D1095564

BASIC MATHEMATICS
FOR ELECTRICITY, RADIO, AND TELEVISION

BASIC

McGraw-Hill Book Company, Inc.

MATHEMATICS

for electricity, radio, and television

BERTRAND B. SINGER

Instructor of Radio and Television Mathematics, Samuel Gompers Vocational and Technical High School, New York

NEW YORK
TORONTO
LONDON

1957

Frontispiece photograph courtesy of General Electric Co.

THE MAPLE PRESS COMPANY, YORK, PA.

PREFACE

The purpose of this volume is to provide (1) a practical course in basic mathematics for students of electricity, radio, or television and (2) a refresher course in the mathematics needed by the skilled mechanic in these trades.

The objective is to present the mathematical principles as the direct result of a need encountered in the development of the electrical theory. This theory is built up in slow, simple stages and directly and immediately applied to the solution of actual practical problems in electrical installation and radio and television servicing.

Very little is taken for granted. Whenever a new mathematical operation is needed—no matter how simple—a check-up and brush-up on the operation is provided. Each check-up is a mathematical diagnostic test and motivation for the following job. The problems are electrical in nature but can be solved purely on the basis of the mathematical principle involved without any knowledge of the electrical theory to follow. Each brush-up reviews the mathematical concepts immediately necessary for the continuance of the electrical development and application. For example, Jobs 2-4 and 2-5 (Check-up and Brush-up on Formulas) immediately precede the algebraic manipulation of the Ohm's law formula to find the current or resistance.

Each chapter is broken down into a set of short "jobs" which concentrate on a small portion of the large concept involved in the chapter. Each job develops either a new mathematical operation or a new electrical concept and is illustrated by a series of examples which increase in both arithmetical difficulty and electrical scope. It is believed that this "illustration method" makes this volume particularly suitable for the mechanic in the trade as well as for all basic courses in electricity, radio, or television. The problems in each job are very carefully graded, starting with simple whole numbers through fractions and decimals to provide answers which are first whole numbers, then fractions, and finally decimals. Answers to the problems are provided to enhance the "self-help" features of the volume. Continuing review and drill in both mathematical and electrical concepts are obtained by extending the electrical theory and application.

Diagrams are used extensively, with particular attention being paid to the process of changing the words of a problem into a simple sketch, properly labeled with all the information given and to be found. A summary and set of review problems are included in each chapter as well as one or more tests. The review jobs attempt to attack the problems in the chapter from a slightly different point of view so as to round up any possible loose ends in the student's mind.

The author wishes to acknowledge his indebtedness to Mr. Nathan Clark, Science Supervisor for the New York City Board of Education, at whose suggestion this book was begun, for many years of guidance. He also wishes to thank Mr. Oscar Fisch and the many other members of the Related Technical Subjects Department of the George West-inghouse Vocational High School for their many constructive criticisms and contributions.

BERTRAND B. SINGER

CONTENTS

Chapter 6.   Combination Circuits   127

Chapter 7.   Electrical Power   148

Chapter 8.   Applications of Series and Parallel Circuits   174

Chapter 9.   Efficiency   218

SYMBOLS AND ABBREVIATIONS

TERM	SYMBOL	ABBRE-VIATION	TERM	SYMBOL	ABBRE-VIATION
Alternating current		a-c	Diameter	D, d	diam
Ampere (unit of current)	I	amp	Degree	°	deg
			Direct current		d-c
Milliampere		ma	Efficiency		Eff
Microampere		μa	Electromotive force	E	emf
American Wire Gage		AWG	Energy	W	
Apparent power	P	va	Farad (unit of capacitance)	C	
Angle	$\angle$		Microfarad	C	μf
Area	A		Micromicro-farad	C	$\mu\mu$f
Circular mils		cir mils	Foot		ft
Square inches		sq in.	Frequency	f	freq
Candlepower		cp	Audio		a-f
Capacitance	C		Intermediate		i-f
Constant	K		High		h-f
Continuous wave		cw	Low		l-f
Cosine		cos	Radio		r-f
Coulomb	Q		Resonant		f
Current	I		Ground		gnd
Average value	I_{av}		Henry (unit of inductance)	L	
Change in current	ΔI		Millihenry		mh
Effective value	I		Microhenry		μh
Instantaneous current	i		High pass		h-p
Maximum value	I_{max}		Horsepower		hp
			Horsepower-hour		hp-hr
Cycles			Hour	T	hr
Cycles per second		cps	Impedance	Z	
Kilocycles		kc	Inch		in.
Megacycles		Mc	Inductance	L	
Decibel		db	Kilo (1,000)		k
Delta (Greek letter)	Δ		Low pass		l-p
			Maximum		max

TERM	SYMBOL	ABBRE-VIATION	TERM	SYMBOL	ABBRE-VIATION
Mega (1,000,000)		Meg	Time	T	
Micro (one-millionth)	μ	micro	Tuned radio frequency		trf
Micromicro (one-millionth of a millionth)	$\mu\mu$	micromicro	Turns ratio		TR
			Vacuum tube		VT
Milli (one-thousandth)	m	milli	Cathode	K	
Minimum		min	Cathode current	I_k	
Ohm (unit of resistance)	R	ohm	Cathode resistance	R_k	
Pi (Greek letter)	π		Cathode voltage	E_k	
Phase angle (theta)	θ		Plate	P	
Power	P		Plate current	I_p	
Apparent power	P		Plate resistance	R_p	
Effective power	W		Plate voltage	E_p	
Input power	P_i		Screen current	I_s	
Output power	P_o		Volt	E	v
Reactive power	VA	va	Kilovolt		kv
Power factor		pf	Millivolt		mv
Push-pull		pp	Microvolt		μv
Quality	Q		Voltage	E	
Radius	R, r	rad	Average value	E_{av}	
Reactance	X		Effective value	E	
Capacitive reactance	X_c		Instantaneous value	e	
Inductive reactance	X_L		Maximum value	E_{max}	
Resistance	R		Volt-ampere	VA	volt-amp
Root mean square		rms	Kilovolt-ampere	KVA	kv-amp
Revolutions per minute		rpm	Voltage ratio	VR	
Second	T	sec	Watt (unit of electrical power)	P	w
Microsecond		μsec	Kilowatt		kw
Sine		sin	Kilowatthour		kwhr
Specific resistance	K		Milliwatt		mw
Tangent		tan	Microwatt		μw
Television		TV	Watthour		whr
			Wavelength	λ	

CHAPTER 1

INTRODUCTION TO ELECTRICITY

JOB 1-1: BASIC THEORY OF ELECTRICITY

We shall start our study of electricity with an examination of the materials from which electrical energy is produced.

Elements. Science has discovered 98 different kinds of material called elements. These cannot be made from other materials and cannot be broken up to form other materials by ordinary methods. Gold, iron, copper, oxygen, and carbon are some examples of elements.

Atoms. An atom is the smallest amount of an element which has all the properties of the element. An atom may be broken down into smaller pieces, but these pieces have none of the properties of the element. It is now believed that all material is electrical in nature. All matter is made of combinations of elements, which, in turn, are made of atoms. The atoms themselves are merely combinations of different kinds of electrical energy. The presently accepted theory is that an atom, because it is electrically neutral, is made of positive charges of electricity called *protons* and an equal number of negative charges called *electrons*. There are also a number of electrically neutral particles called *neutrons*. Similarly

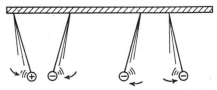

Fig. 1-1. Opposite charges attract, like charges repel each other.

charged particles will repel each other, while particles of opposite charge will attract each other. For example, two electrons will repel each other, and two protons will repel each other, but an electron will be attracted to a proton as shown in Fig. 1-1.

Structure of the Atom. An atom is believed to resemble our solar system with the sun at the center and the planets revolving around it as shown in Fig. 1-2a. An atom consists of electrons revolving around a nucleus, which contains the protons and neutrons as shown in Fig. 1-2b. The number of revolving or *planetary* electrons is equal to the number of positively charged protons in the nucleus.

Free Electrons.   The electrons farthest from the nucleus are called *free electrons* because they are bound very loosely to the nucleus. The word "electricity" comes from *elektron*, the Greek word for amber. Thales, a Greek philosopher, observed that if amber was rubbed, it would attract small objects.   You can observe the same effect by running a hard-rubber comb through your hair or by rubbing the

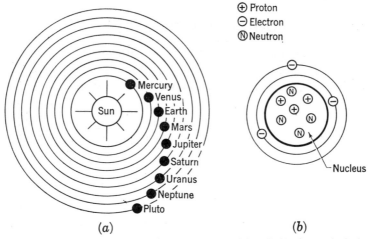

FIG. 1-2. The resemblance between the solar system (a) and the theoretical diagram of an atom of lithium (b).

comb on your coat sleeve.   The comb will then attract small pieces of paper.   As the comb is rubbed on the sleeve, some of the free electrons are rubbed off the cloth and deposited on the comb.   The comb is now considered to be *negatively charged* because it has accumulated an *excess* of electrons.   On the other hand, the coat sleeve is *positively charged* because of the *shortage* of electrons.   A small bit of paper will now be attracted and held by the charged comb.   A similar transfer of electrons occurs if you shuffle your feet over a rug on a dry day.   Electrons are rubbed off the rug and are accumulated on your body.   Touching a metal doorknob or some other conductor will produce a slight shock as the electrons *flow* through your body to the ground.

Electron Flow.   Notice that no shock will be experienced while the body is accumulating the electrons.   The shock will occur only when the electrons *flow* through your body in one concerted surge.   This

directed flow, or movement, of the electrons is one of the most important ideas in electricity. In order to understand this better, let us
compare the particles of matter with a brick wall, as in Fig. 1-3. A
brick in a wall is like an atom, since it is the smallest part of the wall
that has the characteristics of the wall. If an individual brick were
to be powdered into dust, we could compare a single grain of dust
with an electron. The grains of brick cannot do any useful work by
themselves, but if a powerful pressure like a blast of compressed air
were allowed to hit the particles as would occur in a sandblasting
machine, then enormous energies would be available.

We can also consider the drops of water in a stream to be like the
electrons in a piece of matter. If the drops of water move aimlessly,
as in a water sprinkler, then their energy is small. But if all the drops

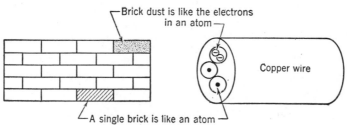

FIG. 1-3. Comparison of brick dust to electrons.

are forced to move in the *same direction*, as in a high-pressure fire hose,
then their energy is large. We can see, then, that if electrons are to do
useful work, they must be *moving under pressure* as do the grains of
sand or drops of water.

Electrical Pressure: Voltage. In order to move the drops of water
or the grains of sand, a mechanical pressure supplied by a water pump
or an air compressor is required. Similarly, an electron pressure is
required to move the electrons along a wire. This electrical pressure
is called the *voltage* and is measured in units of *volts*. This unit of
measurement was named after Count Alessandro Volta, an Italian
physicist (1745–1827).

Producing Electrical Pressures. A working pressure is considered
to exist when there is a *difference* in energies. Water in a high tank
will exert a pressure because of the *difference* in the height of the water
levels as shown in Fig. 1-4. Elements differ not only in the number of
electrons which make up their individual "solar systems" but also in
the energies of their electrons. Therefore, if two different materials
are brought together under suitable conditions, there will be a *dif-*

ference of electron energies. This difference produces the electrical pressure that we call the *voltage*.

Different combinations of materials will produce different voltages. A dry cell of carbon and zinc produces 1.5 volts, a lead and sulfuric acid cell produces 2.1 volts, and an Edison storage cell of nickel and iron produces 1.2 volts. These combinations are called *batteries*. A voltage pressure may be produced in several other ways which we shall learn about later. For example, the 110–120 volts supplied by an ordinary house outlet is produced by a machine called a generator. An automobile spark coil delivers about 1,500 volts. The purpose of all voltages, however produced, is to provide a force to *move* the electrons. It is appropriately termed an electron-moving or *electromotive force*, which is abbreviated as emf. Very often the simple symbol E is used to indicate voltage.

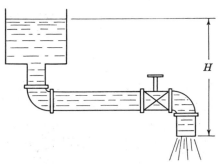

FIG. 1-4. The difference in height between the water levels causes pressure.

Quantity of Electricity. The amount of electricity represented by a single electron is very small—much too small to be used as a measure of quantity in practical electrical work. The electron has already been compared with a drop of water. It is obviously ridiculous to measure quantities of water by the number of drops. Instead, we use quantities like a gallon or a quart, each of which represents a certain number of drops. Similarly, the practical unit of electrical quantity represents a certain number of electrons and is called a *coulomb*. This unit was named after C. A. Coulomb, a French physicist (1736–1806). The coulomb is equal to about 6 billion billion electrons (6,000,000,000,000,000,000). The symbol for the coulomb is Q, since it represents a definite quantity of electrons.

Current. When a voltage is applied across the ends of a conductor, the electrons, which up to now have been moving in many different directions (Fig. 1-5*a*), are forced to move in the *same direction* along the wire (Fig. 1-5*b*). Individual electrons all along the path are forced to leave the atoms to which they are attached. They travel only a short distance until they find an atom that needs an electron. This motion is transmitted along the path from atom to atom, as motion in a whip is transmitted from one end to the other. This *flow* of electrons is called an *electric current* (Fig. 1-6). The speed of this flow is very nearly equal to the speed of light, which is about 186,000 miles per second. The actual speed of the individual electrons is much slower, but the effect of a pressure at one end of a wire is felt almost instantaneously at the other end.

(a)   (b)

Fig. 1-5. (a) The electrons in the wire move in many different directions. (b) When a voltage pushes the electrons, they all move in the same direction and make an electric current.

The flow of water is measured as the number of gallons per minute, barrels per hour, etc. Similarly, the flow of electricity is measured by the number of electrons that pass a point in a wire in one second. We do not have special names for the flow of water, but we do have a special name for the flow of electrons. This name is *ampere* of current. A current of one ampere represents a flow of one coulomb of electricity (6 billion billion electrons) past a point in a wire in one second.

The symbol for current is I. The ampere was named after André Marie Ampère, a French physicist and chemist (1775–1836). Since

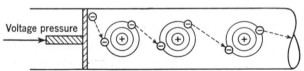

Fig. 1-6. An electric current is produced by billions of electrons *moving* through a wire.

an electron is so small (about 25 trillion to an inch) and since there are so many of them, it is impossible actually to count them as they go by. However, when electrons are moving as an electric current, they can do useful work such as lighting lamps, running motors, producing heat, and plating metals. We can make use of this last ability of an electric current to measure and define it accurately. An international commission has thus defined an ampere as that number of electrons which can deposit a definite amount of silver (0.001118 gram) from a silver solution in one second. A 100-watt 110-volt lamp uses about 1 amp. A 600-watt 110-volt electric iron uses about

5.5 amp, and the current required by a radio or television tube may be as low as 0.001 amp.

Resistance. We have learned that "free" electrons may be forced to move from atom to atom when a voltage pressure is applied. Different materials vary in their number of free electrons and in the ease with which electrons may be transferred between atoms. A *conductor* (Fig. 1-7*a*) is a material through which electrons may travel freely. Most metals are good conductors. An *insulator* (Fig. 1-7*b*) is a material which prevents the electrons from traveling through it easily. Nonmetallic materials like glass, mica, porcelain, rubber, and textiles are good insulators. No material is a perfect insulator or a perfect conductor.

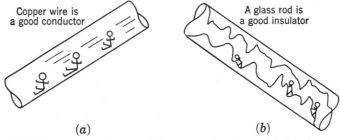

Copper wire is a good conductor

A glass rod is a good insulator

(*a*)   (*b*)

FIG. 1-7. (*a*) Electrons travel freely through conductors. (*b*) Insulators prevent electrons from flowing freely.

The ability of a material to resist the flow of electrons is called its *resistance* and is measured in units called *ohms*. This unit of measurement was named after Georg Simon Ohm, a German physicist (1787–1854). The symbol for resistance is R. An international agreement defines the ohm as the resistance offered by a column of mercury of uniform cross section, 106.3 cm long (about 41.8 in.), and weighing 14.45 grams (about $\frac{1}{2}$ oz). For example, 1,000 ft of No. 10 copper wire has a resistance of almost exactly 1 ohm, the resistance of a 40-watt electric light is 300 ohms when hot, and a 150-volt voltmeter has a resistance of 15,000 ohms.

There are many electrical devices which make use of the fact that materials offer resistance to the flow of an electric current. Soldering irons, electric heaters, and electric-light bulbs contain conductors which have a high resistance compared with the resistance of the connecting wires. Radio and television circuits contain many resistance elements which are called *resistors*. They are not always made of special resistance wire. Carbon and mixtures of carbon and insulating materials are molded to form resistors.

JOB 1-2: ELECTRICAL MEASUREMENTS AND CIRCUITS

The voltage, current, and resistance of an electrical circuit are measured with special instruments. An *ammeter* measures the current I in units of amperes. A *voltmeter* measures the voltage E in units of volts. An *ohmmeter* measures the resistance R in units of ohms.

How to Use the Ammeter. In order to measure the flow of water in a pipe, a flowmeter is inserted into the pipe as shown in Fig. 1-8a. The pump supplies the pressure to force the water through the pipe and flowmeter against the resistance of the faucet valve. Since all the water in the system must flow through the flowmeter, it must indicate the number of gallons per minute that flow through the pipe.

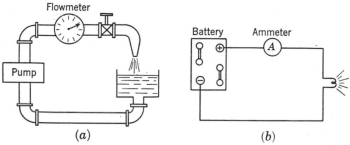

Fig. 1-8. (a) A flowmeter is inserted in the line of flow of the water. (b) An ammeter is inserted in the line of flow of the electrons.

In the same way, in order to measure the flow of current in a wire, an ammeter must be inserted *directly into the circuit* so that all the electrons will be forced through it. The ammeter has a very low resistance and so does not stop the flow of current. When large currents are measured, certain adjustments must be made in order to prevent the ammeter from burning out (Job 8-6). In Fig. 1-8b, the battery supplies the electrical pressure that forces the electrons through the lamp against the resistance of the lamp. Since all the electrons in the circuit must pass through the ammeter, it will indicate the number of electrons per second, or amperes, passing through it.

How to Use the Voltmeter. As we have already learned, the amount of water that will flow in a pipe depends on the *difference* in the pressure between any two points. In the same way, the electric current that will flow through a resistance depends on the *difference* in electrical pressure (voltage) between the two ends of the resistance. In order to measure this difference, a voltmeter must be connected across the ends of the resistance as in Fig. 1-9. Note that the current that flows through the resistance does *not* flow through the voltmeter. Since a voltmeter is designed to measure the electrical pressure, it should be placed in the circuit so that the pressure across the resistance is also across the voltmeter.   An ammeter, on the other hand, is inserted *into* the circuit and receives the full current of the circuit.

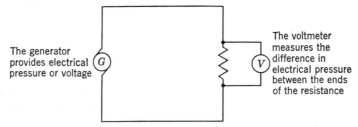

The generator provides electrical pressure or voltage

The voltmeter measures the difference in electrical pressure between the ends of the resistance

Fig. 1-9. A voltmeter is always connected across the ends of a part when measuring the voltage across it.

A voltmeter is merely attached to the ends of the part across which the voltage is to be measured.

How to Use the Ohmmeter.   An ohmmeter is really an ammeter whose dial has been marked to read the resistance in ohms instead of the current in amperes according to a very simple relationship called *Ohm's law*, which we shall study soon.   An ohmmeter will measure the resistance of the individual parts of a circuit by connecting the leads of the instrument across the ends of the part as is done with a voltmeter.

Electrical Circuits.   A *circuit* is simply a *complete* path along which the electrons can move.   A complete circuit must have an *unbroken* path as shown in Fig. 1-10*a* with the source of energy acting as an

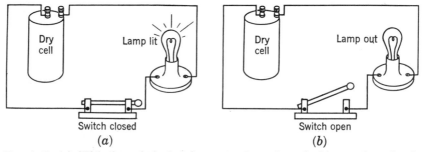

Dry cell — Lamp lit — Switch closed
(a)

Dry cell — Lamp out — Switch open
(b)

Fig. 1-10. (*a*) With the switch closed, current flows through this complete circuit. (*b*) With the switch open, no current flows through this broken or open circuit.

electron pump to force the electrons through the conductor (usually a copper wire) against the resistance of the device to be operated. When the switch is opened as in Fig. 1-10*b*, the electrons cannot leave one side of the switch to enter the other side and so return to their source because of the very high resistance of the air gap. This is an *open circuit*, and no current will flow.

Fuses. One of the effects of the passage of an electric current is the production of heat. The larger the current, the more heat produced. In order to prevent large currents from accidentally flowing through our expensive apparatus and burning it up, a device called a *fuse* is placed directly into the circuit as in Fig. 1-11 so as to form a part of the circuit through which all the electrons must flow. To protect a circuit, a fuse must be a device which will *open* the circuit whenever a dangerously large current starts to flow. Accordingly, a fuse completes a circuit with a piece of special metal designed to melt quickly when heated excessively as would occur when a large current flows. The fuse will permit currents smaller than the fuse value to flow but

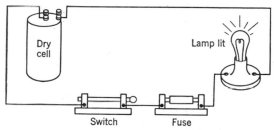

FIG. 1-11. A fuse completes an electrical circuit and protects it against the flow of dangerously large currents.

will melt and therefore break the circuit if a larger, dangerous current ever appears. A dangerously large current will flow, for instance, when a "short circuit" occurs. A short circuit is usually caused by an accidental connection between two points in a circuit which offer very little resistance to the flow of the electrons. If the resistance is small, there will be nothing to stop the flow of the electrons and the current will increase enormously. The resulting heat generated might cause a fire. However, if the circuit is protected by a fuse, the heat caused by the short-circuit current will melt the fuse wire, thus breaking the circuit and reducing the current to zero.

Fuse Ratings. Fuses are rated by the number of amperes of current that can flow through them before they melt and break the circuit. Thus we have 10-, 15-, 30-amp, etc., fuses. We must be careful that any fuse inserted in a circuit be rated low enough to melt, or "blow," before the apparatus is damaged. For example, in a house wired to carry a current of 15 amp it is best to use a fuse no larger than 15 amp so that a current larger than 15 amp could never flow.

Delayed Fuses. In ordinary house wiring, a 15-amp fuse is used to protect the line wires from overheating and producing a fire hazard.

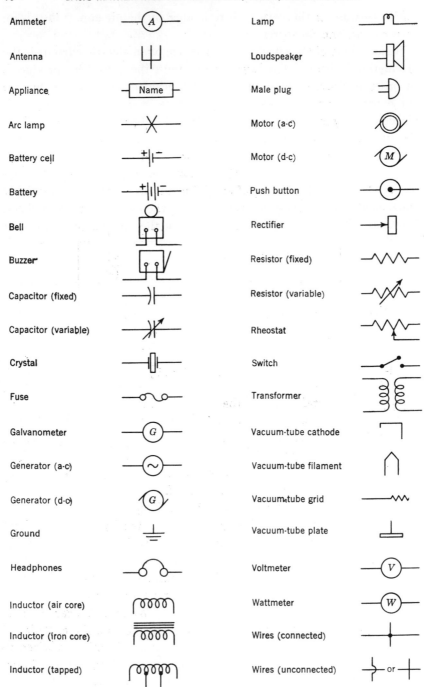

Ammeter	Lamp
Antenna	Loudspeaker
Appliance	Male plug
Arc lamp	Motor (a-c)
Battery cell	Motor (d-c)
Battery	Push button
Bell	Rectifier
Buzzer	Resistor (fixed)
Capacitor (fixed)	Resistor (variable)
Capacitor (variable)	Rheostat
Crystal	Switch
Fuse	Transformer
Galvanometer	Vacuum-tube cathode
Generator (a-c)	Vacuum-tube filament
Generator (d-c)	Vacuum-tube grid
Ground	Vacuum-tube plate
Headphones	Voltmeter
Inductor (air core)	Wattmeter
Inductor (iron core)	Wires (connected)
Inductor (tapped)	Wires (unconnected)

Fig. 1-12. Standard circuit symbols.

However, if a current larger than 15 amp were to flow for only a few seconds, it would not harm the wires. There are many times when a wire must carry a current larger than it was designed to carry—but only for a short time. For example, a normal 5 amp may be flowing in a line. If the motor of a washing machine is suddenly turned on, the current drawn may go up to 35 amp for a few seconds but then drop to a normal 10 amp after the motor is running. The ordinary fuse would blow, since the current is larger than the rated 15 amp. However, since there is no danger, as the current drops again very quickly, we would like a fuse that could carry larger currents for a short time. This type of fuse is called a *time-delay* fuse. It is designed to carry about twice its rated current for 20 to 30 sec but to blow if the rated current is exceeded for 1 min. The net effect is that the fuse will hold for *temporary* overloads but will blow on continuous, small overloads or short circuits.

Symbols. Most of our diagrams up to this point have used pictures of the various electrical devices. However, everybody cannot draw pictures quickly and accurately, and so we shall substitute special simple diagrams to illustrate the various parts of any circuit. Each circuit element is represented by a simple diagram called the *symbol* for the part. The standard symbols for the commonly used electrical and electronic components are given in Fig. 1-12.

Circuit Diagrams. Every electrical circuit must contain the following:

1. A source of electrical pressure or voltage E, measured in volts.

2. An unbroken conductor through which the electrons may flow easily. The amount of electron flow is the current I, measured in amperes.

3. A load, or resistance R to this flow of current, measured in ohms.

Example 1-1. Draw a circuit containing two battery cells, an ammeter, a fuse, a single-pole switch, a resistor, and a lamp. Label each part, using E for voltage, R for resistance, and I for current.

Solution: See Fig. 1-13.

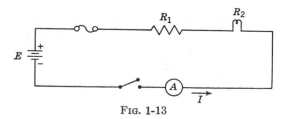

Fɪɢ. 1-13

Note: The numbers 1 and 2 under the letter R are a convenient way to indicate the first resistance R_1 and the second resistance R_2.

Problems

Using the circuit symbols shown in Fig. 1-12, draw a circuit for each problem to include the elements indicated. Label the diagram completely, using the subscripts 1, 2, 3, etc., to indicate the parts of the circuit.

1. A battery of two cells, a fuse, and two resistors.

2. An a-c generator, a switch, an ammeter, a bell, and a buzzer.

3. A battery, a switch, an ammeter, two resistors, and a lamp with a voltmeter across it.

4. A battery, a switch, and four vacuum-tube filaments.

5. A d-c generator, a switch, a rheostat, and a d-c motor.

6. A d-c generator, a switch, a fuse, an arc lamp, and a resistor.

7. A male plug, an electric iron, a rheostat, and a switch.

8. A male plug, four vacuum-tube filaments, a switch, and a resistor.

Summary

1. All material is made of electrical charges.

2. Negative charges are called *electrons*.

3. Positive charges are called *protons*.

4. Similar charges repel each other, and opposite charges attract each other.

5. A *coulomb* represents a quantity of 6 billion billion electrons.

6. An *ampere* is a current of one coulomb per second. The symbol for current is I.

7. Current is measured by an *ammeter*, which is always inserted directly into the circuit and reads *amperes*.

8. Electrons move because of the pressure of an electromotive force, or *voltage*. The symbol for voltage is E.

9. Voltage is measured by a *voltmeter*, which is always connected across the ends of the circuit element and reads *volts*.

10. The *resistance* of a circuit is the resistance offered by the circuit to the flow of electrons. The symbol for resistance is R.

11. Resistance is measured by an *ohmmeter*, which is always connected across the ends of the circuit element and reads *ohms*.

12. A *conductor* is a material which allows current to flow.

13. An *insulator* is a material which prevents current from flowing easily.

14. A *fuse* is a thin strip of easily melted metal. It protects a circuit from large currents by melting quickly and thereby breaking the circuit.

15. *Symbols* are simple diagrams which are used to draw circuit diagrams neatly and quickly.

CHAPTER 2

SIMPLE ELECTRICAL CIRCUITS

JOB 2-1: CHECK-UP ON FRACTIONS

Before we go any further into our study of electrical circuits, let's stop to check up on our knowledge of the multiplication of fractions. The following are some problems often met by electricians and radio men in their daily work. They are all solved by multiplying the numbers involved in the problem. If you have difficulty solving any of these problems, see Job 2-2, which follows.

Problems

1. What length of two-conductor BX cable is needed to obtain 6 pieces each $4\frac{1}{4}$ ft long?

2. What is the total horsepower delivered by five $\frac{3}{4}$-hp motors?

3. If the resistance of one turn of a variable wire-wound resistor is $2\frac{1}{3}$ ohms, what is the resistance of three turns?

4. What is the cost of $2\frac{1}{4}$ lb of magnet wire at 30 cents per pound?

5. A voltage divider develops an emf of $\frac{1}{20}$ volt for each ohm of resistance. What voltage would be measured across 1,800 ohms of resistance?

6. An industrial shop uses $9\frac{1}{2}$ kwhr of electricity per day. How many kilowatthours are used in a month of 24 working days?

7. How many hours of work were spent on an electrical installation if five men each worked $7\frac{1}{2}$ hr?

8. A neon electric sign uses $4\frac{1}{2}$ watts of power per foot of tubing. How many watts are used for a sign which uses 21 ft of tubing?

9. Number 9191 Fiberduct conduit adapters weigh $1\frac{1}{2}$ lb each. Find the weight of 24 such fittings.

10. How many feet of antenna wire are there in a $1\frac{1}{8}$-lb coil if the wire runs 18 ft to the pound?

11. $2\frac{1}{2} \times 3\frac{1}{5}$

12. $\frac{2}{5} \times 20$

13. $\frac{22}{7} \times 21$

14. $\frac{1}{2} \times \frac{1}{3}$

15. $20 \times \frac{1}{1000}$

16. $\frac{2}{3} \times \frac{3}{4}$

17. $\frac{3}{8} \times \frac{1}{4}$

18. $\frac{1}{10} \times 25$

19. $5\frac{1}{3} \times 8\frac{1}{2}$

20. $3\frac{1}{7} \times 5\frac{1}{11}$

JOB 2-2: BRUSH-UP ON FRACTIONS

Meaning of a Fraction. A fraction is a shorthand way of describing some part of a total amount. Figure 2-1*a* shows a whole pie. If the pie is cut into four equal pieces as shown in Fig. 2-1*b*, then each piece is just one part out of the total of four parts. This is written

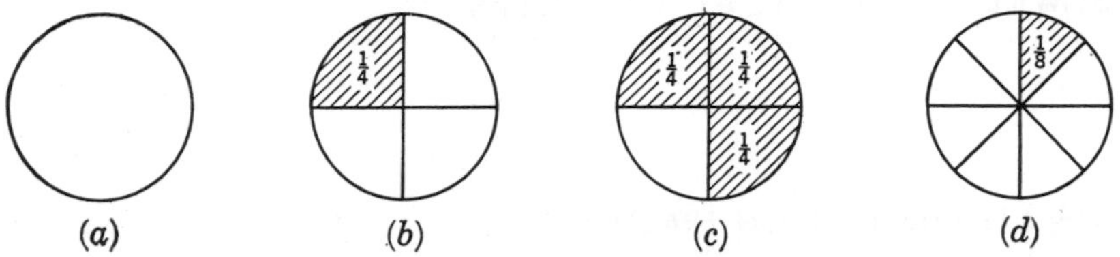

FIG. 2-1. Fractional parts of a pie.

as the *fraction* $\frac{1}{4}$ and means 1 part out of 4 equal parts. The fraction $\frac{3}{4}$, as shown by the shaded portion in Fig. 2-1*c*, says that a whole was divided into 4 equal parts and that 3 of these parts were used. The fraction $\frac{1}{8}$, as shown in Fig. 2-1*d*, says that a whole was divided into 8 equal parts and that 1 of these parts was used. It is evident that we can divide the pie into any number of equal parts. Each part will be 1 part out of the total number of parts. In Fig. 2-2*a* the pie

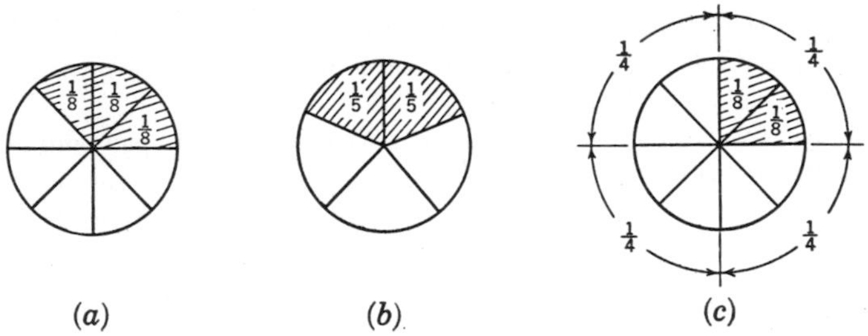

FIG. 2-2

is cut into 8 equal parts. Each part is $\frac{1}{8}$ of the pie. The shaded portion is 3 of these, or $\frac{3}{8}$ of the pie. In Fig. 2-2*b* the pie is cut into 5 equal parts. Each part is $\frac{1}{5}$ of the pie. The shaded portion is 2 of these, or $\frac{2}{5}$ of the pie. In Fig. 2-2*c* the pie is again cut into 8 equal parts. Each part is $\frac{1}{8}$ of the pie. The shaded portion is 2 of these, or $\frac{2}{8}$ of the pie. If the pie were cut into 4 equal parts, our shaded portion would then be $\frac{1}{4}$. Thus,

$$\frac{2}{8} = \frac{1}{4}$$

Reducing Fractions. We have seen that a portion of a total may be expressed in two different ways, as $\frac{1}{4}$ is the same as $\frac{2}{8}$. $\frac{1}{4}$ is called the *reduced* form of $\frac{2}{8}$. To reduce a fraction means to change it into another *equal* fraction. The numbers of this new fraction should not be divisible by any number except itself and 1.

Rule: To reduce a fraction, divide the numerator (top number) **and the denominator** (bottom number) **by the same number.**

Example 2-1. Reduce $\frac{4}{12}$ to lowest terms.
Solution: Divide the 4 and the 12 by 4. The top $4 \div 4 = 1$. The bottom $12 \div 4 = 3$. Therefore,

$$\frac{4}{12} = \frac{1}{3} \qquad Ans.$$

Example 2-2. Reduce $\frac{24}{96}$ to lowest terms.
Solution: We could divide both the 24 and the 96 by 24 to get $\frac{1}{4}$ in one step, or we could reduce by a series of steps. Reducing by dividing the 24 and the 96 by 8 gives $\frac{3}{12}$. Now, dividing the 3 and the 12 by 3 gives $\frac{1}{4}$. *Ans.*

Problems

Reduce the following fractions to lowest terms:

1. $\frac{4}{8}$
2. $\frac{3}{9}$
3. $\frac{4}{16}$
4. $\frac{4}{80}$
5. $\frac{12}{16}$

6. $\frac{20}{32}$
7. $\frac{5}{20}$
8. $\frac{3}{12}$
9. $\frac{24}{72}$
10. $\frac{12}{36}$

11. $\frac{30}{1000}$
12. $\frac{12}{48}$
13. $\frac{24}{64}$
14. $\frac{40}{100}$
15. $\frac{14}{32}$

16. $\frac{15}{60}$
17. $\frac{15}{45}$
18. $\frac{15}{75}$
19. $\frac{60}{100}$
20. $\frac{42}{72}$

21. The ratio of the output voltage of a 50L6 audio output tube to the input voltage was found to be 27/3. Reduce to lowest terms.

22. The resistance of iron wire compared with nichrome wire is 90/600. Reduce to lowest terms.

23. The ratio of the plate impedance of a 6K6 audio output tube to the impedance of the voice coil is 5,600/8. Reduce to lowest terms.

24. The turns ratio of a step-up transformer is 6/120. Reduce to lowest terms.

25. The current in a certain parallel circuit divides in the ratio of 12/30. Reduce to lowest terms.

Reducing Mixed Numbers to Improper Fractions. In a *proper fraction* the top number (the numerator) is always *smaller* than the bottom number (the denominator). Some examples of proper fractions are $\frac{1}{2}$, $\frac{3}{4}$, and $\frac{8}{11}$. A *mixed number* is made of two numbers—a whole number and a proper fraction. Some examples are $2\frac{1}{2}$, $3\frac{1}{4}$, and

$5\frac{3}{16}$. In an *improper fraction* the top number is always *larger* than the bottom number. Some examples are $\frac{5}{3}$, $\frac{8}{5}$, and $\frac{22}{7}$.

Example 2-3. Change $3\frac{3}{4}$ to an improper fraction.

Solution: The improper fraction will be a certain number of fourths. Each whole = $\frac{4}{4}$. In the number 3, there are 3×4 fourths or 12 fourths or $\frac{12}{4}$. But in addition to the 3 wholes, we have $\frac{3}{4}$ more. Therefore,

$$3\frac{3}{4} = \frac{12}{4} + \frac{3}{4} = \frac{15}{4} \quad Ans.$$

Rule: To change a mixed number to an improper fraction, multiply the denominator of the fraction by the whole number and add the numerator of the fraction. Place this answer over the denominator to make the improper fraction.

Example 2-4. Change $2\frac{3}{8}$ to an improper fraction.

Solution: The numerator is equal to 2×8, or 16, plus the 3, which equals 19. Placing this 19 over the denominator 8 gives

$$\frac{19}{8} \quad Ans.$$

Problems

Change each of the following mixed numbers to improper fractions:

1. $2\frac{1}{4}$	4. $5\frac{3}{8}$	7. $4\frac{1}{6}$	10. $10\frac{1}{2}$
2. $3\frac{3}{8}$	5. $1\frac{3}{10}$	8. $3\frac{7}{10}$	11. $3\frac{1}{8}$
3. $2\frac{2}{9}$	6. $4\frac{3}{4}$	9. $4\frac{5}{8}$	12. $2\frac{1}{12}$

Changing Improper Fractions to Mixed Numbers

Example 2-5. Change $\frac{15}{2}$ to a mixed number.

Solution: $\frac{15}{2}$ means 15 divided by 2 or $15 \div 2$. This means that 2 is contained in 15 only 7 times, which is 14, leaving a remainder of 1. This is written as

$$\frac{15}{2} = 7\frac{1}{2} \quad Ans.$$

Rule: To change an improper fraction into a mixed number, divide the numerator by the denominator. Any remainder is placed over the denominator. The resulting whole number and proper fraction form the required mixed number.

Example 2-6. Change $\frac{25}{10}$ to a mixed number.

Solution: $25 \div 10 = 2$ with 5 remaining, or $2\frac{5}{10}$. Any remaining fraction like $\frac{5}{10}$ should be reduced to lowest terms. Therefore,

$$2\frac{5}{10} = 2\frac{1}{2} \quad Ans.$$

Problems

Change the following improper fractions to mixed numbers or whole numbers:

1. $\frac{7}{4}$ 7. $\frac{8}{5}$ 13. $\frac{29}{3}$ 19. $\frac{96}{8}$ 25. $\frac{47}{9}$

2. $\frac{9}{2}$ 8. $\frac{23}{4}$ 14. $\frac{26}{8}$ 20. $\frac{31}{4}$ 26. $\frac{19}{6}$

3. $\frac{13}{3}$ 9. $\frac{33}{10}$ 15. $\frac{64}{4}$ 21. $\frac{70}{10}$ 27. $\frac{108}{9}$

4. $\frac{8}{3}$ 10. $\frac{14}{5}$ 16. $\frac{16}{9}$ 22. $\frac{38}{3}$ 28. $\frac{47}{11}$

5. $\frac{15}{4}$ 11. $\frac{20}{2}$ 17. $\frac{18}{5}$ 23. $\frac{17}{10}$ 29. $\frac{147}{12}$

6. $\frac{23}{5}$ 12. $\frac{43}{10}$ 18. $\frac{52}{4}$ 24. $\frac{59}{8}$ 30. $\frac{66}{10}$

Multiplication of Fractions

Rule: To multiply fractions, place the multiplication of the numerators over the multiplication of the denominators and reduce to lowest terms.

Example 2-7. Multiply $\frac{1}{2} \times \frac{3}{4}$.
Solution: $\frac{1}{2} \times \frac{3}{4}$ means

$$\frac{1 \times 3}{2 \times 4} = \frac{3}{8} \qquad Ans.$$

Example 2-8. Multiply $\frac{1}{2} \times 5$.

Solution:

$$\frac{1}{2} \times 5 = \frac{1}{2} \times \frac{5}{1} = \frac{1 \times 5}{2 \times 1} = \frac{5}{2} = 2\frac{1}{2} \qquad Ans.$$

Cancellation. To cancel numerators and denominators means to divide both a numerator and a denominator by the same number.

Example 2-9. Multiply $\frac{3}{8} \times \frac{4}{9}$.
Solution: Notice that the 3 on the top and the 9 on the bottom can both be divided by 3. Cross out the 3, and write 1 over it. Cross out the 9, and write 3 under it. Also, the 4 on the top and the 8 on the bottom can both be divided by 4. Cross out the 4 on the top, and write 1 over it. Cross out the 8, and write 2 under it as shown below.

$$\frac{3}{8} \times \frac{4}{9} = \frac{\overset{1}{\cancel{3}}}{\underset{2}{\cancel{8}}} \times \frac{\overset{1}{\cancel{4}}}{\underset{3}{\cancel{9}}} = \frac{1 \times 1}{2 \times 3} = \frac{1}{6} \qquad Ans.$$

Problems

Multiply the following fractions and reduce to lowest terms:

1. $8 \times \frac{1}{2}$ 4. $\frac{1}{4} \times 3$ 7. $\frac{1}{3} \times \frac{1}{5}$

2. $\frac{2}{5} \times \frac{1}{3}$ 5. $5 \times \frac{1}{2}$ 8. $\frac{3}{8} \times 4$

3. $\frac{1}{10} \times 3$ 6. $\frac{1}{4} \times 7$ 9. $\frac{3}{8} \times 16$

10. A 40-watt lamp uses about $\frac{3}{8}$ amp. How many amperes would four lamps use when connected in parallel?

11. A motor delivers only seven-eighths of the power it receives. Find the power delivered if it receives 6 hp.

12. What is the total thickness of three $\frac{1}{8}$-in.-thick washers?

13. The actual value of the resistance of many radio resistors may be off as much as one-fifth of the rated value. What would be the error in a 230-ohm resistor of this type?

14. What total horsepower is required for the operation of three ⅙-hp single-phase capacitor motors?

15. The resistance of No. 19 copper wire is about one-half the resistance of No. 22 wire. What is the resistance of 1,000 ft of No. 19 wire if No. 22 wire has a resistance of about 16 ohms per 1,000 ft?

16. Only four-fifths of the wattage of an electric range is used in computing the size of entrance wires. Find the wattage to use if the range is rated at 4,000 watts.

17. What is the cost of ¾ lb of magnet wire at 28 cents per pound?

18. In transmitting 2 hp by belts, one-twentieth of the energy is lost in slippage. How much horsepower is lost?

19. What is the total thickness of three insulating plates if each plate is ⁵⁄₆₄ in. thick?

20. A capacitor charges to about ⅔ the applied voltage in 1 time constant. If the applied voltage is 10 volts, what is the voltage after 1 time constant?

21. $\frac{2}{3} \times \frac{1}{2}$ **24.** $\frac{3}{5} \times \frac{5}{9}$ **27.** $\frac{3}{4} \times \frac{2}{15}$ **29.** $\frac{7}{8} \times \frac{3}{5}$

22. $\frac{7}{10} \times \frac{5}{14}$ **25.** $\frac{3}{5} \times \frac{4}{5}$ **28.** $\frac{2}{9} \times 11$ **30.** $\frac{3}{4} \times \frac{2}{5}$

23. $\frac{1}{7} \times 5$ **26.** $\frac{4}{5} \times \frac{1}{16}$

Multiplication of Mixed Numbers

Example 2-10. Multiply $2\frac{1}{4} \times 10$.

Solution: Before we can multiply, we must change all mixed numbers into improper fractions.

$$2\frac{1}{4} \times 10 = \frac{9}{4} \times 10$$

$$= \frac{9}{\underset{2}{\cancel{4}}} \times \frac{\overset{5}{\cancel{10}}}{1} = \frac{45}{2} = 22\frac{1}{2} \qquad Ans.$$

Example 2-11. Multiply $1\frac{7}{8} \times 3\frac{1}{3}$.

Solution:

$$1\frac{7}{8} \times 3\frac{1}{3} = \frac{15}{8} \times \frac{10}{3}$$

$$= \frac{\overset{5}{\cancel{15}}}{\underset{4}{\cancel{8}}} \times \frac{\overset{5}{\cancel{10}}}{\underset{1}{\cancel{3}}} = \frac{5 \times 5}{4 \times 1} = \frac{25}{4} = 6\frac{1}{4} \qquad Ans.$$

Problems

Multiply the following fractions and mixed numbers. Reduce to lowest terms.

1. $1\frac{7}{9} \times \frac{3}{8}$ 4. $1\frac{1}{4} \times 3\frac{2}{5}$ 7. $1\frac{1}{3} \times 3\frac{3}{4}$

2. $\frac{1}{5} \times 4\frac{3}{8}$ 5. $2\frac{1}{3} \times \frac{1}{7}$ 8. $2\frac{1}{4} \times 3\frac{3}{5}$

3. $3\frac{1}{6} \times 3$ 6. $3\frac{1}{3} \times 1\frac{1}{5}$ 9. $\frac{1}{5} \times 3\frac{1}{3}$

10. One gallon of water weighs about $8\frac{1}{3}$ lb. Find the weight of 4 gallons of water.

11. Find the total voltage supplied by three $1\frac{1}{2}$-volt dry cells connected in series.

12. Number 70G77 G-E autotransformers weigh $1\frac{9}{10}$ lb each. How much do a dozen weigh?

13. About two-fifths of the electrolyte in a storage battery is acid. If the battery contains $5\frac{1}{4}$ oz of electrolyte, how many ounces of acid are in the cells of the battery?

14. UTC power transformers are given a surge test for insulation breakdown of $2\frac{1}{2}$ times the normally developed voltage. What is the test voltage for a transformer which delivers 510 volts?

15. If one-twentieth of the energy put into a motor is lost by friction, copper, and iron losses, how many kilowatts are lost if the motor receives $\frac{2}{5}$ kw?

16. Deltabeston aircraft cable No. AN-22 weighs $5\frac{7}{10}$ lb per 1,000 ft. What is the weight of 500 ft?

17. The weight of $\frac{1}{16}$-in. gray fiber is $\frac{1}{3}$ lb per sq ft. What is the weight of a sheet of 16 sq ft?

18. If one electrical outlet requires $13\frac{1}{2}$ ft of flexible conduit, how many feet of conduit are required for five such outlets?

19. What is the total resistance of three $7\frac{1}{4}$-ohm resistors in series?

20. A capacitor should be checked for dielectric breakdown at $1\frac{1}{2}$ times its rated working voltage. If the capacitor to be tested has a working voltage of 600 volts, what test voltage should be applied?

Summary

1. A fraction is a way to describe some portion of a total amount.

2. To reduce a fraction to lowest terms, divide both the numerator and the denominator by the same number until it cannot be reduced any further.

3. Mixed numbers should be changed to improper fractions before multiplying.

4. To change a mixed number to an improper fraction, multiply the denominator of the fraction by the whole number and add the numerator of the fraction. Place this answer over the denominator to form the improper fraction.

5. To change an improper fraction to a mixed number, divide the numerator by the denominator. Any remainder is placed over the denominator.

6. To multiply fractions, place the multiplication of the numer-

ators over the multiplication of the denominators and reduce to lowest terms.

7. To cancel means to divide both the numerator and the denominator by the same number.

Test—Fractions

1. Reduce to lowest terms (a) $^{10}\!/_{16}$, (b) $^{8}\!/_{20}$, (c) $^{20}\!/_{64}$, (d) $^{30}\!/_{45}$, and (e) $\dfrac{40}{1,000}$.

2. Change to improper fractions (a) $1\frac{3}{8}$, (b) $3\frac{1}{4}$, (c) $5\frac{1}{2}$, (d) $2\frac{7}{10}$, and (e) $4\frac{1}{8}$.

3. Change to mixed numbers (a) $^{9}\!/_{4}$, (b) $^{23}\!/_{3}$, (c) $^{19}\!/_{5}$, (d) $^{42}\!/_{5}$, and (e) $^{61}\!/_{8}$.

4. Multiply and reduce to lowest terms (a) $^{23}\!/_{7} \times 28$, (b) $\frac{3}{2} \times 1\frac{1}{3}$, (c) $1\frac{5}{4} \times ^{20}\!/_{3}$, and (d) $\frac{5}{3} \times 2\frac{1}{5}$.

5. Multiply and reduce to lowest terms (a) $4\frac{1}{2} \times ^{3}\!/_{16}$, (b) $^{3}\!/_{32} \times 5\frac{1}{3}$, (c) $3\frac{1}{4} \times 4\frac{1}{2}$, and (d) $5\frac{1}{16} \times ^{3}\!/_{32}$.

JOB 2-3: OHM'S LAW

In Job 1-2 we learned that the following three factors must be present in every electrical circuit:

1. The *electromotive force E* expressed in *volts*, which causes the current to flow.

2. The *resistance* of the circuit *R* expressed in *ohms*, which attempts to stop the flow of current.

3. The *current I* expressed in *amperes*, which flows as a result of the voltage pressure exceeding the resistance.

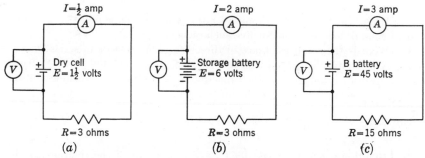

FIG. 2-3. The voltage equals the current multiplied by the resistance in a simple circuit.

A definite relationship exists among these three factors, which is known as *Ohm's law*. This relationship is very important, since it is the basis for most of the calculations in electrical, radio, and television work. In the three circuits shown in Fig. 2-3, the voltage E of the battery is measured by a voltmeter. The current I that flows is measured by an ammeter. The resistance R of the resistor is indicated by the manufacturer by distinctive markings on the resistor

as described in Job 3-2.   Let us put the information from Fig. 2-3
into a table.

Figure	E	I	R	$I \times R$
a	$1\frac{1}{2}$	$\frac{1}{2}$	3	$\frac{1}{2} \times 3 = 1\frac{1}{2}$
b	6	2	3	$2 \times 3 = 6$
c	45	3	15	$3 \times 15 = 45$

In the last column we have multiplied the current I by the resistance
R for each circuit.   Evidently, the result of this multiplication is
always equal to the voltage E of the circuit.   This is true for all
circuits and was first discovered by Georg S. Ohm.   This simple
relationship is called *Ohm's law.*

Rule: Voltage equals current multiplied by resistance.

Formula
$$E = I \times R \tag{2-1}$$
In this formula,
 E must always be expressed in volts (v).
 I must always be expressed in amperes (amp).
 R must always be expressed in ohms (Ω).

Solving Problems

 1. Read the problem carefully.
 2. Draw a simple diagram of the circuit.
 3. Record the given information directly on the diagram.   Indicate
the values to be found by question marks.
 4. Write the formula.
 5. Substitute the given numbers for the letters in the formula.
If the number for the letter is unknown, merely write the letter again.
Be sure to include all mathematical signs like ($\times$) or ($=$), etc.
 6. Do the indicated arithmetic at the side so as not to interrupt
the continued progress of the solution.
 7. In the answer, indicate the letter, its numerical value, and the
units of measurement.

Example 2-12.   Find the voltage needed to operate a circuit if the
current is 2 amp and the resistance is 55 ohms.
 Solution: The diagram for the circuit is shown in Fig. 2-4.
 1. Write the formula.

$$E = I \times R$$

2. Substitute numbers.

$$E = 2 \times 55$$

3. Multiply the numbers.

$$E = 110 \text{ volts} \quad Ans.$$

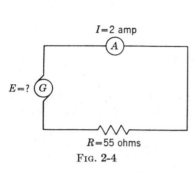

FIG. 2-4

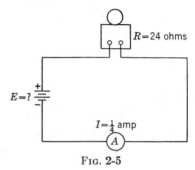

FIG. 2-5

Example 2-13. A doorbell requires $\frac{1}{4}$ amp in order to ring. The resistance of the coils in the bell is 24 ohms. What voltage must be supplied in order to ring the bell?

Solution: The diagram for the circuit is shown in Fig. 2-5.

1. Write the formula.

$$E = I \times R$$

2. Substitute numbers.

$$E = \tfrac{1}{4} \times 24$$

3. Multiply the numbers.

$$E = 6 \text{ volts} \quad Ans.$$

Example 2-14. The filament of a type 1T4 radio tube is rated at a resistance of 28 ohms. What voltage is required if the filament current must be 0.05 amp?

Solution: The diagram for the circuit is shown in Fig. 2-6.

1. Write the formula.

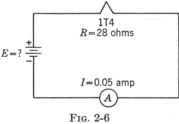

FIG. 2-6

$$E = I \times R$$

2. Substitute numbers.

$$E = 0.05 \times 28$$

3. Multiply the numbers.

$$E = 1.4 \text{ volts} \quad Ans.$$

Problems

1. What voltage is needed to light a lamp if the current required is 2 amp and the resistance of the lamp is 55 ohms?

2. A 20-ohm heating-element resistor draws 3 amp from a line. Find the voltage across the resistor.

3. If the total resistance (impedance) of a radio receiver is 240 ohms and it draws ½ amp, what voltage is needed?

4. A certain radio tube takes 0.15 amp. Its resistance is 80 ohms. What voltage does it need?

5. An arc lamp whose hot resistance is 9 ohms draws 6.2 amp. What voltage is required?

6. What voltage is required to operate a 5,500-ohm electric clock which draws 0.02 amp?

7. A 52-ohm electric toaster uses 2¼ amp. Find the required voltage.

8. A 180-ohm line cord resistor carries 0.15 amp. Find the voltage drop in the resistor.

9. What voltage is needed to energize the field coil of a loudspeaker if its resistance is 1,100 ohms and it uses 0.04 amp?

10. The coils of a washing-machine motor have a resistance of 21 ohms. What voltage does it require if the motor draws 5.3 amp?

11. What voltage is registered by a voltmeter whose internal resistance is 150,000 ohms when 0.001 amp flows through it?

12. What voltage is required for an electroplating tank whose resistance is 0.35 ohm and which requires a current of 80 amp?

13. A neon electric sign draws 1.07 amp. If its resistance is 98 ohms, find the voltage needed.

14. An electric bell has a resistance of 25 ohms and will not operate on a current of less than 0.25 amp. What is the smallest voltage that will ring the bell?

15. The resistance of a telephone receiver is 1,000 ohms. If the current is 0.032 amp, what is the voltage across the receiver?

16. What voltage is supplied to a 0.015-ohm d-c arc welder drawing 650 amp?

17. A 125-ohm relay coil needs 0.15 amp to operate. What is the lowest voltage needed to operate the relay?

18. The cathode bias voltage for a 50L6 power amplifier is created by a resistor of 150 ohms carrying a current of 0.05 amp as shown in Fig. 2-7. Find the value of the bias voltage.

19. What is the voltage across the shunt of an ammeter if the shunt has a resistance of 0.005 ohm and carries 9.99 amp?

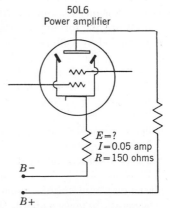

FIG. 2-7. Cathode-bias resistor for a 50L6 power amplifier. The circuit is completed from the source of energy *B* through the tube via the electrons streaming from the cathode to the plate.

20. A 250,000-ohm resistor in the plate circuit of a 12SQ7 tube draws 0.0003 amp. Find the voltage across the resistor.

JOB 2-4: CHECK-UP ON FORMULAS IN ELECTRICAL WORK

In our last job we used our first *formula*. When Ohm's law is written using only the letters which represent the words of Ohm's law it is called a *formula*. As we continue with our study of electricity, we shall meet many new formulas. Some are simple like Ohm's law, but others are more complicated. Let us check up on our knowledge of how to use formulas. The following problems involve the use of formulas. The electrician and the radio and television man find it necessary to solve problems like these in their daily work. If you have any difficulty with these problems, see Job 2-5 which follows.

Problems

1. Using Ohm's law ($E = I \times R$), find the current I drawn by a 10-ohm automobile horn R from a 6-volt battery E.

2. Using Ohm's law, find the number of ohms of resistance R needed to obtain a bias voltage E of 6 volts if the current I is 0.02 amp.

3. Using the formula for electrical power, $P = E \times I$, find the voltage E necessary to operate a 500-watt electric percolator P if it draws a current I of 4.5 amp.

4. Using the formula $P = E \times I$, find the current I drawn by a 440-watt vacuum cleaner P from a 110-volt line E.

5. Write the formula for the following rule: Kilowatts (kw) equals current I multiplied by voltage E and divided by 1,000.

6. Using the series circuit formula $I = E/(R_1 + R_2)$, find I if $E = 100$ volts, $R_1 = 20$ ohms, and $R_2 = 30$ ohms.

7. Using the a-c formula $I = E/Z$, find the impedance Z of an a-c circuit if the voltage E is 50 volts and the current I is 2 amp.

8. Using the formula ma = amp $\times$ 1,000, find the number of amperes which is the equivalent of 125 milliamperes (ma).

9. The formula for the total current in a parallel circuit is $I_T = I_1 + I_2 + I_3$. Find the total current I_T if $I_1 = 2$ amp, $I_2 = 5$ amp, and $I_3 = 4$ amp.

10. The formula for the number of coulombs of electricity which can be placed on the plates of a capacitor is $Q = C \times E$. Find the voltage E which is necessary to place a charge Q of 0.0000002 coulomb on the plates of a capacitor whose capacitance C is 0.000000002 farad.

JOB 2-5: BRUSH-UP ON FORMULAS

Meaning. A formula is a convenient shorthand method for expressing and writing a rule or relationship among several quantities.

Signs of Operation. The quantities involved in any simple relationship are held together by one or more of the following operations:

1. Multiplication ($\times$).
2. Division ($\div$).
3. Addition ($+$).
4. Subtraction ($-$).
5. Equality ($=$).

Each of these operations may be written in several ways.

Multiplication. The multiplication of two quantities is often expressed as the "product of" the two quantities. This may be written as follows:

1. Using a multiplication sign ($\times$) between the numbers or letters.
2. Using a dot ($\cdot$) between the numbers or letters.
3. Writing nothing at all between the numbers or letters.

For example, the product of 3 and 4 may be written as (1) 3×4 or (2) $3 \cdot 4$. The third method cannot be used when only numbers are involved because the meaning would not be clear. For example, 34 would mean the number thirty-four and *not* 3×4. This method of indicating multiplication by omitting all signs between the quantities can be used only for combinations of numbers and letters or combinations of letters.

The product of 6 and R may be written as (1) $6 \times R$, (2) $6 \cdot R$, or (3) $6R$. All three forms indicate that 6 is to be multiplied by the quantity called R.

The product of P, R, and T may be written as (1) $P \times R \times T$, (2) $P \cdot R \cdot T$, or (3) PRT. All three forms indicate that the quantity P is to be multiplied by the quantity R and then multiplied by the quantity T.

Division. The division of two quantities is often expressed as the "quotient of" the two quantities. This may be written as follows:

1. Using a division sign ($\div$) between the numbers or letters.
2. Using a fraction bar to indicate division.

For example, the quotient of 8 divided by 2 may be written as (1) $8 \div 2$ or (2) $\frac{8}{2}$.

The quotient of 12 divided by I may be written as (1) $12 \div I$ or (2) $12/I$.

The quotient of E divided by R may be written as (1) $E \div R$ or (2) E/R.

Addition. The addition of two or more quantities is often expressed as the "sum of" the quantities and is indicated by a plus sign ($+$) between the quantities. For example,

The sum of 6 and 4 is written as $6 + 4$.

The sum of 3 and R is written as $3 + R$.

The sum of E_1 and E_2 is written as $E_1 + E_2$.

Subtraction. The subtraction of two quantities is often expressed as the "difference between" the quantities and is indicated by a minus sign $(-)$ between them. For example,

The difference between 9 and 4 is written as $9 - 4$. This is read as (1) 9 minus 4 or (2) 4 subtracted from 9.

The difference between 20 and R is written as $20 - R$. This is read as (1) 20 minus R or (2) R subtracted from 20.

The difference between E_T and E_1 is written as $E_T - E_1$. This is read as (1) E_T minus E_1 or (2) E_1 subtracted from E_T.

Equality. An equals sign $(=)$ is used to indicate that the combination of numbers and letters on one side of the equals sign has the same value as the combination of numbers and letters on the other side. For example,

$$3 \times 4 = 12$$
$$a \cdot b = ab$$
$$2R = 10$$

Changing Rules into Formulas. To change a rule into a formula

1. Replace each quantity with a convenient letter.

2. Rewrite the rule. Substitute these letters for the words of the rule. Include the symbols for the signs of operation.

Note: The letters used to replace the words are usually the first letter of the word representing the quantity. However, any letter may be used. For example, if a letter has already been used to represent some quantity, it cannot be used again in the same formula to represent another quantity. In this event, a letter which is *not* the first letter of the word would be used.

Example 2-15. Change the following rule into a formula. The area of a rectangle is equal to its length multiplied by its width.

Solution:

The length is replaced by the letter L.

The width is replaced by the letter W.

The area is replaced by the letter A.

The area is equal to the length multiplied by the width.

$$A \qquad = \qquad L \qquad \times \qquad W$$

Thus,

$$A = L \times W \text{ or } A = L \cdot W \text{ or } A = LW \qquad Ans.$$

Example 2-16. Change the following rule into a formula. The voltage is equal to the current multiplied by the resistance.

Solution:

The voltage is replaced by the letter E.
The current is replaced by the letter I.
The resistance is replaced by the letter R.

The voltage is equal to the current multiplied by the resistance.
$\quad E \qquad = \qquad I \qquad \times \qquad R$

Thus,

$$E = I \times R \text{ or } E = I \cdot R \text{ or } E = IR \qquad Ans.$$

Problems

Write the formula for each of the rules given. Use the italic letters and abbreviations in parentheses to indicate each word.

1. The electrical power P is equal to the current I multiplied by the voltage E.

2. The effective voltage E of an a-c voltage wave is equal to 0.707 times the maximum value E_{max}.

3. The efficiency (Eff) of a motor is equal to the power output P_o divided by the power input P_i.

4. The total resistance R_T of a series circuit is equal to the sum of the individual resistances R_1, R_2, and R_3.

5. The capacitive reactance X_c of a capacitor is equal to 159,000 divided by the product of the frequency f and the capacitance C.

6. The total capacitance C_T of a group of capacitors in parallel is equal to the sum of the individual capacitances C_1, C_2, and C_3.

7. The power factor (pf) of an a-c circuit is equal to the total resistance R_T divided by the impedance Z.

8 The total resistance R_T of two resistors in parallel is equal to the product of the resistances R_1 and R_2 divided by the sum of the resistances.

9. The resistance R_s of an ammeter shunt is equal to the product of the meter current I_m and the meter resistance R_m divided by the shunt current I_s.

10. The current I_m in an ammeter is the difference between the line current I and the shunt current I_s.

Changing Formulas into Rules

Example 2-17. Express the formula $P = EI$ as a rule if P is the number of watts of power used, E is the voltage, and I is the current.

Solution: The number of watts of power used is equal to the voltage multiplied by the current in the circuit. *Ans.*

Problems

Express the formula in each problem as a rule.

1. $E = IZ$

where E = voltage of an a-c circuit
    I = current in the circuit
    Z = impedance of the circuit

2. $R = \dfrac{e}{I}$

where R = internal resistance of a dry cell
    e = voltage delivered by the cell
    I = current delivered by the cell

3. $c = 1,000 \ kc$

where kc = number of kilocycles
    c = number of cycles

4. $\lambda = 300,000/kc$

where λ = wavelength of a radio wave
    kc = number of kilocycles

Substitution in Formulas. As we have learned, we can change a rule into a formula by substituting letters for words. Since each word or letter actually represents some number in a specific problem, we can go one step further and substitute specific numbers for the letters in any formula or expression. This is called *substitution in a formula.* The numbers are then combined according to the signs of operation shown by the formula.

Example 2-18. Using the formula $P = EI$, find the power P necessary to operate an incandescent lamp rated at 110 volts E and 2 amp I.
Solution: The diagram for the circuit is shown in Fig. 2-8.

1. Write the formula.

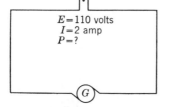

$E = 110$ volts
$I = 2$ amp
$P = ?$

$$P = EI$$

2. Substitute numbers.

$$P = 110 \times 2$$

3. Multiply the numbers.

Fig. 2-8

$$P = 220 \text{ watts} \qquad Ans.$$

Example 2-19. Using the formula $I = E/R$, find the current I drawn from a 117-volt line E by a washing-machine motor of 39 ohms resistance R.

Solution: The diagram for the circuit is shown in Fig. 2-9.

1. Write the formula.

$$I = \frac{E}{R}$$

2. Substitute numbers.

$$I = \frac{117}{39}$$

3. Divide the numbers.

$$I = 3 \text{ amp} \qquad Ans.$$

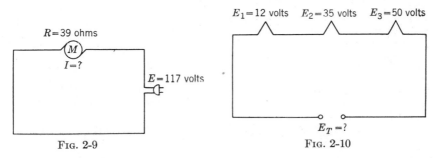

FIG. 2-9   FIG. 2-10

Example 2-20. Using the formula $E_T = E_1 + E_2 + E_3$, find the total voltage E_T required for a series heater circuit if E_1 is 12 volts, E_2 is 35 volts, and E_3 is 50 volts.

Solution: The diagram for the circuit is shown in Fig. 2-10.

1. Write the formula.

$$E_T = E_1 + E_2 + E_3$$

2. Substitute numbers.

$$E_T = 12 + 35 + 50$$

3. Add the numbers.

$$E_T = 97 \text{ volts} \qquad Ans.$$

Example 2-21. Using the formula $I_m = I - I_s$, find the current I_m in an ammeter if the line current I is 50 amp and the shunt current I_s is 49 amp.

Solution: The diagram for the circuit is shown in Fig. 2-11.

1. Write the formula.

$$I_m = I - I_s$$

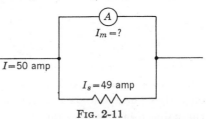

FIG. 2-11

2. Substitute numbers.

$$I_m = 50 - 49$$

3. Subtract the numbers.

$$I_m = 1 \text{ amp} \qquad Ans.$$

Problems

Solve the following problems using the formulas that are given in each problem. If there is no diagram that applies to the problem, set down the given information in the space ordinarily used for the diagram.

1. Using the formula $A = LW$, find the number of square feet of area A in a rectangle if the length L is 15 ft and the width W is 9 ft.

2. Using the formula $I = E/Z$, find the number of amperes I if E is 110 volts and Z is 22 ohms.

3. Using the formula $I_T = I_1 + I_2 + I_3$, find the total number of amperes I_T if $I_1 = 2$ amp, $I_2 = 3$ amp, and $I_3 = 5$ amp.

4. Using the formula $P = SP - C$, find the profit P if the selling price SP is \$1.50 and the cost C is \$1.22.

5. $I = PRT$ is the formula that is used to calculate the interest I on an investment. Using this formula, find the interest I if P is \$2,000, R is $\frac{1}{20}$, and T is 3 years.

6. Using the formula kw $= EI/1,000$, find the kilowatts of power (kw) if the voltage E is 200 volts and the current I is 2 amp.

7. Using the formula $R_T = R_1 + R_2 + R_3$, find the total resistance R_T of a series circuit if R_1 is 18.2 ohms, R_2 is 45.8 ohms, and R_3 is 76.4 ohms.

8. The formula for the shunt current in an ammeter hookup is $I_s = I - I_m$. Find the current I_s through the shunt if the line current I is 0.045 amp and the meter current I_m is 0.009 amp.

JOB 2-6: SOLVING THE OHM'S LAW FORMULA FOR CURRENT
OR RESISTANCE

Formulas Are Equations. As you may have noticed, every formula contains the sign of equality. The statement that a combination of quantities is *equal* to another combination of quantities is called an *equation*. In this sense, every formula is an equation. Examples of some equations are

$$3 \times 4 = 12$$
$$2 \times I = 10$$
$$12 = 3 \times R$$
$$E = IR$$

In order that a statement be termed an equation, it is necessary only that the value on the left side of the equals sign be *truly equal* to the value on the right side.

Working with Equations. Many mathematical operations may be performed on an equation. Whatever is done, however, the basic equality of the statements on each side of the equals sign must not be destroyed. This equality must be maintained if the equation is to remain an equation. This is accomplished by applying the following basic principle:

Basic Principle: Any mathematical operation performed on one side of an equals sign must also be performed on the other side.

For example, let us subject the equation $3 \times 4 = 12$ to different mathematical operations.

Rule 1: The same number may be added to both sides of an equals sign without destroying the equality.

1. Write the equation.

$$3 \times 4 = 12$$

2. Add **3** to both sides.

$$(3 \times 4) + \mathbf{3} = 12 + \mathbf{3}$$

3. Do the arithmetic.

$$12 + \mathbf{3} = 12 + \mathbf{3}$$

or

$$15 = 15$$

which is a true equation, since the left side is still equal to the right side.

Rule 2: The same number may be subtracted from both sides of an equals sign without destroying the equality.

1. Write the equation.

$$3 \times 4 = 12$$

2. Subtract **3** from both sides.

$$(3 \times 4) - \mathbf{3} = 12 - \mathbf{3}$$

3. Do the arithmetic.

$$12 - \mathbf{3} = 12 - \mathbf{3}$$

or

$$9 = 9$$

which is a true equation, since the left side is still equal to the right side.

Rule 3: Both sides of an equals sign may be multiplied by the same number without destroying the equality.

1. Write the equation.

$$3 \times 4 = 12$$

2. Multiply both sides by **3**.

$$(3 \times 4) \times 3 = 12 \times 3$$

3. Do the arithmetic.

$$12 \times 3 = 12 \times 3$$

or

$$36 = 36$$

which is a true equation, since the left side is still equal to the right side.

Rule 4: Both sides of an equals sign may be divided by the same number without destroying the equality.

1. Write the equation.

$$3 \times 4 = 12$$

2. Divide both sides by **3**.

$$\frac{3 \times 4}{3} = \frac{12}{3}$$

3. Do the arithmetic.

$$\frac{12}{3} = \frac{12}{3}$$

or

$$4 = 4$$

which is a true equation, since the left side is still equal to the right side.

Solving Equations.   Consider the equation $2R = 10$.   To solve this equation means to find the value of the unknown letter R in the equation.   This value is found *when the letter stands all alone on one side of the equals sign.*   When this occurs, the equation has the form

$$R = \text{some number}$$

This number will obviously be the value of the letter R, and the equation will be solved.

How Do We Get the Letter All Alone?   In the equation $2R = 10$, the letter will be alone on the left side of the equals sign if we can somehow eliminate the number 2 on that side. The number 2 will actually be eliminated if we can change it to a 1, since $1R$ means the same as R. This can be done by applying Rule 4 above. In order to eliminate the 2, we shall *divide both sides* of the equation *by that same number*.

1. Write the equation.

$$2R = 10$$

2. Divide both sides by 2.

$$\frac{2R}{2} = \frac{10}{2}$$

3. Reduce each side separately.

$$\frac{\overset{1}{\cancel{2}R}}{\underset{1}{\cancel{2}}} = \frac{\overset{5}{\cancel{10}}}{\underset{1}{\cancel{2}}}$$

or

$$1R = 5$$

or

$$R = 5$$

Notice that the number that is multiplied by the unknown letter will be canceled out *only* if we divide both sides of the equals sign *by that same number*. Dividing both sides by any other number will *not* eliminate this number.

Rule 5: To eliminate the number which is multiplied by the unknown letter, divide both sides of the equals sign by the multiplier of the letter.

Example 2-22. Solve the following equations for the values of the unknown letters.

Solution:

1. Write the equations.

$$2R = 10 \qquad\qquad 14 = 7E$$

2. Divide both sides of each equation by the multiplier of the letter.

$$\frac{2R}{2} = \frac{10}{2} \qquad\qquad \frac{14}{7} = \frac{7E}{7}$$

3. Cancel out the multiplier of the letters.

$$R = \frac{10}{2} \qquad\qquad \frac{14}{7} = E$$

4. Dividing,

$$R = 5 \quad Ans. \qquad 2 = E \quad Ans.$$

We are now in a position to shorten our work. Notice that in each example, the effect of dividing both sides of the equals sign by the multiplier of the letter has been to *move* the multiplier *across the equals sign* into the position shown in step 3.   Since this will always occur, we can eliminate step 2 and proceed as shown in Example 2-23.

Example 2-23.   Solve the following equations for the values of the unknown letters:

Solution:

1. Write the equations.

$$2R = 10 \qquad\qquad 14 = 7E$$

2. Divide the quantity all alone on one side of the equals sign by the multiplier of the letter.

$$R = \frac{10}{2} \qquad\qquad \frac{14}{7} = E$$

3. Dividing,

$$R = 5 \quad Ans. \qquad 2 = E \quad Ans.$$

Rule 6: To solve a simple equation of the form "a number multiplied by a letter equals a number," divide the number all alone on one side of the equals sign by the multiplier of the letter.

Example 2-24.   Solve the equation $4I = 21$ for the value of I.

Solution:

$$4I = 21$$
$$I = \frac{21}{4}$$
$$I = 5\tfrac{1}{4} \qquad Ans.$$

Example 2-25.   Solve the equation $18 = 0.3Z$ for the value of Z.

Solution:

$$18 = 0.3Z$$
$$\frac{18}{0.3} = Z$$
$$60 = Z \text{ or } Z = 60 \qquad Ans.$$

Problems

Solve the following equations for the value of the unknown letter.

1. $3I = 15$	**6.** $4L = 21$	**11.** $0.3R = 120$
2. $5R = 20$	**7.** $3R = 41$	**12.** $40 = 0.2Z$
3. $2E = 12$	**8.** $20I = 117$	**13.** $0.15R = 120$
4. $48 = 8R$	**9.** $19 = 2E$	**14.** $0.003R = 78$
5. $7I = 63$	**10.** $\tfrac{1}{2}W = 20$	**15.** $117 = 0.3Z$

Solving the Formula for Ohm's Law. The formula for Ohm's law is actually an equation. By applying Rule 6, we can solve Ohm's law for any unknown value of current or resistance.

Example 2-26. The total resistance of a relay coil is 50 ohms. What current will it draw from a 20-volt source?

Solution: The diagram for the circuit is shown in Fig. 2-12.

1. Write the formula.

$$E = IR$$

2. Substitute numbers.

$$20 = I \times 50$$

3. Solve for I.

$$\frac{20}{50} = I$$

4. Divide the numbers.

$$0.4 = I \quad \text{or} \quad I = 0.4 \text{ amp} \quad Ans.$$

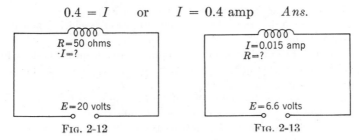

Fɪɢ. 2-12   Fɪɢ. 2-13

Example 2-27. Find the total resistance of a telegraph coil if it draws 0.015 amp from a 6.6-volt source.

Solution: The diagram for the circuit is shown in Fig. 2-13.

1. Write the formula.

$$E = IR$$

2. Substitute numbers.

$$6.6 = 0.015 \times R$$

3. Solve for R.

$$\frac{6.6}{0.015} = R$$

4. Divide the numbers.

$$440 = R \quad \text{or} \quad R = 440 \text{ ohms} \quad Ans.$$

Problems

1. What is the hot resistance of an arc lamp if it draws 15 amp from a 30-volt line?

2. The resistance of the motor windings of an electric vacuum cleaner is 20 ohms. If the voltage is 120 volts, find the current drawn.

3. An electric enameling kiln draws 9 amp from a 117-volt line. Find the resistance of the coils.

4. The field magnet of a loudspeaker carries 0.04 amp when connected to a 40-volt supply.   Find its resistance.

5. What is the hot resistance of a tungsten lamp if it draws 0.25 amp from a 110-volt line?

6. What current would flow in a 0.3-ohm short circuit of a 6-volt automobile ignition system?

7. A 6BG6 is used as a horizontal output tube in a television receiver.   If the "hot" heater resistance is 7 ohms, how much current flows through the heater when the rated voltage of 6.3 volts is applied?

8. The heater of a 6AU6 video amplifier tube draws 0.3 amp from a 6.3-volt circuit.   What is the hot resistance of the heater filament?

9. A dry cell indicates a terminal voltage of 1.2 volts when a wire of 0.2-ohm resistance is connected across it.   What current flows in the wire?

10. What is the hot resistance of the heater of a 6L6 beam-power amplifier pentode if it draws 0.9 amp from a 6.3-volt power source?

11. What is the resistance of a telephone receiver if there is a voltage drop of 24 volts across it when the current is 0.02 amp?

12. What current is drawn by a 5,000-ohm electric clock when operated from a 110-volt line?

13. Find the current drawn by a 52-ohm toaster from a 117-volt line.

14. Find the resistance of an electric furnace drawing 41 amp from a 230-volt line.

15. The resistance of the field coils of a shunt motor is 60 ohms.   What is the field current when the voltage across the coils is 220 volts?

16. The resistance of a common Christmas-tree lamp is about 50 ohms. What is the current through it if the voltage across the lamp is 14 volts?

17. The large copper leads on switchboards are called bus bars.   What is the resistance of a bus bar carrying 400 amp if the voltage across its ends is 0.6 volt?

18. If a radio receiver draws 0.85 amp from a 110-volt line, what is the total resistance (impedance) of the receiver?

19. A 32-candlepower lamp in a truck headlight draws 3.4 amp from the 6-volt battery.   What is the resistance of the lamp?

20. What current is carried by a 135-ohm line cord resistor if the voltage drop across it is 30 volts?

21. What current flows through an automobile headlight lamp of 1.2 ohms resistance if it is operated from the 6-volt battery?

22. What is the resistance of a buzzer if it draws 0.14 amp from a 3-volt source?

23. Find the resistance of an iron if it draws 3.8 amp from a 110-volt line.

24. A 160-ohm telegraph relay coil operates on a voltage of 9.6 volts.   What is the current drawn by the relay?

JOB 2-7: CHECK-UP ON DECIMALS

Did you have any difficulty with the decimals in the last job?   The following problems occur in the everyday work of the electrician and radio man.   They all involve decimals and will help you to check up on their use. If you have difficulty with any of these problems, see Job 2-8 which follows.

Problems

1. Find the total current drawn by the following appliances by adding the currents: electric iron, 4.12 amp; electric clock, 0.02 amp; 100-watt lamp, 0.91 amp; and radio, 0.5 amp.

2. Find, by addition, the total heater voltage required by a five-tube radio receiver using tubes rated at 12.6, 12.6, 12.6, 50, and 35 volts.

3. Find the total capacitance of a parallel group of capacitors by adding these values: 0.00025, 0.01, and 0.005 μf.

4. How much larger in diameter is No. 10 copper wire (0.1019 in.) than No. 14 wire (0.0641 in.)?

5. The current drawn by a motor is 1.21 amp at no load and 1.56 amp at full load. What is the increase in the current?

6. The heaters of a five-tube radio receiver are connected in series to a 110-volt line. The heaters require only 76.9 volts. How many volts are not needed?

7. The laminated core of a power transformer is made of 15 sheets of steel each 0.079 in. thick. Find the total thickness of the core.

8. The maximum value of an a-c voltage wave is 1.414 times its a-c meter reading of 46.5 volts. Find the maximum value of the voltage wave.

9. If 65 ft of BX cable costs $14.95, what is the cost of 1 ft of this cable?

10. The resistance of 24.5 ft of No. 16 copper wire is 0.0982 ohm. Find the resistance of 1 ft of this wire.

11. Add 7.05, 2, 3.5.

12. Subtract: 6.75 − 3

13. Which current is larger—0.4 or 0.25 amp?

14. Write the following decimals in words: (a) 4.3, (b) 0.359, and (c) 0.41.

15. Multiply $\frac{3}{10}$ by 0.05.

16. Write as a decimal (a) $\frac{1}{4}$, (b) $\frac{4}{7}$, (c) $\frac{5}{8}$, and (d) $\frac{1}{16}$.

17. Subtract 12 from 18.24.

18. Arrange the following numbers starting with the largest: 0.050, 0.30, 0.0070, 1.1.

19. Find the difference between three-tenths and twenty-five hundredths.

20. What is the excess of 5 over 2.75?

JOB 2-8. BRUSH-UP ON DECIMAL FRACTIONS

Meaning of a Decimal Fraction. A decimal fraction is a fraction in which the denominator is not written. The denominator is always a number like 10, 100, 1,000, etc. We know the value of the denominator by the way in which the numerator is written. The denominator is indicated by the number of digits to the right of a dot called a *decimal point*.

Equal Fractions

Words	Fraction	Decimal
Seven-tenths.........................	$\frac{7}{10}$	0.7
Twenty-three hundredths..............	$\frac{23}{100}$	0.23
Seventy-hundredths...................	$\frac{70}{100}$	0.70
Three-hundredths.....................	$\frac{3}{100}$	0.03
Three-thousandths....................	3/1,000	0.003
Fifteen-thousandths..................	15/1,000	0.015
One hundred and forty-nine thousandths	149/1,000	0.149
Seven hundred thousandths............	700/1,000	0.700

Meaning of the Digits in a Decimal. The number of digits to the right of a decimal point determine the denominator of the decimal fraction according to the following table.

No. of Places to the Right of the Decimal Point	Meaning
1	Tenths
2	Hundredths
3	Thousandths
4	Ten-thousandths

Note: Zeros placed at the *end* of a decimal do *not* change the value of the decimal but merely describe the decimal in another way. For example, 0.5 (5 tenths) = 0.50 (50 hundredths) = 0.500 (500 thousandths).

Comparing the Value of Decimals. When comparing the value of various decimal fractions, we must first be certain that they have the same denominators. This means that the decimals must be written so that they have the same number of decimal places.

Example 2-28. Which is larger—0.3 or 0.25?
Solution: Since 0.3 has only one decimal place and 0.25 has two decimal places, we must change 0.3 into a two-place decimal by adding a zero. This does *not* change the value but merely expresses it differently. Therefore 0.3 or 0.30 (thirty-hundredths) is larger than 0.25 (twenty-five hundredths).   *Ans.*

Problems

Write the following fractions as decimal fractions:

1. $\frac{7}{10}$
2. $\frac{29}{100}$
3. $\frac{114}{1000}$
4. $\frac{3}{10}$

5. $\frac{6}{100}$
6. $\frac{9}{1000}$
7. $\frac{18}{1000}$
8. $\frac{3}{1000}$

9. $\frac{11}{100}$
10. $\frac{4}{10}$
11. $\frac{13}{1000}$
12. $\frac{74}{100}$

13. $\frac{45}{1000}$
14. $\frac{316}{1000}$
15. $\frac{6}{10}$

Arrange the following decimals in order starting with the largest:

16. 0.007, 0.16, 0.4   **20.** 0.5, 0.051, 0.18   **23.** 0.006, 0.05, 0.3
17. 0.2, 0.107, 0.28   **21.** 0.90, 0.018, 0.06   **24.** 0.19, 0.004, 0.08
18. 0.8, 0.06, 0.040   **22.** 0.1228, 0.236, 0.4   **25.** 0.060, 0.40, 0.0080
19. 0.496, 0.8, 0.02

Changing Mixed Numbers to Decimals. When a mixed number is read as a decimal, the word "and" appears as a decimal point. For example, $2\frac{7}{10}$ is read as two *and* seven-tenths and is written as 2.7. A whole number may be written as a decimal if a decimal point is placed at the *end* of the number. For example, the number 4 means 4.0 or 4.00 or 4.000

Problems

Change the following mixed numbers to decimals:

1. $2\frac{3}{10}$ **4.** $1\frac{17}{100}$ **7.** $2\frac{20}{1000}$ **9.** $1\frac{2}{1000}$
2. $18\frac{5}{100}$ **5.** $2\frac{25}{1000}$ **8.** $3\frac{9}{100}$ **10.** $62\frac{90}{100}$
3. $3\frac{144}{1000}$ **6.** $7\frac{35}{100}$

Changing Fractions to Decimals. We shall discover that many of the answers to our electrical problems will be fractions like $\frac{1}{8}$ amp, $\frac{7}{40}$ µf, and $\frac{3}{13}$ ohm. These will be perfectly correct mathematical answers, but they will be completely worthless to a practical electrician or television mechanic. Electrical measuring instruments give values expressed as decimals and *not* as fractions. In addition, the manufacturers of electrical components give the values of the parts in terms of decimals.

Suppose we worked out a problem and found that the current in the circuit should be $\frac{1}{8}$ amp. Then, using an ammeter, we tested the circuit and found that 0.125 amp flowed. Is our circuit correct? How would we know? How can we compare $\frac{1}{8}$ and 0.125? The easiest way is to change the fraction $\frac{1}{8}$ into its equivalent decimal and then to compare the decimals.

Rule: To change a fraction into a decimal, divide the numerator by the denominator.

Example 2-29. Change $\frac{1}{8}$ into an equivalent decimal.

Solution: ⅛ means 1 ÷ 8. To write this as a long-division example, place the numerator inside the long-division sign and the denominator outside the sign as shown below.

$$8 \overline{)1}$$

We can't divide 8 into 1, but remember that every whole number may be written with a decimal point at the end of the number. As many zeros may be added as we desire without changing the value. Our problem now looks like this:

$$8 \overline{)1.000}$$

1. Put the decimal point in the answer directly above its position in 1.000.

$$8 \overline{)1.000}^{\qquad .}$$

2. Try to divide the 8 into the first digit. 8 does not divide into 1. Then try to divide the 8 into the first two digits. 8 divides into 10 one time. Place this number 1 in the answer directly above the last digit of the number into which the 8 was divided.

$$8 \overline{)1.000}^{\;0.1}$$

3. Multiply this 1 by the divisor 8 and place as shown below. Draw a line and subtract.

$$\begin{array}{r} 0.1 \\ 8 \overline{)1.000} \\ \underline{8} \\ 2 \end{array}$$

4. Bring down the next digit 0 and divide this new number 20 by the 8. The 8 will divide into 20 two times.

$$\begin{array}{r} 0.1 \\ 8 \overline{)1.000} \\ \underline{8} \\ 20 \end{array}$$

5. Place this 2 in the answer directly above the last digit brought down.

$$\begin{array}{r} 0.12 \\ 8 \overline{)1.000} \\ \underline{8} \\ 20 \end{array}$$

6. Multiply the 2 by the divisor 8, and continue steps 3 to 5. The answer comes out even as 0.125. This means that $\frac{1}{8} = 0.125$ *Ans.*

$$
\begin{array}{r}
0.125 \\
8\overline{)1.000} \\
8 \\
\hline
20 \\
16 \\
\hline
40 \\
40 \\
\hline
0
\end{array}
$$

Example 2-30. Change $\frac{7}{40}$ into an equivalent decimal.

Solution:

$$
\frac{7}{40} = 40\overline{)7.000} \quad \begin{array}{c} 0.175 \quad Ans. \end{array}
$$

$$
\begin{array}{r}
0.175 \\
40\overline{)7.000} \\
4\,0 \\
\hline
3\,00 \\
2\,80 \\
\hline
200 \\
200 \\
\hline
0
\end{array}
$$

Example 2-31. Change $\frac{6}{13}$ into an equivalent decimal.
Solution: The answer does not come out evenly:

$$
\frac{6}{13} = 13\overline{)6.000} \quad \begin{array}{r} 0.461 \end{array}
$$

$$
\begin{array}{r}
0.461 \\
13\overline{)6.000} \\
5\,2 \\
\hline
80 \\
78 \\
\hline
20 \\
13 \\
\hline
7
\end{array}
$$

We see that there is a remainder. If the remainder is more than half of the divisor, we drop it and add an extra unit to the last place of the answer. Since 7 is more than half of 13,

$$
\begin{array}{r}
0.461\frac{7}{13} \text{ becomes } 0.461 \\
+\quad 1 \\
\hline
0.462 \quad Ans.
\end{array}
$$

If any remainder is less than half of the divisor, drop it completely and leave the answer unchanged. For example,

$$0.236\frac{5}{12} = 0.236 \quad \text{(since 5 is less than half of 12)}$$
$$0.483\frac{1}{4} = 0.483 \quad \text{(since 1 is less than half of 4)}$$

Table 2-1. Table of Decimal Equivalents

Fraction	$\frac{1}{32}$ds	$\frac{1}{64}$ths	Decimal	Fraction	$\frac{1}{32}$ds	$\frac{1}{64}$ths	Decimal
		1	0.015625			33	0.515625
	1	2	0.03125		17	34	0.53125
		3	0.046875			35	0.546875
$\frac{1}{16}$	2	4	0.0625	$\frac{9}{16}$	18	36	0.5625
		5	0.078125			37	0.578125
	3	6	0.09375		19	38	0.59375
		7	0.109375			39	0.609375
$\frac{1}{8}$	4	8	0.125	$\frac{5}{8}$	20	40	0.625
		9	0.140625			41	0.640625
	5	10	0.15625		21	42	0.65625
		11	0.171875			43	0.671875
$\frac{3}{16}$	6	12	0.1875	$\frac{11}{16}$	22	44	0.6875
		13	0.203125			45	0.703125
	7	14	0.21875		23	46	0.71875
		15	0.234375			47	0.734375
$\frac{1}{4}$	8	16	0.25	$\frac{3}{4}$	24	48	0.75
		17	0.265625			49	0.765625
	9	18	0.28125		25	50	0.78125
		19	0.296875			51	0.796875
$\frac{5}{16}$	10	20	0.3125	$\frac{13}{16}$	26	52	0.8125
		21	0.328125			53	0.828125
	11	22	0.34375		27	54	0.84375
		23	0.359375			55	0.859375
$\frac{3}{8}$	12	24	0.375	$\frac{7}{8}$	28	56	0.875
		25	0.390625			57	0.890625
	13	26	0.40625		29	58	0.90625
		27	0.421875			59	0.921875
$\frac{7}{16}$	14	28	0.4375	$\frac{15}{16}$	30	60	0.9375
		29	0.453125			61	0.953125
	15	30	0.46875		31	62	0.96875
		31	0.484375			63	0.984375
$\frac{1}{2}$	16	32	0.5	1	32	64	1.

A big question may have occurred to you by now: "If it doesn't come out even, how long shall I continue to divide?" The answer to this depends on the use to which the answer is to be put. Some jobs require five or six decimal places, while others need only one place or none at all. For example, the value of a grid leak capacitor should be worked out to an answer like 0.00025 μf; a grid bias resistor of 203.4 ohms is just as well written as 203 ohms or even 200 ohms.

Degree of Accuracy. A very general rule for the number of decimal places required in an answer is given in the following table:

Answer	No. of decimal places	Examples
Less than 1	3	0.132, 0.008
From 1–10	2	3.48, 6.07
From 10–100	1	28.3, 52.9
From 100 up	None	425, 659

Problems

Change the following fractions to equivalent decimals:

1. $\frac{1}{4}$ 5. $\frac{2}{5}$ 9. $\frac{7}{8}$ 13. $\frac{3}{32}$ 16. $\frac{9}{16}$

2. $\frac{3}{8}$ 6. $\frac{3}{10}$ 10. $\frac{3}{16}$ 14. $\frac{21}{25}$ 17. $\frac{1}{50}$

3. $\frac{5}{8}$ 7. $\frac{3}{20}$ 11. $\frac{4}{9}$ 15. $\frac{25}{40}$ 18. $\frac{1}{200}$

4. $\frac{1}{3}$ 8. $\frac{2}{7}$ 12. $\frac{13}{15}$

Using the Decimal Equivalent Chart. There are some fractions that are used very often. These are the fractions which represent the parts of an inch on a ruler, like $\frac{1}{16}$, $\frac{3}{8}$, $\frac{5}{32}$, $\frac{9}{64}$, etc. Since they are so widely used, a table of decimal equivalents has been prepared. In order to find the decimal equivalent of a fraction of this type, refer to Table 2-1.

Addition of Decimals. When adding decimals, be sure to write the numbers so that the decimal points will be kept in a straight vertical line.

Example 2-32. Add $2.52 + 0.007 + 13.03 + 0.7 + 26$.

Solution:

$$
\begin{array}{ccc}
2.52 & & 2.520 \\
0.007 & & 0.007 \\
13.03 & \text{or} & 13.030 \\
0.7 & & 0.700 \\
\underline{26.} & & \underline{26.000} \\
& & 42.257 \quad Ans.
\end{array}
$$

The empty spaces are filled in with zeros as shown in the column at the right in order to aid in keeping the numbers in the correct column.

Problems

Add the following decimals:
1. $3.28 + 9.5 + 0.634 + 0.078$
2. $56.09 + 14 + 4.876 + 49.007$
3. $13 + 3.072 + 0.7 + 6.06$
4. $54 + 0.033 + 0.713 + 8.05$
5. $0.087 + 6.18 + 4 + 1.7$

6. Find the total drop in voltage in a distribution system if the voltage drops across each section are 1.06, 36.4, and 8 volts.

7. Find the total thickness of insulation on shielded radio wire covered with resin (0.022 in.), lacquered cotton braid (0.018 in.), and copper shielding (0.03 in.).

8. The diameter of a motor shaft bearing is 0.0025 in. larger than the shaft of the motor.   What is the diameter of the bearing if the shaft has a diameter of 2.25 in.?

9. Find the total resistance of the leads of an installation if the resistances are 0.054, 1.004, 1.2, and 1.2 ohms.

10. A four-tube pentode beam-power receiver uses tubes with the following heater voltage ratings: 25L6, 25 volts; 6K7, 6.3 volts; 25Z6, 25 volts; and 6J7, 6.3 volts.   Find the total voltage required by all the heaters.

Subtracting Decimals.   When subtracting decimals, write the numbers in columns as for addition, lining up the decimal points in a straight vertical column.

Example 2-33.   Subtract 2.36 from 4.79.
Solution: The number *after* the word "from" is written on top.   The number *after* the word "subtract" is written underneath.

$$
\begin{array}{r}
4.79 \\
- \ 2.36 \\
\hline
2.43 \quad Ans.
\end{array}
$$

Example 2-34.   Subtract 1.04 from 3.
Solution: The number 3 is written as 3.00 to locate the decimal point correctly.

$$
\begin{array}{r}
3.00 \\
- \ 1.04 \\
\hline
1.96 \quad Ans.
\end{array}
$$

Example 2-35.   Find the value of $0.1 - 0.05$.

Solution:

$$
\begin{array}{r}
0.10 \\
- \ 0.05 \\
\hline
0.05 \quad Ans.
\end{array}
$$

Example 2-36. $2\frac{1}{2} - 1.32$.

Solution: Since $2\frac{1}{2} = 2.5$ or 2.50, we have

$$
\begin{array}{r}
2.50 \\
-\ 1.32 \\
\hline
1.18 \quad \textit{Ans.}
\end{array}
$$

Problems

1. $0.26 - 0.03$	**7.** $0.627 - 0.31$	**13.** $2.89 - 0.5$
2. $1.36 - 0.18$	**8.** $0.827 - 0.31$	**14.** $12.6 - 7$
3. $0.4 - 0.06$	**9.** $3 - 0.08$	**15.** $0.316 - 0.054$
4. $0.05 - 0.004$	**10.** $0.5 - 0.02$	**16.** $14 - 8.06$
5. $18.92 - 11.36$	**11.** $6 - 0.1$	**17.** $5\frac{1}{4} - 2.63$
6. $\frac{5}{8} - 0.002$	**12.** $0.83 - \frac{1}{2}$	**18.** $3.125 - \frac{1}{8}$

19. Subtract $\frac{1}{4}$ from 0.765.

20. Find the difference between 110 and 54.9.

21. Find the difference between (*a*) 0.316 and 0.012, (*b*) 3.006 and 1.9, (*c*) 0.5 and 0.11, (*d*) 7.07 and 1.32, and (*e*) 2 and 0.02.

22. Subtract (*a*) 0.008 from 0.80 and (*b*) 0.216 from 2.16.

23. From 0.4 subtract 0.08.

24. From 6.04 subtract 2.3.

25. From 2.004 subtract 1.09.

26. What is the difference in the diameters of No. 1 wire (0.2893 in.) and No. 7 wire (0.1447 in.)?

27. The electric-meter readings on successive months were 70.08 and 76.49. Find the difference.

28. A circuit in a television receiver calls for a 0.0005-μf capacitor. A capacitor valued at 0.00035 μf is available. How much extra capacitance is needed if connected in parallel?

29. A 6J5 tube used as an audio amplifier in a short-wave receiver draws current from the 350-volt tap of the power transformer. If the voltage loss in the plate load is 108.6 volts, what voltage is available at the plate of the tube?

30. The intermediate frequency at the output of a converter stage is found by obtaining the difference between the oscillator frequency and the radio frequency. If the radio frequency is 1.1 Mc and the oscillator frequency is 1.555 Mc, what will be the intermediate frequency?

Multiplication of Decimals. Decimals are multiplied in exactly the same way that ordinary numbers are multiplied. However, in addition to the normal multiplication, the decimal point must be correctly set in the answer.

Rule: The number of decimal places in a product is equal to the sum of the number of decimal places in the numbers being multiplied.

Example 2-37. Multiply 0.62 by 0.3.

Solution:

$$0.62 \text{ (multiplicand—2 places)}$$
$$\times\ 0.3 \text{ (multiplier—1 place)}$$
$$\overline{0.186} \text{ (product} = 2 + 1 = 3 \text{ places)}\qquad Ans.$$

Example 2-38. Multiply 0.35 by 0.004

Solution:

$$0.35 \text{ (multiplicand—2 places)}$$
$$\times\ 0.004 \text{ (multiplier—3 places)}$$
$$\overline{0.00140} \text{ (product} = 2 + 3 = 5 \text{ places)}\qquad Ans.$$

In this problem, extra zeros must be inserted between the decimal point and the digits of the answer to make up the required number of decimal places.

Problems

Find the product of

1. 0.005×82
2. 1.732×40
3. 1.13×0.41
4. 0.9×0.09

5. 0.866×35
6. 44.6×805
7. 7.63×0.029
8. 0.354×0.008

9. 6.2×0.003
10. 0.033×0.0025
11. $106 \times .045$
12. 73.8×1.09

13. If a 100-watt lamp uses 0.91 amp, how much current would be used by five such lamps in parallel?

14. If BX cable costs $0.235 per foot, what would be the cost of 52.5 ft?

15. If a portable B battery is made of 45 small 1.5-volt dry cells in series, find the total voltage of the battery.

16. The number of milliamperes is found by multiplying the number of amperes by 1,000. Find the number of milliamperes equal to (*a*) 0.25 amp, (*b*) 0.025 amp, and (*c*) 2.5 amp.

17. The standard unit of resistance is measured by the resistance of a column of mercury 106.3 cm high. If 1 cm equals 0.3937 in., what is the height of the mercury column correct to the nearest thousandth of an inch?

Division of Decimals

Example 2-39. Divide 4.788 by 14.

Solution: The division is accomplished in the same manner as in changing fractions to decimals.

$$\begin{array}{r} 0.342 \quad \textit{Ans.} \\ 14\overline{)4.788} \\ 4\ 2 \\ \hline 58 \\ 56 \\ \hline 28 \\ 28 \\ \hline 0 \end{array}$$

Example 2-40. Divide 1.38 by 0.06.

Solution: When dividing by a decimal, it is best to move the decimal point all the way over to the right so as to bring it to the end of the divisor.

$$\odot 06.\overline{)1.38}$$

If this is done, the decimal point in the dividend must also be moved to the right *for the same number of places.* Then we can divide as before.

$$\begin{array}{r} 23. \quad \textit{Ans.} \\ \odot 06.\overline{)1 \odot 38.} \\ 1\ \ 2 \\ \hline 18 \\ 18 \\ \hline 0 \end{array}$$

Example 2-41. Divide 3.6 by 0.08.

Solution: A zero must be added after the 6 to provide the two places that the decimal point must be moved to the right.

$$\begin{array}{r} 45. \quad \textit{Ans.} \\ \odot 08.\overline{)3 \odot 60.} \\ 3\ \ 2 \\ \hline 40 \\ 40 \\ \hline 0 \end{array}$$

Example 2-42. Divide 0.0007 by 0.125.

Solution:

$$\begin{array}{r} 0.0056 \quad \textit{Ans.} \\ \odot 125.\overline{)\odot 000.7000} \\ 625 \\ \hline 750 \\ 750 \\ \hline 0 \end{array}$$

Problems

1. $3.9 \div 0.3$
2. $12.56 \div 0.4$
3. $80.5 \div 0.5$

4. $51 \div 0.06$
5. $38.54 \div 8.2$
6. $1{,}591 \div 0.43$

7. $2.8296 \div 0.0036$
8. $140.7 \div 0.021$
9. $9.1408 \div 3.94$

10. Using the formula $I = E/R$, find I if $E = 79.5$ volts and $R = 265$ ohms.

11. Shielded rubber-jacketed microphone cable weighs 0.075 lb per foot. How many feet of cable are there in a coil weighing 15 lb?

12. What is the smallest number of insulators, each rated at 12,000 volts, that should be used to safeguard a 220,000-volt transmission line?

13. If 440,000 lines of magnetic force are cut in 4.4 sec and produce 1 volt of electrical pressure, how many lines of force were cut per second?

14. The Q, or "quality," of a coil is a measure of its worth in a tuned circuit. It is found by dividing the reactance of the coil by its resistance (see Job 15-3). Find the Q of a coil if its reactance is 1,820 ohms and its resistance is 30 ohms.

15. A 50-ft-long wire has a resistance of 10.35 ohms. What is the resistance of 1 ft of this wire?

Multiplication of Fractions and Decimals

Example 2-43.   Multiply $\frac{1}{5}$ by 2.5.

Solution:

$$\frac{1}{5} \times 2.5 = \frac{1}{5} \times \frac{2.5}{1} = \frac{2.5}{5} = 0.5 \qquad Ans.$$

Example 2-44.   Multiply $\frac{3}{10}$ by 0.5.

Solution:

$$\frac{3}{10} \times 0.5 = \frac{3}{10} \times \frac{0.5}{1} = \frac{1.5}{10} = 0.15 \qquad Ans.$$

Example 2-45.   Multiply $\frac{2}{3}$ by 0.19.

Solution:

$$\frac{2}{3} \times 0.19 = \frac{2}{3} \times \frac{0.19}{1} = \frac{0.38}{3} = 0.127 \qquad Ans.$$

Example 2-46.   Multiply $2\frac{1}{4}$ by 0.35.

Solution: If the fraction is one that can be easily changed to a decimal, do so and multiply the resulting decimals. Since $2\frac{1}{4}$ is equal to 2.25 (from the decimal equivalent chart),

$$2\frac{1}{4} \times 0.35 = 2.25 \times 0.35 = 0.788 \qquad Ans.$$

Problems

1. $\frac{1}{5} \times 3.5$
2. $\frac{2}{5} \times 0.25$
3. $\frac{1}{5} \times 0.05$
4. $\frac{1}{2} \times 2.4$
5. $\frac{1}{10} \times 0.5$

6. $\frac{1}{10} \times 0.01$
7. $\frac{1}{3} \times 0.27$
8. $\frac{1}{5} \times 30.5$
9. $\frac{1}{8} \times 12.6$
10. $\frac{1}{10} \times 2.5$

11. $1\frac{1}{2} \times 0.3$
12. $\frac{2}{5} \times 0.1$
13. $\frac{1}{8} \times 0.13$
14. $\frac{3}{5} \times 2.7$
15. $\frac{1}{6} \times 4.9$

16. $\frac{2}{7} \times 3.12$
17. $5\frac{3}{4} \times 0.192$
18. $1\frac{1}{3} \times 0.23$
19. $0.056 \times 3\frac{1}{2}$
20. $0.91 \times 2\frac{1}{5}$

Summary—Working with Decimals

1. Decimal fractions are fractions whose denominators are numbers like 10, 100, 1,000, etc.

2. The denominator is shown by the number of digits to the right of the decimal point. Each digit represents a zero in the denominator of the fraction.

3. Decimals can be compared only when they have the same number of decimal places.

4. The word "and" in a mixed number is written as a decimal point.

5. Fractions are changed to decimals by dividing the numerator by the denominator.

6. A whole number always has a decimal point understood to be at the end of the number.

7. When dividing decimals, if a remainder is more than half of the divisor, drop it and add a full unit to the last digit of the answer. If the remainder is less than half, drop it completely.

8. When adding or subtracting decimals, line up the decimal points in a vertical column.

9. The product of two decimals has as many decimal places as the sum of the places in the numbers being multiplied.

10. When you divide decimals, move the decimal point in the divisor to the right as many places as is necessary to bring the point behind the last digit. Then move the point in the dividend to the right for the same number of places.

Test—Decimals

1. Add two and seventy-three thousandths, four and one hundred five thousandths, seven, and sixty-seven hundredths.

2. Add $5.04 + 8 + 19.243 + 62.7$.

3. Arrange in order of size starting with the largest: (a) 0.05, 0.2, 0.0035; (b) 0.0061, 0.063, 0.62.

4. Subtract fifty-one and fifty-eight thousandths from seventy-nine and ninety-nine hundredths.

5. From $16\frac{1}{2}$ subtract 10.359.

6. Change $\frac{3}{7}$ to a three-place decimal.

7. Change $\frac{2}{3}$ to a three-place decimal.

8. Multiply 14.32×0.035.

9. Divide 4.092 by 0.31.

10. Multiply $2\frac{1}{2} \times 0.66$.

JOB 2-9: REVIEW OF OHM'S LAW

In any electrical circuit,

1. The voltage forces the current through a conductor against its resistance.

2. The resistance tries to stop the current from flowing.

3. The current that flows in a circuit depends on the voltage and the resistance.

The relationship among these three quantities is described by Ohm's law. Ohm's law applies to an entire circuit or to any component part of a circuit.

Formula

$$E = IR \qquad\qquad (2\text{-}1)$$

where E = voltage, volts
$\quad I$ = current, amp
$\quad R$ = resistance, ohms

The formula for Ohm's law may be used to find the value of any one of the quantities in the formula. It is of equal importance that the student be able to determine the relative values of each quantity as one of the other quantities is changed in amount.

1. When the resistance remains constant,

  a. The larger the voltage, the larger the current.
  b. The smaller the voltage, the smaller the current.

2. When the voltage remains constant,

  a. The larger the resistance, the smaller the current.
  b. The smaller the resistance, the larger the current.

Formulas in Electrical Work. A formula is a shorthand method for writing a rule. Each letter in a formula represents a number which may be substituted for it. The signs of operation tells us what to do with these numbers.

Steps in Solving Problems

1. Read the problem carefully.
2. Draw a simple diagram of the circuit.
3. Record the given information directly on the diagram. Indicate the values to be found by question marks.
4. Write the formula.
5. Substitute the given numbers for the letters in the formula. If the number for the letter is unknown, merely write the letter again. Include all mathematical signs.
6. Do the indicated arithmetic.

a. If, after substitution, the unknown letter is multiplied by some number, divide the number all alone on one side of the equals sign by the multiplier of the unknown letter.

7. In the answer, indicate the letter, its numerical value, and the units of measurement.

Example 2-47.   Solve the equation $6.3 = 0.3R$ for the letter R.

Solution:

1. Write the equation.

$$6.3 = 0.3R$$

2. Solve for R.

$$\frac{6.3}{0.3} = R$$

3. Divide the numbers.

$$21 = R \text{ or } R = 21 \qquad Ans.$$

Problems

1. The resistance of an electric percolator is 22 ohms.   If it draws 5 amp, what is the operating voltage?

2. An electric heater whose coil is wound with No. 18 iron wire is connected across 110 volts.   If it draws a current of 10 amp, what is the value of its resistance?

3. According to the National Electrical Code, No. 14 asbestos-covered type A wire should never carry more than 32 amp.   Is this wire safe to use to carry power to a 10-ohm 230-volt motor?

4. A washing-machine motor has a total resistance of 39 ohms and operates on 117 volts.   Find the current taken by the motor.

5. What is the voltage drop across an Allied model BK relay of 12,000 ohms resistance if it carries 0.0015 amp?

6. What is the voltage across a telephone receiver of 800 ohms resistance if the current flowing is 0.03 amp?

7. A 600-watt soldering iron is used on a 120-volt line and has a resistance of 24 ohms.   Find the current used.

8. The heater of a 25BQ6-GT horizontal deflection output tube operates at 25 volts and draws 0.3 amp.   Find its resistance.

9. If the full-scale reading of an ammeter is 10 amp, what is its resistance if this current causes a voltage drop of 0.05 volt?

10. What is the resistance of a bus bar carrying 300 amp if the voltage drop across it is 1.2 volts?

11. A sensitive d-c meter takes 0.009 amp from a line when the voltage is 108 volts.   What is the resistance of the meter?

12. An electromagnet draws 5 amp from a 110-volt line.   What current will it draw from a 220-volt line?

13. The resistance of the series field coils of a compound motor is 0.24 ohm, and they carry a current of 72 amp.   Find the voltage drop across these coils.

14. If a 0.6-ohm rail connector accidentally shorted the 12-volt system of a model railroad, what current would flow?

15. An automobile dashboard ammeter shows 5.5 amp of current flowing when the headlights are lit. If the current is drawn from the 6-volt storage battery, what is the resistance of the headlights?

16. A voltmeter has a resistance of 27,000 ohms. What current will flow through the meter when it is placed across a 220-volt line?

17. A 110-volt line is protected with a 15-amp fuse. Will the fuse "carry" a 5.5-ohm load?

18. A voltage of 28.8 volts is required to send 7.2 amp of current through a wire 5 miles long. What is the resistance of the wire? What is the resistance per mile of wire?

19. What bias voltage is developed across a grid leak resistor of 2,000,000 ohms resistance if the current through it is 0.0000002 amp?

20. A series of insulators leak 0.00003 amp at 9,000 volts. Find the resistance of the insulator string.

Test—Ohm's Law

Draw a diagram for each problem, and label it completely. Write the formula, substitute, and show all steps necessary for the solution of the problem. Show all arithmetical calculations at the side.

1. The heater of a 6J7 class A amplifier tube takes 0.3 amp at 6.3 volts. What is the resistance of the heater?

2. A neon electric sign draws 1¼ amp. If its resistance is 92 ohms, find the voltage needed.

3. What current is drawn by a 6,000-ohm electric clock when operated from a 110-volt line?

4. What is the resistance of a motor if it draws 5 amp from a 110-volt line?

5. The resistance of a telephone receiver is 425 ohms. If the current is 0.06 amp, what voltage is required?

6. Find the current used by a bell of 8.5 ohms resistance when used on a 12.6-volt circuit.

7. What is the resistance of a truck windshield-wiper motor if it draws ¾ amp from the 6-volt battery?

8. A 24-ohm soldering iron requires 5 amp for proper operation. What voltage is necessary?

9. An arc lamp whose resistance is 2½ ohms operates on a 70-volt line. What current does it draw?

10. What is the voltage across a voltmeter of 24,000 ohms resistance if it carries 0.0015 amp?

CHAPTER 3

ELECTRICAL MEASUREMENTS

JOB 3-1: MEASURING ELECTRICAL ENERGY

The Kilowatthour Meter. The amount of electrical energy used by a consumer is measured by a kilowatthour meter. The meter is just a small motor whose speed depends on the amount of energy passing through it to the user. The shaft of the motor is connected to a mechanism that turns the hands on each of four dials. The energy used is found by subtracting the meter reading at any particular time from the reading at some future time.

Example 3-1. The meter reading last month was 4,812 kwhr. This month the reading is 4,864 kwhr. Find the number of kilowatthours of energy that has been used during the month.

Solution:

$$\begin{array}{r} 4,864 \\ -\ 4,812 \\ \hline 52 \text{ kwhr used} \qquad Ans. \end{array}$$

Reading a Kilowatthour Meter. The ordinary meter has four dials as shown in Fig. 3-1. Each dial represents one of the digits in a four-figure number. The dials are arranged to read the number of kilowatthours from left to right. To get the reading, however, write down the reading of the fourth dial at the extreme right. To the left of this number, write the reading of the third dial. To the left of these numbers, write the reading of the second dial. To the left of these numbers, write the reading of the first dial. When reading the dials, always take the number which the hand has *just passed*, and *not* the number nearest to the hand.

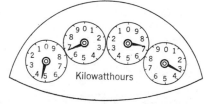

Fig. 3-1. Dial faces of a kilowatthour meter.

Example 3-2. Find the reading of the meter shown in Fig. 3-1.

Solution:

1. The fourth dial reads clockwise, and the fourth hand is between the 3 and the 4. Write the 3 at the extreme right as shown (_ _ _ 3).

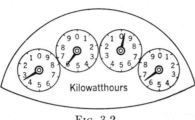

FIG. 3-2

2. The third dial reads counterclockwise, and the third hand is between the 7 and the 8. Write the 7 to the left of the 3 just noted as shown (_ _ 7 3).

3. The second dial reads clockwise, and the second hand is between the 6 and the 7. Write the 6 to the left of the 73 just noted as shown (_ 6 7 3).

4. The first dial reads counterclockwise, and the first hand is between the 4 and the 5. Write the 4 to the left of the 673 just noted as shown (4 6 7 3).

Kilowatthour reading = 4,673   *Ans.*

Example 3-3. Find the reading of the meter shown in Fig. 3-2.

Solution: The reading is 3,596 kwhr. It is *not* 3,696 kwhr. It is not clear whether the second dial has passed the 6 or is just coming up to it. However, the third dial has passed the 9, indicating that the reading is coming *up* to the next unit (the 6 in the second dial) and *not* just passed the 6—in which case the third dial would probably be on the 1, 2, or 3.

Problems

Find the readings indicated by the following dials:

1.   2.

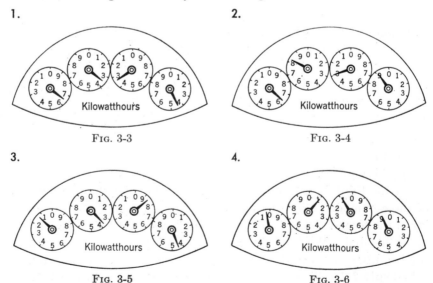

FIG. 3-3   FIG. 3-4

FIG. 3-5   FIG. 3-6

5.

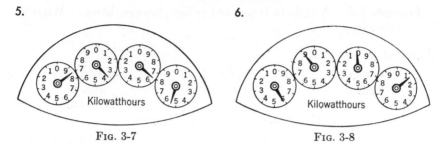

Fig. 3-7   **6.**   Fig. 3-8

JOB 3-2: FINDING THE VALUE OF FIXED RESISTORS

Instead of the number of ohms of resistance being stamped on carbon-type resistors, the resistors are colored according to a definite system approved by the Radio-Electronics-Television Manufacturers Association (RETMA). Each color represents a number according to the following plan.

Color	Number	Color	Number
Black	0	Green	5
Brown	1	Blue	6
Red	2	Violet	7
Orange	3	Gray	8
Yellow	4	White	9

Gold—multiply by 0.1.

Silver—multiply by 0.01.

The value of the resistor is obtained by reading the colors according to the following systems.

The Three-band System. The first band represents the first number in the value. The second band represents the second number. The third band represents the number of zeros to be added after the first two numbers. If the third band is gold or silver, multiply the value indicated by the first two bands by 0.1 or 0.01, respectively, as indicated above.

Example 3-4. Find the resistance of a resistor marked red, violet, yellow as shown in Fig. 3-9.

Solution:

1st band	2d band	3d band
Red	Violet	Yellow
2	7	0000

Resistance = 270,000 ohms   *Ans.*

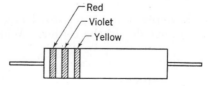

Red

Violet

Yellow

Fig. 3-9. The resistance value is indicated by three bands of color read in order from left to right.

Example 3-5.   A resistor is marked yellow, orange, black.   What is its resistance?

Solution:

1st band	2d band	3d band
Yellow	Orange	Black
4	3	No zeros

$$\text{Resistance} = 43 \text{ ohms} \quad Ans.$$

Example 3-6.   A resistor is marked green, blue, gold.   What is its resistance?

Solution:

1st band	2d band	3d band
Green	Blue	Gold
5	6	Multiply by 0.1

The first two bands indicate a value of 56 ohms.   Therefore,

$$56 \times 0.1 = 5.6 \text{ ohms} \quad Ans.$$

The Body-Tip-Dot System.   The colors must be read in the following order; body, tip, and dot.   The body color represents the first number, the right-hand tip represents the second number, and the center dot represents the number of zeros to be added after the first two numbers.   If the dot is gold or silver, multiply the value indicated by the first two numbers by 0.1 or 0.01, respectively.

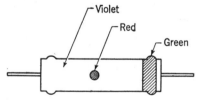

FIG. 3-10. The resistance value is indicated by the colors in the order body, right-end tip, and center dot.

Example 3-7.   What is the resistance of the resistor shown in Fig. 3-10?

Solution:

Body	Tip	Dot
Violet	Green	Red
7	5	00

$$\text{Resistance} = 7{,}500 \text{ ohms} \quad Ans.$$

Example 3-8.   A resistor has a brown body, a blue right end, and an orange dot in the center.   What is its resistance?

Solution:

Body	Tip	Dot
Brown	Blue	Orange
1	6	000

$$\text{Resistance} = 16{,}000 \text{ ohms} \quad Ans.$$

Example 3-9. A resistor has a gray body, a red right end, and a silver dot in the center. What is its resistance?

Solution:

Body	Tip	Dot
Gray	Red	Silver
8	2	Multiply by 0.01

The first two colors indicate a value of 82 ohms. Therefore,

$$82 \times 0.01 = 0.82 \text{ ohm} \quad Ans.$$

Example 3-10. A mechanic needs a 510,000-ohm resistor. What combination of colors in the body-tip-dot system is needed?

Solution:

The first digit is a 5, indicating green.
The second digit is a 1, indicating brown.
The four zeros that remain indicate yellow.
Therefore, the resistor will be color-coded as follows:

Body, green; right-end tip, brown; dot, yellow   *Ans.*

Example 3-11. What color combination is needed to indicate a 6.8-ohm resistor in the three-band system?

Solution:

The first digit is a 6, indicating blue.
The second digit is a 8, indicating gray.
To obtain the number 6.8 from the number 68 it is necessary to multiply 68 by 0.1, which indicates gold. Therefore, the resistor will be color-coded as follows:

First band, blue; second band, gray; third band, **gold**   *Ans.*

Tolerance Markings. A fourth band of color in the band system or a color on the left-hand side of the resistor in the body-tip-dot system is used to indicate how accurately the part is made to conform to the indicated markings. Gold means that the value is not more than 5 per cent away from the indicated value. Silver indicates a tolerance of 10 per cent, and black a tolerance of 20 per cent. If the tolerance is not indicated by a color, it is assumed to be 20 per cent.

Problems

What value of resistance is indicated by each of the following color combinations?

1. Brown, black, yellow.	11. Brown, gray, green.
2. Red, yellow, red.	12. Orange, white, silver.
3. Gray, red, orange.	13. Blue, red, brown.
4. Green, brown, red.	14. Brown, gray, brown.
5. Violet, green, black.	15. White, brown, red.
6. Red, black, green.	16. Orange, orange, gold.
7. Yellow, violet, gold.	17. Yellow, violet, silver.
8. Brown, green, yellow.	18. Orange, white, silver.
9. Brown, red, gold.	19. Gray, red, black.
10. Brown, red, red.	20. Green, blue, gold.

What color combination is needed to indicate each of the following resistances?

21. 240,000 ohms	31. 0.68 ohm
22. 430,000 ohms	32. 1.2 ohms
23. 51 ohms	33. 2.2 ohms
24. 150 ohms	34. 100 ohms
25. 10,000,000 ohms	35. 1.8 ohms
26. 5.6 ohms	36. 1,000,000 ohms
27. 3,900 ohms	37. 360 ohms
28. 0.47 ohm	38. 6,200 ohms
29. 12 ohms	39. 1.5 ohms
30. 750,000 ohms	40. 1 ohm

JOB 3-3: FINDING THE VALUE OF FIXED CAPACITORS

The 1948 RMA color code and the JAN color code are the systems in use at the present time. The meaning of the dots is given in Fig. 3-11. The colors have the same meaning as for resistors. The

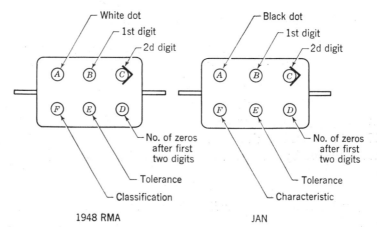

Fig. 3-11. Molded mica capacitor color codes. All capacitances are measured in micromicrofarads ($\mu\mu f$).

classification or characteristic as shown by dot F is relatively unimportant and is omitted from the following examples.

Example 3-12. A capacitor is color-coded as follows: A, white; B, red; C, green; D, brown; E, black. Find the capacitance of the capacitor.

Solution:

$$B(\text{red}) \qquad\qquad C(\text{green}) \qquad\qquad D(\text{brown})$$
$$2 \qquad\qquad\qquad 5 \qquad\qquad\qquad 0$$
Capacitance = 250 $\mu\mu$f, 20 per cent tolerance   *Ans.*

Example 3-13. A capacitor is color-coded as follows: A, black; B, brown; C, green; D, red; E, silver. Find the capacitance of the capacitor.

Solution:

$$B(\text{brown}) \qquad\qquad C(\text{green}) \qquad\qquad D(\text{red})$$
$$1 \qquad\qquad\qquad 5 \qquad\qquad\qquad 00$$
Capacitance = 1,500 $\mu\mu$f, 10 per cent tolerance   *Ans.*

Problems

What value of capacitance is indicated by each of the following color combinations?

Problem	A	B	C	D	E
1	White	Green	Black	Black	Gold
2	Black	Brown	Orange	Red	Silver
3	Black	Orange	Blue	Brown	Silver
4	Black	Brown	Green	Red	Black
5	White	White	Brown	Brown	Black
6	Black	Violet	Black	Black	Silver
7	White	Yellow	Black	Brown	Silver
8	Black	Brown	Gray	Orange	Black
9	White	Yellow	Orange	Black	Gold
10	Black	Brown	Black	Red	Silver

JOB 3-4: READING ELECTRICAL METERS

The entire range of an instrument dial is divided into a number of equal parts called *main divisions*, the value of which varies from dial to dial. The main divisions are usually numbered, but some numbers may be omitted in order to make the dial easier to read. The main divisions are further indicated as either the heaviest or the longest lines on the dial.

Each of the main divisions is divided into a number of smaller parts which we shall call "spaces." Just as the main divisions of different instruments are not always the same, the small spaces will also vary. There may be several scales on the same dial, as the meter may be used for different ranges. This is accomplished by the use of special shunts or multipliers which are discussed in Chapter 8. The range of a meter means the highest value on that particular scale.

Reading Meter Dials. To read the value indicated,

1. Determine which of the several scales is to be read.

2. Determine the value of each main division and how many main divisions have been passed by the indicator.

3. Determine the value of each small space and how many small spaces past the last main division have been passed.

4. Add the small-space value to the main-division value to obtain the total reading.

Value of the Main Divisions. To determine the value of the main divisions, merely subtract the value of *any* main division from the next *larger* one.

Example 3-14. Find the value of the main division on each scale of the meter shown in Fig. 3-12.

Solution:

$$\text{Top scale: Main division} = 100 - 75 = 25 \quad Ans.$$
$$\text{Middle scale: Main division} = 20 - 15 = 5 \quad Ans.$$
$$\text{Bottom scale: Main division} = 1 - 0.75 = 0.25 \quad Ans.$$

Fig. 3-12. Model 281 ammeter-voltmeter. (*Weston Electrical Instrument Corp.*)

Value of the Small Spaces: To find the value of the small spaces,

1. Count the number of spaces between any two main divisions.

2. Each small space equals the value of the main division divided by the number of spaces.

Example 3-15. Find the value of each small space on the dial shown in Fig. 3-13.

FIG. 3-13. Model 269 d-c voltmeter. (*Weston Electrical Instrument Corp.*)

Solution:

$$\text{Main division} = 10 \text{ volts}$$
$$\text{Each main division} = 10 \text{ small spaces}$$
$$\text{Each small space} = {}^{10}\!/_{10} = 1 \text{ volt} \qquad Ans.$$

Example 3-16. Find the value of each small space on the dial shown in Fig. 3-14.

FIG. 3-14. Model 301 d-c voltmeter. (*Weston Electrical Instrument Corp.*)

Solution:

$$\text{Main division} = 5 \text{ volts}$$
$$\text{Each main division} = 10 \text{ small spaces}$$
$$\text{Each small space} = \frac{5}{10} = 0.5 \text{ volt} \qquad Ans.$$

Example 3-17. Find the value of each small space on the dial shown in Fig. 3-15.

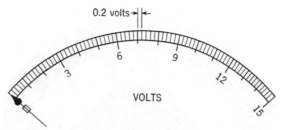

Fig. 3-15. (*Weston Electrical Instrument Corp.*)

Solution:

$$\text{Main division} = 1 \text{ volt}$$
$$\text{Each main division} = 5 \text{ small spaces}$$
$$\text{Each small space} = \frac{1}{5} = 0.2 \text{ volt} \qquad Ans.$$

Finding the Meter Reading

1. Find the value of the main division just before the indicator.

2. Find the number of spaces between this main division and the indicator.

3. Find the value of each small space.

4. Multiply the number of spaces found in step 2 by the value of each space found in step 3.

5. Add steps 1 and 4 to get the meter reading.

Example 3-18. Find the reading indicated by the arrow for each scale of the dial shown in Fig. 3-16.

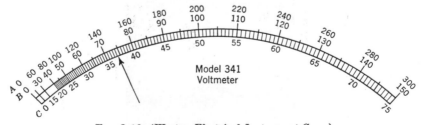

Fig. 3-16. (*Weston Electrical Instrument Corp.*)

Solution:

Scale *A*: The main division just before the arrow is 140 volts.

Number of spaces covered by arrow = 4

Main division = 20 volts, divided into 10 spaces

Each small space = $^{20}/_{10}$ = 2 volts

Value of spaces covered = 4 × 2 = 8 volts

Meter reading = 140 + 8 = 148 volts   *Ans.*

Scale *B*: The main division just before the arrow is 70 volts.

Number of spaces covered by arrow = 4

Main division = 10 volts, divided into 10 spaces

Each small space = $^{10}/_{10}$ = 1 volt

Value of spaces covered = 4 × 1 = 4 volts

Meter reading = 70 + 4 = 74 volts   *Ans.*

Scale *C*: The main division just before the arrow is 35 volts.

Number of spaces covered by arrow = 4

Main division = 5 volts, divided into 10 spaces

Each small space = $^{5}/_{10}$ = 0.5 volt

Value of spaces covered = 4 × 0.5 = 2 volts

Meter reading = 35 + 2 = 37 volts   *Ans.*

Example 3-19.   Find the reading indicated by the arrow for each scale of the dial shown in Fig. 3-17.

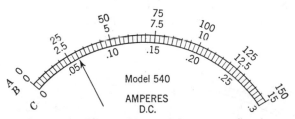

Fig. 3-17. (*Weston Electrical Instrument Corp.*)

Solution:

Scale *A*: The main division just before the arrow is 25 amp.

Number of spaces covered by arrow = 2 spaces

Main division = 25 amp, divided into 10 spaces

Each small space = $^{25}/_{10}$ = 2.5 amp

Value of spaces covered = 2 × 2.5 = 5 amp

Meter reading = 25 + 5 = 30 amp   *Ans.*

Scale *B*: The main division just before the arrow is 2.5 amp.

Number of spaces covered by arrow = 2 spaces

Main division = 2.5 amp, divided into 10 spaces

Each small space = $\dfrac{2.5}{10}$ = 0.25 amp

Value of spaces covered = 2 × 0.25 = 0.5 amp

Meter reading = 2.5 + 0.5 = 3.0 amp   *Ans.*

Scale C: The main division just before the arrow is 0.05 amp.

$$\text{Number of spaces covered by arrow} = 2 \text{ spaces}$$
$$\text{Main division} = 0.05 \text{ amp, divided into 10 spaces}$$
$$\text{Each small space} = \frac{0.05}{10} = 0.005 \text{ amp}$$
$$\text{Value of spaces covered} = 2 \times 0.005 = 0.01 \text{ amp}$$
$$\text{Meter reading} = 0.05 + 0.01 = 0.06 \text{ amp} \qquad Ans.$$

Problems

Find the meter reading for each scale at the points indicated by the arrows in the following figures:

1.

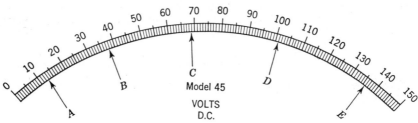

Fig. 3-18. (*Weston Electrical Instrument Corp.*)

2.

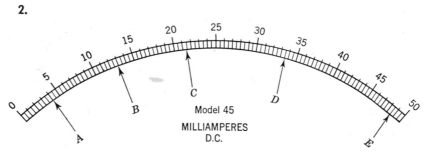

Fig. 3-19. (*Weston Electrical Instrument Corp.*)

3.

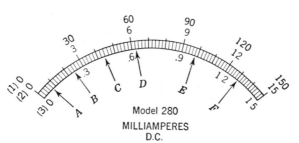

Fig. 3-20. (*Weston Electrical Instrument Corp.*)

4.

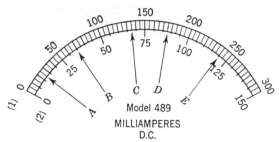

Model 489
MILLIAMPERES
D.C.

FIG. 3-21. (*Weston Electrical Instrument Corp.*)

Summary

1. To read a kilowatthour meter, write down the reading of each dial, starting with the dial at the right and proceeding to the left.

2. The order of colors in reading fixed resistors is (1) first band, second band, third band; (2) body, right-hand tip, dot.

3. The order of colors in reading fixed capacitors is shown by the arrow printed on the capacitor.

4. The meaning of the colors applies to both resistors and capacitors.

5. To determine the value of a dial reading:

a. Find the value of the main division just before the indicator.

b. Find the number of spaces between this main division and the indicator.

c. Find the value of each small space.

d. Multiply the number of spaces found in step *b* by the value of each space found in step *c*.

e. Add steps *a* and *d* to get the meter reading.

Test—Electrical Measurements

1. Find the number of kilowatt-hours of energy used if the meter appeared as shown in Fig. 3-22.

2. Find the value of the following fixed resistors: (*a*) gray, black, red; (*b*) red, green, orange; (*c*) brown,

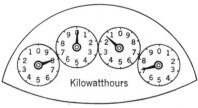

January

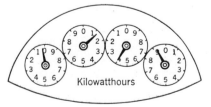

February

FIG. 3-22

black, brown; and (*d*) yellow, green, brown.

3. Find the value of the following fixed capacitors: (*a*) *A*, white; *B*, red; *C*, green; *D*, black; *E*, gold;

and (*b*) *A*, black; *B*, brown; *C*, violet; *D*, red; *E*, black.

4. Find the meter reading for each scale at the points indicated by the arrows in Fig. 3-23.

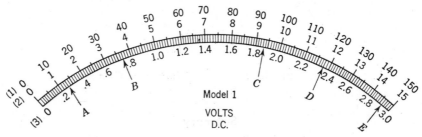

Fig. 3-23. (*Weston Electrical Instrument Corp.*)

CHAPTER 4

SERIES CIRCUITS

JOB 4-1: VOLTAGE, CURRENT, AND RESISTANCE IN SERIES CIRCUITS

Wiring a Series Circuit. A series circuit is one in which all the component parts are connected in succession from plus (+) to minus (−) as shown in Fig. 4-1. In a series circuit there is *only one path* through which the electrons may flow. The flow of current in a series circuit may be compared to the flow of water in a series-connected water system. In Fig. 4-2a, the pump forces the water through the three valves in succession. In Fig. 4-2b, the electron-moving pump—the battery—forces the electrons through the three resistors in succession. In both series circuits there is *only one path* that the water

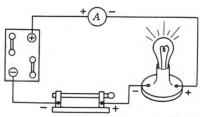

FIG. 4-1. A simple series circuit. The parts are connected so that the current can flow in only one path.

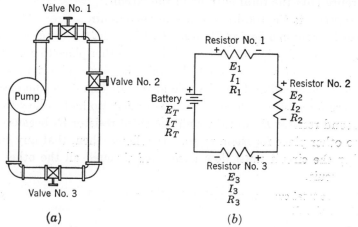

FIG. 4-2. (a) Valves in series in a water-supply system. (b) Resistors in series in an electrical circuit.

or the electrons may travel. If the water circuit is broken at any point, by either closing a valve or breaking a pipe, the flow of water around the system will stop. If the electrical series circuit is broken at any point, no energy will be available to any part of the circuit,

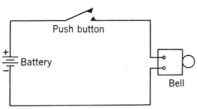

FIG. 4-3. A push button in series controls the flow of current from the battery to the bell by opening or closing the circuit.

since there will be no return path for the electrons to follow. For example, in Fig. 4-3, a push button is usually placed in series with the bell it controls. As long as the button is held up by the force of the spring inside it, the circuit is broken. Since no current can flow in a broken, or "open," circuit, the bell will not ring. When the button is depressed, the wires make contact, completing the circuit. The current then flows through the bell and the bell rings.

Symbols for Series Circuits. Numbers or letters written underneath other numbers or letters are called *subscripts*. Numbers like 1, 2, or 3 are written under the letters E, I, or R to indicate these quantities in the first, second, or third part of the circuit. For example, in Fig. 4-2b,

E_1 represents the voltage across the first resistor.

I_2 represents the current through the second resistor.

R_3 represents the resistance of the third resistor.

E_T represents the total voltage in the circuit.

I_T represents the total current in the circuit.

R_T represents the total resistance in the circuit.

Total Current in a Series Circuit. In Fig. 4-2a, the water was forced through each valve in turn because it had no other place to go. Whatever quantity of water flowed through the first valve had to flow through the second and third valve also. In Fig. 4-2b, the electrons that were forced through the first resistor R_1 also had to flow through the second resistor R_2 and through the third resistor R_3 because there was no other place for them to go. It follows, then, that any current entering the circuit must flow *unchanged* through all the other parts of the circuit.

Rule: The total current in a series circuit is equal to the current in any other part of the circuit.

Formula

$$I_T = I_1 = I_2 = I_3 = \ \cdot \ \cdot \ \cdot \ \text{etc.} \qquad (4\text{-}1)$$

where I_T = total current

  I_1 = current in first part

  I_2 = current in second part

  I_3 = current in third part, etc.

Total Voltage in a Series Circuit. In Fig. 4-4a, the total force required to lift the weights must be equal to the *sum* of the forces required to lift the individual weights. In Fig. 4-4b, the total electrical pressure supplied by the battery must be equal to the *sum* of the pressures required by each lamp.

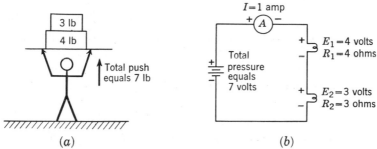

(a) (b)

Fig. 4-4. Similarity between (a) a force system and (b) an electrical system.

Rule: The total voltage in a series circuit is equal to the sum of the voltages across all the parts of the circuit.

Formula

$$E_T = E_1 + E_2 + E_3 + \cdots \text{ etc.} \tag{4-2}$$

where E_T = total voltage

  E_1 = voltage across first part

  E_2 = voltage across second part

  E_3 = voltage across third part, etc.

Total Resistance in a Series Circuit. In Fig. 4-4a, the resistance that must be overcome by the body is equal to the *sum* of the weights. In Fig. 4-4b, the total electrical resistance of the circuit is equal to the *sum* of the resistances of all the lamps.

Rule: The total resistance of a series circuit is equal to the sum of the resistances of all the parts of the circuit.

Formula

$$R_T = R_1 + R_2 + R_3 + \cdots \text{ etc.} \tag{4-3}$$

where R_T = total resistance

  R_1 = resistance of first part

  R_2 = resistance of second part

  R_3 = resistance of third part, etc.

Example 4-1. A 45- and a 90-volt battery are connected in series as shown in Fig. 4-5. What is the total voltage available?

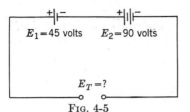

$E_1 = 45$ volts $E_2 = 90$ volts

$E_T = ?$

FIG. 4-5

Solution:

1. Write the formula.

$$E_T = E_1 + E_2 \quad (4\text{-}2)$$

2. Substitute numbers.

$$E_T = 45 + 90$$

3. Add the numbers.

$$E_T = 135 \text{ volts} \qquad Ans.$$

Example 4-2. The heaters of a 6J7 tube (6 volts, 20 ohms) and a 12Z3 tube (12 volts, 40 ohms) are connected in series with a 20-ohm ballast resistor using 6 volts and 0.3 amp. Find (*a*) the total voltage, (*b*) the total current, and (*c*) the total resistance.

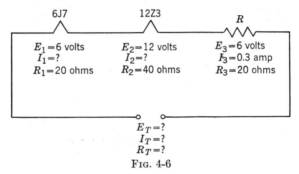

6J7   12Z3   R

$E_1 = 6$ volts $E_2 = 12$ volts $E_3 = 6$ volts
$I_1 = ?$ $I_2 = ?$ $I_3 = 0.3$ amp
$R_1 = 20$ ohms $R_2 = 40$ ohms $R_3 = 20$ ohms

$E_T = ?$
$I_T = ?$
$R_T = ?$

FIG. 4-6

Solution: Draw the circuit diagram as shown in Fig. 4-6.

a. Find the total voltage.

1. Write the formula.

$$E_T = E_1 + E_2 + E_3 \qquad (4\text{-}2)$$

2. Substitute numbers.

$$E_T = 6 + 12 + 6$$

3. Add the numbers.

$$E_T = 24 \text{ volts} \qquad Ans.$$

b. Find the total current.

1. Write the formula.

$$I_T = I_1 = I_2 = I_3 \qquad (4\text{-}1)$$

2. Substitute numbers.

$$I_T = I_1 = I_2 = 0.3$$

3. Total current is

$$I_T = 0.3 \text{ amp} \qquad Ans.$$

c. Find the total resistance.

1. Write the formula.

$$R_T = R_1 + R_2 + R_3 \qquad (4\text{-}3)$$

2. Substitute numbers.

$$R_T = 20 + 40 + 20$$

3. Add the numbers.

$$R_T = 80 \text{ ohms} \qquad Ans.$$

Problems

1. In the circuit shown in Fig. 4-7, find (a) the total voltage, (b) the total current, and (c) the total resistance.

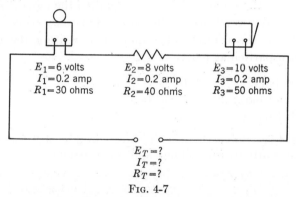

$$E_T = ?$$
$$I_T = ?$$
$$R_T = ?$$

FIG. 4-7

2. In an antique car, a 3-volt 1.5-ohm dash light and a 3-volt 1.5-ohm taillight are connected in series to a battery delivering 2 amp as shown in Fig. 4-8. Find (a) the total voltage and (b) the total resistance.

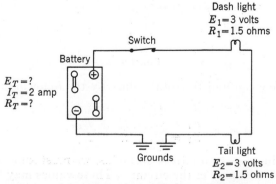

FIG. 4-8. Series-connected automobile dash and taillight for Prob. 2.

3. Three resistances are connected in series. $E_1 = 6.3$ volts, $I_1 = 0.3$ amp, $R_1 = 21$ ohms, $E_2 = 12.6$ volts, $R_2 = 42$ ohms, $E_3 = 24$ volts, and $R_3 = 80$ ohms. Find (a) the total voltage, (b) the total current, and (c) the total resistance.

4. The receiver, transmitter, and line coil of a telephone circuit are connected in series. For the receiver: $E = 2.5$ volts, $I = ?$, and $R = 12.5$ ohms. For the transmitter: $E = 18.6$ volts, $I = 0.2$ amp, and $R = 93$ ohms. For the line coil: $E = 6.7$ volts, $I = ?$, and $R = 33.5$ ohms. Find (a) the total voltage, (b) the total current, and (c) the total resistance.

JOB 4-2: USING OHM'S LAW IN SERIES CIRCUITS

Ohm's law may be used for the individual parts of a series circuit. When it is used on a particular part of a circuit, great care must be taken to use *only* the voltage, current, and resistance of that particular part. That is, the *voltage of a part* is equal to the *current in that part* multiplied by the *resistance of that part*. This may be easily remembered by using the correct subscripts when writing the Ohm's law formula for a particular part.

For the first part: $E_1 = I_1 \times R_1$ (4-4)

For the second part: $E_2 = I_2 \times R_2$ (4-5)

For the third part: $E_3 = I_3 \times R_3$ (4-6)

Example 4-3. Solve the circuit shown in Fig. 4-9 for all missing values of (a) current, (b) voltage, and (c) resistance.

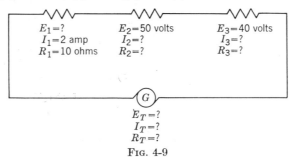

$$I_T = I_1 = I_2 = I_3 \qquad (4\text{-}1)$$

FIG. 4-9

Solution: We can find the total values by the following formulas:

$$I_T = I_1 = I_2 = I_3 \qquad (4\text{-}1)$$
$$E_T = E_1 + E_2 + E_3 \qquad (4\text{-}2)$$
$$R_T = R_1 + R_2 + R_3 \qquad (4\text{-}3)$$

However, in order to use these formulas, we must know the individual values for each part of the circuit. These values may be found by using the Ohm's law formulas for each part.

$$E_1 = I_1 \times R_1 \qquad\qquad (4\text{-}4)$$
$$E_2 = I_2 \times R_2 \qquad\qquad (4\text{-}5)$$
$$E_3 = I_3 \times R_3 \qquad\qquad (4\text{-}6)$$

a. Since the current has the same value at every point in a series circuit, it is easiest to find the currents first.

1. Write the formula.

$$I_T = I_1 = I_2 = I_3 \qquad\qquad (4\text{-}1)$$

2. Substitute numbers.

$$I_T = 2 = I_2 = I_3$$

3. The current value is

$$I_T = I_1 = I_2 = I_3 = 2 \text{ amp} \qquad Ans.$$

b. Find E_1.

1. Write the formula.

$$E_1 = I_1 \times R_1 \qquad\qquad (4\text{-}4)$$

2. Substitute numbers.

$$E_1 = 2 \times 10$$

3. Multiply numbers.

$$E_1 = 20 \text{ volts} \qquad Ans.$$

Find E_T.   Use $E_1 = 20$ from step (*b*).
1. Write the formula.

$$E_T = E_1 + E_2 + E_3 \qquad\qquad (4\text{-}2)$$

2. Substitute numbers.

$$E_T = 20 + 50 + 40$$

3. Add the numbers.

$$E_T = 110 \text{ volts} \qquad Ans.$$

c. Find R_2 and R_3.   Use $I_2 = I_3 = 2$ amp from step (*a*).
1. Write the formula.

$$E_2 = I_2 \times R_2 \quad (4\text{-}5) \qquad E_3 = I_3 \times R_3 \qquad (4\text{-}6)$$

2. Substitute the numbers.

$$50 = 2 \times R_2 \qquad\qquad 40 = 2 \times R_3$$

3. Solve.

$$\frac{50}{2} = R_2 \qquad\qquad\qquad \frac{40}{2} = R_3$$
$$R_2 = 25 \text{ ohms} \qquad Ans. \qquad R_3 = 20 \text{ ohms} \qquad Ans.$$

Find R_T.   Use $R_2 = 25$ and $R_3 = 20$ from step (c).

1. Write the formula.

$$R_T = R_1 + R_2 + R_3 \qquad\qquad (4\text{-}3)$$

2. Substitute numbers.

$$R_T = 10 + 25 + 20$$

3. Add the numbers.

$$R_T = 55 \text{ ohms} \qquad Ans.$$

Problems

1. A lamp using 10 volts, a 10-ohm resistor drawing 4 amp, and a 24-volt motor are connected in series.   Find (a) the total current, (b) the total voltage, and (c) the total resistance.

2. The plate voltage of the vacuum-tube circuit shown in Fig. 4-10 is 60 volts.   What is the total B-battery voltage?

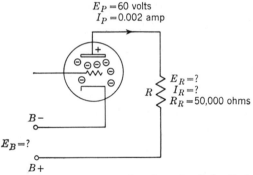

FIG. 4-10. Simple vacuum-tube plate circuit for Prob. 2.

3. A small arc lamp designed to operate on a current of 6 amp has a resistance of 14 ohms.   It is used in series with a limiting resistor of 6 ohms.   Find (a) total current, (b) total voltage, and (c) total resistance.

4. A series-connected automobile dash- and taillight circuit similar to that shown in Fig. 4-8 operates from a 6-volt battery.   The dash operates on 2 volts and 0.8 amp.   The taillight requires 4 volts.   Find (a) the resistance of each light, (b) the total resistance, and (c) the total current.

5. A lamp, a resistor, and a soldering iron are connected in series.   The lamp has a voltage across it of 16 volts.   The voltage across the resistor is 12.8 volts.   The iron has a resistance of 6 ohms and carries a current of 3.2 amp.   Find (a) total current, (b) total voltage, and (c) total resistance.

6. The 6AC7 horizontal oscillator control tube in the RCA 630 TS chassis uses a screen dropping resistor of 27,000 ohms resistance in series with the screen grid whose voltage is 150 volts.   If the screen current is 0.0025 amp, find (a) the voltage across the screen dropping resistor and (b) the total B-supply voltage.

Test—Ohm's Law in Series Circuits

1. Figure 4-11 shows the heater circuit for a modern a-c–d-c radio receiver using the following tubes: 35Z5, 50L6, 12SK7, 12SA7, 12SQ7. If all the tubes take 0.15 amp, find (a) total voltage and (b) total resistance of the circuit.

2. A 100-volt 25-ohm motor and a 15-volt rheostat are in series with a d-c source delivering 4 amp. Find the (a) total current, (b) total voltage, and (c) total resistance.

3. In a circuit similar to that shown in Fig. 4-10, the plate voltage E_p is 120 volts. If the plate current I_p is 0.003 amp and R equals 20,000 ohms, find the total B-battery voltage E_b required.

4. Three resistors are in series. The first resistance is 100 ohms, and the second resistance is 20 ohms. The third resistor uses 0.5 amp and has a voltage drop of 30 volts across it. Find (a) total current, (b) total voltage, and (c) total resistance.

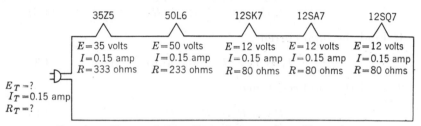

FIG. 4-11. Heater circuit of a modern a-c–d-c radio receiver.

JOB 4-3: USING OHM'S LAW FOR TOTAL VALUES IN SERIES CIRCUITS

Ohm's law was used in the last job to find the voltage, current, and resistance of the individual parts of a series circuit. Ohm's law may also be used to find the *total values* of voltage, current, and resistance in a series circuit.

Rule: In a series circuit, the total voltage is equal to the total current multiplied by the total resistance.

Formula

$$E_T = I_T \times R_T \qquad\qquad (4\text{-}7)$$

where E_T = total voltage, volts

$\quad I_T$ = total current, amp

$\quad R_T$ = total resistance, ohms

Finding the Total Voltage

Example 4-4. A resistor of 45 ohms, a bell of 60 ohms, and a buzzer of 50 ohms are connected in series as shown in Fig. 4-12. The current in each is 0.2 amp. What is the total voltage?

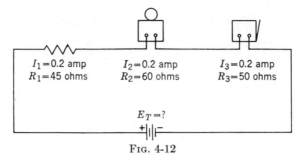

$$I_1 = 0.2 \text{ amp} \qquad I_2 = 0.2 \text{ amp} \qquad I_3 = 0.2 \text{ amp}$$
$$R_1 = 45 \text{ ohms} \qquad R_2 = 60 \text{ ohms} \qquad R_3 = 50 \text{ ohms}$$

$$E_T = ?$$

FIG. 4-12

Solution: In order to use Ohm's law to find the total voltage, we must first obtain the values for the total current and the total resistance. These values may be found by the following formulas:

$$I_T = I_1 = I_2 = I_3 \qquad \text{(4-1)}$$
$$R_T = R_1 + R_2 + R_3 \qquad \text{(4-3)}$$

1. Find the total current.

$$I_T = I_1 = I_2 = I_3 = 0.2 \text{ amp} \qquad Ans. \qquad \text{(4-1)}$$

2. Find the total resistance.

$$R_T = R_1 + R_2 + R_3 \qquad \text{(4-3)}$$
$$R_T = 45 + 60 + 50$$
$$R_T = 155 \text{ ohms} \qquad Ans.$$

3. Find the total voltage.

$$E_T = I_T \times R_T \qquad \text{(4-7)}$$
$$E_T = 0.2 \times 155$$
$$E_T = 31 \text{ volts} \qquad Ans.$$

Finding the Total Current

Example 4-5. A portable spotlight of 3 ohms resistance is connected to a 6-volt power pack with two wires, each of 0.4 ohm resistance. Find the total current drawn from the power pack.

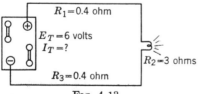

$$R_1 = 0.4 \text{ ohm}$$
$$E_T = 6 \text{ volts}$$
$$I_T = ?$$
$$R_2 = 3 \text{ ohms}$$
$$R_3 = 0.4 \text{ ohm}$$

FIG. 4-13

Solution: The diagram for the circuit is shown in Fig. 4-13.

In order to use Ohm's law to find the total current, we must first obtain the values for the total voltage and the total resistance. These values may be found by the following formulas:

$$E_T = E_1 + E_2 + E_3 \qquad \text{(4-2)}$$
$$R_T = R_1 + R_2 + R_3 \qquad \text{(4-3)}$$

1. The total voltage is known: $E_T = 6$ volts.
2. Find the total resistance.

$$R_T = R_1 + R_2 + R_3 \qquad (4\text{-}3)$$
$$R_T = 0.4 + 3 + 0.4$$
$$R_T = 3.8 \text{ ohms} \qquad Ans.$$

3. Find the total current.

$$E_T = I_T \times R_T \qquad (4\text{-}7)$$
$$6 = I_T \times 3.8$$
$$\frac{6}{3.8} = I_T$$

or $\qquad\qquad I_T = 1.58 \text{ amp} \qquad Ans.$

Example 4-6. A three-tube a-c–d-c amplifier uses a 12SQ7, a 50L6, and a 35Z5. The voltage across the first heater is 12.5 volts, across the second heater 50 volts, and across the third heater 35 volts. The total resistance of the circuit is 650 ohms. Find the total current.

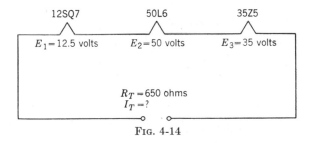

Fig. 4-14

Solution: The diagram for the circuit is shown in Fig. 4-14.

In order to use Ohm's law to find the total current, we must first obtain the values for the total voltage and the total resistance.

1. The total resistance is known: $R_T = 650$ ohms.
2. Find the total voltage.

$$E_T = E_1 + E_2 + E_3 \qquad (4\text{-}2)$$
$$E_T = 12.5 + 50 + 35$$
$$E_T = 97.5 \text{ volts} \qquad Ans.$$

3. Find the total current.

$$E_T = I_T \times R_T \qquad (4\text{-}7)$$
$$97.5 = I_T \times 650$$
$$\frac{97.5}{650} = I_T$$

or $\qquad\qquad I_T = 0.15 \text{ amp} \qquad Ans.$

Finding the Total Resistance

Example 4-7. A motor, a lamp, and a rheostat are connected in series. The motor uses 80 volts, the lamp takes 10 volts and 2 amp, and the rheostat uses 30 volts. Find the total resistance of the circuit.

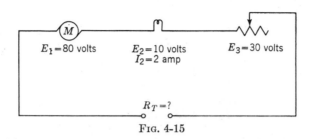

$E_1 = 80$ volts $E_2 = 10$ volts $E_3 = 30$ volts
$I_2 = 2$ amp

$R_T = ?$

FIG. 4-15

Solution: The diagram for the circuit is shown in Fig. 4-15.

In order to use Ohm's law to find the total resistance, we must first obtain the values for the total voltage and the total current.

1. Find the total voltage.

$$E_T = E_1 + E_2 + E_3 \qquad (4\text{-}2)$$
$$E_T = 80 + 10 + 30$$
$$E_T = 120 \text{ volts} \qquad Ans.$$

2. Find the total current.

$$I_T = I_1 = I_2 = I_3 = 2 \text{ amp} \qquad Ans. \qquad (4\text{-}1)$$

3. Find the total resistance.

$$E_T = I_T \times R_T \qquad (4\text{-}7)$$
$$120 = 2 \times R_T$$
$$\frac{120}{2} = R_T$$

or

$$R_T = 60 \text{ ohms} \qquad Ans.$$

Problems

1. Five lamps are connected in series for use in a subway lamp bank. Each lamp has a resistance of 110 ohms. What is the subway circuit total voltage if the total current drawn is 1 amp?

2. A railroad signal lamp and the coil of a semaphore are connected in series. The resistance of the lamp is 16 ohms, and that of the coil is 5 ohms. The current is 2 amp. What is the total voltage?

3. In a telephone circuit, the receiver, transmitter, and line coil are connected in series. The receiver resistance is 2.2 ohms; the transmitter resistance is 6.2 ohms; the coil resistance is 1.2 ohms. If the current in the receiver is 0.5 amp, what is the total voltage of the circuit?

4. A motor, a lamp, and a rheostat are connected in series. The voltage across the motor is 96 volts, across the lamp 24 volts, and across the rheostat 40 volts. If the current in the motor is 2 amp, find (a) total current, (b) total voltage, and (c) total resistance.

5. A 70L7 combination rectifier and beam-power tube requires 70 volts and 0.15 amp for its heater. The heater is in series with a ballast resistor using 45 volts. Find (a) total voltage, (b) total current, and (c) total resistance.

6. A series circuit consists of a heating coil, an ultraviolet lamp, and a motor for an electric clothes drier. The current in the motor is 5 amp. The voltages are 50 volts for the lamp, 80 volts for the motor, and 100 volts for the heating coil. Find (a) total current, (b) total voltage, and (c) total resistance.

7. The heating filaments of the six tubes of the G-E model 221 a-c-d-c superheterodyne receiver are connected in series. The voltages required are 12.6, 12.6, 12.6, 12.6, 35, and 35 volts. Each requires a current of 0.15 amp. Find (a) total current, (b) total voltage, and (c) total resistance.

8. Four lamps are wired in series. The resistance of each lamp is 0.5 ohm. The voltage across each lamp is 0.4 volt. Find (a) total current, (b) total voltage, and (c) total resistance.

9. Three arc lights are connected in series with a resistance of 21 ohms. The resistance of each arc light when hot is 10 ohms. The voltage across each arc light is 40 volts, and the voltage across the resistance is 84 volts. Find (a) total voltage, (b) total current, and (c) total resistance.

10. A voltage divider in a television receiver consists of a 6,000-, a 3,000-, and a 1,500-ohm resistor in series. If the total current is 0.015 amp, find the total voltage drop.

JOB 4-4: INTERMEDIATE REVIEW OF SERIES CIRCUITS

Finding the Total Voltage. The total voltage in a series circuit may be found by use of the following formulas:

$$E_T = E_1 + E_2 + E_3 \qquad (4\text{-}2)$$
$$E_T = I_T \times R_T \qquad (4\text{-}7)$$

Finding the Total Resistance. The total resistance in a series circuit may be found by use of the following formulas:

$$R_T = R_1 + R_2 + R_2 \qquad (4\text{-}3)$$
$$E_T = I_T \times R_T \qquad (4\text{-}7)$$

Finding the Total Current. The total current in a series circuit may be found by use of the following formulas:

$$I_T = I_1 = I_2 = I_3 \qquad (4\text{-}1)$$
$$E_T = I_T \times R_T \qquad (4\text{-}7)$$

Example 4-8. Find the total resistance of the circuit shown in Fig. 4-16.

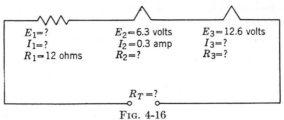

$E_1 = ?$
$I_1 = ?$
$R_1 = 12$ ohms

$E_2 = 6.3$ volts
$I_2 = 0.3$ amp
$R_2 = ?$

$E_3 = 12.6$ volts
$I_3 = ?$
$R_3 = ?$

$R_T = ?$

FIG. 4-16

Solution: In order to use the formula $E_T = I_T \times R_T$ to find the total resistance, we must know the value of E_T and I_T. If the individual voltages are unknown, we must find them in order to get E_T.

1. Find the currents in the circuit.

$$I_T = I_1 = I_2 = I_3 \qquad (4\text{-}1)$$
$$I_T = I_1 = I_2 = I_3 = 0.3 \text{ amp} \qquad Ans.$$

2. Find E_1.

$$E_1 = I_1 \times R_1 \qquad (4\text{-}4)$$
$$E_1 = 0.3 \times 12$$
$$E_1 = 3.6 \text{ volts} \qquad Ans.$$

3. Find E_T.

$$E_T = E_1 + E_2 + E_3 \qquad (4\text{-}2)$$
$$E_T = 3.6 + 6.3 + 12.6$$
$$E_T = 22.5 \text{ volts} \qquad Ans.$$

4. Find R_T.

$$E_T = I_T \times R_T \qquad (4\text{-}7)$$
$$22.5 = 0.3 \times R_T$$
$$\frac{22.5}{0.3} = R_T$$

or
$$R_T = 75 \text{ ohms} \qquad Ans.$$

Problems

1. The heaters of three radio tubes are connected in series. The first tube has a resistance of 40 ohms. The second tube uses 6 volts, and the third tube has a resistance of 120 ohms. Find the total voltage if the series current is 0.3 amp.

2. A 40-ohm resistor is in series with a 25-ohm resistor. Find the total voltage if the series current is 0.5 amp.

3. Three resistors are in series. $I_1 = 0.5$ amp, $R_1 = 2$ ohms, $R_2 = 3$ ohms, and $E_3 = 3.5$ volts. Find the total voltage.

4. Two resistors and a motor are connected in series. The motor current is 3 amp, and its resistance is 25 ohms. The voltage across each resistor is 37.5 volts. Find (*a*) total current, (*b*) total voltage, and (*c*) total resistance.

5. A voltage divider consists of a 3,000-, a 5,000-, and a 10,000-ohm resistor in series. The series current is 0.015 amp. Find (a) the voltage drop across each resistance, (b) the total voltage, and (c) the total resistance.

6. A lamp and two bells are connected in series in a burglar-alarm circuit. The lamp draws a current of 0.25 amp and has a resistance of 160 ohms. Each bell uses 35 volts. Find (a) total current, (b) total voltage, and (c) total resistance.

7. Three resistors are in series: $E_1 = 31.2$ volts, $E_2 = 48$ volts, $I_2 = 1.2$ amp, and $R_3 = 44$ ohms. Find (a) total current, (b) total voltage, and (c) total resistance of the circuit.

8. Find the total voltage of the circuit shown in Fig. 4-17.

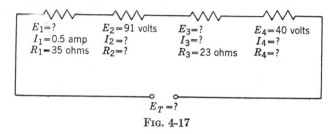

$E_1 = ?$ $E_2 = 91$ volts $E_3 = ?$ $E_4 = 40$ volts
$I_1 = 0.5$ amp $I_2 = ?$ $I_3 = ?$ $I_4 = ?$
$R_1 = 35$ ohms $R_2 = ?$ $R_3 = 23$ ohms $R_4 = ?$

$E_T = ?$

FIG. 4-17

9. Three resistances are in series. They use 8, 10, and 14 volts, respectively. The total resistance of the circuit is 80 ohms. Find all missing values of current, voltage, and resistance including the total values.

10. Three resistances of 30, 40, and 50 ohms are in series. The total voltage impressed across the circuit is 24 volts. Find all missing values of current, voltage, and resistance including the total values.

Test—Series Circuits

1. Four lamps are in series. The first two lamps take $1\frac{1}{2}$ volts each. The third lamp draws 0.5 amp and has a resistance of 2 ohms. The fourth lamp has a resistance of 4 ohms. Find the total voltage required by the circuit.

2. A 12A7 half-wave rectifier-amplifier whose heater requires 12.6 volts and 0.3 amp is in series with a limiting resistor using 104.4 volts. Find (a) the total current, (b) the total voltage, and (c) the total resistance.

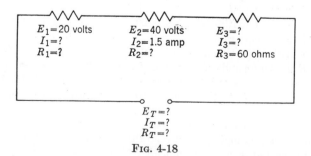

$E_1 = 20$ volts $E_2 = 40$ volts $E_3 = ?$
$I_1 = ?$ $I_2 = 1.5$ amp $I_3 = ?$
$R_1 = ?$ $R_2 = ?$ $R_3 = 60$ ohms

$E_T = ?$
$I_T = ?$
$R_T = ?$

FIG. 4-18

3. Find all missing values of current, voltage, and resistance in the circuit shown in Fig. 4-18.

4. Find all missing values of current, voltage, and resistance in the circuit shown in Fig. 4-19.

5. A 10,000-ohm voltmeter draws a current of 0.01 amp. If a multiplying resistor of 5,000 ohms is connected in series with the voltmeter, find the voltage drop across the combination.

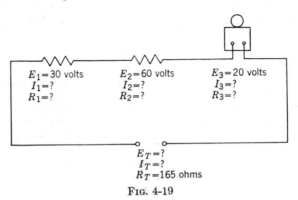

$$E_1 = 30 \text{ volts} \qquad E_2 = 60 \text{ volts} \qquad E_3 = 20 \text{ volts}$$
$$I_1 = ? \qquad\qquad I_2 = ? \qquad\qquad I_3 = ?$$
$$R_1 = ? \qquad\qquad R_2 = ? \qquad\qquad R_3 = ?$$

$$E_T = ?$$
$$I_T = ?$$
$$R_T = 165 \text{ ohms}$$

Fig. 4-19

JOB 4-5: CHECK-UP ON FORMULAS INVOLVING ADDITION AND SUBTRACTION

In our next electrical job we shall be required to solve some formulas which are slightly different from any we have solved up to this point. The following 10 problems are of this type. If you have any difficulty with them, see Job 4-6 which follows.

Problems

1. Using the formula $E_T = E_1 + E_2 + E_3$, find E_2 if $E_T = 78$, $E_1 = 17$, and $E_3 = 32$.

2. Using the formula $P = 2L + 2W$, find L if $P = 80$ and $W = 14$.

3. Using the formula $I_T = I_1 + I_2 + I_3$, find I_3 if $I_T = 5$ amp, $I_1 = 1.6$ amp, and $I_2 = 2.3$ amp.

4. Find R in the equation $7 + R = 5.4 + 19$.

5. Find E in the equation $3E + 8 = 29$.

6. Find I in the equation $I - 5 = 40$.

7. Find I in the equation $3I - 4 = 32$.

8. Find R in the formula $R + r = E/I$ if $E = 60$, $I = 5$, $r = 9$.

9. What resistance must be placed in series with six 15-volt Christmas-tree lights in order to operate them on a 110-volt circuit? Each light requires 0.8 amp.

10. What ballast resistor is necessary to operate the heaters of the five tubes of an a-c–d-c radio receiver if the tubes need 79 volts at 0.3 amp and the set is to be operated from a 110-volt line?

JOB 4-6: BRUSH-UP ON FORMULAS INVOLVING ADDITION AND SUBTRACTION

Solving a formula means to find the value of the unknown letter in the formula. In Job 2-6, after substituting the numbers for the letters, we obtained statements of equality such as $3 \times I = 60$ or $110 = 24R$. In each instance, a number *multiplied* by a letter was equal to another number. We obtained the value of the unknown letter by eliminating the number multiplied by it. This was accomplished by *dividing both sides* of the equals sign by that *same* number. In general, to solve *any* formula or equation, we must eliminate all numbers and letters on the same side of the equals sign as the *unknown* letter. This is done by applying the basic principle given in Job 2-6.

Basic Principle: Any mathematical operation performed on one side of an equals sign must also be performed on the other side.

In simple language this says, "whatever we do to one side of an equals sign must also be done to the other side."

Formulas Involving Addition

Rule: The same number may be subtracted from both sides of an equals sign without destroying the equality.

Example 4-9. In an antique car a 6-volt battery supplies a 2-volt dash light and a taillight in series. What is the voltage available at the taillight?

Solution: The diagram for the circuit is shown in Fig. 4-20.

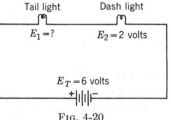

1. Write the formula.

$$E_T = E_1 + E_2 \quad (4\text{-}2)$$

2. Substitute numbers.

$$6 = E_1 + 2$$

Fig. 4-20

Step 2 asks the question, "2 plus what number equals 6?" We can find E_1 if we can eliminate the number 2. This may easily be done by *subtracting 2 from both sides* of the equals sign.

3. Subtract 2 from both sides.

$$\begin{array}{r} 6 = E_1 + 2 \\ -2 \qquad -2 \\ \hline \end{array}$$

4. Subtract.

$$4 = E_1 + 0$$

5. The voltage is

$$E_1 = 4 \text{ volts} \quad Ans.$$

Example 4-10. Using the formula $R_T = R_1 + R_2 + R_3$, find the resistance R_3 if $R_T = 100$, $R_1 = 20$, and $R_2 = 40$.

Solution:

1. Write the formula.

$$R_T = R_1 + R_2 + R_3$$

2. Substitute numbers.

$$100 = 20 + 40 + R_3$$

3. Simplify (add $20 + 40$).

$$100 = 60 + R_3$$

Step 3 asks the question "60 plus what number equals 100?"   We can find R_3 if we can eliminate the number 60.   This may easily be done by *subtracting* 60 *from both sides* of the equals sign.

4. Subtract 60 from both sides.

$$\begin{array}{r} 100 = 60 + R_3 \\ -\quad 60 - 60 \\ \hline \end{array}$$

5. Subtract.

$$40 = 0 + R_3$$

6. Resistance is

$$R_3 = 40 \qquad Ans.$$

Problems

Solve each of the following equations for the value of the unknown letter:

1. $E + 3 = 9$
2. $2 + R = 10$
3. $10 + P = 80$

4. $110 = E + 60$
5. $I + \frac{1}{2} = 5$
6. $I + 3.5 = 10.8$

7. $20 + 10 + E = 110$
8. $0.2 + 1.3 + I = 7.6$

Formulas Involving Subtraction

Rule: The same number may be added to both sides of an equals sign without destroying the equality.

Example 4-11. Using the formula $C = SP - P$, find the selling price SP if the cost C is \$10 and the profit P is \$2.

Solution:

1. Write the formula.

$$C = SP - P$$

2. Substitute numbers.

$$10 = SP - 2$$

Step 2 asks the question "what number may 2 be subtracted from in order to give 10?"   We can find the SP if we can eliminate the -2

from the right side of the equals sign. This may easily be done by *adding* 2 *to both sides* of the equals sign.

3. Add 2 to both sides.

$$10 = SP - 2$$
$$+\ 2 \qquad +2$$

4. Add.

$$12 = SP + 0$$

5. Selling price is

$$SP = 12 \qquad Ans.$$

Problems

Solve each of the following equations for the value of the unknown letter:

1. $R - 5 = 12$
2. $12 = E - 3$
3. $I - 4 = 12$
4. $30 + R - 10 = 50$

5. $I - \frac{1}{2} = 4\frac{1}{2}$
6. $P - 3.2 = 8.3$
7. $9 = I - 3.5$
8. $E - 2.2 - 1.8 = 6.3$

Transposition. The method of eliminating a number from one side of an equals sign by adding or subtracting the same number may be shortened by the method known as *transposition.* Let us investigate the following four examples in an effort to determine the rule for the transposition of quantities.

Example 4-12. Find R in the equation $R + 2 = 10$.

Solution:

1. Write the equation.

$$R + 2 = 10$$

2. Subtract 2 from both sides.

$$R + 2 - 2 = 10 - 2$$

3. Subtract.

$$R + 0 = 10 - 2$$
$$R = 8 \qquad Ans.$$

Example 4-13. Find E in the equation $8 = E + 3$.

Solution:

1. Write the equation.

$$8 = E + 3$$

2. Subtract 3 from both sides.

$$8 - 3 = E + 3 - 3$$

3. Subtract.

$$8 - 3 = E + 0$$
$$5 = E \text{ or } E = 5 \qquad Ans.$$

Example 4-14. Find S in the equation $S - 4 = 10$.

Solution:

1. Write the equation.

$$S - 4 = 10$$

2. Add 4 to both sides.

$$S - 4 + 4 = 10 + 4$$

3. Add.

$$S + 0 = 10 + 4$$
$$S = 14 \qquad Ans.$$

Example 4-15. Find I in the equation $9 = I - 5$.

Solution:

1. Write the equation.

$$9 = I - 5$$

2. Add 5 to both sides.

$$9 + 5 = I - 5 + 5$$

3. Add.

$$9 + 5 = I + 0$$
$$14 = I \text{ or } I = 14 \qquad Ans.$$

Notice that in each of the last four examples, the number to be eliminated—the number in the heavy type—seems to have *moved* from one side of the equals sign to the *other side*. Also, the sign in front of the number changed from (+) to (−) or from (−) to (+). This gives us the following rule for transposing.

Rule: Plus or minus quantities may be moved from one side of an equals sign to the other if the sign of the quantity is changed from (+) to (−) or from (−) to (+).

Example 4-16. Find E in the equation $E + 8 = 12$.

Solution:

1. Write the equation.

$$E + 8 = 12$$

2. Transpose the 8.

$$E = 12 - 8$$

3. Subtract.

$$E = 4 \qquad Ans.$$

Example 4-17. Find R in the equation $9 = R + 3$.

Solution:

1. Write the equation.

$$9 = R + 3$$

2. Transpose the 3.

$$9 - 3 = R$$

3. Subtract.

$$6 = R \text{ or } R = 6 \qquad Ans.$$

Example 4-18. Find S in the equation $S - 5 = 16$.

Solution:

1. Write the equation.

$$S - 5 = 16$$

2. Transpose the 5.

$$S = 16 + 5$$

3. Add.

$$S = 21 \qquad Ans.$$

Example 4-19. Find I in the equation $4 = I - 9$.

Solution:

1. Write the equation.

$$4 = I - 9$$

2. Transpose the 9.

$$4 + 9 = I$$

3. Add.

$$13 = I \text{ or } I = 13 \qquad Ans.$$

Problems

Solve the following equations by transposition:

1. $E + 3 = 14$
2. $16 = E + 3$
3. $2 + R = 8$
4. $13 = I + 2$
5. $6 + 4 + E = 20$
6. $3 + R + 2 = 15$
7. $21 = 4 + 5 + I$

8. $6 + I = 15$
9. $P - 2 = 6$
10. $14 = R - 4$
11. $0.6 + I = 1.6$
12. $20 = E - 2$
13. $18 - 3 + R = 25$
14. $16 = R - 4 - 5$

15. Using the formula $P_T = P_1 + P_2 + P_3$, find P_1 if $P_T = 600$, $P_2 = 120$, and $P_3 = 300$.

16. Using the formula $I_1 = I_T - I_2$, find I_T if $I_1 = 8$ and $I_2 = 3$.

17. Using the formula $E_T = E_1 + E_2 + E_3$, find E_3 if $E_T = 110$, $E_1 = 30$, and $E_2 = 50$.

18. Using the formula $R_T = R_1 + R_2 + R_3$, find R_2 if $R_T = 245$, $R_1 = 85$, and $R_3 = 90$.

19. Using the formula $I_s = I_l - I_m$, find I_l if $I_s = 99$ and $I_m = 1$.

20. Using the formula $C_T = C_1 + C_2$, find C_1 if $C_T = 0.00035$ and $C_2 = 0.0001$.

JOB 4-7: CONTROL OF CURRENT IN A SERIES CIRCUIT

In Job 2-9 we learned that the resistance affected the current in an electrical circuit. The greater the resistance, the smaller the current; the smaller the resistance, the greater the current. There are many instances where a certain current must be maintained in a circuit. We can accomplish this by adjusting the resistance of the circuit so as to obtain any required current.

Example 4-20. How much resistance must be added to the circuit shown in Fig. 4-21 in order to allow only the rated current of 2 amp to flow?

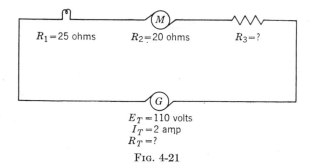

$E_T = 110$ volts
$I_T = 2$ amp
$R_T = ?$

Fig. 4-21

Solution: The diagram for the circuit is shown in Fig. 4-21.

If we can find the total resistance required to limit the current to 2 amp, then we can use formula (4-3) to find the missing extra resistance.

Find R_T.

1. Write the formula.

$$E_T = I_T \times R_T \tag{4-7}$$

2. Substitute numbers.

$$110 = 2 \times R_T$$

3. Solve for R_T.

$$\frac{110}{2} = R_T$$

4. Divide.

$$R_T = 55 \text{ ohms} \qquad Ans.$$

Find R_3, the resistance to be added.

1. Write the formula.

$$R_T = R_1 + R_2 + R_3 \qquad\qquad (4\text{-}3)$$

2. Substitute numbers.

$$55 = 25 + 20 + R_3$$

3. Simplify (add $25 + 20$).

$$55 = 45 + R_3$$

4. Transpose the 45.

$$55 - 45 = R_3$$

5. Subtract.

$$10 = R_3 \text{ or } R_3 = 10 \text{ ohms} \qquad Ans.$$

Example 4-21. What resistance must be added in series with a lamp rated at 12 volts and 0.3 amp in order to operate it on a 110-volt line?

Solution: The diagram for the circuit is shown in Fig. 4-22.

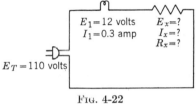

If we can discover how many volts are available in excess of that required by the lamp, then we can find the resistance which will use up that extra voltage at the rated 0.3 amp.

Fig. 4-22

Find the extra voltage E_x supplied.

1. Write the formula.

$$E_T = E_1 + E_x \qquad\qquad (4\text{-}2)$$

2. Substitute numbers.

$$110 = 12 + E_x$$

3. Transpose the 12.

$$110 - 12 = E_x$$

4. Subtract.

$$98 = E_x \text{ or } E_x = 98 \text{ volts} \qquad Ans.$$

Find the current I_x in the unknown resistor.

1. Write the formula.

$$I_T = I_1 = I_x \qquad\qquad (4\text{-}1)$$

2. Substitute numbers.

$$I_T = 0.3 = I_x$$
$$I_x = 0.3 \text{ amp} \qquad Ans.$$

Find the resistance R_x which will use up this voltage.

1. Write the formula.

$$E_x = I_x \times R_x \tag{2-1}$$

2. Substitute numbers.

$$98 = 0.3 \times R_x$$

3. Solve for R_x.

$$\frac{98}{0.3} = R_x$$

4. Divide.

$$327 = R_x \text{ or } R_x = 327 \text{ ohms} \qquad Ans.$$

Example 4-22. A 20,000-ohm resistor is connected in series with a 300-volt B power supply and the plate of a radio tube. If the plate current I_p is thereby limited to 0.006 amp, (a) what is the voltage drop in the resistor and (b) what is the voltage available at the plate?

Solution: The diagram for the circuit is shown in Fig. 4-23.

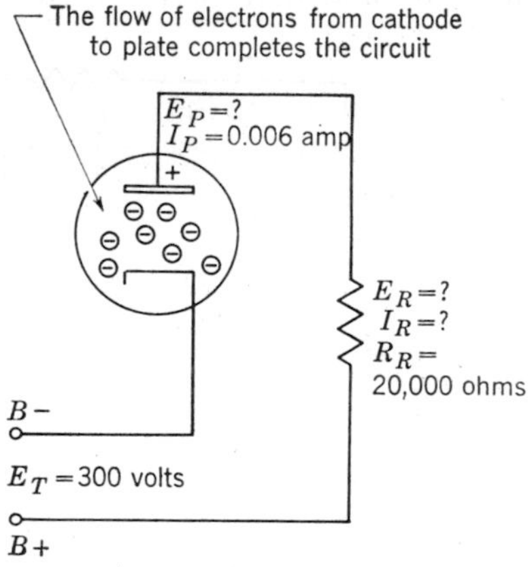

a. Find I_R.

1. Write the formula.

$$I_T = I_R = I_p \tag{4-1}$$

2. Substitute numbers.

$$I_T = I_R = 0.006$$

3. Answer

$$I_R = 0.006 \text{ amp} \qquad Ans.$$

The flow of electrons from cathode to plate completes the circuit

$E_P = ?$
$I_P = 0.006$ amp

$E_R = ?$
$I_R = ?$
$R_R = 20,000$ ohms

$B -$

$E_T = 300$ volts

$B +$

Fig. 4-23

Find E_R.

1. Write the formula.

$$E_R = I_R \times R_R \tag{2-1}$$

2. Substitute numbers.

$$E_R = 0.006 \times 20,000$$

3. Multiply.

$$E_R = 120 \text{ volts} \qquad Ans.$$

b. Find the voltage E_p at the plate.

1. Write the formula.

$$E_T = E_R + E_p \tag{4-2}$$

2. Substitute numbers.

$$300 = 120 + E_p$$

3. Transpose the 120.

$$300 - 120 = E_p$$

4. Subtract.

$$180 = E_p \text{ or } E_p = 180 \text{ volts} \qquad Ans.$$

Problems

1. A motor of 22 ohms resistance and a signal lamp of 25 ohms resistance are connected in series across 110 volts. Find the series resistor that must be added to limit the current to 2 amp.

2. A boy wants to illuminate five houses on his model railroad, using five 20-ohm lamps in series. What resistance must be connected in series in order to limit the current to the 0.5 amp needed by the lamps if the circuit is to be operated from the ordinary 110-volt house line?

3. What resistance must be placed in series with a 12-ohm bell if it is to draw exactly ¼ amp from a 24-volt source?

4. Five ordinary 0.90-amp 110-volt lamps must be used in series when operated from the 550-volt subway system. If only one of these lamps were used, what resistance must be placed in series with it to operate it from the 550-volt line?

5. If a vacuum tube rated at ¼ amp and 5 volts is to be operated from a 6-volt battery, what series resistor is needed?

6. The plate circuit of the first sync amplifier in the RCA 630TS chassis is similar to that shown in Fig. 4-10. If $E_p = 163$ volts, $I_p = 0.012$ amp, and $E_b = 275$ volts, find R.

7. A 3-volt airplane instrument lamp is to be operated from the 12-volt electrical system. What resistance should be inserted in series so that the lamp will receive its rated 0.1 amp?

8. What voltage is available at the plate of a resistance-coupled amplifier stage (Fig. 4-24) if the B supply voltage is 250 volts, the plate current I_p is 0.002 amp, and the load resistance is 50,000 ohms?

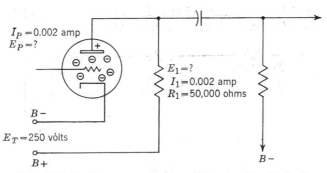

Fig. 4-24. Resistance-coupled amplifier stage for Prob. 8.

9. An 80-amp motor is connected to a 250-volt generator through leads which have a resistance of 0.3 ohm for each lead.   What is the voltage available at the motor?

10. The wiring in a house has a resistance of 0.4 ohm.   What is the voltage available at an electric range using 12 amp if the voltage at the meter is 117 volts?

JOB 4-8: REVIEW OF SERIES CIRCUITS

Definition.   A series circuit is a circuit in which the electrons can flow in only one path.

Rule 1: The total resistance is equal to the sum of the resistances of all the parts of the circuit.

$$R_T = R_1 + R_2 + R_3 \qquad (4\text{-}3)$$

Rule 2: The total voltage is equal to the sum of the voltages across all the parts of the circuit.

$$E_T = E_1 + E_2 + E_3 \qquad (4\text{-}2)$$

Rule 3: The total current is equal to the current in any part of the circuit.

$$I_T = I_1 = I_2 = I_3 \qquad (4\text{-}1)$$

Rule 4: Ohm's law may be used for any part of a series circuit.

$$E_1 = I_1 \times R_1 \qquad (4\text{-}4)$$
$$E_2 = I_2 \times R_2 \qquad (4\text{-}5)$$
$$E_3 = I_3 \times R_3 \qquad (4\text{-}6)$$

Rule 5: Ohm's law may be used for total values in a series circuit.

$$E_T = I_T \times R_T \qquad (4\text{-}7)$$

Problems

1. Three resistors are connected in series as shown in Fig. 4-25.   Find all missing values of voltage, current, and resistance.

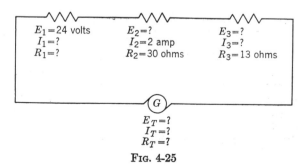

$E_1 = 24$ volts $E_2 = ?$ $E_3 = ?$
$I_1 = ?$ $I_2 = 2$ amp $I_3 = ?$
$R_1 = ?$ $R_2 = 30$ ohms $R_3 = 13$ ohms

$E_T = ?$
$I_T = ?$
$R_T = ?$

Fig. 4-25

2. The two field coils of a generator have a resistance of 55 ohms each and are connected in series across the brushes, which deliver 110 volts. What is the current in the field coils?

3. An electric heater whose resistance is 10 ohms is to be used on a 220-volt line. The maximum current permitted through it is 10 amp. What resistance must be added in series with the heater in order to hold the current to 10 amp?

4. The heaters of the four tubes of the Admiral model 5622 radio receiver are connected in series. The heaters are rated at 35, 50, 12.6, and 12.6 volts each. If the tubes draw 0.15 amp, find the total voltage and total resistance of the heater circuit.

5. The field coils of a motor draw 4 amp from a 112-volt line. What is the resistance of the coils? If a 14-ohm resistor is added in series with the coils, find the current in the coils and the voltage across the coils.

6. What value of resistance must be placed in series with two 50-ohm lamps, each taking 50 volts, if they are to be operated from a 220-volt line?

7. Three resistors are connected in series across 220 volts. $R_1 = 15$ ohms, $R_2 = 25$ ohms, and $R_3 = 60$ ohms. (*a*) Find the total current. (*b*) If the maximum permissible current is 2 amp, how much resistance must be added in series to keep the current at this value?

8. In order to dim a bank of stage lights, a rheostat may be connected in series with the lights to reduce the current and therefore the brightness of the lights. What value of resistance must be connected in series with a lamp bank drawing 20 amp from a 120-volt line in order to reduce the total current drawn to 5 amp?

9. Two 25-volt 25-ohm incandescent lamps are connected in series with a demonstration motor requiring 30 volts at 1 amp. What extra resistance should be added in series in order to draw the required current from a 110-volt line?

10. When a voltmeter indicates its maximum rated voltage of 150 volts, it is drawing a current of 0.01 amp. What value of resistance is in series with the moving coil of the voltmeter if its resistance is 20 ohms?

Test—Series Circuits

1. A lamp, a coil, and a resistor are in series. The voltage across the lamp is 16 volts and across the resistor 44 volts. The coil has a resistance of 30 ohms and carries a current of 2 amp. Find all missing values of current, voltage, and resistance, including the total values.

2. Three resistances are connected in series. $E_1 = 30$ volts, $R_1 = 60$ ohms, $E_2 = 50$ volts, and $R_3 = 76$ ohms. Find all missing values of current, voltage, and resistance, including the total values.

3. Three resistances are in series. $E_1 = 50$ volts, $I_1 = 0.4$ amp, $E_3 = 40$ volts, and $E_T = 110$ volts. Find all missing values of voltage, current, and resistance, including the total values.

4. What resistance must be placed in series with a 48-ohm bell if it is to draw exactly 0.25 amp from a 20-volt source?

5. A buzzer is designed to operate at 0.15 amp and 2.5 volts. What resistance must be placed in series with the buzzer in order to operate it from a 10-volt source?

CHAPTER 5

PARALLEL CIRCUITS

JOB 5-1: TOTAL VOLTAGE, TOTAL CURRENT, AND TOTAL RESISTANCE IN PARALLEL CIRCUITS

Recognizing a Parallel Circuit. A parallel circuit is a circuit connected in such a manner that the current flowing into it may divide

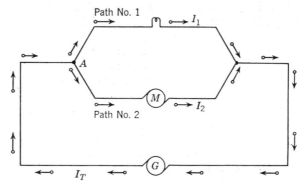

FIG. 5-1. The current in a parallel circuit flows in more than one path.

and flow in *more than one path*. In the parallel circuit shown in Fig. 5-1, the current divides at point A, part of the current flowing

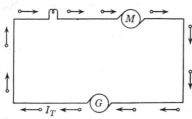

FIG. 5-2. The current in a series circuit can flow in only one path.

through the lamp in path 1 and the rest of the current flowing through the motor in path 2. The various paths of a parallel circuit are called the branches of the circuit. Notice how different this is from a series circuit shown in Fig. 5-2, in which the current can flow in *only one path.*

Total Voltage in a Parallel Circuit. Figure 5-3 shows a water-distribution system which might be called a parallel system because the water can flow in more than one pipe. A similar electrical system

94

is shown in Fig. 5-4. In this circuit, the 110-volt outlet acts as an electrical pump and supplies an equal pressure to all the branches in parallel.

Rule: The voltage across any branch in parallel is equal to the voltage across any other branch and is also equal to the total voltage.

Formula

$$E_T = E_1 = E_2 = E_3 = \cdots \text{ etc.} \qquad (5\text{-}1)$$

Total Current in a Parallel Circuit. In Fig. 5-3, we can see that the total number of gallons per minute flowing in the main pipe equals the

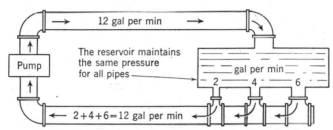

FIG. 5-3. A water-distribution system in "parallel."

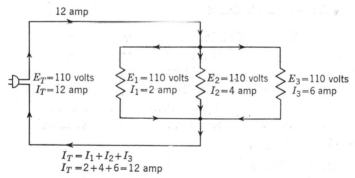

FIG. 5-4. Three resistors in parallel. The voltages across all the branches are equal.

number of gallons per minute discharged by all the pipes together, or 12 gpm. In the same way, the total current that flows in the circuit of Fig. 5-4 is equal to $2 + 4 + 6 = 12$ amp.

Rule: The total current in a parallel circuit is equal to the sum of the currents in all the branches of the circuit.

Formula

$$I_T = I_1 + I_2 + I_3 + \cdots \text{ etc.} \qquad (5\text{-}2)$$

Distribution of Current in Parallel.   The current in a parallel circuit might be distributed as shown in Fig. 5-5.   A total of 12 amp is drawn from the line.   At A, 2 amp is drawn off through R_1, leaving only 10 amp to flow along to point B.   At B, 4 amp is drawn off through R_2, leaving 6 amp to flow through the rest of the circuit R_3 around to C.   At C, this 6 amp combines with the 4 amp from R_2 to give 10 amp, which flows along to D.   Here it combines with the 2 amp from R_1 to make up the total of 12 amp available originally.

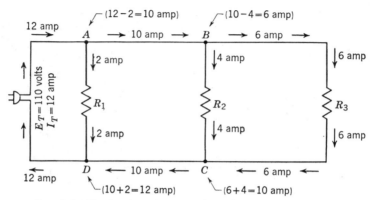

Fig. 5-5. Distribution of current in a simple parallel circuit.

Line Drop.   The distribution of the current as indicated above is based on the assumption that the connecting wires have no resistance, which is never true.   In most instances, however, the resistance of the connecting wires is so small that we may neglect it completely. If the line wires are so long that their resistance is large, its effect must be included.   This case will be taken up later in Job 6-4 under Line Drop.

Total Resistance in a Parallel Circuit

Rule: The total resistance in a parallel circuit is found by applying Ohm's law to the total values of the circuit.

Formula

$$E_T = I_T \times R_T \tag{4-7}$$

Example 5-1.   A toaster, a waffle iron, and a hot plate are connected in parallel across a house line delivering 110 volts.   The current through the toaster is 2 amp, through the waffle iron 6 amp, and through the hot plate 3 amp.   Find (a) the total current drawn from the line, (b) the voltage across each device, and (c) the total resistance of the circuit.

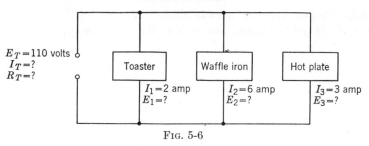

FIG. 5-6

Solution: The diagram for the circuit is shown in Fig. 5-6.

a. Find the total current I_T.

1. Write the formula.

$$I_T = I_1 + I_2 + I_3 \qquad (5\text{-}2)$$

2. Substitute numbers.

$$I_T = 2 + 6 + 3$$

3. Add.

$$I_T = 11 \text{ amp} \qquad Ans.$$

b. Find the voltage across each device.

1. Write the formula.

$$E_T = E_1 - E_2 = E_3 \qquad (5\text{-}1)$$

2. Substitute numbers.

$$E_T = E_1 = E_2 = E_3 = 110 \text{ volts} \qquad Ans.$$

c. Find the total resistance R_T.

1. Write the formula.

$$E_T = I_T \times R_T \qquad (4\text{-}7)$$

2. Substitute numbers.

$$110 = 11 \times R_T$$

3. Solve for R_T.

$$\tfrac{110}{11} = R_T$$

4. Divide.

$$R_T = 10 \text{ ohms} \qquad Ans.$$

Problems

1. Two lamps each drawing 2 amp and a third lamp drawing 1 amp are connected in parallel across a 110-volt line. Find (*a*) the total current drawn from the line, (*b*) the voltage across each lamp, and (*c*) the total resistance of the circuit.

2. The ignition coil and the starting motor of an automobile are connected in parallel across a 6-volt battery through the ignition switch as shown in

Fig. 5-7. Find (*a*) the total current drawn from the battery, (*b*) the voltage across the coil and the motor, and (*c*) the total resistance of the circuit.

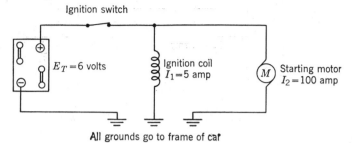

Ignition switch

$E_T = 6$ volts

Ignition coil
$I_1 = 5$ amp

(M) Starting motor
$I_2 = 100$ amp

All grounds go to frame of car

FIG. 5-7. The ignition coil and the starting motor of an automobile are in parallel.

3. Find the total current drawn by eight trailer-truck warning lights in parallel if each takes 0.5 amp.

4. A motor drawing 5 amp, a coil drawing 3 amp, and a lamp drawing 1 amp are connected in parallel across 110 volts. Find (*a*) the total current drawn, (*b*) the voltage across each device, and (*c*) the total resistance of the circuit.

5. A motor, a heating coil, and an ultraviolet lamp of a modern clothes drier are connected in parallel across 117 volts. The lamp current is 1 amp, the coil current is 4 amp, and the motor current is 3 amp. Find (*a*) the total current drawn and (*b*) the total resistance of the circuit.

6. In Table 12-1, page 277, the National Electrical Code specifies that No. 14 rubber-covered wire can safely carry only 15 amp. How many 0.5-amp lamps could be safely operated at a time on a line using this wire? How many lamps could be safely operated at one time if a 5-amp electric iron were connected in the circuit?

7. A toaster drawing 2 amp, a coffee percolator drawing 3.5 amp, and a refrigerator motor drawing 4.5 amp are connected in parallel across a 110-volt line. Find (*a*) the total current drawn, (*b*) the voltage across each device, and (*c*) the total resistance.

8. A bank of ten 110-volt 100-watt lamps is connected in parallel in a stage lighting circuit. Each lamp uses 0.91 amp. Find the total current drawn. Will a fuse rated at 10 amp safely carry this load?

9. A 40-watt lamp drawing 0.36 amp, a 60-watt lamp drawing 0.54 amp, and a 100-watt lamp drawing 0.9 amp are connected in parallel across 110 volts as shown in Fig. 5-8. Find (*a*) the total current, (*b*) the voltage across each lamp, and (*c*) the total resistance of the circuit.

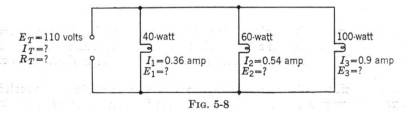

$E_T = 110$ volts
$I_T = ?$
$R_T = ?$

40-watt
$I_1 = 0.36$ amp
$E_1 = ?$

60-watt
$I_2 = 0.54$ amp
$E_2 = ?$

100-watt
$I_3 = 0.9$ amp
$E_3 = ?$

FIG. 5-8

10. A radio receiver uses four tubes whose heaters are connected in parallel across the 2.5-volt winding of the power transformer. What is the total current drawn from this winding if each tube draws 0.3 amp? What is the total resistance of the heater circuit?

11. Two 32-candlepower headlight lamps each drawing 3.9 amp and two taillight lamps (4 candlepower, 0.85 amp each) are wired in parallel to the 6-volt storage battery. Find the total current drawn and the total resistance of the circuit.

12. A washing machine drawing 7.5 amp, an electric fan drawing 0.85 amp, and an electric clock drawing 0.02 amp are in parallel with a 110-volt line. Find the total current and the total resistance.

JOB 5-2: USING OHM'S LAW IN PARALLEL CIRCUITS

In some instances, it may be impossible to find the total current by adding the individual currents because the individual currents may be unknown. Therefore, the current in each branch must be found before we can find the total current.

Example 5-2. The circuit of an electric clothes drier is shown in Fig. 5-9. The ultraviolet lamp R_1 is 120 ohms and draws 1 amp. The

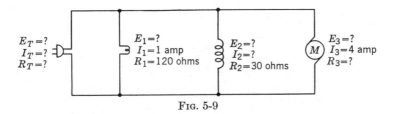

FIG. 5-9

heating coil R_2 is 30 ohms, and the motor R_3 draws a current of 4 amp. Find (a) the voltage for each part and the total voltage, (b) the current in each part and the total current, and (c) the resistance of each part and the total resistance.

Solution:

a. Find E_1.

1. Write the formula.

$$E_1 = I_1 \times R_1 \qquad (4\text{-}4)$$

2. Substitute numbers.

$$E_1 = 1 \times 120$$

3. Multiply.

$$E_1 = 120 \text{ volts} \qquad Ans.$$

Find E_T and the voltage across each part of the circuit.

1. Write the formula.

$$E_T = E_1 = E_2 = E_3 \tag{5-1}$$

2. Substitute numbers.

$$E_T = E_1 = E_2 = E_3 = 120 \text{ volts} \qquad Ans.$$

b. Find the current I_2.

1. Write the formula.

$$E_2 = I_2 \times R_2 \tag{4-5}$$

2. Substitute numbers.

$$120 = I_2 \times 30$$

3. Solve for I_2.

$$\frac{120}{30} = I_2$$

4. Divide.

$$I_2 = 4 \text{ amp} \qquad Ans.$$

Find the total current I_T.

1. Write the formula.

$$I_T = I_1 + I_2 + I_3 \tag{5-2}$$

2. Substitute numbers.

$$I_T = 1 + 4 + 4$$

3. Add.

$$I_T = 9 \text{ amp} \qquad Ans.$$

c. Find the resistance R_3.

1. Write the formula.

$$E_3 = I_3 \times R_3 \tag{4-6}$$

2. Substitute numbers.

$$120 = 4 \times R_3$$

3. Solve for R_3.

$$\frac{120}{4} = R_3$$

4. Divide.

$$R_3 = 30 \text{ ohms} \qquad Ans.$$

Find the total resistance R_T.

1. Write the formula.

$$E_T = I_T \times R_T \tag{4-7}$$

2. Substitute numbers.

$$120 = 9 \times R_T$$

3. Solve for R_T.

$$\frac{120}{9} = R_T$$

4. Divide.

$$R_T = 13.3 \text{ ohms} \qquad Ans.$$

In the last example, R_2 and R_3 are both equal to 30 ohms. They both draw 4 amp of current. This gives us the following rules.

Rule: If the branches of a parallel circuit have the same resistance, then each will draw the same current.

Rule: If the branches of a parallel circuit have different resistances, then each will draw a different current.

Problems

1. Two resistors of 3 and 6 ohms are connected in parallel across 18 volts. Find (a) the voltage across each resistor, (b) the current in each resistor and the total current, and (c) the total resistance.

2. Find all missing values of voltage, current, and resistance in the circuit shown in Fig. 5-10.

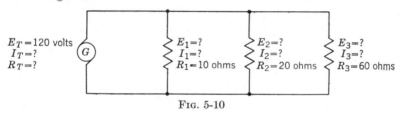

$E_T = 120$ volts
$I_T = ?$
$R_T = ?$

$E_1 = ?$
$I_1 = ?$
$R_1 = 10$ ohms

$E_2 = ?$
$I_2 = ?$
$R_2 = 20$ ohms

$E_3 = ?$
$I_3 = ?$
$R_3 = 60$ ohms

FIG. 5-10

3. A parallel circuit has three branches of 12, 6, and 4 ohms resistance. If the current in the 6-ohm branch is 4 amp, what current will flow in each of the other branches? What is the total current?

4. The secondary of a power transformer is connected across the motors of three toy trains in parallel. Motor 1 has a resistance of 50 ohms and draws 0.4 amp. Motor 2 has a resistance of 40 ohms. Motor 3 draws a current of 0.3 amp. Find (a) the total voltage, (b) the total current, and (c) the total resistance.

5. Three resistors are in parallel. $I_1 = 12$ amp, $E_2 = 114$ volts, $R_2 = 19$ ohms, and $R_3 = 57$ ohms. Find (a) the voltage across each resistor and the total voltage, (b) the current in each resistor and the total current, and (c) the resistance of each resistor and the total resistance.

6. Three buzzers are wired in parallel. They draw currents of 0.2, 0.4 and 0.6 amp, respectively. If their total resistance is 6 ohms, find (a) the resistance of each buzzer and (b) the voltage across each buzzer.

7. A portable radio receiver employs four 1½-volt tubes wired in parallel. Three of these tubes draw a current of 0.05 amp each. The fourth draws a current of 0.1 amp. (a) What is the resistance of each filament? (b) What is the total current drawn? (c) What is the total voltage required? (d) What is the total resistance of the four filaments in parallel?

8. Solve the circuit shown in Fig. 5-11 for the values indicated.

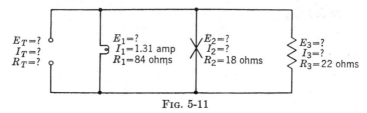

$$E_T = ?$$
$$I_T = ?$$
$$R_T = ?$$

$$E_1 = ?$$
$$I_1 = 1.31 \text{ amp}$$
$$R_1 = 84 \text{ ohms}$$

$$E_2 = ?$$
$$I_2 = ?$$
$$R_2 = 18 \text{ ohms}$$

$$E_3 = ?$$
$$I_3 = ?$$
$$R_3 = 22 \text{ ohms}$$

FIG. 5-11

9. The following RCA panel lights are to be wired in parallel from an 8-volt source: two No. 40 lamps (0.15 amp) and three No. 44 lamps (0.15 amp). Find the total current, total voltage, and the total resistance of the circuit.

10. What is the total current drawn from the 6-volt automobile battery by two 4-ohm headlights and a 12-ohm taillight if they are all connected in parallel?

JOB 5-3: CHECK-UP ON ADDITION OF FRACTIONS

Our next electrical job considers problems which are solved by the addition of fractions. In order to prepare for them, let us try the following problems which are often met by the electrician and radio and television man in his work. If you have any difficulty with any of these, see Job 5-4 which follows.

Problems

1. What is the total horsepower delivered by a $\frac{1}{3}$-, a $\frac{1}{4}$-, and a $\frac{1}{8}$-hp motor in parallel?

2. Add the following conductances in a circuit to obtain the total conductance: $\frac{1}{60}$, $\frac{1}{20}$, and $\frac{1}{10}$.

3. In rewinding the armature of a motor, the following thicknesses of insulation were used: $\frac{1}{16}$, $\frac{1}{32}$, and $\frac{3}{64}$ in. What was the total thickness of the insulation?

4. What length of a bolt is covered by a lock washer ($\frac{1}{32}$ in.), a washer ($\frac{1}{8}$ in.), and a nut ($\frac{5}{16}$ in.)?

5. What is the total weight of three coils of wire weighing $16\frac{1}{4}$, $4\frac{1}{8}$, and $2\frac{1}{2}$ lb?

6. Add $\frac{1}{5}$, $\frac{1}{3}$, and $\frac{1}{10}$.

7. Add $\frac{3}{4}$, $\frac{7}{8}$, and $\frac{3}{16}$.

8. Add $\frac{3}{4}$, $\frac{5}{6}$, and $\frac{7}{8}$.

9. Add $\frac{5}{6}$, $\frac{1}{9}$, and $\frac{2}{3}$.

10. Add $\frac{1}{2}$, $\frac{5}{7}$, and $\frac{3}{4}$.

JOB 5-4: BRUSH-UP ON ADDITION OF FRACTIONS

Adding Fractions with the Same Denominator

Rule: To add fractions with the same denominator, add the numerators and place the sum over the same denominator.

Example 5-3. Add ⅛, ⅜, and ⅔.

Solution:

$$\frac{1}{8} + \frac{3}{8} + \frac{2}{8} = \frac{1+3+2}{8} = \frac{6}{8} = \frac{3}{4} \qquad Ans.$$

Adding Fractions with Different Denominators

Procedure:

1. Find the *least common denominator.*
2. Change the fractions to *equivalent* fractions using this new denominator.
3. Add these fractions with the same denominator.

Example 5-4. Add ¼ + ⅜.
Solution: The least common denominator is a number *into which* all the denominators will evenly divide. Both the 4 and the 8 will divide into 8 evenly. Therefore, 8 is the least common denominator. Since ¼ = ²⁄₈, we have

$$\tfrac{2}{8} + \tfrac{3}{8} = \tfrac{5}{8} \qquad Ans.$$

In this problem, it was very easy to change all the fractions into equivalent fractions with the same denominator. All problems are not so simple. One of the difficulties will be to decide on what the new denominator will be. This least common denominator is abbreviated as the LCD.

How to Find the Least Common Denominator

Example 5-5. Find the LCD for ½ + ⅓ + ⅛.

Solution:

1. Start with the largest denominator—the 8.
2. Try to divide the other denominators into the 8. They must divide exactly. If not,
3. Multiply the 8 by 2 to get 16.
4. Try to divide the other denominators into the 16. If they all divide evenly, then 16 is the LCD. If not, multiply the 8 by 3 and then 4, etc., until you find a number into which all the denominators will evenly divide. This last number will be the LCD.

Following this method, we multiply the 8 by 2 and get 16. The 2 and the 8 will divide evenly into the 16, but the 3 will not. We multiply the 8 by 3 and get 24. The 2, the 3, and the 8 all divide into 24 evenly. Therefore,

24 is the LCD *Ans.*

Example 5-6.   Add: $\frac{1}{7} + \frac{1}{2} + \frac{1}{4}$.

Solution:

1. Find the LCD.   Start with the **7**.   This is not the LCD because the 2 and the 4 do not divide evenly into 7.   Multiply the 7 by 2 to get 14.   This is not the LCD because the 4 does not divide evenly into 14.   Multiply the 7 by 3 to get 21.   This is not the LCD because neither the 2 nor the 4 will divide evenly into 21.   Multiply the 7 by 4 to get 28.   This *is* the LCD because the numbers 2, 4, and 7 *all divide evenly into* 28.

2. Set up the problem like this:

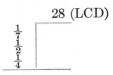

3. Divide each denominator into the LCD, and then multiply the quotient by the numerator of the fraction.

   a. 7 into 28 is 4. $4 \times 1 = 4$.   Therefore $\frac{1}{7} = \frac{4}{28}$.
   b. 2 into 28 is 14. $14 \times 1 = 14$.   Therefore $\frac{1}{2} = \frac{14}{28}$.
   c. 4 into 28 is 7. $7 \times 1 = 7$.   Therefore, $\frac{1}{4} = \frac{7}{28}$.

The problem now looks like this.   Add the equivalent fractions and reduce to lowest terms or divide to a decimal.

$$+ \begin{array}{c} \frac{1}{7} \\ \frac{1}{2} \\ \frac{1}{4} \end{array} \left| \begin{array}{c} 28 \\ \hline \frac{4}{28} \\ \frac{14}{28} \\ \frac{7}{28} \\ \hline \frac{25}{28} \end{array} \right. \quad \textit{Ans.}$$

Example 5-7.   Add $\frac{3}{4} + \frac{5}{6} + \frac{7}{8}$.

Solution:

1. Find the LCD.   The LCD is not 8.   The LCD is not $8 \times 2 = 16$. The LCD *is* $8 \times 3 = 24$ because the 4, 6, and 8 will divide evenly into 24.

2. Find the equivalent fractions and put them in the proper form.

   a. 4 into 24 is 6. $6 \times 3 = 18$.   Therefore, $\frac{3}{4} = \frac{18}{24}$.
   b. 6 into 24 is 4. $4 \times 5 = 20$.   Therefore, $\frac{5}{6} = \frac{20}{24}$.
   c. 8 into 24 is 3. $3 \times 7 = 21$.   Therefore, $\frac{7}{8} = \frac{21}{24}$.

3. The problem now looks like this.   Add the equivalent fractions, and reduce to lowest terms or divide to a decimal as shown.

$$\begin{array}{r} 24 \\ \hline \end{array}$$

$$+\begin{array}{c} \frac{3}{4} \\ \frac{5}{6} \\ \frac{7}{8} \end{array} \left| \begin{array}{c} \frac{18}{24} \\ \frac{20}{24} \\ \frac{21}{24} \\ \hline \frac{59}{24} = 2\frac{11}{24} = 2.46 \quad Ans. \end{array}\right.$$

Problems

Add the following fractions and reduce to lowest terms.

1. $\frac{1}{8} + \frac{3}{8} + \frac{7}{8}$

2. $\frac{3}{4} + \frac{5}{8} + \frac{9}{16}$

3. $\frac{1}{4} + \frac{5}{6} + \frac{3}{8}$

4. $\frac{5}{6} + \frac{1}{9} + \frac{2}{3}$

5. $\frac{1}{60} + \frac{1}{20} + \frac{1}{10}$

6. $\frac{1}{3} + \frac{1}{6} + \frac{1}{9}$

7. $\frac{1}{4} + \frac{1}{12} + \frac{1}{15}$

8. $\frac{1}{5} + \frac{1}{7} + \frac{1}{9}$

9. $\frac{1}{200} + \frac{1}{300}$

10. $\frac{1}{50} + \frac{1}{100}$

JOB 5-5: CHECK-UP ON SOLUTION OF FORMULAS INVOLVING FRACTIONS

In addition to adding fractions, our next electrical job will require that we be able to solve formulas which contain fractions. Following are some problems of this type. If you have any difficulty solving any of them, see Job 5-6 which follows.

Problems

1. Using the formula $f = PS/120$, find the speed S of an alternator if the frequency f is 60 cps and the number of poles P is 4.

2. $R_1/R_2 = L_1/L_2$ is a formula used to compare the resistances of different lengths of wire. Find R_1 if $R_2 = 100$, $L_1 = 500$, $L_2 = 800$.

3. $E_1/E_2 = I_2/I_1$ is the formula for the relation between the voltages and the currents in the primary and secondary windings of a transformer. Find I_1 if $E_1 = 110$ volts, $E_2 = 22$ volts, and $I_2 = 10$ amp.

4. The fundamental equation for the Wheatstone bridge (a resistance-measuring device) is $R_1/R_2 = R_3/R_x$. Find R_x if $R_1 = 1,000$, $R_2 = 10,000$, and $R_3 = 84.3$.

5. In series circuits, the voltage drops are proportional to the resistances. This is stated mathematically as $E_1/E_2 = R_1/R_2$. Find E_1 if $E_2 = 8$ volts, $R_1 = 3$ ohms, and $R_2 = 4$ ohms.

JOB 5-6: BRUSH-UP ON SOLUTION OF FRACTIONAL EQUATIONS

Solving Simple Fractional Equations. Many electrical formulas are stated in the form of a fraction. After substituting the given numbers for the letters of the formula, we might get an equation like $E/4 = 5$. To find the value of E, we must get the letter E all by itself on one side of the equals sign. In other words, we must eliminate the number 4. We can do this by applying the general rule which says that we may do anything to one side of an equals sign provided we do the same thing to the other side. To eliminate the number 4 which is in the denominator of the fraction, we use the following specific rule:

Rule: Both sides of an equals sign may be multiplied by the same number without destroying the equality.

Example 5-8. Find the value of E in the equation $\dfrac{E}{4} = 5$.

Solution:

1. Write the equation.

$$\frac{E}{4} = 5$$

2. Multiply both sides by 4.

$$\overset{1}{\cancel{4}} \times \frac{E}{\underset{1}{\cancel{4}}} = 5 \times 4$$

3. Multiply each side separately.

$$1 \times E = 20$$

or
$$E = 20 \qquad Ans.$$

Example 5-9. Using the formula $I = \dfrac{E}{R}$, find E if $I = 2$, $R = 6$.

Solution:

1. Write the formula.

$$I = \frac{E}{R}$$

2. Substitute numbers.

$$2 = \frac{E}{6}$$

3. Multiply both sides by 6.

$$6 \times 2 = \frac{E}{\underset{1}{\cancel{6}}} \times \overset{1}{\cancel{6}}$$

4. Multiply each side separately.

$$12 = E \times 1$$

or
$$E = 12 \qquad Ans.$$

Notice that in each of the last two examples we eliminated the number in the denominator by *multiplying both sides by that same number*. If we were to multiply both sides by any other number, we would still be left with a number in the denominator and the letter would not stand alone. Therefore, to eliminate a number in the denominator of a fraction, we use the following rule:

Rule: To eliminate a number divided into a letter, multiply both sides of the equals sign by that same number.

Problems

Find the value of the unknown letter in each problem.

1. $\dfrac{E}{3} = 8$ 4. $0.5 = \dfrac{E}{3}$ 7. $\dfrac{E}{3} = \dfrac{2}{3}$ 9. $\dfrac{P}{\frac{1}{2}} = 16$

2. $4 = \dfrac{E}{10}$ 5. $\dfrac{M}{0.2} = 5$ 8. $0.4 = \dfrac{M}{0.8}$ 10. $\dfrac{E}{4} = 2\frac{1}{2}$

3. $\dfrac{P}{6} = 2$ 6. $\dfrac{A}{10} = 0.35$

11. In the formula $I = \dfrac{E}{R}$, find E if $I = 3$ and $R = 18$.

12. In the formula $E = \dfrac{P}{I}$, find P if $E = 110$ and $I = 5$.

13. In the formula $Q = \dfrac{X_L}{R}$, find X_L if $Q = 100$ and $R = 40$.

14. In the formula $\text{Eff} = \dfrac{0}{I}$, find 0 if $I = 36$ and $\text{Eff} = 0.85$.

Using the Least Common Denominator to Solve Fractional Equations

Example 5-10. Find E in the equation $\dfrac{2E}{9} = \dfrac{4}{3}$.

Solution: When fractions appear on both sides of the equals sign, the solution will be simplified if we eliminate *all* denominators first. We could do this one denominator at a time by the method used in Examples 5-8 and 5-9, but it is faster if we eliminate both denominators at the same time. In order to eliminate *both* the 9 and the 3 at the same time, we must multiply both sides of the equals sign by some number so that *both* denominators will be canceled out. This must be a number into which *both* denominators will evenly divide—which is the *least common denominator*. In this problem, the LCD of 9 and 3 is 9.

1. Write the equation.

$$\frac{2E}{9} = \frac{4}{3}$$

2. Multiply both sides by the LCD (9).

$$\overset{1}{\cancel{9}} \times \frac{2E}{\underset{1}{\cancel{9}}} = \frac{4}{3} \times \overset{3}{\cancel{9}}$$

3. Multiply each side separately.

$$2E = 12$$

4. Solve for E.

$$E = \frac{12}{2}$$

5. Divide.

$$E = 6 \qquad Ans.$$

Example 5-11. Find R in the equation $\dfrac{2R}{3} = \dfrac{9}{4}$.

Solution: The LCD for 3 and 4 is 12.   That is, both 3 and 4 will divide evenly into 12.   In general, the LCD is equal to the product of the denominators.

1. Write the equation.

$$\frac{2R}{3} = \frac{9}{4}$$

2. Multiply both sides by the LCD (12).

$$\overset{4}{\cancel{12}} \times \frac{2R}{\underset{1}{\cancel{3}}} = \frac{9}{\underset{1}{\cancel{4}}} \times \overset{3}{\cancel{12}}$$

3. Multiply each side separately.

$$8R = 27$$

4. Solve for R.

$$R = \frac{27}{8}$$

5. Divide.

$$R = 3\tfrac{3}{8} \qquad Ans.$$

Example 5-12. Find L in the equation $\dfrac{6}{L} = \dfrac{2}{3}$.

Solution: The LCD is $3 \times L$ or $3L$.
1. Write the equation.

$$\frac{6}{L} = \frac{2}{3}$$

2. Multiply both sides by the LCD (3L).

$$3\cancel{L} \times \frac{\overset{1}{6}}{\cancel{L}} = \frac{2}{\cancel{3}} \times \overset{1}{\cancel{3}}L$$

3. Multiply each side separately.

$$18 = 2L$$

4. Solve for L.

$$\frac{18}{2} = L$$

5. Divide.

$$L = 9 \qquad Ans.$$

Rule: When fractions appear on both sides of the equals sign, eliminate the denominators by multiplying both sides by the least common denominator.

Problems

Solve each equation for the value of the unknown letter.

1. $\dfrac{R}{3} = \dfrac{2}{3}$ 5. $\dfrac{M}{5} = \dfrac{2}{3}$ 9. $\dfrac{N}{20} = \dfrac{3}{4}$ 13. $\dfrac{2}{L} = \dfrac{6}{30}$

2. $\dfrac{E}{8} = \dfrac{3}{4}$ 6. $\dfrac{4}{5} = \dfrac{T}{2}$ 10. $\dfrac{4}{7} = \dfrac{S}{2}$ 14. $\dfrac{10}{C} = \dfrac{150}{200}$

3. $\dfrac{2}{3} = \dfrac{P}{6}$ 7. $\dfrac{2E}{5} = \dfrac{3}{5}$ 11. $\dfrac{3}{E} = \dfrac{1}{4}$ 15. $\dfrac{22}{7} = \dfrac{11}{R}$

4. $\dfrac{2E}{3} = \dfrac{4}{9}$ 8. $\dfrac{2B}{5} = \dfrac{7}{10}$ 12. $\dfrac{3}{5} = \dfrac{2}{R}$

16. $N_1/N_2 = E_1/E_2$ is a formula used in transformer calculations.   Find N_2 if $N_1 = 40$ turns, $E_1 = 6$ volts, and $E_2 = 18$ volts.

17. Using the formula of Prob. 16, find E_1 if $N_1 = 30$ turns, $N_2 = 70$ turns, and $E_2 = 21$ volts.

18. $A_2/A_1 = R_1/R_2$ is a formula used to calculate the sizes of wires in electrical installations.   Find A_2 if $A_1 = 100$, $R_1 = 1,000$, $R_2 = 3,000$.

19. $I_1/I_2 = R_2/R_1$ is a formula used for calculating the way the current divides in a parallel circuit.   Find I_1 if $I_2 = 2$ amp, $R_2 = 100$ ohms, and $R_1 = 25$ ohms.

20. Using the same formula as in Prob. 19, find R_2 if $I_1 = 3$ amp, $I_2 = 5$ amp, and $R_1 = 100$ ohms.

21. $R_1/R_2 = R_3/R_x$ is the formula used for calculations in the Wheatstone-bridge method for measuring resistance.   Find R_x if $R_1 = 1,000$, $R_3 = 26.9$, and $R_2 = 10,000$.

22. $R_s/R_m = I_m/I_s$ is the formula for finding the shunt resistor needed to extend the range of an ammeter.   Find R_s if $I_m = 0.001$, $R_m = 50$, and $I_s = 0.049$.

Cross Multiplication. When a fractional equation contains *only two fractions* equal to each other, the equation may be solved by a very simple method known as cross multiplication. This method automatically multiplies both sides of the equals sign by the LCD and therefore eliminates one step in the solution. This method is most useful when the unknown letter is in the denominator of one of the fractions.

Rule: To cross-multiply, the product of the numerator of the first fraction and the denominator of the second is set equal to the product of the numerator of the second fraction and the denominator of the first.

It is easier to understand this rule by putting it in picture form. The multiplication of the numbers along one line is equal to the multiplication of the numbers along the other line.

$$\frac{2}{3} \times \frac{4}{6}$$

$$2 \times 6 = 4 \times 3$$

or

$$3 \times 4 = 6 \times 2$$

$$\frac{A}{B} \times \frac{C}{D}$$

$$A \times D = C \times B$$

or

$$B \times C = D \times A$$

Example 5-13. Find the value of R in the equation $\dfrac{3}{R} = \dfrac{2}{5}$.

Solution:

1. Write the equation.

$$\frac{3}{R} = \frac{2}{5}$$

2. Cross-multiply.

$$2 \times R = 3 \times 5$$

3. Simplify each side.

$$2R = 15$$

4. Solve for R.

$$R = \frac{15}{2}$$

5. Divide.

$$R = 7\tfrac{1}{2} \qquad Ans.$$

Example 5-14.   Find the value of E in the equation $\dfrac{4}{20} = \dfrac{3}{E}$.

Solution:

1. Write the equation.

$$\frac{4}{20} = \frac{3}{E}$$

2. Cross-multiply.

$$4 \times E = 20 \times 3$$

3. Simplify each side.

$$4E = 60$$

4. Solve for E.

$$E = \frac{60}{4}$$

5. Divide.

$$E = 15 \qquad Ans.$$

Problems

Find the value of the unknown letter in each equation.

1. $\dfrac{E}{10} = \dfrac{3}{5}$

2. $\dfrac{8}{3} = \dfrac{R}{6}$

3. $\dfrac{60}{A} = \dfrac{3}{4}$

4. $\dfrac{9}{E} = \dfrac{15}{40}$

5. $\dfrac{84}{E} = \dfrac{28}{17}$

6. $\dfrac{84}{28} = \dfrac{66}{R}$

7. $\dfrac{E}{18} = \dfrac{3}{2}$

8. $9 = \dfrac{54}{R}$

9. $\dfrac{50}{T} = 2$

10. $\dfrac{2R}{3} = \dfrac{10}{5}$

11. $\dfrac{24}{2} = \dfrac{6M}{5}$

12. $\dfrac{3P}{0.4} = 6$

13. $\dfrac{3.6}{5} = \dfrac{A}{2}$

14. $0.88 = \dfrac{R}{3}$

15. $\dfrac{3}{12} = \dfrac{4}{3T}$

16. $5 = \dfrac{1}{0.2E}$

17. $\dfrac{1}{R} = 10$

18. $80 = \dfrac{1}{R}$

19. $\dfrac{1}{R} = \dfrac{13}{24}$

20. $\dfrac{10}{R} = 50$

JOB 5-7: TOTAL RESISTANCE IN A PARALLEL CIRCUIT

When resistances are connected in parallel, the total resistance is always *less* than the resistance of any branch. When resistances are added to a circuit in parallel, they merely provide extra paths for the current to follow. Each extra path will draw its own current from the voltage source, *increasing* the total current drawn. But resistance is that quality of a circuit which attempts to stop the flow of current. If the addition of a resistance *increases* the current, then this resistance must have *reduced* the total resistance. For example, in the circuit of Fig. 5-12a, the current that flows in the resistor is 1 amp and the total resistance R_T is 50 ohms. Now let us add an extra 50-ohm resistor in parallel as shown in Fig. 5-12b. Since equal resistors carry

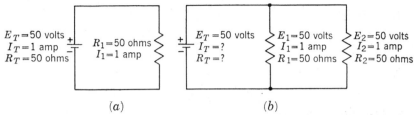

$$E_T = 50 \text{ volts}$$
$$I_T = 1 \text{ amp}$$
$$R_T = 50 \text{ ohms}$$
$$R_1 = 50 \text{ ohms}$$
$$I_1 = 1 \text{ amp}$$

$$E_T = 50 \text{ volts}$$
$$I_T = ?$$
$$R_T = ?$$
$$E_1 = 50 \text{ volts}$$
$$I_1 = 1 \text{ amp}$$
$$R_1 = 50 \text{ ohms}$$
$$E_2 = 50 \text{ volts}$$
$$I_2 = 1 \text{ amp}$$
$$R_2 = 50 \text{ ohms}$$

(a)   (b)

Fig. 5-12. Adding resistances in parallel reduces the total resistance.

equal currents, the total current equals $I_1 + I_2 = 2$ amp. The total resistance will be

$$E_T = I_T \times R_T \tag{4-7}$$
$$50 = 2 \times R_T$$
$$R_T = \frac{50}{2} = 25 \text{ ohms}$$

Thus we see that the net effect of adding another resistance in parallel *reduced* the total resistance from 50 to 25 ohms. Also, the current drawn by the new circuit *increased* from 1 to 2 amp.

The total resistance in parallel is given by the

Formula

$$\frac{1}{R_T} = \frac{1}{R_1} + \frac{1}{R_2} + \frac{1}{R_3} \cdots \text{ etc.} \tag{5-3}$$

where R_T is the total resistance in parallel and R_1, R_2, and R_3 are the branch resistances.

Example 5-15. Find the total resistance of a 10-, a 20-, and a 60-ohm resistor in parallel.

Solution: The diagram for the circuit is shown in Fig. 5-13.

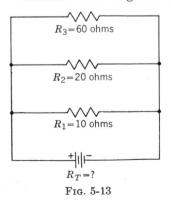

$$R_3 = 60 \text{ ohms}$$
$$R_2 = 20 \text{ ohms}$$
$$R_1 = 10 \text{ ohms}$$
$$R_T = ?$$

Fig. 5-13

1. Write the formula.

$$\frac{1}{R_T} = \frac{1}{R_1} + \frac{1}{R_2} + \frac{1}{R_3} \tag{5-3}$$

2. Substitute numbers.

$$\frac{1}{R_T} = \frac{1}{10} + \frac{1}{20} + \frac{1}{60}$$

3. Add fractions.

$$\frac{1}{R_T} = \frac{1}{6}$$

4. Cross-multiply.

$$1 \times R_T = 1 \times 6$$

5. Simplify.

$$R_T = 6 \text{ ohms} \qquad Ans.$$

Example 5-16. A 3-, a 4-, and an 8-ohm resistor are connected in parallel. Find the total resistance.

Solution:

Given: $R_1 = 3$ ohms   Find: $R_T = ?$
$R_2 = 4$ ohms
$R_3 = 8$ ohms

1. Write the formula.

$$\frac{1}{R_T} = \frac{1}{R_1} + \frac{1}{R_2} + \frac{1}{R_3} \qquad (5\text{-}3)$$

2. Substitute numbers.

$$\frac{1}{R_T} = \frac{1}{3} + \frac{1}{4} + \frac{1}{8}$$

3. Add fractions.

$$\frac{1}{R_T} = \frac{17}{24}$$

4. Cross-multiply.

$$17 \times R_T = 1 \times 24$$

5. Simplify.

$$17R_T = 24$$

6. Solve for R_T.

$$R_T = \frac{24}{17}$$

7. Divide.

$$R_T = 1.4 \text{ ohms} \qquad Ans.$$

Example 5-17. A 40-, a 70-, and a 150-ohm resistor are connected in parallel. Find the total resistance.

Solution:

Given: $R_1 = 40$ ohms   Find: $R_T = ?$
$R_2 = 70$ ohms
$R_3 = 150$ ohms

1. Write the formula.

$$\frac{1}{R_T} = \frac{1}{R_1} + \frac{1}{R_2} + \frac{1}{R_3} \qquad (5\text{-}3)$$

2. Substitute numbers.

$$\frac{1}{R_T} = \frac{1}{40} + \frac{1}{70} + \frac{1}{150}$$

The next step would be to add these fractions. However, it is very difficult to find the LCD when the denominators are as large as these. In this situation, it is best to find the decimal equivalent for each fraction and use these decimals instead of the fractions.

$$\frac{1}{40} = 40\overline{)1.000} \quad\begin{array}{r} 0.025 \\ \hline \end{array}\quad \frac{1}{70} = 70\overline{)1.000} \quad\begin{array}{r} 0.014 \\ \hline \end{array}\quad \frac{1}{150} = 150\overline{)1.000} \quad 0.006\tfrac{2}{3} = 0.007$$

$$\begin{array}{r} 0.025 \\ 40\overline{)1.000} \\ 80 \\ \hline 200 \\ 200 \\ \hline \end{array} \qquad \begin{array}{r} 0.014 \\ 70\overline{)1.000} \\ 70 \\ \hline 300 \\ 280 \\ \hline 20 \end{array} \qquad \begin{array}{r} 0.006\tfrac{2}{3} = 0.007 \\ 150\overline{)1.000} \\ 900 \\ \hline 100 \end{array}$$

3. Substitute the decimals for the fractions.

$$\frac{1}{R_T} = 0.025 + 0.014 + 0.007$$

4. Add the decimals.

$$\frac{1}{R_T} = \frac{0.046}{1}$$

5. Cross-multiply.

$$0.046R_T = 1$$

6. Solve for R_T.

$$R_T = \frac{1}{0.046}$$

7. Divide.

$$R_T = 21.7 \text{ ohms} \qquad Ans.$$

Example 5-18. A television mechanic needs a 120-ohm resistor. He has 200-, 300-, and 500-ohm resistors available. How can he combine these to form a combination worth 120 ohms?

Solution:

1. Try the 200- and the 500-ohm in parallel.

$$\frac{1}{R_T} = \frac{1}{R_1} + \frac{1}{R_2} \tag{5-3}$$

$$\frac{1}{R_T} = \frac{1}{200} + \frac{1}{500}$$

$$\frac{1}{R_T} = \frac{7}{1,000}$$

$$7R_T = 1,000$$

$$R_T = \frac{1,000}{7} = 144 \text{ ohms (not equal to 120)}$$

2. Try the 200- and the 300-ohm in parallel.

$$\frac{1}{R_T} = \frac{1}{200} + \frac{1}{300}$$

$$\frac{1}{R_T} = \frac{1}{120}$$

$R_T = 120$ ohms   *Ans.* (This combination works)

Problems

1. Find the total resistance of a 3-, a 4-, and a 12-ohm resistor in parallel.

2. Find the total resistance of the circuit shown in Fig. 5-14.

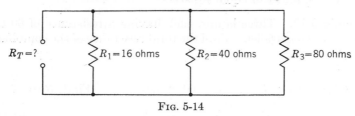

$R_T = ?$ $R_1 = 16$ ohms $R_2 = 40$ ohms $R_3 = 80$ ohms

Fig. 5-14

3. A 12SQ7 radio tube is substituted for another tube by placing its 42-ohm heater in parallel with a shunt of 42 ohms. Find the total resistance of the combination.

4. Three resistances of 3, 6, and 9 ohms are in parallel. What is the combined resistance?

5. Find the total resistance of a 25-ohm coffee percolator and a 30-ohm toaster in parallel.

6. Find the total resistance of 4, 8, 12, and 15 ohms in parallel.

7. Find the total resistance of 6, 8, and 4.8 ohms in parallel.

8. How can a radio mechanic combine a 30-, a 40-, and a 60-ohm resistor to get a combination worth 24 ohms?

9. How can a mechanic combine the resistors of Prob. 8 to get a resistance of 20 ohms?

10. Find the total resistance of 15, 7.5, and 5 ohms in parallel.

11. Find the total resistance of 100, 250, and 500 ohms when connected in parallel.

12. Find the resistance of each group of resistors in the circuit shown in Fig. 5-15.

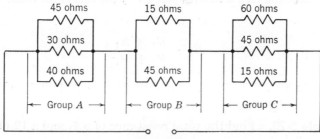

Fig. 5-15

Total Resistance of a Number of Equal Branches

Rule: The total resistance of a number of equal resistors in parallel is equal to the resistance of one resistor divided by the number of resistors.

Formula

$$R_T = \frac{R}{N} \tag{5-4}$$

where R_T = total resistance of equal resistors in parallel

R = resistance of one of the equal resistors

N = number of equal resistors

Example 5-19.   Three lamps, each having a resistance of 60 ohms, are connected in parallel.   Find the total resistance of the combination.

Solution:

Given: $R_1 = R_2 = R_3 = 60$ ohms   Find: $R_T = ?$

$$R_T = \frac{R}{N} \tag{5-4}$$

$$R_T = \frac{60}{3} = 20 \text{ ohms} \qquad Ans.$$

Problems

1. Find the total resistance of two 100-ohm lamps in parallel.

2. Find the total resistance of three 48-ohm bells in parallel.

3. Find the total resistance of two 1.5-ohm headlight lamps in parallel.

4. If the total resistance of two identical bells in parallel is 20 ohms, what is the resistance of each bell?

5. A toaster, an electric iron, and a coffee percolator, all of 22 ohms resistance, are connected in parallel across a 110-volt line.   Find (*a*) the total resistance and (*b*) the total current.

Two Resistors in Parallel.   When only two resistors are in parallel, the total resistance may be calculated by a simple rule.

Rule: To find the total resistance of only two resistors in parallel, multiply the resistances and then divide the product by the sum of the resistors.

Formula

$$R_T = \frac{R_1 \times R_2}{R_1 + R_2} \tag{5-5}$$

where R_T is the total resistance in parallel and R_1 and R_2 are the two resistors in parallel.

Example 5-20.   Find the total resistance of a 4- and a 12-ohm resistor in parallel.

Solution:

    Given: $R_1 = 4$ ohms   Find: $R_T = ?$
            $R_2 = 12$ ohms

$$R_T = \frac{R_1 \times R_2}{R_1 + R_2} \qquad\qquad (5\text{-}5)$$

$$R_T = \frac{4 \times 12}{4 + 12}$$

$$R_T = \frac{48}{16} = 3 \text{ ohms} \qquad Ans.$$

Problems

1. Find the total resistance of two 40-ohm coils in parallel.

2. Find the total resistance of a 20- and a 60-ohm motor in parallel.

3. What is the combined resistance of a 14C5 radio-tube filament ($R = 56$ ohms) and a 41-ohm shunt in parallel for operation in a 0.3-amp series heater circuit?

4. Find the total resistance of a 90-ohm galvanometer in parallel with a 10-ohm shunt resistor.

5. A section of the picture-control circuit of a television receiver uses a 10,000- and a 25,000-ohm resistor in parallel. Find the total resistance of the combination.

JOB 5-8: TOTAL VOLTAGE IN A PARALLEL CIRCUIT

Example 5-21. What voltage is needed to send 3 amp through a parallel combination consisting of a 3-, a 4-, and a 12-ohm resistance?

Solution: The diagram for the circuit is shown in Fig. 5-16.

In order to find the total voltage E_T, we must know the value of the total current I_T and the total resistance R_T. If either value is unknown, it must be found first.

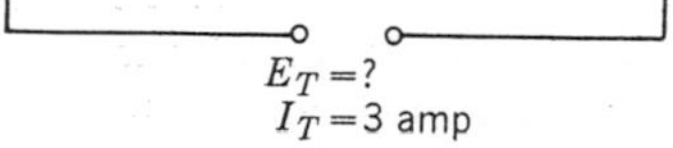

    1. Find the total resistance R_T.

$R_1 = 3$ ohms
$R_2 = 4$ ohms
$R_3 = 12$ ohms

$E_T = ?$
$I_T = 3$ amp
Fig. 5-16

$$\frac{1}{R_T} = \frac{1}{R_1} + \frac{1}{R_2} + \frac{1}{R_3} \qquad (5\text{-}3)$$

$$\frac{1}{R_T} = \frac{1}{3} + \frac{1}{4} + \frac{1}{12}$$

$$\frac{1}{R_T} = \frac{2}{3}$$

$$2R_T = 3$$

$$R_T = \frac{3}{2} = 1.5 \text{ ohms} \qquad Ans.$$

2. Find the total voltage E_T.

$$E_T = I_T \times R_T \qquad\qquad (4\text{-}7)$$
$$E_T = 3 \times 1.5 = 4.5 \text{ volts} \qquad Ans.$$

Example 5-22.   Find the total voltage required by the circuit shown in Fig. 5-17.

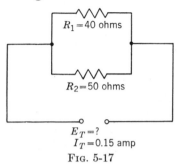
$R_1 = 40$ ohms

$R_2 = 50$ ohms

$E_T = ?$
$I_T = 0.15$ amp
FIG. 5-17

Solution:

1. Find the total resistance R_T.

$$R_T = \frac{R_1 \times R_2}{R_1 + R_2} \qquad\qquad (5\text{-}5)$$

$$R_T = \frac{40 \times 50}{40 + 50}$$

$$R_T = \frac{2,000}{90} = 22.2 \text{ ohms} \qquad Ans.$$

2. Find the total voltage E_T.

$$E_T = I_T \times R_T \qquad\qquad (4\text{-}7)$$
$$E_T = 0.15 \times 22.2 = 3.33 \text{ volts} \qquad Ans.$$

Problems

1. Find the voltage needed to send 2 amp through a parallel combination of three 60-ohm resistors.

2. Find the total voltage needed to send 9 amp through a parallel circuit of a 25-ohm percolator and a 30-ohm refrigerator motor.

3. Find the voltage needed to send 3 amp through a parallel combination of a 2- and an 8-ohm resistor.

4. Find the voltage needed to send 2 amp through a parallel combination of a 3- and a 6-ohm resistor.

5. Find the voltage required to send a current of 2.4 amp through a 10-ohm coil, a 20-ohm coil, and a 60-ohm motor if they are wired in parallel.

6. In Fig. 5-18, a 25-ohm galvanometer is shunted with a 4-ohm resistor when indicating a current of 0.003 amp. What is the voltage across the galvanometer?

7. Two tubes have heaters of 40 and 60 ohms wired in parallel. What voltage is needed to send a current of 0.6 amp through the combination?

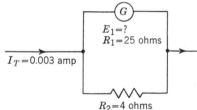
$E_1 = ?$
$R_1 = 25$ ohms
$I_T = 0.003$ amp
$R_2 = 4$ ohms

FIG. 5-18. A shunt across the galvanometer carries most of the line current.

8. Find the voltage required to send 2 amp through a parallel combination of a 20-, a 30-, and a 40-ohm resistance.

9. Find the total voltage required to send 0.15 amp through three coils in parallel if their resistances are 200, 400, and 800 ohms, respectively.

10. The cathode bias resistor for the 50L6 in an a-c–d-c receiver burned out. Not having a replacement in stock, the serviceman replaced it with a 200- and an 800-ohm resistor in parallel as shown in Fig. 5-19. If the cathode current was 0.05 amp, what bias voltage was developed across the parallel combination?

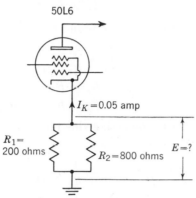

F$_{IG}$. 5-19. A burned-out cathode bias resistor is replaced with an equivalent parallel combination.

JOB 5-9: DIVISION OF CURRENT IN A PARALLEL CIRCUIT

In our study of Ohm's law we learned that the resistance of a circuit affected the current in the circuit. The greater the resistance, the smaller the current. The smaller the resistance, the greater the current. When the current in a parallel circuit reaches a point at which it may divide and flow in more than one path, the largest current will naturally flow in that portion of the circuit which offers the smallest resistance and the smallest current will flow through the largest resistance. The exact manner in which a current will divide in a parallel circuit is shown in the following example.

Example 5-23. Find the current that flows in each branch of the parallel circuit shown in Fig. 5-20.

Solution:

1. We can find the current in each branch if we know the voltage and the resistance of each branch by the formulas

$$E_1 = I_1 \times R_1 \quad (4\text{-}4)$$
$$E_2 = I_2 \times R_2 \quad (4\text{-}5)$$
$$E_3 = I_3 \times R_3 \quad (4\text{-}6)$$

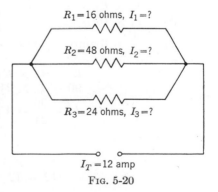

F$_{IG}$. 5-20

2. If the individual voltages are unknown, we can find them if we know E_T, since

$$E_T = E_1 = E_2 = E_3 \tag{5-1}$$

3. If E_T is unknown, it may be found by the formula

$$E_T = I_T \times R_T \tag{4-7}$$

4. If R_T is unknown, it may be found by the formula

$$\frac{1}{R_T} = \frac{1}{R_1} + \frac{1}{R_2} + \frac{1}{R_3} \tag{5-3}$$

or
$$R_T = \frac{R_1 \times R_2}{R_1 + R_2} \tag{5-5}$$

The problem is solved by reversing this plan.

1. Find the total resistance R_T.

$$\frac{1}{R_T} = \frac{1}{R_1} + \frac{1}{R_2} + \frac{1}{R_3} \tag{5-3}$$

$$\frac{1}{R_T} = \frac{1}{16} + \frac{1}{48} + \frac{1}{24}$$

$$\frac{1}{R_T} = \frac{1}{8}$$

$$R_T = 8 \text{ ohms}$$

2. Find the total voltage E_T.

$$E_T = I_T \times R_T \tag{4-7}$$
$$E_T = 12 \times 8 = 96 \text{ volts}$$

3. Find the branch voltages.

$$E_T = E_1 = E_2 = E_3 = 96 \text{ volts} \tag{5-1}$$

4. Find the branch currents.

$$E_1 = I_1 \times R_1 \qquad\qquad E_2 = I_2 \times R_2$$
$$96 = I_1 \times 16 \qquad\qquad 96 = I_2 \times 48$$
$$I_1 = \frac{96}{16} = 6 \text{ amp} \quad Ans. \qquad I_2 = \frac{96}{48} = 2 \text{ amp} \quad Ans.$$

$$E_3 = I_3 \times R_3$$
$$96 = I_3 \times 24$$
$$I_3 = \frac{96}{24} = 4 \text{ amp} \quad Ans.$$

5. Check.

$$I_T = I_1 + I_2 + I_3 \tag{5-2}$$
$$12 = 6 + 2 + 4$$
$$12 = 12$$

Example 5-24. The 25L6 beam-power tube in a 0.3-amp series heater circuit burned out. An emergency replacement was made with a tube whose resistance was 56 ohms in parallel with a shunt of 168

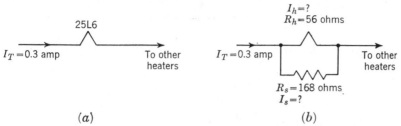

(a)   (b)

FIG. 5-21. (a) Original heater circuit. (b) Replacement circuit.

ohms as shown in Fig. 5-21b. Find the current flowing in the heater and the shunt.

Solution:

1. Find the total resistance of the parallel combination.

$$R_T = \frac{R_h \times R_s}{R_h + R_s} \tag{5-5}$$

$$R_T = \frac{56 \times 168}{56 + 168}$$

$$R_T = \frac{9,408}{224} = 42 \text{ ohms}$$

2. Find the total voltage.

$$E_T = I_T \times R_T \tag{4-7}$$
$$E_T = 0.3 \times 42 = 12.6 \text{ volts}$$

3. Find the branch voltages.

$$E_T = E_h = E_s = 12.6 \text{ volts} \tag{5-1}$$

4. Find the branch currents.

Heater circuit	Shunt circuit	
$E_h = I_h \times R_h$	$E_s = I_s \times R_s$	(2-1)
$12.6 = I_h \times 56$	$12.6 = I_s \times 168$	
$I_h = \dfrac{12.6}{56}$	$I_s = \dfrac{12.6}{168}$	
$I_h = 0.225$ amp *Ans.*	$I_s = 0.075$ amp *Ans.*	

Division of Current in Two Branches in Parallel

Rule: When only two branches are involved, the current in one branch will be only some fraction of the total current. This fraction is the quotient of the second resistance divided by the sum of the resistances.

Formula

$$I_1 = \frac{R_2}{R_1 + R_2} \times I_T \qquad (5\text{-}6)$$

$$I_2 = \frac{R_1}{R_1 + R_2} \times I_T \qquad (5\text{-}7)$$

Example 5-25. We can solve Example 5-24 using these formulas.

Solution:

Given: $R_h = 56$ ohms   Find: $I_h = ?$
$R_s = 168$ ohms $I_s = ?$
$I_T = 0.3$ amp

1. Find the heater current I_h.

$$I_h = \frac{R_s}{R_h + R_s} \times I_T \qquad (5\text{-}6)$$

$$I_h = \frac{168}{56 + 168} \times 0.3 = \frac{168}{224} \times 0.3$$

$$I_h = 0.75 \times 0.3 = 0.225 \text{ amp} \qquad Ans.$$

2. Find the shunt current I_s.

$$I_s = \frac{R_h}{R_h + R_s} \times I_T \qquad (5\text{-}7)$$

$$I_s = \frac{56}{56 + 168} \times 0.3 = \frac{56}{224} \times 0.3$$

$$I_s = 0.25 \times 0.3 = 0.075 \text{ amp} \qquad Ans.$$

Problems

1. In a circuit similar to that shown in Fig. 5-17, $R_1 = 48$ ohms, $R_2 = 48$ ohms, and $I_T = 8$ amp. Find the current flowing in each branch. On the basis of your answers, state a rule about the division of current between equal resistors in parallel.

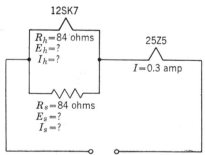

2. Find the current in each branch of a parallel circuit consisting of a 20-ohm percolator and a 30-ohm toaster if the total current is 9 amp.

3. In Fig. 5-22, a 12SK7 tube whose heater resistance is 84 ohms is shunted with an 84-ohm resistor in parallel in order to operate it in series with a 25Z5 rectifier. The 25Z5 heater draws 0.3 amp. Find (a) the total resistance of the parallel group, (b) the voltage across the 12SK7 heater, (c) the current through the 12SK7, and (d) the current through the shunt.

FIG. 5-22. A resistor must be placed in parallel with the 12SK7 heater to operate it in series with a 25Z5 heater (see Job 8-5).

4. Two 1.5-ohm automobile headlight lamps in parallel draw a total of 8 amp. Find the total voltage supplied and the current drawn by each lamp.

5. A galvanometer whose resistance is 48 ohms and its parallel shunt of 2 ohms draw a total current of 0.2 amp. Find the current through the galvanometer and through the shunt.

6. A generator supplies a current of 19.5 amp to three small electroplating tanks arranged in parallel. The resistances of the tanks are 8, 12, and 16 ohms. What current does each tank draw?

7. A generator supplies a current of 26 amp to three motors arranged in parallel. The resistances of the motors are 24, 36, and 48 ohms. What current does each motor draw?

8. The plate circuit of a radio tube is shown in Fig. 5-23. The 18,000-ohm load resistance includes the plate resistance of the tube. Find the current in the load I_L and the current in the bleeder resistor I_b.

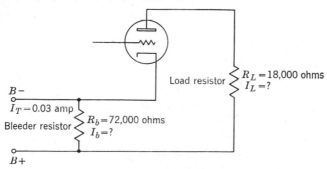

FIG. 5-23. A load resistor and bleeder resistor in parallel.

9. The resistance of an ammeter is 2.8 ohms. A shunt of 0.02 ohm is connected in parallel with it. If the combination is inserted into a line carrying 10 amp, how much current actually flows through the ammeter?

10. In a circuit similar to that shown in Fig. 5-16, $R_1 = 5$ ohms, $R_2 = 7$ ohms, $R_3 = 8$ ohms, and $I_T = 13.1$ amp. Find (a) the total resistance of the circuit, (b) the total voltage of the circuit, (c) the voltage across each branch, and (d) the current in each branch.

11. The 25L6 amplifier tube in a 0.3-amp series heater circuit was replaced with a 35L6 whose heater resistance is 233 ohms and shunted with a 233-ohm resistor in parallel. Find the current in the 35L6 heater and in its shunt resistor.

12. The ballast resistor in a 0.3-amp series heater circuit overheated. It was replaced with a 200-ohm and a 300-ohm resistor in parallel. Find (a) the total resistance of the parallel group, (b) the voltage drop across the group, and (c) the current in each resistor of the group.

JOB 5-10: REVIEW OF PARALLEL CIRCUITS

Definition. A parallel circuit is a circuit in which the current may divide so as to flow in more than one path.

Rules and Formulas

1. The total voltage across a parallel circuit is equal to the voltage across any branch of the circuit.

$$E_T = E_1 = E_2 = E_3 \qquad (5\text{-}1)$$

2. The total current in a parallel circuit is equal to the *sum* of the currents in all the branches of the circuit.

$$I_T = I_1 + I_2 + I_3 \qquad (5\text{-}2)$$

3. The total resistance in a parallel circuit may be found by applying Ohm's law to the total values of the circuit.

$$E_T = I_T \times R_T \qquad (4\text{-}7)$$

4. The total resistance may also be found by
    a. For any number of resistors

$$\frac{1}{R_T} = \frac{1}{R_1} + \frac{1}{R_2} + \frac{1}{R_3} \qquad (5\text{-}3)$$

   b. For just two resistors

$$R_T = \frac{R_1 \times R_2}{R_1 + R_2} \qquad (5\text{-}5)$$

   c. For any number N of equal resistors

$$R_T = \frac{R}{N} \qquad (5\text{-}4)$$

5. Ohm's law may be used on any branch of a parallel circuit.

$$E_1 = I_1 \times R_1 \qquad (4\text{-}4)$$
$$E_2 = I_2 \times R_2 \qquad (4\text{-}5)$$
$$E_3 = I_3 \times R_3 \qquad (4\text{-}6)$$

6. The total resistance in parallel is always *less* than the resistance of any branch.

7. Division of current between two branches in parallel.

$$I_1 = \frac{R_2}{R_1 + R_2} \times I_T \qquad (5\text{-}6)$$

$$I_2 = \frac{R_1}{R_1 + R_2} \times I_T \qquad (5\text{-}7)$$

8. Adding fractions,

a. In order to add fractions, all the fractions must have the same denominator.

b. The LCD is the smallest number into which *all* the denominators will evenly divide.

9. Solving fractional equations:

a. Simplify fractions whenever possible.

b. When a fractional equation contains only two fractions equal to each other, the equation may be solved by cross multiplication.

c. To cross-multiply, the product of the numerator of the first fraction and the denominator of the second is set equal to the product of the numerator of the second fraction and the denominator of the first. For example, if

$$\frac{C}{D} = \frac{E}{F}$$

then $\qquad C \times F = D \times E \qquad$ or $\qquad E \times D = F \times C$

Problems

1. An electric iron, a radio, and an electric clock are connected to a three-way 110-volt kitchen outlet which puts the appliances in parallel. The iron draws 5 amp, the radio draws 0.5 amp, and the clock draws 0.25 amp. Find (*a*) the total current drawn from the line, (*b*) the voltage across each device, and (*c*) the total resistance of the circuit.

2. A semaphore signal, a floodlight tower, and a coal loader of a model railroad are connected in parallel across the 12-volt winding of the power transformer. The signal draws 0.1 amp, and the coal loader draws 0.2 amp. The floodlight tower has a resistance of 48 ohms. Find (*a*) the voltage across each device, (*b*) the resistance of the semaphore and the coal loader, (*c*) the total current, and (*d*) the total resistance of the circuit.

3. Three motors are wired in parallel across 440 volts. Motor 1 draws a current of 10 amp, and motor 3 draws 15 amp. Motor 2 has a resistance of 20 ohms. Solve the circuit for all missing values of current, voltage, and resistance.

4. Find all missing values of voltage, current, and resistance in the circuit shown in Fig. 5-24.

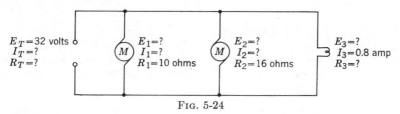

Fig. 5-24

5. Find the total resistance of a 60-, an 80-, and a 120-ohm resistor in parallel.

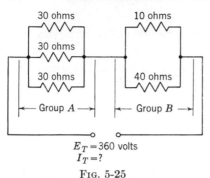

Fig. 5-25

$E_T = 360$ volts
$I_T = ?$

6. In the circuit shown in Fig. 5-25, find (*a*) the total resistance R_A of group A and (*b*) the total resistance R_B of group B. (*c*) Draw a new circuit using a single resistor (R_A and R_B) in place of the groups they represent. (*d*) Is the new circuit a series or a parallel circuit? (*e*) What is the total resistance of the new circuit? (*f*) Find the total current in the new circuit.

7. What is the combined resistance of a 480-ohm galvanometer and its parallel 20-ohm shunt?

8. Find the voltage needed to send 2 amp through a parallel combination of a 75- and a 100-ohm resistor.

9. Using a circuit similar to that shown in Fig. 5-23, R_L equals 3,000 ohms, R_b equals 17,000 ohms, and I_T equals 0.04 amp. Find (*a*) the total resistance and (*b*) the total voltage.

10. A generator supplies 26 amp to three motors in parallel. The resistances of the motors are 12, 18, and 24 ohms. What current does each motor draw?

11. The Bell model 2122C 10-watt audio amplifier uses two 6SC7 tubes, one 6SL7 tube, and two 6V6 tubes with their heaters connected in parallel across a 6.3-volt winding. The 6V6 uses 0.45 amp, and the other tubes use 0.3 amp. Find (*a*) the total current, (*b*) the total resistance, and (*c*) the resistance of each heater.

12. A 6SL7 whose heater resistance is 21 ohms is substituted for a 6SN7 in a 0.6-amp series heater circuit. If the 6SL7 is placed in parallel with a 21-ohm shunt resistor, find (*a*) the total resistance of the parallel combination, (*b*) the voltage drop across the 6SL7 heater, (*c*) the current through the heater, and (*d*) the current through the parallel shunt.

Test—Parallel Circuits

1. Three motors are connected in parallel. $I_1 = 3$ amp, $R_1 = 40$ ohms, $R_2 = 30$ ohms, and $I_3 = 1$ amp. Find (*a*) the total voltage, (*b*) the total current, and (*c*) the total resistance.

2. Add (*a*) $\frac{1}{4} + \frac{5}{6} + \frac{3}{8}$ and (*b*) $\frac{1}{2} + \frac{7}{32} + \frac{3}{16}$.

3. Solve for the value of the unknown letter:

(*a*) $\frac{2M}{5} = \frac{3}{5}$ and (*b*) $\frac{0.8}{R} = \frac{2}{5}$.

4. Find the total voltage needed to send 2 amp of current through a parallel combination of a 10-, a 20-, and a 60-ohm motor.

5. A parallel combination of a 5- and a 15-ohm resistor draws 10 amp from a line. Find the current in each resistor.

CHAPTER 6

COMBINATION CIRCUITS

JOB 6-1: INTRODUCTION TO COMBINATION CIRCUITS

Each simple circuit has its own advantages and disadvantages.

Series Circuits. An advantage of a series circuit is that it may be used to connect small voltages to obtain high voltages. Also, high voltages may be reduced by connecting resistances in series. Series circuits provide a means for reducing and controlling the current by connecting resistances in series. However, this series current remains unchanged throughout the circuit. This is a serious disadvantage. Since the current is constant, we are forced to use only those devices which require the same current. Thus it would be impossible to use any two household appliances at the same time because their current requirements range from 0.25 to 10 amp. In addition, if any part of a series circuit should burn out, it would cause an open circuit and put the entire circuit out of operation. Lights are never wired in series for this reason, because the circuit demands that we have either *all* the lights on or none at all. Series circuits are used where different voltage drops and a constant current are needed.

Parallel Circuits. If a break should occur in any branch of a parallel circuit, it would not affect the other branch circuits. Houses are wired in parallel so that any device may be operated independently of any other device. This is both an advantage and a disadvantage. In a parallel circuit, more branches may be added at any time. Each new load draws current from the line. So much current may be drawn that the original line wires may not be able to carry the new current and the fuse will "blow." In this event, it is necessary to rewire the circuits completely, using wire capable of carrying the larger currents or to put in extra independent circuits to supply the installation. Parallel circuits are used wherever a constant voltage and a large supply of current are required.

127

Combination Circuits. If we combine series circuits with parallel circuits, we produce a combination circuit which makes use of the best features of each. A combination circuit makes it possible to obtain the different voltages of a series circuit and the different currents of a parallel circuit. This is the condition most generally required, particularly when the different voltages and currents must be supplied from the same source of power. In the electrical system of an automobile, the voltage and current needs of the lights, ignition system, and accessories are all different and yet the power is drawn from a single storage battery. The different voltage and current needs of the different circuits of a radio receiver are all obtained from combination circuits drawing power from a single power supply.

Simple combination circuits are of two types:

1. A *series-parallel* circuit (Fig. 6-1) is a circuit in which one or more *groups* of resistances in parallel are connected in series.

2. A *parallel-series* circuit (Fig. 6-10) is a circuit in which one or more *groups* of resistances in series are connected in parallel.

General Method for Solving Combination Circuits

1. A *group* of resistances is a simple combination of two or more resistances which are arranged in either a *simple* series or a *simple* parallel circuit. Locate these groups.

2. Every group must be removed from the circuit as a unit and *replaced* by a single resistor which offers the identical resistance. This equivalent resistance is the total resistance of the group.

3. Redraw the circuit, using the equivalent resistance in place of each group.

4. Solve the resulting simple circuit for all missing values.

5. Go back to the *original* circuit to find the voltage, current, and resistance for each resistance in the circuit.

JOB 6-2: SOLVING SERIES-PARALLEL CIRCUITS

Example 6-1. Solve the circuit shown in Fig. 6-1 for all values of voltage, current, and resistance.

Solution:

1. Find the equivalent resistance of group A. This means that the circuit is broken at points 1 and 2; resistors R_2 and R_3 are removed and replaced by a *single* resistance. This single resistance will do the work of the combination of R_2 and R_3.

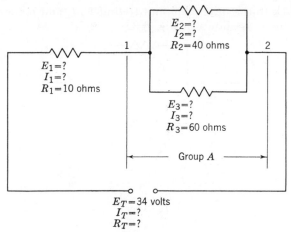

FIG. 6-1. A series-parallel circuit.

2. Since R_2 and R_3 are in parallel,

$$R_A = \frac{R_2 \times R_3}{R_2 + R_3} \qquad\qquad (5\text{-}5)$$

$$R_A = \frac{40 \times 60}{40 + 60} = \frac{2,400}{100} = 24 \text{ ohms} \qquad Ans.$$

3. Redraw the circuit using this 24-ohm resistor R_A in place of the combination as shown in Fig. 6-2.

4. Solve the new circuit. Notice that we have a simple *series* circuit.

Find the total resistance R_T.

$R_T = R_1 + R_A \qquad (4\text{-}3)$
$R_T = 10 + 24 = 34 \text{ ohms} \qquad Ans.$

Find the total current I_T.

$E_T = I_T \times R_T \qquad (4\text{-}7)$
$34 = I_T \times 34$
$I_T = \frac{34}{34} = 1 \text{ amp} \qquad Ans.$

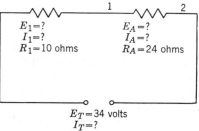

FIG. 6-2. The parallel group A is replaced with its equivalent resistance R_A.

Find the current in each part of the series circuit.

$$I_T = I_1 = I_A = 1 \text{ amp} \qquad Ans. \qquad (4\text{-}1)$$

Find the voltage in each part of the series circuit.

$$
\begin{array}{llr}
E_1 = I_1 \times R_1 & E_A = I_A \times R_A & (4\text{-}4) \\
E_1 = 1 \times 10 & E_A = 1 \times 24 & \\
E_1 = 10 \text{ volts} & E_A = 24 \text{ volts} \qquad Ans. &
\end{array}
$$

5. Go back to the original circuit to find E, I, and R for each resistance in group A as shown in Fig. 6-3.

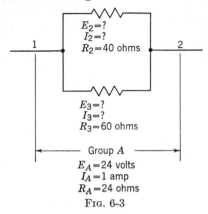

$$E_2 = ?$$
$$I_2 = ?$$
$$R_2 = 40 \text{ ohms}$$

$$E_3 = ?$$
$$I_3 = ?$$
$$R_3 = 60 \text{ ohms}$$

Group A
$$E_A = 24 \text{ volts}$$
$$I_A = 1 \text{ amp}$$
$$R_A = 24 \text{ ohms}$$

FIG. 6-3

Since E_A represents the total voltage of the parallel group A,

$$E_A = E_2 = E_3 = 24 \text{ volts} \qquad Ans. \qquad (5\text{-}1)$$

Find the current in each resistor of group A.

$E_2 = I_2 \times R_2$	$E_3 = I_3 \times R_3$ $\qquad\qquad$ (4-6)
$24 = I_2 \times 40$	$24 = I_3 \times 60$
$I_2 = \frac{24}{40} = 0.6 \text{ amp}$	$I_3 = \frac{24}{60} = 0.4 \text{ amp} \qquad Ans.$

6. Check.

$$I_T = I_2 + I_3 \qquad (5\text{-}2)$$
$$I_T = 0.6 + 0.4$$
$$1 = 1 \qquad Check$$

Example 6-2. In the Motorola Ch 120174B noise-control circuit shown in Fig. 6-4, find (a) the cathode current I_k, (b) the cathode voltage E_k, (c) the voltage drop in the plate circuit E_L, and (d) the plate-circuit current I_L.

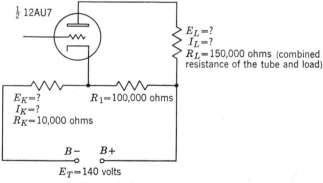

$\frac{1}{2}$ 12AU7

$$E_L = ?$$
$$I_L = ?$$
$$R_L = 150,000 \text{ ohms (combined resistance of the tube and load)}$$

$$E_K = ?$$
$$I_K = ?$$
$$R_K = 10,000 \text{ ohms}$$

$$R_1 = 100,000 \text{ ohms}$$

$B-$ $B+$

$$E_T = 140 \text{ volts}$$

FIG. 6-4. A noise-control circuit.

Solution: It is usually difficult for the beginning student to trace a radio circuit because of the unusual twists and turns of the wires. Therefore, let us redraw the circuit in the familiar standard form as

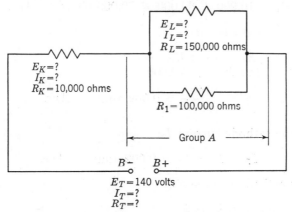

$E_L=?$
$I_L=?$
$R_L=150,000$ ohms

$E_K=?$
$I_K=?$
$R_K=10,000$ ohms

$R_1-100,000$ ohms

Group *A*

B-   B+

$E_T=140$ volts
$I_T=?$
$R_T=?$

FIG. 6-5. The diagram of Fig. 6-4 is redrawn in standard form.

shown in Fig. 6-5.   *Note:* R_L represents the combined resistance of the plate of the tube and the load resistance.

a. Find the cathode current I_k.
    1. Find the equivalent resistance of group *A*.

$$R_A = \frac{R_L \times R_1}{R_L + R_1} \tag{5-5}$$

$$R_A = \frac{150,000 \times 100,000}{150,000 + 100,000}$$

$$R_A = \frac{15,000,000,000}{250,000} = 60,000 \text{ ohms} \qquad Ans.$$

    2. Redraw the circuit using this 60,000-ohm resistor in place of the combination as shown in Fig. 6-6.

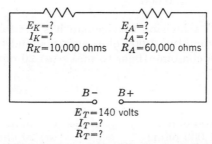

$E_K=?$
$I_K=?$
$R_K=10,000$ ohms

$E_A=?$
$I_A=?$
$R_A=60,000$ ohms

B-   B+

$E_T=140$ volts
$I_T=?$
$R_T=?$

FIG. 6-6. The parallel group is replaced by its equivalent resistance R_A.

3. Solve the new *series* circuit.
Find the total resistance R_T.

$$R_T = R_k + R_A \qquad\qquad (4\text{-}3)$$
$$R_T = 10,000 + 60,000 = 70,000 \text{ ohms} \qquad Ans.$$

Find the total current I_T.

$$E_T = I_T \times R_T \qquad\qquad (4\text{-}7)$$
$$140 = I_T \times 70,000$$
$$I_T = \frac{140}{70,000} = 0.002 \text{ amp} \qquad Ans.$$

Find the cathode current I_k.

$$I_T = I_k = I_A = 0.002 \text{ amp} \qquad Ans. \qquad (4\text{-}1)$$

b. Find the cathode voltage E_k.

$$E_k = I_k \times R_k \qquad\qquad (4\text{-}4)$$
$$E_k = 0.002 \times 10,000 = 20 \text{ volts} \qquad Ans.$$

c. Find the voltage drop in the plate circuit E_L.
1. Find the voltage drop across group A.

$$E_A = I_A \times R_A \qquad\qquad (4\text{-}5)$$
$$E_A = 0.002 \times 60,000 = 120 \text{ volts}$$

2. In Fig. 6-5, since E_A represents the total voltage of the parallel group A,

$$E_L = E_A = 120 \text{ volts} \qquad Ans.$$

d. Using group A in Fig. 6-5, find the plate-circuit current I_L.

$$E_L = I_L \times R_L \qquad\qquad (2\text{-}1)$$
$$120 = I_L \times 150,000$$
$$I_L = \frac{120}{150,000} = 0.0008 \text{ amp} \qquad Ans.$$

Example 6-3. A television serviceman has the following resistors: two 100-ohm resistors, two 1,000-ohm resistors, and two 25-ohm resistors. How can he combine them to make (*a*) 20 ohms, (*b*) 75 ohms, and (*c*) 600 ohms?

Solution:

Given: Two—100 ohms   Find: Combinations to make
        Two—1,000 ohms   (*a*) 20 ohms
        Two—25 ohms   (*b*) 75 ohms
                      (*c*) 600 ohms

a. Combine a 100- and a 25-ohm resistor in parallel.

$$R_T = \frac{R_1 \times R_2}{R_1 + R_2} \qquad (5\text{-}5)$$

$$R_T = \frac{100 \times 25}{100 + 25} = \frac{2,500}{125} = 20 \text{ ohms} \qquad Ans.$$

b. Combine two 100-ohm resistors in parallel with a 25-ohm resistor in series with the parallel group.
For the parallel group:

$$R_A = \frac{R}{N} \qquad (5\text{-}4)$$

$$R_A = \tfrac{100}{2} = 50 \text{ ohms}$$

Placing this in series with a 25-ohm resistor:

$$R_T = R_A + R_1 \qquad (4\text{-}3)$$
$$R_T = 50 + 25 = 75 \text{ ohms} \qquad Ans.$$

c. Combine two 1,000-ohm resistors in parallel with a 100-ohm resistor in series with the parallel group.
For the parallel group:

$$R_A = \frac{R}{N} \qquad (5\text{-}4)$$

$$R_A = \frac{1,000}{2} = 500 \text{ ohms}$$

Placing this in series with a 100-ohm resistor:

$$R_T = R_A + R_1 \qquad (4\text{-}3)$$
$$R_T = 500 + 100 = 600 \text{ ohms} \qquad Ans.$$

Problems

1. In a circuit similar to that shown in Fig. 6-1, $E_T = 130$ volts, $R_1 = 10$ ohms, $R_2 = 4$ ohms, and $R_3 = 12$ ohms. Find all missing values of voltage, current, and resistance.

2. Find all missing values in the circuit shown in Fig. 6-7.

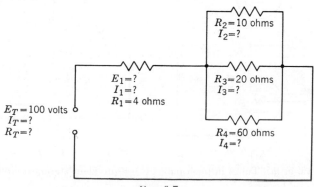

$R_2 = 10$ ohms
$I_2 = ?$

$E_1 = ?$
$I_1 = ?$
$R_1 = 4$ ohms

$R_3 = 20$ ohms
$I_3 = ?$

$E_T = 100$ volts
$I_T = ?$
$R_T = ?$

$R_4 = 60$ ohms
$I_4 = ?$

Fig. 6-7

3. The heater circuit of a tuned r-f receiver using a 6K7, 6J7, 25L6, 25Z5, and a shunted type 46 pilot light is shown in Fig. 6-8. Find the total line current and the voltage and the current of the No. 46 lamp.

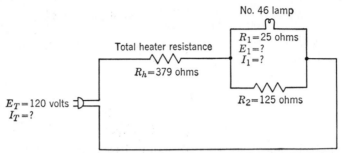

FIG. 6-8. The heater circuit of a tuned r-f receiver for Prob. 3.

4. A mechanic has the following resistors available: three 50-, two 100-, and three 500-ohm. How should he connect them to make combinations worth (a) 125 ohms, (b) 275 ohms, and (c) 350 ohms?

5. In a circuit similar to that shown in Fig. 6-4, $E_T = 174$ volts, $R_k = 10,000$ ohms, $R_1 = 80,000$ ohms, and $R_L = 120,000$ ohms. Find (a) the cathode current I_k, (b) the cathode voltage E_k, (c) the voltage drop in the plate load E_L, and (d) the plate-load current I_L.

6. In a circuit similar to that shown in Fig. 6-4, $R_k = 10,000$ ohms, $R_1 = 100,000$ ohms, $R_L = 200,000$ ohms, and $I_L = 0.0007$ amp. Find (a) the voltage drop in the plate circuit, (b) the voltage drop across R_1, (c) the current in R_1, (d) the cathode current I_k, (e) the cathode voltage E_k, and (f) the total B-supply voltage.

7. A typical circuit for the operation of tubes in push-pull is shown in Fig. 6-9a. Its equivalent standard circuit is shown in Fig. 6-9b. Find the total current.

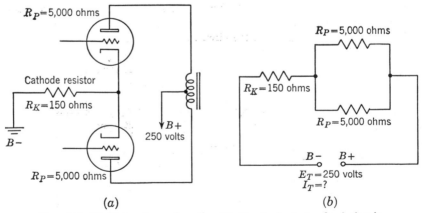

(a)   (b)

FIG. 6-9. (a) Tubes in push-pull. (b) Equivalent standard circuit.

8. In a circuit similar to that shown in Fig. 6-7, find the total current if $E_T = 8.5$ volts, $R_1 = 12$ ohms, $R_2 = 10$ ohms, $R_3 = 15$ ohms, and $R_4 = 30$ ohms.

JOB 6-3: SOLVING PARALLEL-SERIES CIRCUITS

Example 6-4. Solve the circuit shown in Fig. 6-10 for all missing values of voltage, current, and resistance.

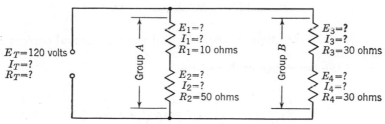

FIG. 6-10. A parallel-series circuit.

Solution:

1. Locate groups A and B as simple series circuits.
2. Find the equivalent resistance of each group.

$$R_A = R_1 + R_2 \quad\quad\quad (4\text{-}3)$$
$$R_A = 10 + 50 = 60 \text{ ohms} \quad Ans.$$

$$R_B = R_3 + R_4 \quad\quad\quad (4\text{-}3)$$
$$R_B = 30 + 30 = 60 \text{ ohms} \quad Ans.$$

3. Redraw the circuit, using these 60-ohm resistors in place of the series groups as shown in Fig. 6-11.

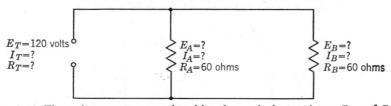

FIG. 6-11. The series groups are replaced by the equivalent resistors R_A and R_B.

4. Solve the new *parallel* circuit.
   Find the voltage for each group.

$$E_T = E_A = E_B = 120 \text{ volts} \quad Ans. \quad (5\text{-}1)$$

   Find the current in each group.

$$E_A = I_A \times R_A \quad\quad\quad\quad E_B = I_B \times R_B \quad\quad (4\text{-}4)$$
$$120 = I_A \times 60 \quad\quad\quad\quad 120 = I_B \times 60$$
$$I_A = \tfrac{120}{60} = 2 \text{ amp} \quad Ans. \quad I_B = \tfrac{120}{60} = 2 \text{ amp} \quad Ans.$$

Find the total current I_T.

$$I_T = I_A + I_B \qquad (5\text{-}2)$$
$$I_T = 2 + 2 = 4 \text{ amp} \qquad Ans.$$

Find the total resistance R_T.

$$E_T = I_T \times R_T \qquad (4\text{-}7)$$
$$120 = 4 \times R_T$$
$$R_T = \tfrac{120}{4} = 30 \text{ ohms} \qquad Ans.$$

5. Go back to the original circuit to find the voltage and current for each resistor.

Find the current in each resistor.

$$I_A = I_1 = I_2 = 2 \text{ amp} \qquad Ans. \qquad (5\text{-}2)$$
$$I_B = I_3 = I_4 = 2 \text{ amp} \qquad Ans. \qquad (5\text{-}2)$$

Find the voltage drop across each resistor.

$E_1 = I_1 \times R_1$	$E_3 = I_3 \times R_3$	(2-1)
$E_1 = 2 \times 10$	$E_3 = 2 \times 30$	
$E_1 = 20$ volts $Ans.$	$E_3 = 60$ volts $Ans.$	
$E_2 = I_2 \times R_2$	$E_4 = I_4 \times R_4$	(2-1)
$E_2 = 2 \times 50$	$E_4 = 2 \times 30$	
$E_2 = 100$ volts $Ans.$	$E_4 = 60$ volts $Ans.$	

Problems

1. Find all missing values in the circuit shown in Fig. 6-12.

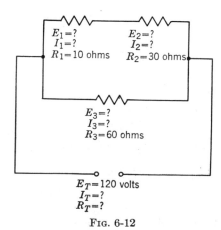

$E_1=?$
$I_1=?$
$R_1=10$ ohms

$E_2=?$
$I_2=?$
$R_2=30$ ohms

$E_3=?$
$I_3=?$
$R_3=60$ ohms

$E_T=120$ volts
$I_T=?$
$R_T=?$

Fig. 6-12

2. Find the total resistance and the total current for the circuit shown in Fig. 6-13.

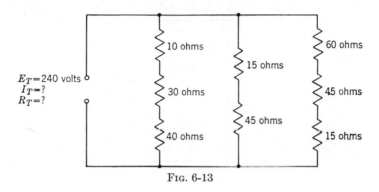

FIG. 6-13

3. Find the total resistance and the total current for the circuit shown in Fig. 6-14.

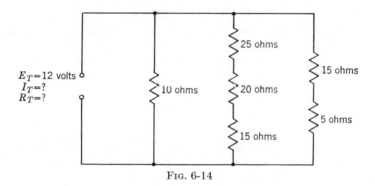

FIG. 6-14

4. Find all missing values in the circuit shown in Fig. 6-15.

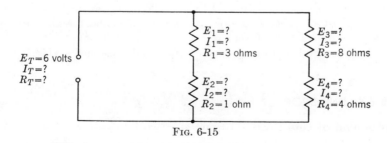

FIG. 6-15

5. In the plate circuit shown in Fig. 6-16, find (*a*) the total resistance, (*b*) the total current, (*c*) the voltage across the bleeder E_b, (*d*) the bleeder current

I_b, (e) the plate-circuit current I_L, (f) the plate voltage E_p, and (g) the load voltage E_L.

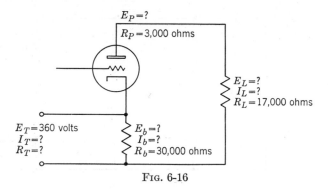

FIG. 6-16

Test—Combination Circuits

1. A 50-ohm resistor is connected in series with a parallel combination of a 40- and a 60-ohm resistor. The entire circuit is placed across a total voltage of 37 volts. Find (a) the total resistance of the parallel group, (b) the total resistance of the entire circuit, (c) the total current, and (d) the current and the voltage drop in each resistor.

2. A mechanic has three 300-ohm resistors and two 50-ohm resistors. How can they be combined to form a combination worth 175 ohms?

3. A 50- and a 30-ohm resistor are connected in series. In parallel with this series group is another series group consisting of a 20- and a 28-ohm resistor. The two groups are supplied from a 120-volt source. Find (a) the total resistance and total voltage for each series group, (b) the total current for each series group, (c) the total current for the entire combination, (d) the total resistance of the entire combination, and (e) the current and the voltage drop in each resistor.

4. A television receiver damper circuit consists of a 30- and a 50-ohm resistor in parallel. In series with this group is another parallel group of a 60- and an 80-ohm resistor. Find the total resistance of the entire circuit.

5. The brightness-control circuit of the DeWald model ET-140R television receiver is essentially a 220,000-ohm resistor in series with a parallel combination of a 100,000- and a 180,000-ohm resistor. Find the total resistance of the circuit.

JOB 6-4: LINE DROP

Meaning of Line Drop. In our last two jobs, we worked with circuits in which the connecting wires were very short. The resistances of these short lengths were so very small that we did not bother to include them in our calculations. In home and factory installations, however, where long lines of wire (feeders) are used, the resistance of these long lengths must be included in all calculations.

The voltage that is needed to force the current through the resistance of the line wires is called the *line drop*. For example, if a generator delivers 120 volts but the voltage available at a motor some distance away is only 116 volts, then there has been a "drop" in voltage of 4 volts. Apparently, the connecting wires had enough resistance to use up 4 volts of electrical pressure.

We must be very careful about the kind and size of wires used in any installation. If the wires are poorly chosen, then the *line drop* may be very large and the voltage available to the electrical apparatus will be too low for proper operation. The National and City Electrical Codes permit definite amounts of line drop for specific installations. This limitation of the line drop is accomplished by specifying definite sizes of wire to be used in specific installations. We shall study this in detail in Chap. 12.

You may have noticed the effect of line drop in your home. The lights may suddenly get dim when the refrigerator motor starts. The large current drain required to start the motor increases the line drop in the house wiring so that the voltage left over for the lights is less than normal. Since the running current is much less than the starting current, as soon as the motor has started the current drain decreases—the line drop decreases—and the lights once again come up to full brilliance.

Definitions

1. Generator voltage: The total voltage supplied to the circuit from the source of voltage (E_G).

2. Load voltage: The voltage which is available to operate the devices or loads (E_L).

3. Line drop: The voltage which is lost in sending the current through the line wires (E_l).

Rules and Formulas

1. By Ohm's law, the total line drop is equal to the line current multiplied by the total line resistance.

$$E_{\text{line}} = I_{\text{line}} \times R_{\text{line}}$$
$$E_l = I_l \times R_l \tag{6-1}$$

2. The generator voltage is the total voltage of the series circuit made up of the line drop and the load voltage.

$$E_T = E_1 + E_2 \qquad (4\text{-}2)$$

or $\qquad E_{\text{generator}} = E_{\text{line}} + E_{\text{load}}$

or $\qquad E_G = E_l + E_L \qquad (6\text{-}2)$

3. The load voltage is equal to the generator voltage minus the line drop. From

$$E_l + E_L = E_G \qquad (6\text{-}2)$$

we get, by transposing the E_l,

$$E_L = E_G - E_l \qquad (6\text{-}3)$$

When using these formulas, be sure that

1. The line current I_l is the current flowing in the line wires and *not* the current in the load.

2. The line drop E_l is the voltage lost in the line wires only.

3. The line resistance is the resistance of the connecting wires only. The resistance of both lead and return wires must be considered when finding the total resistance of the line.

Example 6-5. A lamp bank consisting of three lamps, each drawing 2 amp, is connected to a 120-volt source. Each line wire has a resistance of 0.2 ohm. Find the drop in voltage in the line and the voltage available at the load.

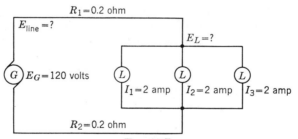

Fig. 6-17

Solution: The diagram for the circuit is shown in Fig. 6-17.

1. Find the current drawn by the load.

$$I_L = I_1 + I_2 + I_3 \qquad (5\text{-}2)$$
$$I_L = 2 + 2 + 2 = 6 \text{ amp} \qquad Ans.$$

2. Find the line current. Since the line wires are in series with the load,

$$I_l = I_L = 6 \text{ amp} \qquad Ans. \qquad (4\text{-}1)$$

3. Find the resistance of the line wires. Since the line wires are in series,

$$R_l = R_1 + R_2 \qquad (4\text{-}3)$$
$$R_l = 0.2 + 0.2 = 0.4 \text{ ohm} \qquad Ans.$$

4. Find the total line drop.

$$E_l = I_l \times R_l \qquad\qquad (6\text{-}1)$$
$$E_l = 6 \times 0.4 = 2.4 \text{ volts} \qquad Ans.$$

5. Find the voltage available at the load.

$$E_L = E_G - E_l \qquad\qquad (6\text{-}3)$$
$$E_L = 120 - 2.4 = 117.6 \text{ volts} \qquad Ans.$$

Example 6-6. Find the generator voltage required for the circuit shown in Fig. 6-18.

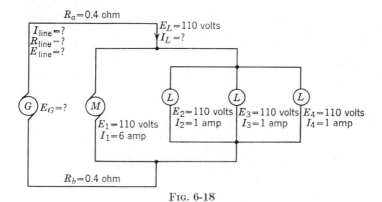

Fig. 6-18

Solution:

1. Find the current drawn by the load.

$$I_L = I_1 + I_2 + I_3 + I_4 \qquad\qquad (5\text{-}2)$$
$$I_L = 6 + 1 + 1 + 1 = 9 \text{ amp} \qquad Ans.$$

2. Find the line current.

$$I_l = I_L = 9 \text{ amp} \qquad Ans. \qquad\qquad (4\text{-}1)$$

3. Find the resistance of the line wires.

$$R_l = R_a + R_b \qquad\qquad (4\text{-}3)$$
$$R_l = 0.4 + 0.4 = 0.8 \text{ ohm} \qquad Ans.$$

4. Find the total line drop.

$$E_l = I_l \times R_l \qquad\qquad (6\text{-}1)$$
$$E_l = 9 \times 0.8 = 7.2 \text{ volts} \qquad Ans.$$

5. Find the generator voltage.

$$E_G = E_l + E_L \qquad\qquad (6\text{-}2)$$
$$E_G = 7.2 + 110 = 117.2 \text{ volts} \qquad Ans.$$

Problems

1. In a circuit similar to that shown in Fig. 6-17, the generator voltage is 117 volts. Each line wire has a resistance of 0.4 ohm, and each lamp draws 1 amp. Find the line drop and the voltage available at the lamps.

2. A motor is connected by two wires of 0.15 ohm each to a generator. The motor takes 30 amp at 211 volts. What must be the generator voltage?

3. If the voltage at a load drawing 6 amp is 117 volts while the generator voltage is 120 volts, what is the resistance of each line wire? *Hint:* Find the line drop, then the line resistance, and finally the resistance of each wire.

4. Home wiring is often done with No. 16 wire which has a resistance of 0.401 ohm for a 100-ft length. What is the loss in voltage from the house meter to an electric broiler using 12 amp and located 100 ft from the meter?

5. What would be the voltage drop if No. 14 wire (0.252 ohm per 100 ft) were used in Prob. 4? Which size of wire is better for wiring homes?

6. In a circuit similar to that shown in Fig. 6-17, the generator voltage is 117 volts. Each line wire has a resistance of 0.45 ohm, and the lamps draw currents of 0.9, 1.4 and 1.8 amp. Find the line drop and the voltage available at the lamps.

7. In a circuit similar to that shown in Fig. 6-18, the motor draws 8.2 amp and each of the three lamps draws 0.92 amp. Each line wire has a resistance of 0.15 ohm. Find the generator voltage if the load voltage must be 110 volts.

8. In a circuit similar to that shown in Fig. 6-17, the generator voltage is 117 volts, the resistance of each line wire is 0.2 ohm, and the total resistance of the lamp bank is 16.1 ohms. Find (*a*) the total resistance of the circuit, (*b*) the current delivered to the lamp bank, and (*c*) the voltage across the lamp bank.

JOB 6-5: DISTRIBUTION SYSTEMS

In order to distribute current throughout an installation, the various loads are connected in parallel across the feeder lines. The feeder lines form various combination circuits with the loads. To solve circuits like these, we must first break down the combination into simple series or parallel circuits. It is best to follow a definite system like the following:

1. Find the current distribution. Start with the section *farthest* from the generator. Find the current in this section and work backward toward the generator, finding the current in the different parts of the circuit.

2. Name the sections. Call the section nearest to the generator section *A*, the next section *B*, etc.

3. Find the resistance of each *pair* of line wires for each section using formula (4-3).

4. Find the line drop for each section of the circuit using formula (6-1). The line wires connecting the generator to section A are called line 1, the next line wire pair is called line 2, etc.

5. Find the voltage across each section. Start where the voltage is known, and apply formulas (6-2) and (6-3).

Example 6-7. Find the voltage across the motor and across the lamp bank of the circuit shown in Fig. 6-19.

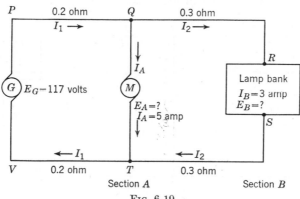

FIG. 6-19

Solution:

1. Find the current distribution. Start with the section B farthest from the generator. $I_B = 3$ amp. Line 2, from Q to R and from S to T must carry these 3 amp. Therefore, $I_2 = 3$ amp.

Since $I_A = 5$ amp, the wire from Q to T must carry these 5 amp. At point Q, we have the beginning of a parallel circuit made of the motor (section A) and the lamp bank (section B).

$$I_1 = I_A + I_2 \qquad (5\text{-}2)$$
$$I_1 = 5 + 3 = 8 \text{ amp}$$

Thus, the current in line 1 from P to Q equals 8 amp. Similarly, at T, the current I_A from the motor and the current I_2 from the lamp bank will combine.

$$I_1 = I_A + I_2 \qquad (5\text{-}2)$$
$$I_1 = 5 + 3 = 8 \text{ amp}$$

Thus, the current in line 1 from T to V equals 8 amp.

2. Find the resistance of the *pairs* of line wires.

$$R_{l_1} = 0.2 + 0.2 = 0.4 \text{ ohm} \qquad R_{l_2} = 0.3 + 0.3 = 0.6 \text{ ohm} \qquad (4\text{-}3)$$

3. Find the line drop for each section.

$$E_{l_1} = I_1 \times R_{l_1} \qquad\qquad E_{l_2} = I_2 \times R_{l_2} \qquad (6\text{-}1)$$
$$E_{l_1} = 8 \times 0.4 = 3.2 \text{ volts} \qquad E_{l_2} = 3 \times 0.6 = 1.8 \text{ volts}$$

4. Find the load voltages.

$$E_A = E_G - E_{l_1} \qquad\qquad (6\text{-}3)$$
$$E_A = 117 - 3.2 = 113.8 \text{ volts} \qquad Ans.$$

$$E_B = E_A - E_{l_2} \qquad\qquad (6\text{-}3)$$
$$E_B = 113.8 - 1.8 = 112 \text{ volts} \qquad Ans.$$

Example 6-8. Find the generator voltage and the voltage across the motor in the circuit shown in Fig. 6-20.

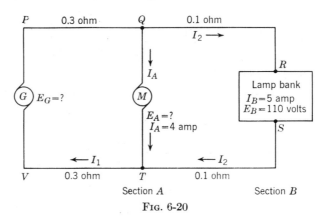

Fig. 6-20

Solution:

1. Find the current distribution. Start with the section B farthest from the generator. $I_B = 5$ amp. Line 2, from Q to R and from S to T, must carry these 5 amp. Therefore, $I_2 = 5$ amp. Since $I_A = 4$ amp, the wire from Q to T must carry these 4 amp.

$$\begin{array}{ll} \text{At point } Q: & \text{At point } T: \\ I_1 = I_A + I_2 & I_1 = I_A + I_2 \qquad (5\text{-}2) \\ I_1 = 4 + 5 = 9 \text{ amp} & I_1 = 4 + 5 = 9 \text{ amp} \end{array}$$

2. Find the resistance of the *pairs* of line wires.

$$R_{l_1} = 0.3 + 0.3 = 0.6 \text{ ohm} \qquad R_{l_2} = 0.1 + 0.1 = 0.2 \text{ ohm} \quad (4\text{-}3)$$

3. Find the line drop for each section.

$$\begin{array}{ll} E_{l_1} = I_1 \times R_{l_1} & E_{l_2} = I_2 \times R_{l_2} \qquad (6\text{-}1) \\ E_{l_1} = 9 \times 0.6 = 5.4 \text{ volts} & E_{l_2} = 5 \times 0.2 = 1 \text{ volt} \end{array}$$

4. Find the load and generator voltages.

$$E_A = E_{l_2} + E_B \qquad\qquad (6\text{-}2)$$
$$E_A = 1 + 110 = 111 \text{ volts} \qquad Ans.$$

$$E_G = E_{l_1} + E_A \qquad\qquad (6\text{-}2)$$
$$E_G = 5.4 + 111 = 116.4 \text{ volts} \qquad Ans.$$

Problems

1. In the circuit shown in Fig. 6-21, the motor takes 30 amp and the lamp bank takes 8 amp. The generator voltage is 117 volts. Find (*a*) the line drop in each section, (*b*) the voltage across the motor, and (*c*) the voltage across the lamp bank.

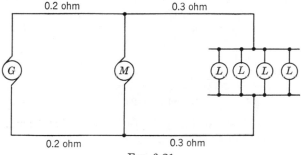

FIG. 6-21

2. Each lamp in the circuit shown in Fig. 6-21 takes 1.5 amp. The motor takes 12 amp. The generator voltage is 115 volts. Find (*a*) the line drop in each section, (*b*) the voltage across the motor, and (*c*) the voltage across the lamp bank.

3. Each lamp in the diagram shown in Fig. 6-22 takes 0.5 amp. Find E_A and E_B.

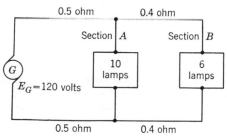

FIG. 6-22

4. In the circuit shown in Fig. 6-23, the resistance of the wires AB is 0.3 ohm, BC is 0.5 ohm, EF is 0.5 ohm, and DE is 0.3 ohm. If each lamp takes 1 amp, what is the terminal voltage of the generator? The voltage across CF is 105 volts.

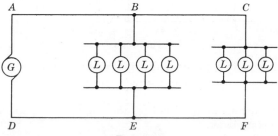

FIG. 6-23

5. In the circuit shown in Fig. 6-24, each lamp takes 1.2 amp. $E_A = 113$ volts, and $I_A = 12$ amp. Find E_G and E_B.

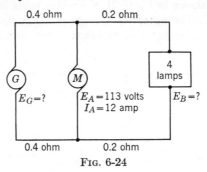

FIG. 6-24

6. In the circuit shown in Fig. 6-25, each lamp takes 1 amp. $E_A = 114$ volts, and $E_G = 117$ volts. Find E_B and I_A.

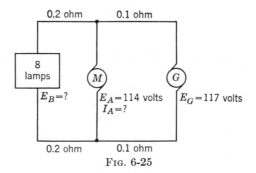

FIG. 6-25

7. Find the generator voltage in the circuit shown in Fig. 6-26.

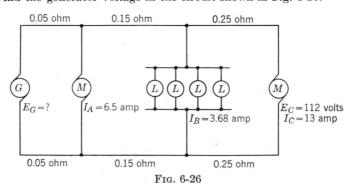

FIG. 6-26

8. Each line wire of a two-wire distribution system has a resistance of 0.2 ohm. A motor drawing 10 amp is connected by two of these wires to a generator delivering 121 volts. Two more of these line wires carry current to a lamp bank drawing 4.5 amp. Find (*a*) the voltage at the motor and (*b*) the voltage at the lamp bank.

Test—Distribution Systems

1. In a circuit similar to that shown in Fig. 6-21, the motor draws 22 amp and the lamp bank draws 10 amp from the 132-volt generator. Find (a) the voltage across the motor and (b) the voltage across the lamp bank.

2. In a circuit similar to that shown in Fig. 6-22, $E_G = 135$ volts and each lamp draws 0.91 amp. Find (a) E_A and (b) E_B.

3. In a circuit similar to that shown in Fig. 6-24, each lamp draws 1.4 amp, $E_A = 115$ volts, and $I_A = 10$ amp. Find (a) E_G and (b) E_B.

4. In a circuit similar to that shown in Fig. 6-25, each lamp draws 1 amp at 110 volts and the motor draws 12 amp. Find (a) the voltage at the motor and (b) the generator voltage.

CHAPTER 7

ELECTRICAL POWER

JOB 7-1: ELECTRICAL POWER IN SIMPLE CIRCUITS

Meaning of Electrical Power. Did you know that it is possible to push a candle through a wooden board? You may not be successful when you try it because you may omit an essential element necessary to do this. This missing quantity is *speed*. Power depends on *how fast* a certain amount of work is done. Thus, if you *shoot* the candle from a shotgun, it will have the necessary speed to penetrate the board.

More than speed, however, is necessary to increase the power. In recognition of this fact, the Roman gladiators of long ago wrapped strips of lead around their fists to increase the power of their blows. Our modern boxers are not permitted to increase the weight of their gloves, but they increase their hitting power by punching with short, *fast* blows rather than with looping, slow swings.

Power, then, depends on two quantities—the work done (or the weight moved) and the speed of doing it.

$$\text{Power} = \text{work done} \times \text{speed}$$

In electrical work,

$$\text{Work done} = Q \times E$$

$$\text{Speed} = \frac{1}{t}$$

Therefore,

$$P = Q \times E \times \frac{1}{t}$$

or

$$P = \frac{Q \times E}{t} = \frac{Q}{t} \times E$$

but since $\frac{Q}{t} = I$,

$$P = I \times E$$

148

Rule: The electrical power in any part of a circuit is equal to the current in that part multiplied by the voltage across that part of the circuit.

Formula

$$P = I \times E \qquad (7\text{-}1)$$

where P = power, watts

I = current, amp

E = voltage, volts

A *watt* of electrical power is the power used when one volt causes one ampere of current to flow in a circuit. A *kilowatt* of power is equal to 1,000 watts.

Table 7-1. Power Used by Electrical Devices, Measured in Watts

Electric clocks............	1–3	Vacuum cleaners.........	300–700
Door chimes..............	15	Washers.................	350–450
Electric fans.............	50–300	Toasters................	600–1,100
Lamp bulbs..............	15–200	Air conditioners.........	800–1,500
Sewing machines..........	40–80	Broilers................	800–1,500
Radios..................	50–100	Electric ironers..........	1,000–1,500
Televisions..............	150–250	Clothes driers............	4,000–4,700
Refrigerators............	200–300	Electric ranges..........	Up to 23,000

Example 7-1. A motor draws 12 amp at 110 volts. How much power does it consume?

Solution:

Given: I = 12 amp   Find: P = ?

E = 110 volts

$$P = I \times E \qquad (7\text{-}1)$$
$$P = 12 \times 110 = 1,320 \text{ watts} \qquad Ans.$$

Example 7-2. A power-supply filter circuit supplies 110 volts and 0.05 amp to the plate of a 50B5 beam-power amplifier tube. Find the power used.

Solution:

Given: E = 110 volts   Find: P = ?

I = 0.05 amp

$$P = I \times E \qquad (7\text{-}1)$$
$$P = 0.05 \times 110 = 5.5 \text{ watts} \qquad Ans.$$

Example 7-3. A 1,000-ohm resistor is used in the power-supply filter circuit of many small radio receivers. If the resistor carries 0.06 amp at 60 volts, how many watts of power are developed in the resistor? What must be the wattage rating of the resistor in order to dissipate this power safely as heat?

Solution:

Given: $I = 0.06$ amp   Find: $P = ?$
             $E = 60$ volts   Wattage rating $= ?$

$$P = I \times E \tag{7-1}$$
$$P = 0.06 \times 60 = 3.6 \text{ watts} \quad Ans.$$

The wattage rating of a resistor describes its ability to dissipate the heat produced in it by the passage of an electric current without itself overheating.   For example, a 2-watt resistor could dissipate 2 watts of heat energy without overheating.   However, if 3 watts of power were to be developed in it, it would overheat because of the 1 watt of power which it could not dissipate.   Owing to the lack of ventilation in the close quarters of most radio and television receivers, the wattage ratings of these resistors is usually at least twice the wattage developed in them.

Wattage rating $= 2 \times P$
Wattage rating $= 2 \times 3.6 = 7.2$ watts   *Ans.*

Problems

1. An automobile starting motor draws 80 amp at 6 volts. How much power is drawn from the battery?

2. A 20-hp motor takes 74 amp at 230 volts when operating at full load. Find the power used.

3. What is the wattage dissipated as heat by a 550-ohm resistor operating at 110 volts and 0.2 amp?

4. What is the power consumed by an automobile headlight if it takes 2.8 amp at 6 volts?

5. Find the power used by a 3.4-amp soldering iron at 110 volts.

6. The heater of a 50L6 beam-power tube uses 50 volts and 0.15 amp. Find the power consumed.

7. The high contact resistance of a poorly wired electric toaster plug reduced the current by 1 amp on a 110-volt line. Find the power wasted in the plug.

8. How much power is consumed by an electric clock using 0.02 amp at 110 volts?

9. Find the plate power used by a 70L7GT tube rated at 110 volts and 0.04 amp.

10. A 180-ohm line cord resistor carrying 0.15 amp causes a voltage drop of 27 volts. How much power must be dissipated as heat? What must be the wattage rating of the line cord?

11. A radio resistor carries 0.045 amp at 10 volts. What must be its wattage rating?

12. An electric enameling kiln takes 9.2 amp from a 117-volt line. Find the power used.

13. How much power is used by a ¾-ton air conditioner drawing 11.4 amp from a 220-volt line?

14. How many watts are dissipated as heat by a 135-ohm line cord resistor if it carries 0.22 amp at 30 volts?

15. The heater of a 6V6 tube uses 6.3 volts and 0.45 amp. Find the power used.

JOB 7-2: TOTAL POWER IN AN ELECTRICAL CIRCUIT

When using Ohm's law, we found that it could be used for total values in a circuit as well as for the individual parts of the circuit. In the same way, the formula for power may be used for total values.

Formula

$$P_T = I_T \times E_T \qquad (7\text{-}2)$$

where P_T = total power, watts

I_T = total current, amp

E_T = total voltage, volts

Example 7-4. Two 0.62-amp lamps, each drawing 120 volts, are connected in series. Find the total power used.

Solution:

Given: $I_1 = I_2 = 0.62$ amp   Find: $P_T = ?$
$E_1 = E_2 = 120$ volts

1. Find the total voltage.

$$E_T = E_1 + E_2 = 120 + 120 = 240 \text{ volts} \qquad (4\text{-}2)$$

2. Find the total current.

$$I_T = I_1 = I_2 = 0.62 \text{ amp} \qquad (4\text{-}1)$$

3. Find the total power.

$$P_T = I_T \times E_T \qquad (7\text{-}2)$$
$$P_T = 0.62 \times 240 = 148.8 \text{ watts} \qquad Ans.$$

Example 7-5. If the same lamps were connected in parallel across 120 volts, find the total power used and compare it with the power used when the lamps were connected in series as in Example 7-4.

Solution:

Given: $I_1 = I_2 = 0.62$ amp   Find: $P_T = ?$
$E_1 = E_2 = 120$ volts

1. Find the total voltage.

$$E_T = 120 \text{ volts} \qquad \text{(given)}$$

2. Find the total current.

$$I_T = I_1 + I_2 = 0.62 + 0.62 = 1.24 \text{ amp} \qquad (5\text{-}2)$$

3. Find the total power.

$$P_T = I_T \times E_T \qquad\qquad (7\text{-}2)$$
$$P_T = 1.24 \times 120 = 148.8 \text{ watts} \qquad Ans.$$

The total power in parallel is the same as the total power in series.

If the power used by the parts of a circuit is known, the total power may be found by the following

Formula

$$P_T = P_1 + P_2 + P_3 \qquad\qquad (7\text{-}3)$$

where P_T = total power, watts

P_1, P_2, P_3 are the power used by the parts of the circuit

Example 7-6.   Find the power used by the heaters of two 6J5 tubes connected in series.   From the manufacturer's tube manual, the heater voltage is 6.3 volts and the heater current is 0.3 amp.

Solution:

Given: $E_1 = E_2 = 6.3$ volts   Find: $P_T = ?$
$\qquad\quad I_1 = I_2 = 0.3$ amp

1. Find the power taken by one tube.

$$P = I \times E \qquad\qquad (7\text{-}1)$$
$$P = 0.3 \times 6.3 = 1.89 \text{ watts}$$

2. Find the total power.

$$P_T = P_1 + P_2 \qquad\qquad (7\text{-}3)$$
$$P_T = 1.89 + 1.89 = 3.78 \text{ watts} \qquad Ans.$$

Problems

1. Seven Christmas-tree lamps are connected in series.   Each lamp requires 16 volts and 0.1 amp.   Find the total power used.

2. If the same lamps were connected in parallel across a 16-volt source, what would be the power taken?

3. Three radio tubes have their heaters connected in series.   Each tube requires 12.6 volts and 0.15 amp.   Find the power needed for each tube and the total power.

4. If the same tubes were connected in parallel across the 12.6-volt winding of the power transformer, find the power used by each tube and the total power.

5. The heaters of the following tubes in a radio receiver are connected in series: 12SA7 (12.6 volts, 0.15 amp), 12SK7 (12.6 volts, 0.15 amp), 12SQ7

(12.6 volts, 0.15 amp), 50L6 (50 volts, 0.15 amp), and 35Z5 (35 volts, 0.15 amp). Find the total power used.

6. What is the total power used by a 4.5-amp electric iron, a 0.85-amp fan, and a 2.2-amp refrigerator motor if they are all connected in parallel across a 115-volt line?

7. A 1B3 high-voltage rectifier in a television receiver uses 1.25 volts at 0.2 amp. When it is in series with a 3.3-ohm ballast resistor, what is the total power used by the circuit?

8. Find the power drawn from a 6-volt battery by a parallel circuit of two headlights (4 amp each) and two taillights (0.9 amp each).

9. In Fig. 6-21, the generator voltage is 120 volts. The motor takes 12.4 amp, and each lamp takes 0.92 amp. Neglecting the line drop, find the total power used by the devices.

10. An electric percolator drawing 9 amp and an electric toaster drawing 10.2 amp are connected in parallel to the 117-volt house line. Find the total power consumed.

JOB 7-3: SOLVING THE POWER FORMULA FOR CURRENT OR VOLTAGE

In Job 2-6 we learned how to solve Ohm's law for the current or the resistance. The power formula is the same general type of equation, and we can use the methods learned in Job 2-6 to solve it for values of current or voltage.

Example 7-7. What current flows through the heater of a television tube which consumes 7.5 watts at 25 volts?

Solution:

$$\text{Given: } P = 7.5 \text{ watts} \qquad \text{Find: } I = ?$$
$$E = 25 \text{ volts}$$

$$P = I \times E \qquad\qquad (7\text{-}1)$$
$$7.5 = I \times 25$$
$$I = \frac{7.5}{25} = 0.3 \text{ amp} \qquad Ans.$$

Example 7-8. What is the operating voltage of an electric toaster rated at 600 watts if it draws 5 amp?

Solution:

$$\text{Given: } P = 600 \text{ watts} \qquad \text{Find: } E = ?$$
$$I = 5 \text{ amp}$$

$$P = I \times E \qquad\qquad (7\text{-}1)$$
$$600 = 5 \times E$$
$$E = \frac{600}{5} = 120 \text{ volts} \qquad Ans.$$

Problems

1. A 550-watt neon sign operates on a 110-volt line. Find the current drawn.

2. What current is drawn by a 480-watt soldering iron from a 120-volt line?

3. A radio resistor is capable of dissipating 10 watts of power. If the current is 0.3 amp, what is the maximum voltage drop permitted across the resistor?

4. The filament circuit of a radio receiver uses 6.75 watts. What is the voltage across the circuit if it carries 0.3 amp?

5. A 6K6 tube is used in the vertical output stage of a television receiver and delivers 3.4 watts. If the current is 0.032 amp, what is the voltage across the circuit?

6. What current is drawn by a 1,500-watt electric ironing machine from a 120-volt line?

7. What current is drawn by a 55-candlepower 110-volt lamp if it uses 1 watt per candlepower?

8. Two resistors, each dissipating 2 watts, are connected in series with a 40-volt source. What is the total current drawn? What is the current in each resistor?

9. Twenty 60-watt lamps are connected in parallel to light a stage. Find the current drawn from a 220-volt source.

10. A washing-machine motor requires 350 watts. If it draws $3\frac{1}{8}$ amp, find the operating voltage.

JOB 7-4: INTERMEDIATE REVIEW OF POWER

In some problems, the power cannot be found because either the voltage or the current is unknown. In these instances, the unknown value is found by Ohm's law.

Example 7-9. Find the power taken by a soldering iron of 60 ohms resistance if it draws a current of 2 amp.

Solution:

$$\text{Given: } R = 60 \text{ ohms} \qquad \text{Find: } P = ?$$
$$I = 2 \text{ amp}$$

1. Find the voltage.

$$E = I \times R \qquad\qquad (2\text{-}1)$$
$$E = 2 \times 60 = 120 \text{ volts}$$

2. Find the power.

$$P = I \times E \qquad\qquad (7\text{-}1)$$
$$P = 2 \times 120 = 240 \text{ watts} \qquad Ans.$$

Example 7-10. Find the power used by the 11-ohm resistance element of an electric furnace if the voltage is 110 volts.

Solution:

Given: $R = 11$ ohms   Find: $P = ?$
$E = 110$ volts

1. Find the current.

$$E = I \times R \qquad\qquad (2\text{-}1)$$
$$110 = I \times 11$$
$$I = \tfrac{110}{11} = 10 \text{ amp}$$

2. Find the power.

$$P = I \times E \qquad\qquad (7\text{-}1)$$
$$P = 10 \times 110 = 1{,}100 \text{ watts} \qquad Ans.$$

Problems

1. A 20-ohm neon sign operates on a 120-volt line. Find the power used by the sign.

2. Find the power used by a 55-ohm electric light which draws 2 amp.

3. What is the wattage dissipated by a 10,000-ohm voltage divider if the voltage across it is 250 volts? What is its wattage rating?

4. What is the maximum power obtainable from a Grenet cell of 2 volts which has an internal resistance of 0.02 ohm?

5. What must be the wattage rating of a 40-ohm radio resistor which must carry a current of ¼ amp with a 100 per cent safety factor?

6. The cathode bias resistor for a 50L6 audio power output tube is 150 ohms. If the current through it is 0.05 amp, how many watts are developed in the resistor?

7. What is the power consumed by a 90-ohm subway car heater if the operating voltage is 550 volts?

8. A 6BK5 tube is used as an audio output tube in the Westinghouse model 765T17 television receiver. It has a cathode resistor of 180 ohms which develops a bias of 5 volts. Find the power used by the bias resistor.

9. A 20-ohm toaster operates on a 115-volt line. Find the power used.

10. In a DuMont model RA 306 television receiver, a 4,000-ohm dropping resistor is used to feed voltage to the screen of the 6BQ6 GT horizontal output tube. If the screen current is 0.03 amp, how many watts are developed in the resistor?

Test—Power

1. Find the power used by a 4.5-amp soldering iron when it is operated from a 110-volt line.

2. A motor drawing 5 amp is connected in parallel with another motor drawing 8 amp. The line voltage is 120 volts. Find the total power consumed.

3. A 6F6 power pentode delivers 4.5 watts. If the current is 0.038 amp, what is the voltage across the circuit?

4. A 22-ohm electric toaster operates from a 110-volt line. Find the power used.

5. A 40-ohm neon sign operates on a 120-volt line. Find the power used.

JOB 7-5: CHECK-UP ON USING FORMULAS WITH EXPONENTS

Many problems in electrical work are solved with formulas which use special mathematical symbols called *exponents*. The following problems involve the use of formulas which contain exponents. If you have any difficulty with these problems, see Job 7-6 which follows.

Problems

1. Using the formula $P = E^2/R$, find the value of P if $E = 100$ and $R = 50$.
2. Using the formula $P = I^2R$, find the value of P if $I = 3$ and $R = 40$.
3. Using the formula emf $= (L \times n)/10^8$, find the value of emf if $L = 50 \times 10^6$ and $n = 40$.
4. Using the formula $R = (k \times l)/D^2$, find the value of R if $k = 10.4$, $l = 100$, and $D = 4$.
5. Using the formula farad = microfarad/10^6, find the number of farads equal to 0.5 microfarads.

JOB 7-6: BRUSH-UP ON FORMULAS CONTAINING EXPONENTS

Meaning of an Exponent. Exponents provide a convenient shorthand method for writing and expressing many mathematical operations. For example, $2 \times 2 \times 2$ may be written as 2^3. The number 3 which is written above and to the right of the 2 is called an *exponent*. The exponent says, "Write the number beneath it as many times as the exponent indicates, and then multiply." An exponent may be used with letters as well as numbers. Thus, R^3 means $R \times R \times R$. The exponent 2 is read as the word "square." The exponent 3 is read as the word "cube." When the exponent is any other number, it is read as "to the fourth power" or as "to the seventh power," etc. For example:

$$3^2 \text{ (3 square)} = 3 \times 3 = 9$$
$$5^3 \text{ (5 cube)} = 5 \times 5 \times 5 = 125$$
$$2^4 \text{ (2 to the fourth power)} = 2 \times 2 \times 2 \times 2 = 16$$
$$10^1 \text{ (10 to the first power)} = 10$$
$$10^2 \text{ (10 square)} = 10 \times 10 = 100$$
$$10^3 \text{ (10 cube)} = 10 \times 10 \times 10 = 1,000$$

Example 7-11. The formula for the area of a circle is $A = \pi R^2$. Find the area of a circle if the radius R equals 5 in. and $\pi = 3.14$.

Solution:

Given: $A = \pi R^2$ Find: $A = ?$
$R = 5$ in.
$\pi = 3.14$

1. Write the formula.

$$A = \pi R^2$$

2. Substitute numbers.

$$A = 3.14 \times 5^2$$

3. Simplify the exponent.

$$A = 3.14 \times 25$$

4. Multiply

$$A = 78.5 \text{ sq in.} \qquad Ans.$$

Multiplication of Powers of Ten

Rule: When the base 10 raised to some power is multiplied by the same base 10 raised to a power, the product is equal to the base 10 raised to the sum of the powers.

For example:

$$10^2 \times 10^3 = 10^{(2+3)} = 10^5$$
$$10 \times 10^3 = 10^{(1+3)} = 10^4$$
$$10 \times 10^2 \times 10^6 = 10^{(1+2+6)} = 10^9$$

Multiplying by Powers of 10

Rule: To multiply values by numbers like 100, 1,000, 1,000,000 etc., move the decimal point one place to the right for every zero in the multiplier.

For example:

$1.59 \times 10 = 1\,5.9 = 15.9$ (move point one place to the right)
$4.76 \times 100 = 4\,76. = 476.$ or 476 (move point 2 places to the right)

A decimal point is ordinarily not written at the end of a whole number. However, it may be written if desired. In the following example, the point must be written in together with two zeros so that we can move the decimal point past the required number of places.

$$34 \times 100 = 34\,00. = 3,400. \text{ or } 3,400$$

If the decimal point must be moved past more places than are available, zeros are added at the end of the number to make up the required number of places. This is shown in the following example.

$$0.0259 \times 1,000,000 = 025900. = 25,900.$$

Rule: To multiply values by numbers expressed as 10 raised to some power, move the decimal point to the right as many places as the exponent indicates.

For example:

$$0.345 \times 10^2 = 34.5 \text{ or } 34.5 \text{ (move point 2 places to the right)}$$
$$0.345 \times 10^3 = 345. \text{ or } 345 \text{ (move point 3 places to the right)}$$
$$0.345 \times 10^6 = 345000. \text{ or } 345,000 \text{ (move point 6 places)}$$
$$0.0065 \times 10^3 = 006.5 \text{ or } 6.5 \text{ (move point 3 places)}$$
$$0.00075 \times 10^2 \times 10^3 = 0.00075 \times 10^5 = 00075. \text{ or } 75$$

Problems

1. $0.0072 \times 1{,}000$
2. 45.76×100
3. $3.09 \times 1{,}000$
4. 0.0045×100
5. 37×100
6. 0.08×10^2
7. 0.0006×10^3
8. 0.00056×10^6
9. 27×10^2
10. 15×10^3

11. $0.00078 \times 10 \times 10^2$
12. $3 \times 15 \times 10^2$
13. $0.005 \times 2 \times 10^2$
14. $7.8 \times 10^2 \times 10^6$
15. 15.4×10^3
16. $6 \times 10^2 \times 10^3$
17. $0.008 \times 10 \times 10^2$
18. 0.009×10^4
19. $2.34 \times 10^3 \times 10$
20. $0.0000005 \times 10^2 \times 10^6$

Division of Powers of Ten

Rule: When powers of ten are divided, the new exponent of the base **10** is the exponent in the dividend minus the exponent in the divisor.

For example:

$$10^6 \div 10^2 = 10^{(6-2)} = 10^4$$
$$10^3 \div 10^2 = 10^{(3-2)} = 10^1 = 10$$
$$10^3 \div 10^3 = 1 \text{ (any number divided by itself equals 1)}$$

Dividing by Powers of 10

Rule: To divide values by numbers like **10, 100, 1,000,** etc., move the decimal point one place to the left for every zero in the divisor.

For example:

$$17.4 \div 10 = 1.7\,4 = 1.74 \text{ (move point 1 place left)}$$
$$45 \div 100 = .45 = 0.45 \text{ (move point 2 places left)}$$
$$6.5 \div 1{,}000 = .006\,5 = 0.0065 \text{ (move point 3 places left)}$$

Rule: To divide values by numbers expressed as **10** raised to some power, move the decimal point to the left as many places as the exponent indicates.

For example:

$467.9 \div 10^2 = 4.\underset{\curvearrowleft}{67}9 = 4.679$ (move point 2 places left)

$59 \div 10^2 = .\underset{\curvearrowleft}{59} = 0.59$ (move point 2 places left)

$8.5 \div 10^3 = .\underset{\curvearrowleft}{008}5 = 0.0085$ (move point 3 places left)

$\dfrac{26.7 \times 10^5}{10^2} = 26.7 \times 10^{(5-2)} = 26.7 \times 10^3 = 26\underset{\curvearrowright}{\,700.} = 26,700$

$\dfrac{84.3 \times 10^2}{10^5} = \dfrac{8430.}{10^5} = .\underset{\curvearrowleft}{08430} = 0.0843$ *Ans.*

This problem may also be solved by dividing both the numerator and the denominator by 10^2. This will give

$$\frac{84.3 \times 1}{10^3} = 0.0843 \qquad Ans.$$

Multiplying Large and Small Numbers. When any number is multiplied by the number 1, it does not change the value of the number. Thus, $6 \times 1 = 6$, or $75 \times 1 = 75$. The number 1 may be expressed in any form; 2/2, 4/4, or even 1,000/1,000. It may be to our advantage to multiply an expression by the number 1 expressed in this way. For example, the multiplication $0.004 \times 20,000$ may be multiplied by 1 in the form of 1,000/1,000 to give

$$0.004 \times 20,000 \times \frac{1,000}{1,000}$$

If we *multiply* the 0.004 by 1,000 in the numerator and *divide* the 20,000 by 1,000 in the denominator, we get

$\underset{\curvearrowright}{\,004.} \times 20.\underset{\curvearrowleft}{000}$ or $4 \times 20 = 80$ *Ans.*

Actually, the net effect of multiplying and dividing by the same number has been to move the decimal point in one number to the right and in the other number to the left for the same number of places. This has resulted in eliminating both decimal points and zeros at the end of large numbers.

Rule: When numbers are multiplied, any decimal point may be moved to the right as many places as desired, provided that other decimal points are moved to the left for the same number of places.

For example:

$4,500 \times 0.03 = 45.\underset{\curvearrowleft}{00} \times \underset{\curvearrowright}{\,03.} = 45 \times 3 = 135$

$0.0000005 \times 200,000 = \underset{\curvearrowright}{\,00000.}05 \times 2.\underset{\curvearrowleft}{00000} = 0.05 \times 2 = 0.1$

$0.004 \times 50,000 \times 0.3 = \underset{\curvearrowright}{\,004.} \times 5.\underset{\curvearrowleft}{0000} \times \underset{\curvearrowright}{\,3.} = 4 \times 5 \times 3 = 60$

Problems

1. $32 \div 10^2$

2. $654.8 \div 10^3$

3. $6 \div 10^2$
4. $546 \div 10^6$
5. $17.8 \div 10$
6. $\dfrac{34 \times 100}{0.17 \times 1,000}$
7. $\dfrac{50 \times 10^2 \times 10^3}{10^6}$
8. $\dfrac{0.00025 \times 10^6}{10^2}$
9. $\dfrac{60 \times 100 \times 10^3}{10^6}$
10. $0.0075 \div 10^3$

11. $\dfrac{7.4 \times 10^3}{10^5}$

12. $\dfrac{0.0035 \times 1,000}{10^2}$

13. $0.0004 \times 10^3 \times 30$
14. $250 \times 1,000 \times 0.0003$
15. $20,000 \times 0.006$

16. $0.00035 \times 5,000$

17. $0.6 \times 0.04 \times 2,000$

18. $\dfrac{0.0005 \times 20,000}{2}$

19. $\dfrac{25 \times 10^3 \times 3 \times 10^6}{5 \times 10^4}$

20. $6.28 \times 500,000 \times 0.002$

21. Using the formula $A = \pi R^2$, find the value of A if $\pi = 3.14$ and $R = 9$.

22. Using the formula $P = I^2 R$, find the value of P if $I = 6$ and $R = 200$.

23. Using the formula emf $= (L \times n)/10^8$, find the value of the emf if $L = 4 \times 10^4$ and $n = 80$.

24. Using the formula amp $= \text{ma}/10^3$, find the value of the amperes if ma $= 450$.

25. Using the formula $V = \pi R^2 H$, find the value of V if $\pi = 22/7$, $R = 3.5$, and $H = 14$.

JOB 7-7: THE EXPONENTIAL POWER FORMULA

In Job 7-4, either the voltage or the current was unknown. These values were found by Ohm's law and then used to find the power. The two steps involved in solving problems of this type may be combined into a single formula. The power is given by

$$P = I \times E \qquad (7\text{-}1)$$

But by Ohm's law

$$E = I \times R \qquad (2\text{-}1)$$

Therefore, we may substitute the quantity $I \times R$ for E. This gives

$$P = I \times I \times R$$

Formula

$$P = I^2 R \qquad (7\text{-}4)$$

Also by Ohm's law, $I = E/R$.

Therefore, we may substitute the quantity E/R for I.
Thus,

$$P = I \times E \tag{7-1}$$

Substituting,

$$P = \frac{E}{R} \times E$$

Formula

$$P = \frac{E^2}{R} \tag{7-5}$$

Example 7-12. Calculate the power used by an 8,000-ohm filter resistor if it carries 0.03 amp.

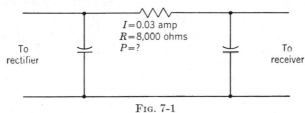

$I = 0.03$ amp
$R = 8,000$ ohms
$P = ?$

To rectifier

To receiver

Fig. 7-1

Solution: The diagram for the circuit is shown in Fig. 7-1.

$$P = I^2R \tag{7-4}$$
$$P = (0.03)^2 \times 8,000$$
$$P = 0.03 \times 0.03 \times 8,000$$
$$P = 0.0009 \times 8,000 = 7.2 \text{ watts} \qquad Ans.$$

Example 7-13. A motor has a total resistance of 20 ohms and operates on a 120-volt line. Find the power used.

Solution:

Given: $R = 20$ ohms   Find: $P = ?$
         $E = 120$ volts

$$P = \frac{E^2}{R} \tag{7-5}$$
$$P = \frac{(120)^2}{20} = \frac{120 \times 120}{20} = 720 \text{ watts} \qquad Ans.$$

Problems

1. A 30-ohm electric toaster draws 4 amp. Find the power used.

2. If the voltage drop across a 10,000-ohm voltage divider is 90 volts, find the power used.

3. Find the power consumed by a 100-ohm electric iron when operating on a 115-volt line.

4. A poorly soldered joint has a contact resistance of 100 ohms. What is the power lost in the joint if the current is 0.5 amp?

5. A 6L6 tube used as a single-tube class A_1 amplifier delivers an average current of 0.05 amp through a 2,600-ohm load resistance. Find the power developed in the load.

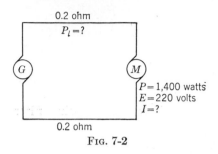

0.2 ohm

$P_l = ?$

G   M

$P = 1,400$ watts
$E = 220$ volts
$I = ?$

0.2 ohm

FIG. 7-2

6. Find the power used by a 15-ohm neon sign on a 110-volt line.

7. The motor shown in Fig. 7-2 takes 1,400 watts at 220 volts. Find the current drawn. How many watts are consumed in the line wires if each has a resistance of 0.2 ohm?

8. How much power is dissipated in the form of heat in a ballast resistor of 60 ohms if the current is 0.3 amp?

9. A 100- and a 260-ohm resistor are connected in series to a 120-volt source. Find the power used by each resistor.

10. Find the total voltage across the circuit shown in Fig. 7-3. What is the voltage across each resistor? What is the power taken by each resistor?

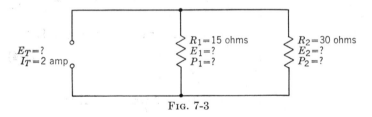

$E_T = ?$
$I_T = 2$ amp

$R_1 = 15$ ohms
$E_1 = ?$
$P_1 = ?$

$R_2 = 30$ ohms
$E_2 = ?$
$P_2 = ?$

FIG. 7-3

JOB 7-8: CHECK-UP ON SQUARE ROOT

In the last job we learned two new formulas which use the exponent 2. This exponent is read as the word "square." We can use these formulas to find the current, voltage, or resistance if we know the power. To do this, we must be able to do the opposite of "squaring" a number. This is called "finding the square root." We shall also use "square root" when we get to the study of a-c circuits. Can you do the following problems? If you have any difficulty with them, turn to Job 7-9 which follows.

Problems

Find the square root of each of the following numbers:

1. 64	**4.** 3,481	**7.** 14	**10.** 30
2. 169	**5.** 12,544	**8.** 567.9	**11.** 0.652
3. 17.64	**6.** 57.76	**9.** 76,432	**12.** 870,000

JOB 7-9: BRUSH-UP ON SQUARE ROOT

The *square root* of a number is that number which must be multiplied by itself in order to obtain the original number. The symbol for the square root is $\sqrt{}$. When a number appears under this symbol, it means that we are to find a number which can be multiplied by itself to give the number under the square-root symbol. For example, the square root of 9 must be the number 3 because only $3 \times 3 = 9$. Also,

$$\sqrt{16} = 4 \text{ because only } 4 \times 4 \text{ will equal } 16$$
$$\sqrt{25} = 5 \text{ because only } 5 \times 5 \text{ will equal } 25$$
$$\sqrt{36} = 6 \text{ because only } 6 \times 6 \text{ will equal } 36$$

We can continue to find the square root of numbers in this manner until our knowledge of the multiplication table is insufficient to keep up with the large numbers involved. For example,

$$\sqrt{49} = 7 \qquad \sqrt{121} = 11$$
$$\sqrt{64} = 8 \qquad \sqrt{144} = 12$$
$$\sqrt{81} = 9 \qquad \sqrt{169} = 13$$
$$\sqrt{100} = 10$$

These numbers under the square-root sign are called "perfect squares" because the square root of each is a whole number.

Somewhere along here we begin to forget whether 14×14 is 196 or not or whether 16×16 is 256 or not. You can see that we will not get very far if we rely on just our knowledge of the multiplication table. Besides, what about all those smaller numbers between these perfect squares like

$$\sqrt{7} = ?$$
$$\sqrt{15} = ?$$
$$\sqrt{32} = ?$$

There doesn't seem to be any number that we can multiply by itself to get 7 or 15 or 32. No, there isn't any *whole* number which is the square root of these numbers, but there are decimal numbers which will satisfy.

Obviously, as the numbers get beyond the range of the ordinary multiplication table, we feel the need for some system that will help us to find the square root of *any* number—large or small, whole number or decimal.

In the following system, it will help if we mark off the numbers into groups of two digits to a group. We start marking off the groups *at the decimal point*. If there is no decimal point indicated, it may be assumed to be at the *end* of the number.

Example 7-14. Group the digits in the number 3,456.
Solution: The decimal point is at the end of the number. Starting at the decimal point, the numbers are grouped two to a group as we move to the left.

$$34\ 56.$$

Example 7-15. Group the digits in the number 546.78.
Solution: Starting at the decimal point and proceeding to the left, we find that the digit 5 is left over. In situations like this, the single digit at the extreme left is considered to be a group. Now, return to the decimal point and group the digits to the *right* of the point—two to a group. We should get

$$5\ 46.\ 78$$

Example 7-16. Group the digits in the number 54,819.8.
Solution: The 5 at the extreme left is again considered a group by itself, but a zero must be added after the 8 at the right to complete the group. We should get

$$5\ 48\ 19\ .\ 80$$

Example 7-17. Find the square root of 5,776.

Solution:

1. Locate the decimal point. In a whole number the decimal point is at the end of the number. Place the point in the answer directly above its position in the number.

$$\sqrt{5\ 7\ 7\ 6\ .}$$

2. Separate the digits into groups—two digits to a group. Start at the decimal point, and group the digits to the left.

$$\sqrt{57\ 76\ .}$$

3. Start with the first group (57). Find a number which when multiplied by itself will give an answer close to or equal to but not larger than 57. 8 squared is 64, but that is too large. 7 squared is 49, which is just right. Place the 7 over the first group in the answer and the 49 under the 57. Draw a line and subtract the 49 from the 57, leaving a remainder of 8.

$$\begin{array}{r} 7 \quad . \\ \sqrt{57\ 76}\ . \\ -\ 49 \\ \hline 8 \end{array}$$

4. Bring down the next *group*. *Never* bring down a single number. Make a little box to the left of this new number 876. *Double* the answer at this point (the 7), and place it in this box. This will be the number 14.

$$\begin{array}{r} 7 \quad . \\ \sqrt{57\ 76}\ . \\ -\ 49 \ \times \\ \hline 14 \quad\big|\ 8\ 76 \end{array}$$

5. Place your finger over the *last digit* in the number 876. The number there will now appear to be 87. Divide the number in the box (14) into this 87. It will go about 6 times. Place this 6 in the answer above the second group, *and also place it next to the 14 in the box.*

$$\begin{array}{r} 7\ 6 \quad . \\ \sqrt{57\ 76}\ . \\ -\ 49 \ \times \\ \hline 14\ 6 \quad\big|\ 8\ 76 \end{array}$$

6. Multiply the 6 by the number just formed (the 146). If the product is larger than 876, we shall be forced to change the 6 to a smaller number. However, $6 \times 146 = 876$. Write this 876 under the 876 already there and subtract. Since there is no remainder, 76 is the exact square root of 5,776. *Check:* $76 \times 76 = 5,776$.

$$\begin{array}{r} 7\ 6 \quad . \\ \sqrt{57\ 76}\ . \\ -\ 49 \ \times \\ \hline 14\ 6 \quad\big|\ 8\ 76 \\ 8\ 76 \\ \hline 0 \end{array}$$

Example 7-18. Find the square root of 930.25.

Solution:

1. Locate the decimal point. Place the point in the answer directly above its position in the number.

$$\sqrt{9\ 30.25}$$

2. Separate the digits into groups—two digits to a group. Start at the decimal point, and group the digits to the left. Return to the decimal point, and group the digits to the right.

$$\sqrt{9\ \overset{.}{30}\ .\overset{.}{25}}$$

3. Start with the first group (9). Find a number which when multiplied by itself will give an answer close to or equal to but not larger than 9. 3 squared is 9, which is exactly right. Place the 3 over the first group in the answer and the 9 under the 9 in the number. Draw a line, and subtract, leaving a remainder of 0.

$$\begin{array}{r} 3\ \ \ \ . \\ \sqrt{9\ 30\ .\ 25} \\ -\ 9 \\ \hline \end{array}$$

4. Bring down the next group (30). Make a little box to the left of this number. *Double* the answer at this point (the 3), and place it in this box. This will be the number 6.

$$\begin{array}{r} 3\ \ \ \ . \\ \sqrt{9\ 30\ .\ 25} \\ 9\ \times \\ 6\ \ \boxed{\ \ 30} \end{array}$$

5. Place your finger over the *last digit* in the number 30. The number there will now appear to be 3. Divide the number in the box (6) into this 3. It will go 0 times. Place this 0 in the answer above the second group, *and also place it next to the 6 in the box.*

$$\begin{array}{r} 3\ \ 0\ . \\ \sqrt{9\ 30\ .\ 25} \\ -\ 9\ \times \\ 6\ 0\ \boxed{\ \ 30} \end{array}$$

6. Multiply the 0 by the number just formed (the 60). The answer is 00. Write this 00 under the 30 and subtract, leaving a remainder of 30.

$$\begin{array}{r} 3\ \ 0\ . \\ \sqrt{9\ 30\ .\ 25} \\ -\ 9\ \times \\ 6\ 0\ \boxed{\ \ 30} \\ -\ 00 \\ \hline 30 \end{array}$$

7. Bring down the next group (25). Make a little box to the left of this new number (3025). *Double* the answer up to this point (the 30), and place the product (60) in this box.

$$
\begin{array}{r}
3 \quad 0 \; . \\
\sqrt{9 \;\; 30 \; . \; 25} \\
- \; 9 \quad \times \\
\end{array}
$$

$$
60 \quad \overline{\bigl)\; 30} \\
- \; 00 \\
60 \quad \overline{\bigr|30 \;\; 25}
$$

8. Place your finger over the *last digit* in the number 3025. The number there will now appear to be 302. Divide the number in the box (60) into this 302. It will go 5 times. Place this 5 in the answer above the third group, *and also place it next to the* 60 *in the box.*

$$
\begin{array}{r}
3 \quad 0 \; . \; 5 \\
\sqrt{9 \;\; 30 \; . \; 25} \\
- \; 9 \quad \times \\
\end{array}
$$

$$
60 \quad \overline{\bigl)\; 30} \\
- \; 00 \\
60 \; 5 \quad \overline{\bigr|30 \;\; 25}
$$

9. Multiply the 5 by the number just formed (the 605). The answer is 3025. Write this 3025 under the 3025 already there and subtract. Since there is no remainder, 30.5 is the exact square root of 930.25. *Check:* $30.5 \times 30.5 = 930.25$.

$$
\begin{array}{r}
3 \quad 0 \; . \; 5 \\
\sqrt{9 \;\; 30 \; . \; 25} \\
- \; 9 \quad \times \\
\end{array}
$$

$$
60 \quad \overline{\bigl)\; 30} \\
- \; 00 \\
605 \quad \overline{\bigr|30 \;\; 25} \\
- \; 30 \;\; 25 \\
\overline{\qquad 0}
$$

Example 7-19. Find the square root of 12.

Solution:

1. Locate the decimal point. In a whole number the decimal point is at the end of the number. Place the point in the answer directly above its position in the number.

$$
\sqrt{12 \; .}
$$

2. Separate the digits into groups—two digits to a group. Start at the decimal point, and group the digits to the left.

$$\sqrt{1\ 2\ .}$$

3. Start with the first group (12).   Find a number which when multiplied by itself will give an answer close to or equal to but not larger than 12.   4 squared is 16, but that is too large.   3 squared is 9, which is less than 12 and so is just right.   Place the 3 over the first group in the answer and the 9 under the 12 in the number.   Draw a line, and subtract, leaving a remainder of 3.

$$
\begin{array}{r}
3\ . \\
\sqrt{1\ 2\ .} \\
-\ 9 \\
\hline
3
\end{array}
$$

4. Since there is a remainder, the square root will be a decimal. Add two *pairs* of zeros after the decimal point.   Bring down the next group (00).   Make a little box to the left of this number (300). *Double* the answer up to this point (the 3), and place the product (6) in this box.

$$
\begin{array}{r}
3\ . \\
\sqrt{1\ 2\ .\ 00\ 00} \\
-\ \ 9 \\
\end{array}
$$
6 | 3 00

5. Place your finger over the *last digit* in the number 300.   The number there will now appear to be 30.   Divide the number in the box (6) into this 30.   It will go 5 times.   Place this 5 in the answer above the second group, *and also place it next to the 6 in the box*.   Multiply the 5 by the number just formed (the 65), and place the product (325) under the 300 already there.   *But 325 is larger than 300, and we have evidently made an error in using the 5.*   Since 5 was too large, use 4 instead of 5.

$$
\begin{array}{r}
3\ .\ 5 \\
\sqrt{1\ 2\ .\ 00\ 00} \\
-\ \ 9\ \ \times \\
\end{array}
$$
6 5 | 3 00
    3 25   Too large!

6. Be sure to change *both* the 5 in the answer and the 5 in the 65 in the box to the number 4.   Now multiply the 4 in the answer by the 64 in the box.   Place the product (256) under the 300 already there, and subtract, leaving a remainder of 44.

$$
\begin{array}{r}
3\,.\,4 \\
\sqrt{1\,2\,.\,00\ 00} \\
-\ \ 9\quad\times \\
\underline{\quad\quad} \\
6\ 4\ \mbig|\ \ 3\ 00 \\
-\ 2\ 56 \\
\underline{\quad\quad} \\
44
\end{array}
$$

7. Bring down the next group (00).   Make a little box to the left of this new number (4400).   Double the answer up to this point (the 34), and place the product (68) in this box.   Always disregard the decimal point in this step.

$$
\begin{array}{r}
3\,.\,4 \\
\sqrt{1\,2\,.\,00\ 00} \\
-\ \ 9\quad\times\ \times \\
6\ 4\ \big|\ \ 3\ 00 \\
-\ 2\ 56 \\
68\ \big|\ \ 44\ 00
\end{array}
$$

8. Place your finger over the *last digit* in the number 4400.   The number there will now appear to be 440.   Divide the number in the box (68) into this 440.   It will go 6 times.   Place this 6 in the answer over the third group, *and also place it next to the 68 in the box.*

$$
\begin{array}{r}
3\,.\,4\ \ 6 \\
\sqrt{1\,2\,.\,00\ 00} \\
-\ \ 9\quad\times\ \times \\
64\ \big|\ \ 3\ 00 \\
-\ 2\ 56 \\
68\ 6\ \big|\ \ 44\ 00
\end{array}
$$

9. Multiply the 6 by the number just formed (the 686), and place the product (4116) under the 4400 already there.   Draw a line, and subtract, leaving a remainder of 284.   This remainder may be disregarded, as we shall rarely need an answer more accurate than two decimal places.   The problem may be worked out to any number of decimal places and then "rounded off" to suit.

$$
\begin{array}{r}
3\,.\,4\ \ 6 \\
\sqrt{1\,2\,.\,00\ 00} \\
-\ \ 9\quad\times\ \times \\
64\ \big|\ \ 3\ 00 \\
-\ 2\ 56 \\
68\ 6\ \big|\ \ 44\ 00 \\
-\ 41\ 16 \\
\underline{\quad\quad} \\
2\ 84
\end{array}
$$

Check: 3.46 × 3.46 = 11.97, or practically 12

Problems

Find the square root of the following numbers:

1. 3,481	**3.** 15.21	**5.** 18,769	**7.** 40	**9.** 65
2. 17.64	**4.** 12,544	**6.** 151.29	**8.** 267	**10.** 53.87

JOB 7-10: APPLICATIONS OF THE EXPONENTIAL POWER FORMULA

The formula $P = I^2R$ may be used to find the current I or the resistance R.   The formula $P = E^2/R$ may be used to find the voltage E or the resistance R.

Example 7-20.   What is the maximum current-carrying capacity of a resistor marked 1,000 ohms and 10 watts?

Solution:

$$\text{Given: } R = 1,000 \text{ ohms} \qquad \text{Find: } I = ?$$
$$P = 10 \text{ watts}$$

$$P = I^2R \tag{7-4}$$
$$10 = I^2 \times 1,000$$
$$I^2 = \frac{10}{1,000} = 0.01 \text{ amp}$$

Now $I^2 = 0.01$ means that some number I multiplied by itself will equal 0.01.   Another way to say this is "What number multiplied by itself will equal 0.01?"   This can be written as

$$I = \sqrt{0.01}$$

Actually, we have transformed the equation $I^2 = 0.01$ into $I = \sqrt{0.01}$ by taking the square root of both sides of the equals sign, as shown in the following step.

$$\sqrt{I^2} = \sqrt{0.01}$$
$$I = \sqrt{0.01} \text{ or } I = 0.1 \text{ amp} \qquad Ans.$$

Example 7-21.   A 6L6 used as a single-tube class A$_1$ amplifier delivers an output power of 4 watts at an average current of 0.05 amp. What is the value of the load resistance?

Solution:

$$\text{Given: } P = 4 \text{ watts} \qquad \text{Find: } R = ?$$
$$I = 0.05 \text{ amp}$$

$$P = I^2R \tag{7-4}$$
$$4 = (0.05)^2 \times R$$
$$4 = 0.0025 \times R$$
$$R = \frac{4}{0.0025} = 1,600 \text{ ohms} \qquad Ans.$$

Example 7-22.   The total resistance of the field coils of a 240-watt motor is 60 ohms.   Find the voltage needed to operate the motor at its rated power.

Solution:

Given: R = 60 ohms   Find: E = ?
P = 240 watts

1. Write the formula.

$$P = \frac{E^2}{R} \qquad\qquad (7\text{-}5)$$

2. Substitute numbers.

$$\frac{240}{1} = \frac{E^2}{60}$$

3. Cross-multiply.

$$E^2 = 240 \times 60$$

4. Multiply.

$$E^2 = 14{,}400$$

5. Take the square root of both sides.

$$\sqrt{E^2} = \sqrt{14{,}400}$$

6. Since $\sqrt{E^2} = E$,

$$E = \sqrt{14{,}400}$$

7. Voltage is

$$E = 120 \text{ volts} \qquad Ans.$$

Problems

1. What current flows through a line supplying 1,500 watts of power to an electric range of 15 ohms resistance?

2. What voltage is necessary to operate an 18-watt automobile headlight bulb of 2 ohms resistance?

3. A 6K6 power-amplifier pentode delivers 4 watts of power at an average current of 0.02 amp.   What is the value of the load resistance?

4. What is the current flowing through a 50-ohm electromagnet drawing 200 watts?

5. What is the maximum current-carrying capacity of a resistor marked 500 ohms and 10 watts?

6. Find the voltage drop across a corroded connection if its contact resistance is 100 ohms and it uses 4 watts of power.

7. Find the internal resistance of a 2-watt electric clock which operates on a 110-volt line.

8. A 60- and a 40-watt lamp are in parallel across 120 volts.   Find the combined resistance of the lamps.

9. What current flows through the heater of a 25Z5 radio tube which has a resistance of 83.3 ohms and uses 7.5 watts of power?

10. The 650-ohm cathode resistor for a 6CB6 television i-f amplifier uses 0.1 watt of power. Find the current in the resistor.

11. What is the voltage necessary to operate a 600-watt neon sign whose resistance is 20 ohms?

12. The screen dropping resistor for a 12SK7 pentode amplifier uses 0.36 watt at 0.0024 amp. Find the resistance of the dropping resistor.

JOB 7-11: REVIEW OF ELECTRICAL POWER

In the following formulas

P = power, watts

E = voltage, volts

I = current, amp

$$P = I \times E \qquad (7\text{-}1)$$
$$P_T = I_T \times E_T \qquad (7\text{-}2)$$
$$P_T = P_1 + P_2 + P_3 \qquad (7\text{-}3)$$
$$P = I^2 R \qquad (7\text{-}4)$$
$$P = \frac{E^2}{R} \qquad (7\text{-}5)$$

Problems

1. Find the power used by an electric toaster if it draws 6 amp from a 110-volt line.

2. Find the power used by a 22-ohm motor if the current is 10 amp.

3. Find the total power drawn by the four lamps shown in Fig. 7-4.

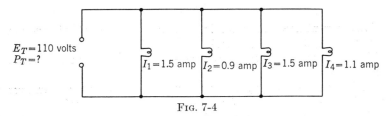

$E_T = 110$ volts
$P_T = ?$

$I_1 = 1.5$ amp $I_2 = 0.9$ amp $I_3 = 1.5$ amp $I_4 = 1.1$ amp

Fig. 7-4

4. What current is drawn by a 250-watt electric vacuum cleaner when operated on 110 volts?

5. Three 18-volt 0.8-amp bells are in series. Find the total power.

6. How many watts of power are dissipated in a 100,000-ohm voltage divider if the voltage across it is 300 volts?

7. A 0.15-amp phonograph amplifier heater circuit uses a 12.6-, a 50-, and a 35-volt tube with the heaters in series. In addition, a ballast resistor which causes a voltage drop of 20 volts is in series with the heaters. What is the total power used by the circuit?

8. What voltage is required to operate a 25-watt automobile headlight bulb properly if the current drawn is 4 amp?

9. Find the resistance of a 1,000-watt electric ironing machine if it uses 5 amp.

10. A typical table-model radio receiver uses a filter resistor of 1,000 ohms and carries a current of 0.06 amp in a circuit similar to that shown in Fig. 7-1. Find the power used in the resistor.

11. The total resistance of a 12SJ7 tube in parallel with a 42-ohm shunt is 21 ohms. Find the power used if the total current is 0.3 amp.

12. The combined resistance of a coffee percolator and toaster in parallel is 22 ohms. Find the total power used if the line voltage is 110 volts.

13. What power is dissipated in the form of heat in a 130-ohm ballast resistor designed to use up 40 volts of excess voltage?

14. What is the voltage needed to operate a 10-watt electric-train accessory whose resistance is 15 ohms?

15. A 100- and a 60-watt lamp are connected in parallel across 120 volts. Find the combined resistance.

16. What is the maximum current-carrying capacity of a resistor marked 5,000 ohms and 20 watts?

17. The cathode resistor for a 7G7 tube uses 0.016 watt while carrying 0.008 amp. What is the resistance of the cathode resistor?

18. A number of incandescent lamps in parallel are supplied by a generator delivering 112 volts at its brushes. The resistance of each of the two leads carrying current to the lamps is 0.05 ohm and causes a voltage drop of 2 volts. If each lamp draws 50 watts, how many lamps are lit? *Hint:*

1. Find the line current.

$$E_l = I_l \times R_l \qquad (6\text{-}1)$$

2. Find the voltage at the load.

$$E_L = E_G - E_l \qquad (6\text{-}3)$$

3. Find the power supplied to the load.

$$P_L = I_l \times E_L \qquad (7\text{-}1)$$

4. The number of lamps $= P_L \div$ wattage per lamp.

Test—Power

1. Find the current drawn by a 1,100-watt electric heater when operated on a 110-volt line.

2. Find the total power used by a 6.3-, a 6.3-, a 6.3-, a 35-, and a 25-volt radio tube when operating in series at 0.3 amp.

3. Find the power taken by a 50-ohm lamp operating at 110 volts.

4. What is the maximum current-carrying capacity of a resistor marked 200 ohms and 10 watts?

5. A 6CD6 horizontal output tube uses a screen dropping resistor which develops 1.28 watts of power. If the current through the resistor is 0.008 amp, what is the resistance of the resistor?

CHAPTER 8

APPLICATIONS OF SERIES AND PARALLEL CIRCUITS

JOB 8-1: ELECTRICAL UNITS OF MEASUREMENT IN RADIO AND TELEVISION

In many problems in radio and television work the usual units of amperes, volts, and ohms are either too large or too small. It has been found more convenient to use new units of measurement. These new units are formed by placing a special word or prefix in front of the unit. Each of these prefixes has a definite meaning.

Milli-unit (m-unit) means 1/1,000 of the unit.

Kilo-unit (k-unit) means 1,000 of these units.

Micro-unit (μ-unit) means 1/1,000,000 of the unit.

Meg-unit (M-unit) means 1,000,000 of these units.

Changing Units of Measurement. There are two factors to be considered when describing any measurement: (1) how many of the measurements and (2) what *kind* of measurement. For example, one dollar may be described as 2 half dollars, 4 quarters, 10 dimes, 20 nickels, or 100 pennies. When the one dollar was changed into each of the new measurements, *both* the unit of measurement as well as the number of them were changed. For example:

$$\text{Since 3 ft} = 1 \text{ yd}, \quad 2 \text{ yd} = \quad 2 \times 3 \quad = 6 \text{ ft}$$
$$\text{Since 2,000 lb} = 1 \text{ ton}, \quad 3 \text{ tons} = \quad 3 \times 2,000 = 6,000 \text{ lb}$$
$$\text{Since 100}\cent = 1 \text{ dollar}, 4 \text{ dollars} = 4 \times 100 \quad = 400\cent$$

Large unit   small unit

small number   Large number

Notice that a *small number* of *large units* is always changed into a *large number* of *small units* by *multiplying* by the number showing the relationship between the units.

Rule: To change from a large unit into a small unit, multiply by the number showing the relationship between the units.

This rule is illustrated for various units in Table 8-1.

Table 8-1. Changing Large Units into Small Units

	To change	Into	Multiply by
1	Volts (v)	Millivolts (mv)	1,000 or 10^3
2	Amperes (amp)	Milliamperes (ma)	1,000 or 10^3
3	Watts (w)	Milliwatts (mw)	1,000 or 10^3
4	Kilovolts (kv)	Volts (v)	1,000 or 10^3
5	Kilowatts (kw)	Watts (w)	1,000 or 10^3
6	Kilocycles (kc)	Cycles (c)	1,000 or 10^3
7	Volts (v)	Microvolts (μv)	10^6
8	Amperes (amp)	Microamperes (μa)	10^6
9	Farads (f)	Microfarads (μf)	10^6
10	Megohms (MΩ)	Ohms (Ω)	10^6
11	Megacycles (Mc)	Cycles (c)	10^6
12	Microfarads (μf)	Micromicrofarads ($\mu\mu$f)	10^6

Example 8-1.

1. 2.4 volts $= 2.4 \times 10^3 = 2,400$ mv
2. 0.56 amp $= 0.56 \times 10^3 = 560$ ma
3. 0.5 watt $= 0.5 \times 10^3 = 500$ mw
4. 0.3 kv $= 0.3 \times 10^3 = 300$ volts
5. 0.15 kw $= 0.15 \times 10^3 = 150$ watts
6. 880 kc $= 880 \times 10^3 = 880,000$ cycles
7. 0.053 volt $= 0.053 \times 10^6 = 53,000$ μv
8. 0.0004 amp $= 0.0004 \times 10^6 = 400$ μa
9. 0.00006 farad $= 0.00006 \times 10^6 = 60$ μf
10. 0.25 Megohm $= 0.25 \times 10^6 = 250,000$ ohms
11. 3.2 Mc $= 3.2 \times 10^6 = 3,200,000$ cycles
12. 0.00035 μf $= 0.00035 \times 10^6 = 350$ $\mu\mu$f

Now let us reverse the process and change small units into large units. For example:

Since 3 ft $=$ 1 yd,   6 ft $= 6 \div 3$ $=$ 2 yd

Since 2,000 lb $=$ 1 ton,   6,000 lb $= 6,000 \div 2,000 =$ 3 tons

Since 100¢ $=$ 1 dollar,   400¢ $= 400 \div 100$ $=$ 4 dollars

small unit ⎯⎯⎯⎯ Large unit

Large number ⎯⎯⎯⎯ small number

Notice that a *large number* of *small units* is always changed into a *small number* of *large units* by *dividing* by the number showing the relationship between the units.

Rule: To change from a small unit into a large unit, divide by the number showing the relationship between the units.

This rule is illustrated for various units in Table 8-2.

Table 8-2. Changing Small Units into Large Units

	To change	Into	Divide by
1	Millivolts (mv)	Volts (v)	10^3
2	Milliamperes (ma)	Amperes (amp)	10^3
3	Milliwatts (mw)	Watts (w)	10^3
4	Volts (v)	Kilovolts (kv)	10^3
5	Watts (w)	Kilowatts (kw)	10^3
6	Cycles (c)	Kilocycles (kc)	10^3
7	Microvolts (μv)	Volts (v)	10^6
8	Microamperes (μa)	Amperes (amp)	10^6
9	Microfarads (μf)	Farads (f)	10^6
10	Ohms (Ω)	Megohms (MΩ)	10^6
11	Cycles (c)	Megacycles (Mc)	10^6
12	Micromicrofarads ($\mu\mu$f)	Microfarads (μf)	10^6

Example 8-2.

1. $356 \text{ mv} = 356 \div 10^3 = 0.356 \text{ volt}$
2. $14.5 \text{ ma} = 14.5 \div 10^3 = 0.0145 \text{ amp}$
3. $700 \text{ mw} = 700 \div 10^3 = 0.7 \text{ watt}$
4. $600 \text{ volts} = 600 \div 10^3 = 0.6 \text{ kv}$
5. $4,000 \text{ watts} = 4,000 \div 10^3 = 4 \text{ kw}$
6. $700 \text{ cycles} = 700 \div 10^3 = 0.7 \text{ kc}$
7. $15,000 \ \mu\text{v} = 15,000 \div 10^6 = 0.015 \text{ volt}$
8. $30,000 \ \mu\text{a} = 30,000 \div 10^6 = 0.03 \text{ amp}$
9. $2.5 \ \mu\text{f} = 2.5 \div 10^6 = 0.0000025 \text{ farad}$
10. $500,000 \text{ ohms} = 500,000 \div 10^6 = 0.5 \text{ Megohm}$
11. $660,000 \text{ cycles} = 660,000 \div 10^6 = 0.66 \text{ Mc}$
12. $350 \ \mu\mu\text{f} = 350 \div 10^6 = 0.00035 \ \mu\text{f}$

Problems

Change the following units of measurement.

1. 225 ma to amperes
2. 0.076 volt to millivolts
3. 3.5 Megohms to ohms
4. 5 kw to watts
5. 550 kc to cycles
6. 0.00008 farad to microfarads
7. 0.065 amp to milliamperes
8. 700,000 cycles to kilocycles
9. 70,000 ohms to Megohms
10. 6,500 watts to kilowatts

11. 75 mv to volts
12. 0.007 farad to microfarads
13. 6,000 μa to amperes
14. 2.3 Mc to cycles
15. 3.9 ma to amperes
16. 75,000 watts to kilowatts
17. 0.005 μf to micromicrofarads
18. $\frac{1}{4}$ amp to milliamperes
19. 1,000 kc to cycles
20. 0.5 Megohm to ohms

21. 0.008 volt to millivolts
22. 0.0045 watt to milliwatts
23. 0.00006 μf to micromicrofarads
24. 0.15 amp to milliamperes
25. 0.15 μf to farads
26. 125 mv to volts
27. 8,000 watts to kilowatts
28. 4.16 kw to watts
29. 0.000004 amp to microamperes
30. 0.6 Mc to cycles

JOB 8-2: USING RADIO AND TELEVISION UNITS IN SIMPLE CIRCUITS

All the formulas for Ohm's law, series circuits, parallel circuits, and power demand that the measurements be given in the units of amperes, volts, and ohms only. If a certain problem gives the measurements in units other than these, we must change all the units into amperes, volts, and ohms before we can use any of these formulas.

Example 8-3. In a 45-volt circuit, the current must be held down to 1 ma. What must be the total resistance of the circuit?

Solution:

$$\text{Given: } E_T = 45 \text{ volts} \qquad \text{Find: } R_T = \text{?}$$
$$I_T = 1 \text{ ma}$$

1. Change ma to amperes.

$$1 \text{ ma} = 1 \div 1,000 = 0.001 \text{ amp}$$

2. Find the resistance.

$$E = 1 \times R \qquad\qquad (2\text{-}1)$$
$$45 = 0.001 \times R$$
$$R = \frac{45}{0.001} = 45,000 \text{ ohms} \qquad Ans.$$

Example 8-4. If 0.15 μamp flows through a 2-Megohm grid leak, what bias voltage will be developed across the resistor?

Solution: The diagram for the circuit is shown in Fig. 8-1.

1. Change the units of measurement.

$$0.15 \ \mu\text{amp} = \frac{0.15}{10^6} \text{ amp}$$
$$2 \text{ Megohms} = 2 \times 10^6 \text{ ohms}$$

2. Find the voltage.

$$E = I \times R \qquad\qquad (2\text{-}1)$$

$$E = \frac{0.15}{10^6} \times 2 \times 10^6$$

$$E = 0.15 \times 2 = 0.3 \text{ volt} \qquad Ans.$$

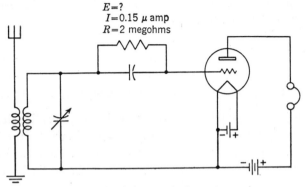

$E = ?$
$I = 0.15 \ \mu \text{ amp}$
$R = 2 \text{ megohms}$

Fig. 8-1. A simple grid-leak detector receiver.

Example 8-5. The series-connected heaters of a 12SQ7 (12.6 volts), a 50L6 (50 volts), and a 35Z5 (35 volts) used in a phonograph amplifier draw 150 ma. Find the total resistance of the circuit.

Solution:

Given: $E_1 = 12.6$ volts   Find: $R_T = ?$
   $E_2 = 50$ volts
   $E_3 = 35$ volts
   $I_T = 150$ ma

1. Change ma to amperes.

$$150 \text{ ma} = 150 \div 1{,}000 = 0.150 = 0.15 \text{ amp}$$

2. Find the total voltage E_T.

$$E_T = E_1 + E_2 + E_3 = 12.6 + 50 + 35 = 97.6 \text{ volts} \quad (4\text{-}2)$$

3. Find the total resistance R_T.

$$E_T = I_T \times R_T \qquad\qquad (4\text{-}7)$$
$$97.6 = 0.15 \times R_T$$
$$R_T = \frac{97.6}{0.15} = 651 \text{ ohms} \qquad Ans.$$

Problems

1. How many milliamperes of current will flow through a 100-ohm resistor if the voltage across its ends is 20 mv?

2. Two microamperes of current flow in an antenna whose resistance is 50 ohms. Find the voltage drop in the antenna.

3. An emf of 200 μv sends 10 ma of current through the primary of a transformer. Find the total resisting effect of the coil.

4. Find the number of microamperes flowing through a 2-Megohm grid leak if the voltage drop across it is 1,000 mv?

5. The heater of a single 25L6 tube draws 0.3 amp. How many milliamperes will the heaters of two such tubes draw if they are connected in parallel?

6. A 6BG6-G horizontal output tube in a television receiver u es a 9,900-ohm screen dropping resistor which carries 15 ma of current. Find the voltage drop in the resistor.

7. An output choke having a d-c resistance of 2,000 ohms passes a plate current of 20 ma as shown in Fig. 8-2. What is the voltage drop in the choke? What is the B-supply voltage if the plate of the tube must receive 180 volts?

8. The radiation resistance of a short-wave antenna is 100 ohms. If the transmitter delivers 900 ma to the antenna, find the number of watts radiated.

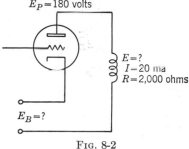

$E_P = 180$ volts

$E = ?$
$I = 20$ ma
$R = 2,000$ ohms

$E_B = ?$

FIG. 8-2

9. A 12SK7 pentode has a resistance of 0.008 Megohm in its plate circuit. Find the voltage drop in this resistance if the plate current is 9.2 ma.

10. A photoelectric cell circuit contains a resistance of 0.12 Megohm and carries a current of 50 μa. Find the voltage drop in the resistance.

JOB 8-3: CATHODE BIAS RESISTORS

The operation of a vacuum tube depends in large measure on the voltage on the grid as compared with the voltage on the cathode. Except for special conditions, the voltage on the grid must never be permitted to become positive with respect to the cathode. Therefore, a special negative voltage, or "bias," is placed on the grid. As a changing signal enters the grid, the grid voltage becomes only more or less negative. These changes in negative voltage on the grid control the plate current in simple triodes.

Producing a Negative Bias with Cathode Resistors. A voltage drop across a resistor in the cathode circuit will produce a negative grid bias as shown in Fig. 8-3. The plate current I_p passes through the B supply to point A and then through the cathode resistor up to B. Some voltage must be used up in sending this current through the cathode resistor— let us say about 10 volts. If the voltage at A

is about 200 volts, then the voltage at B will be only $200 - 10 = 190$ volts. But the voltage at the grid has remained at 200 volts negative, since the grid is connected directly to point A and practically no current flows tnrough the coil. The grid is therefore 10 volts more negative than the cathode, which is equivalent to placing a special negative voltage on the grid.

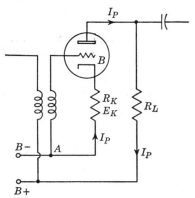

FIG. 8-3. Negative bias produced by a voltage drop across a resistor in the cathode circuit.

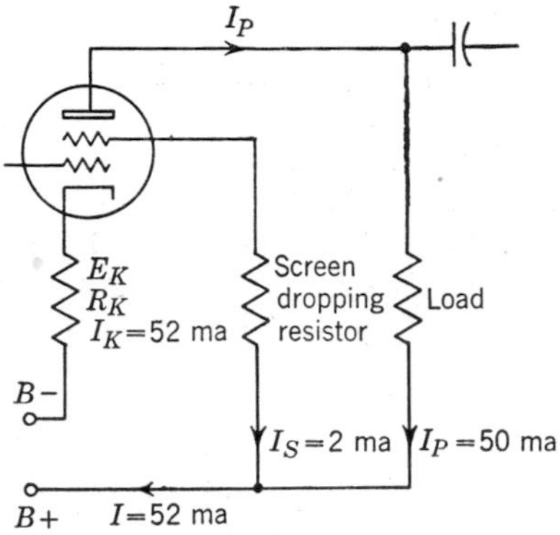

FIG. 8-4. Cathode current for a 50L6 beam-power amplifier.

In a *triode* tube, the cathode current is equal to the plate current. In a *tetrode*, or four-element tube, the cathode current is equal to the plate current *plus* the screen current. In Fig. 8-4, I_k is the cathode current, I_p is the plate current, and I_s is the screen current.

Formula

$$I_k = I_p + I_s \qquad (8\text{-}1)$$
$$I_k = 50 + 2 = 52 \text{ ma}$$

Example 8-6. Find the cathode bias resistor necessary to produce 9 volts of cathode bias for a triode which operates at 3 ma of plate current.

Solution: The circuit is similar to Fig. 8-3.

Given: $E_k = -9$ volts   Find: $R_k = ?$
$I_k = I_p = 3$ ma

1. Change ma to amperes.

$$3 \text{ ma} = 3 \div 1{,}000 = 0.003 \text{ amp}$$

2. Find the cathode bias resistor R_k.

$$E_k = I_k \times R_k \qquad (2\text{-}1)$$
$$9 = 0.003 \times R_k$$
$$R_k = \frac{9}{0.003} = 3{,}000 \text{ ohms} \qquad Ans.$$

Example 8-7. Find the cathode resistor needed for a 12J7GT pentode acting as a class A amplifier if the cathode bias is −3 volts, the plate current is 2 ma, and the screen current is 0.5 ma.

Solution: The circuit is similar to Fig. 8-4.

$$\text{Given: } E_k = -3 \text{ volts} \qquad \text{Find: } R_k = ?$$
$$I_p = 2 \text{ ma}$$
$$I_s = 0.5 \text{ ma}$$

Find the cathode current.

$$I_k = I_p + I_s = 2 + 0.5 = 2.5 \text{ ma} \qquad\qquad (8\text{-}1)$$
$$I_k = 2.5 \text{ ma} = 2.5 \div 1,000 = 0.0025 \text{ amp}$$

Find the cathode resistor.

$$E_k = I_k \times R_k \qquad\qquad\qquad\qquad (2\text{-}1)$$
$$3 = 0.0025 \times R_k$$

$$R_k = \frac{3}{0.0025} = 1,200 \text{ ohms} \qquad Ans.$$

Example 8-8. A 6BA6 used as a sound i-f amplifier in a television receiver has a plate current of 11 ma, a screen current of 4.2 ma, and a cathode resistor of 68 ohms.   Find the grid bias.

Solution:

$$\text{Given: } I_p = 11 \text{ ma} \qquad \text{Find: } E_k = ?$$
$$I_s = 4.2 \text{ ma}$$
$$R_k = 68 \text{ ohms}$$

Find the cathode current.

$$I_k = I_p + I_s = 11 + 4.2 = 15.2 \text{ ma} \qquad\qquad (8\text{-}1)$$
$$I_k = 15.2 \text{ ma} = 15.2 \div 1,000 = 0.0152 \text{ amp}$$

Find the grid bias voltage.

$$E_k = I_k \times R_k \qquad\qquad\qquad\qquad (2\text{-}1)$$
$$E_k = 0.0152 \times 68 = -1.03 \text{ volts} \qquad Ans.$$

Problems

1. Find the cathode resistor needed for a 6L6 class A amplifier (triode connected) if the bias required is −20 volts and the plate current is 40 ma.

2. A 6J5 tube operates at a plate voltage of 250 volts and a plate current of 9 ma.   Find the cathode resistor needed to provide a negative bias of 8.1 volts.

3. The cathode resistor for a 6G6 tube must provide a bias of −9 volts when the plate current is 15 ma and the screen current is 2.5 ma.   Find (a) the resistance of the cathode resistor and (b) the wattage dissipated by the resistor.

4. As tubes get older and deteriorate, the plate current will usually drop. If the plate current in Prob. 3 should drop to 10 ma, find the grid bias obtained if the cathode resistor is unchanged.

5. A 6W6 used as a vertical deflection output tube in a television receiver requires a negative bias of 9 volts. If the plate current is 46 ma, find the resistance of the cathode resistor and the watts dissipated by it.

6. A 6K6GT tube used as a second video amplifier in a television receiver requires a bias voltage of −18 volts. Find the cathode resistor needed if the plate current is 32 ma and the screen current is 5.5 ma.

7. A 6SJ7 tube is used in a phonograph amplifier. If the bias required is −3 volts, find the needed cathode resistor when the plate current is 3 ma and the screen current is 0.8 ma.

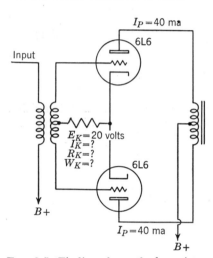

FIG. 8-5. Finding the cathode resistor for two 6L6 tubes in push-pull.

8. Find the cathode resistor needed to provide −1 volt of grid bias for a 6SG7 tube if the plate current is 11.8 ma and the screen current is 4.4 ma.

9. In the G-E model 221 a-c-d-c superheterodyne radio receiver, the 12SK7 r-f amplifier requires a grid bias of −3 volts. Find the needed cathode resistor if the plate current is 9.2 ma and the screen current is 2.6 ma.

10. Two 6L6 tubes (triode connected) are joined in push-pull as shown in Fig. 8-5. Each tube requires a bias of −20 volts and has a plate current of 40 ma. Find the resistance and wattage dissipated by the required cathode resistor. *Hint:* The cathode current will be twice the current of one tube.

11. A 6AG5 used as a first picture i-f amplifier in the RCA model 630TS television receiver has a plate current of 7 ma and a screen current of 2 ma and uses a cathode resistor of 39 ohms. Find the grid bias voltage.

12. A 6AU6 used as the third video i-f amplifier in the Majestic chassis 110 television receiver has a cathode resistor of 150 ohms, a plate current of 10.8 ma, and a screen current of 4.3 ma. Find the grid bias voltage.

JOB 8-4: BALLAST RESISTORS

In order for vacuum tubes to operate, electrons must be emitted from their cathodes. These are comparatively heavy metal plates coated with a material which will emit electrons in a steady flow when it is heated. Many tubes contain a small heating element called the "heater" whose sole purpose is to provide the heat necessary to cause the cathode to emit electrons. Each manufacturer's tube manual specifies the values of voltage and current required by the heater of each tube for proper and efficient operation. Since the heater is only a little stove and is completely independent of the rest of the receiver, the heaters of all the tubes in a set may be connected in series and the whole circuit connected across the line voltage. However, this line voltage may be higher than the total voltage required by all the heaters. If this higher voltage were impressed across the heater circuit, the resulting current would be much larger than the tubes were designed to carry and they would soon burn out.

Therefore, in every situation where the line voltage is larger than the total heater voltage, the excess voltage must be used up by some sort of resistance device inserted in series with the heaters. These are line cord resistors, dropping resistors, or ballast tubes.

Example 8-9. The Crosley model J35 a-c–d-c superheterodyne radio receiver uses a 6SA7, a 6SK7, a 6SQ7, a 25L6, and a 25Z6 with their heaters in series as shown in Fig. 8-6. (a) Find the dropping resistor needed to allow the tubes to operate from a 117-volt line. (b) Calculate the wattage rating of this resistance.

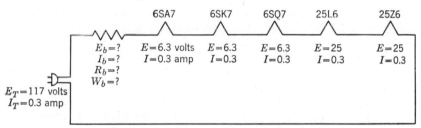

FIG. 8-6. A series-connected heater circuit with dropping resistor.

Solution: The diagram for the circuit is shown in Fig. 8-6.

Note: Since the heaters are connected in series, they all must be rated at the same current of 0.3 amp.

a. 1. Find the voltage to be used up by the ballast resistor.

$$E_T = E_b + E_1 + E_2 + E_3 + E_4 + E_5 \quad (4\text{-}2)$$
$$117 = E_b + 6.3 + 6.3 + 6.3 + 25 + 25$$
$$117 = E_b + 68.9$$
$$117 - 68.9 = E_b$$
$$E_b = 48.1 \text{ volts}$$

2. Find the ballast resistor. The current I_b in the ballast resistor is equal to the series current in the tubes.

$$E_b = I_b \times R_b \quad (2\text{-}1)$$
$$48.1 = 0.3 \times R_b$$
$$R_b = \frac{48.1}{0.3} = 160 \text{ ohms} \qquad Ans.$$

b. Find the wattage rating.   As noted in Job 7-1, the wattage rating of a radio resistor should be at least twice the wattage it is expected to develop.

$$P = I^2R = (0.3)^2 \times 160 = 0.09 \times 160 = 14.4 \text{ watts} \quad (7\text{-}4)$$
$$\text{Wattage rating} = 2 \times P = 2 \times 14.4 = 28.8 \text{ or } 30 \text{ watts} \quad Ans.$$

Problems

1. What value of resistance must be placed in series with the filament of a 3S4 tube if it is operated from a 6.3-volt storage battery?   The filament takes 2.8 volts at 0.05 amp.

Note: In the following problems the heater voltages are given by the first number of the tube as indicated below:

Tubes beginning with the number 6 use 6.3 volts.

Tubes beginning with the number 12 use 12.6 volts.

All other tubes use as many volts as the first number of the tube except as noted.

2. The Knight 2-watt phonograph amplifier uses a 12AU6 and a 50L6GT with the filaments in series in a 0.15-amp circuit.   Find the resistance and wattage dissipated by the ballast resistor needed for operation on a 117-volt line.

3. The Crosley model 417 uses a 6J7G, a 25A6G, and a 25A7G with the heaters in series at 0.3 amp.   Find the resistance and wattage rating of the dropping resistor needed for operation on a 120-volt line.

4. The dial lamp type 49 requires 2 volts and 0.06 amp.   Find the dropping resistor necessary to operate the lamp from two dry cells in series.

5. The G-E model LC-679 uses a 6SA7GT, a 6SK7GT, a 6Q7GT, and a 6J5GT with the heaters in series.   If the 6SA7GT takes 0.3 amp, find the resistance and wattage dissipated by the line cord when it is operated on 110 volts.

6. The DeWald model JD-519 four-tube superheterodyne radio receiver uses a 12AU6, a 12BE6, a 12AB6, and a 50C5 with the heaters connected in series at a current of 0.15 amp.   Find (*a*) the resistance of the required dropping resistor, (*b*) the wattage dissipated by this resistor, and (*c*) the wattage rating of this resistor if the line voltage is 117 volts.

7. The Pilot model T1252 radio receiver uses a 6SA7, a 6SK7, a 6SQ7, a 25L6G, and a 25Z6G with the heaters in series at 0.3 amp.   Find the resistance and wattage rating of the required ballast resistor for operation on a 110-volt line.

8. Without regard for the shunt resistor required (see Job 8-5), find the ballast resistor required to replace a 25L6 beam-power tube with a 6L6 tube (6.3 volts, 0.9 amp).   The heater current will now be the 0.9 amp demanded by the 6L6 tube.

9. The Magnavox model A205 record player uses a 70L7GT rectifier beam-power amplifier (70 volts, 0.15 amp).   If it is replaced with a selenium rectifier and a 50L6 beam-power amplifier (50 volts, 0.15 amp), find (*a*) the series resistor needed and (*b*) the wattage rating of the resistor.

10. An a-c–d-c phonograph amplifier uses a 35Z5, a 50L6, and a 12SQ7 with the heaters connected in series at 0.15 amp. Find the ballast resistor needed to operate the circuit from a 117-volt source.

11. The Knight a-c–d-c "Ocean Hopper" uses a 12AT6, a 50C5, and a 35W4 in a 0.15-amp series-heater circuit. Find the resistance and wattage rating of the ballast resistor needed for operation from a 117-volt source.

12. The Emerson model 107 (UCF) receiver uses a 6A7, a 6K7, a 6H6, a 6F5, a No. 43 (25 volts, 0.3 amp), and a 25Z5 with the heaters in series. Find the ballast resistor needed for operation at 110 volts.

JOB 8-5: SHUNT RESISTORS AND TUBE SUBSTITUTIONS

A *shunt* is a resistance which is placed in *parallel* with another part. Its purpose is to provide an extra path for a line current which is too large for the shunted part.

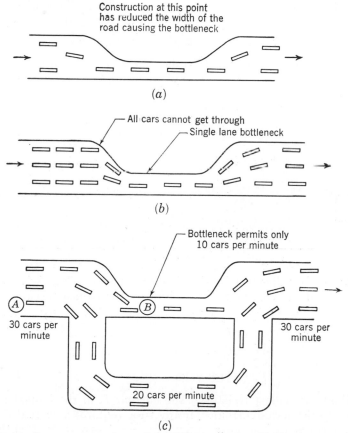

Fig. 8-7. (*a*) Construction reduces the width of a road. (*b*) The large number of cars cannot get through the bottleneck. (*c*) The detour carries the *overflow around* the bottleneck.

The problem is very similar to the problem encountered by the traffic experts on a pleasant Sunday. During the week, a certain highway can easily carry the cars on it even though there may be a bottleneck on the road due to some construction as shown in Fig. 8-7a. This road will be able to carry the relatively few cars using it on weekdays. However, on this pleasant Sunday, the number of cars will probably be very large as shown in Fig. 8-7b. This situation will back up the cars for many miles. In order to alleviate the tie-up, *another path or detour around the bottleneck* must be provided for the overflow as shown in Fig. 8-7c. The size of this detour must be large enough to handle the cars that cannot get through the regular road. For example, if 30 cars per minute are traveling on the road at A, and if only 10 cars per minute can get through at B, then the detour must be able to handle $30 - 10 = 20$ cars per minute. The traffic engineer will therefore provide a detour capable of handling 20 cars per minute. In electricity, we have essentially the same problem.

Example 8-10. If the 6SA7 tube in the a-c–d-c superheterodyne receiver of Example 8-9 is replaced with a 12SA7 tube, find (a) the new ballast resistor and (b) the shunt resistor required across the 12SA7 tube.

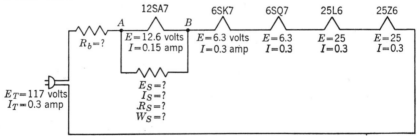

Fig. 8-8

Solution: The diagram for the circuit is shown in Fig. 8-8.

a. 1. Find the voltage to be used up by the ballast resistor.

$$E_T = E_b + E_1 + E_2 + E_3 + E_4 + E_5 \quad (4\text{-}2)$$
$$117 = E_b + 12.6 + 6.3 + 6.3 + 25 + 25$$
$$117 = E_b + 75.2$$
$$117 - 75.2 = E_b$$
$$E_b = 41.8 \text{ volts}$$

2. Find the ballast resistor. The current I_b in the ballast resistor is equal to the series current. If any tube requires a current *different* from the current of any other tube, the series current *must* be the current required by the tube drawing the *largest* current. The largest current is used because it is always possible to *reduce* the current, but

not always possible to *increase* it.   In this example, the series current will be 0.3 amp, since 0.3 or 0.30 amp is larger than 0.15 amp (see Job 2-8, Example 2-28).

$$E_b = I_b \times R_b \qquad\qquad (2\text{-}1)$$
$$41.8 = 0.3 \times R_b$$

$$R_b = \frac{41.8}{0.3} = 139 \text{ ohms} \qquad \textit{Ans.}$$

3. Find the wattage rating.

$$P = I^2R = (0.3)^2 \times 139 = 0.09 \times 139 = 12.5 \text{ watts} \qquad (7\text{-}4)$$
$$\text{Wattage rating} = 2 \times P = 2 \times 12.5 = 25 \text{ watts} \qquad \textit{Ans.}$$

b. The series-heater circuit requires 0.3 amp, but this current is too large for the 12SA7 tube, which can carry only 0.15 amp.   Here, then, is our bottleneck.   Something must be done to allow the extra current to make a detour *around* the 12SA7 tube.   This is accomplished by a *shunt resistor* R_s in *parallel* with the 12SA7 heater which will detour the extra current *around* the tube from *A* to *B*.   In order to find the value of this shunt resistor, we must know its voltage drop and the current through it.

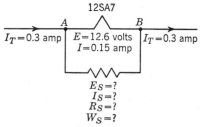

FIG. 8-9. The shunt R_s carries the excess current around the tube.

Finding the shunt current.   In Fig. 8-9, the 0.3 amp in the circuit will divide at point *A*.   The tube needs 0.15 amp.

If we subtract this 0.15 amp from the 0.3 amp coming in to the tube, we shall get the current to be drawn off by the shunt (I_s).

$$I_T = I_s + I_{\text{tube}} \qquad\qquad (5\text{-}2)$$
$$0.3 = I_s + 0.15$$
$$0.3 - 0.15 = I_s$$
$$I_s = 0.15 \text{ amp}$$

Finding the shunt voltage.   Since the shunt is in parallel with the tube heater, they both will receive the *same voltage*.

$$E_s = E_{\text{tube}} = 12.6 \text{ volts} \qquad\qquad (5\text{-}1)$$

Find the shunt resistance.

$$E_s = I_s \times R_s \qquad\qquad (2\text{-}1)$$
$$12.6 = 0.15 \times R_s$$

$$R_s = \frac{12.6}{0.15} = 84 \text{ ohms} \qquad \textit{Ans.}$$

Find the wattage rating of the shunt resistor.

$$P = I^2R = (0.15)^2 \times 84 = 0.0225 \times 84 = 1.89 \text{ watts} \qquad (7\text{-}4)$$
Wattage rating $= 2 \times P = 2 \times 1.89 = 3.78$ or 4 watts   *Ans.*

Example 8-11. An a-c–d-c phonograph amplifier uses a 70L7 rectifier amplifier (70 volts, 0.15 amp) and a 12SK7 (12.6 volts, 0.15 amp) in series with a 230-ohm resistor for operation from a 117-volt line. If the 12SK7 is replaced with a 6AC5 (6.3 volts, 0.4 amp), find (*a*) the new ballast resistor and (*b*) the required shunt resistor.

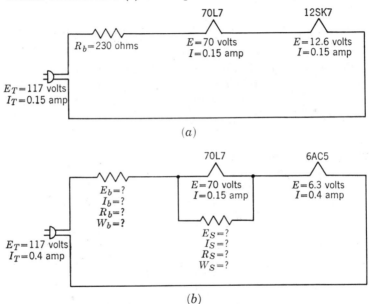

Fig. 8-10. (*a*) Original circuit.   (*b*) Replacement circuit.

Solution: The diagrams for the circuit are shown in Fig. 8-10.
a. 1. Find the voltage to be used up by the ballast resistor.

$$E_T = E_b + E_1 + E_2 \qquad (4\text{-}2)$$
$$117 = E_b + 70 + 6.3$$
$$117 = E_b + 76.3$$
$$117 - 76.3 = E_b$$
$$E_b = 40.7 \text{ volts}$$

2. Find the ballast resistor. The series current and therefore the ballast current must be the *largest* current drawn by any tube in the circuit. The largest current is the 0.4 amp drawn by the 6AC5.

$$E_b = I_b \times R_b \qquad (2\text{-}1)$$
$$40.7 = 0.4 \times R_b$$
$$R_b = \frac{40.7}{0.4} = 102 \text{ ohms} \qquad Ans.$$

3. Find the wattage rating of the ballast resistor.

$$P = I^2R = (0.4)^2 \times 102 = 0.16 \times 102 = 16.3 \text{ watts}$$
$$\text{Wattage rating} = 2 \times P = 2 \times 16.3 = 33 \text{ watts} \qquad Ans.$$

b. The 6AC5 requires 0.4 amp, but this is too large a current for the 70L7, which can carry only 0.15 amp. Therefore, a shunt must be placed around the 70L7 as shown in Fig. 8-10*b* to carry the excess current.

Finding the shunt current:

$$I_T = I_s + I_{\text{tube}} \qquad (5\text{-}2)$$
$$0.4 = I_s + 0.15$$
$$0.4 - 0.15 = I_s$$
$$I_s = 0.25 \text{ amp}$$

Finding the shunt voltage: Since the shunt is in parallel with the tube heater, they both will receive the *same voltage.*

$$E_s = E_{\text{tube}} = 70 \text{ volts} \qquad (5\text{-}1)$$

Find the shunt resistance.

$$E_s = I_s \times R_s \qquad (2\text{-}1)$$
$$70 = 0.25 \times R_s$$
$$R_s = \frac{70}{0.25} = 280 \text{ ohms} \qquad Ans.$$

Find the wattage rating of the shunt resistor.

$$P = I^2R = (0.25)^2 \times 280 = 0.0625 \times 280 = 17.5 \text{ watts}$$
$$\text{Wattage rating} = 2 \times P = 2 \times 17.5 = 35 \text{ watts} \qquad Ans.$$

Problems

1. A 6BQ6 tube (6.3 volts, 1.2 amp) is to be operated in a series-heater circuit with a tube rated at 12.6 volts and 0.3 amp as shown in Fig. 8-11. Find the shunt resistor needed and its wattage rating.

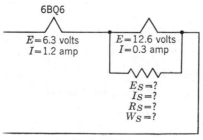

6BQ6

$E = 6.3$ volts
$I = 1.2$ amp

$E = 12.6$ volts
$I = 0.3$ amp

$E_S = ?$
$I_S = ?$
$R_S = ?$
$W_S = ?$

Fig. 8-11

2. A pilot light rated at 6.3 volts and 0.15 amp is to be connected in the circuit shown in Fig. 8-12. Find the resistance and wattage rating of R_b and R_s.

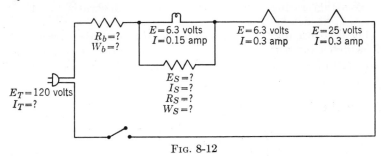

Fig. 8-12

3. If a 12SJ7 (12.6 volts, 0.15 amp) is substituted for a 25B6G (25 volts, 0.3 amp) in a 0.3-amp series-heater circuit, find the ballast and shunt resistors needed.

4. The heaters of a four-tube pentode beam-power receiver are connected in series as shown in Fig. 8-13. Find the resistance and wattage rating of the ballast resistor and the shunt resistors.

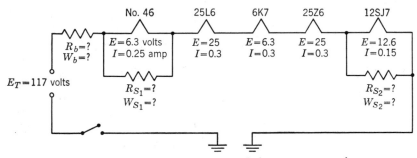

Fig. 8-13. Heater circuit for a pentode beam-power receiver.

5. What resistance must be placed in parallel with the ammeter shown in Fig. 8-14 in order that not more than 0.06 amp flows through the meter? The meter resistance is 30 ohms.

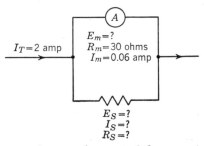

Fig. 8-14. The shunt resistor carries most of the current *around* the meter.

6. Several years ago, the standard a-c–d-c five-tube receiver used the following tubes in a 0.3-amp heater circuit: 6SA7, 6SK7, 6SQ7, 25L6, and 25Z5. (a) Find the ballast resistor needed to operate on 120 volts. If the 6SA7 is replaced with a 12SA7 (12.6 volts, 0.15 amp) and the 25L6 is replaced with a 50L6 (50 volts, 0.15 amp), find (b) the new ballast resistor and (c) the shunts required.

7. The heaters of a 6SJ7, a 6SK7, a 6SQ7, a 25L6, and a 25Z5 used in a tuned r-f receiver are connected in series in a 0.3-amp circuit. If the 25L6 is replaced with a 35L6 (35 volts, 0.15 amp), what is the resistance of the ballast resistor and shunt resistor when the line voltage is 110 volts?

8. A three-way portable receiver uses a IR5 (1.4 volts, 0.05 amp), a 1U4 (1.4 volts, 0.05 amp), a 1U5 (1.4 volts, 0.05 amp), and a 3V4 (1.4 volts, 0.1 amp) with the heaters in series. If the selenium rectifier delivers 110 volts, find the filament dropping resistor and the shunt across the IR5, IU4, and IU5. If individual shunts were used, what would be their values?

9. The Crosley model A 177 receiver uses two 6K7G, a 6A8G, and a 6R7G, all rated at 6.3 volts and 0.3 amp; two 6V6G (6.3 volts, 0.45 amp); and a 6W5G (6.3 volts, 0.9 amp). (a) Find the required ballast resistor. (b) Find the shunt resistor needed across the string of 0.3-amp tubes. (c) Find the shunt resistor needed across the two 6V6G tubes. The line voltage is 117 volts.

10. The Belmont model 526 receiver uses a 5Y3GT (5 volts, 2 amp), a 6K6GT (6.3 volts, 0.4 amp), and a 6Q7G, a 6K7, and a 6A8G, all rated at 6.3 volts and 0.3 amp. The heaters are in series with a 110-volt source. Find (a) the required ballast resistor, (b) the shunt resistor across the string of 0.3-amp tubes, and (c) the shunt resistor for the 6K6GT tube.

Test—Applications of Series and Parallel Circuits

1. Change (a) 0.046 amp to milliamperes, (b) 2.5 kw to watts, (c) 160 mv to volts, (d) 0.00008 farad to microfarads, (e) 30,000 ohms to Megohms.

2. What series resistor is required to operate a 6.3-volt 150-ma tube from a 12-volt battery? Find its wattage rating.

3. Find the cathode resistor for a 6CL6 power pentode if the grid bias needed is −2 volts, the plate current is 30 ma, and the screen current is 7 ma.

4. The Crosley model 10 (1940) receiver uses a 6SK7GT, a 6J7GT, a 25L6GT, and a 25Z6GT with the heaters in series at 0.3 amp. Find the ballast resistor needed for operation from a 117-volt line.

5. A 6BQ7A r-f amplifier (6.3 volts, 0.4 amp) is to be operated in a series-heater circuit with a tube rated at 12.6 volts and 0.3 amp. Find the shunt resistor required and its wattage rating.

JOB 8-6: EXTENDING THE RANGE OF AN AMMETER

An ammeter is a device which is used to measure the current in an electrical circuit. To do this, it must always be inserted directly into the line whose current is to be measured. It is essentially a coil of very fine wire which turns in proportion to the current flowing through it. A pointer attached to the coil moves over a dial and indicates the value of the current. The weight of the coil must be very small in order that it be able to react to the current in it. This weight factor necessitates the use of very fine wire which can carry only about 0.05 amp at best. Yet we can use this ammeter to measure much larger currents by taking advantage of the fact that current in a parallel circuit will divide—the large current flowing through the small resistance and the small current flowing through the large resistance.

Range of an Ammeter. The *range* of an ammeter indicates the value of current required to cause the pointer to swing over the entire scale. This is called "full-scale deflection." Ranges are indicated as "0–1 ma," "0–100 ma," etc. Thus:

0–1 ma requires 1 ma for full-scale deflection.

0–100 ma requires 100 ma for full-scale deflection.

0–10 amp requires 10 amp for full-scale deflection.

Extending the Range of an Ammeter. Suppose we had a milliammeter whose range was 0–1 ma. This means that we can use it to measure currents only up to 1 ma but *not larger* than 1 ma. If we had to measure currents larger than 1 ma, we would need another meter. But this would not be necessary if we could extend the ability of our present meter to read and measure larger currents.

This can be accomplished by connecting a low-resistance resistor called a *shunt* in parallel with the meter. If we keep the shunt resistance small enough, most of the current in the line will pass through the shunt and *not* through the delicate coil of the meter. The object is to use a shunt of such a value that the current in the line will divide so as to keep the current flowing in the coil unchanged. Thus, using a 0–1-ma milliammeter, if the range is to be extended to read 0–50 ma, the shunt should carry 49 ma and the coil should carry its original 1 ma. If the range is to be extended to read 100 ma, then the shunt should carry 99 ma and the coil of the meter should carry its original 1 ma. In general, with *any* shunt, the current through the coil for full-scale deflection is the current necessary for full-scale deflection *before* using the shunt.

Problem. Extend the range of a 0–1-ma milliammeter to carry currents up to 50 ma. In order to carry currents larger than 1 ma, a shunt must be placed in *parallel* with the meter as shown in Fig. 8-15.

The line current I will divide at point A. If the correct shunt is used, the original 1 ma will flow through the meter and the remaining 49 ma will flow through the shunt. In effect, the pointer will cover the full scale (owing to the 1 ma) but it will be indicating the full 50 ma. We shall need a formula to find the shunt needed to extend the range to any value.

In Fig. 8-15,

$$R_s = \frac{E_s'}{I_s} \qquad (2\text{-}1)$$

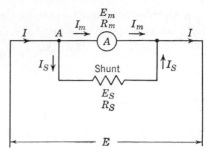

FIG. 8-15. A shunt is placed in parallel with an ammeter. I = line current to be measured, E_m = voltage drop across meter, I_m = current through meter, R_m = resistance of meter, E_s = voltage drop across shunt, I_s = current through shunt, R_s = resistance of shunt.

but since the meter and the shunt are in parallel,

$$E_s = E_m \qquad\qquad (5\text{-}1)$$

therefore,

$$R_s = \frac{E_m}{I_s}$$

but

$$E_m = I_m \times R_m \qquad (2\text{-}1)$$

therefore,

$$R_s = \frac{I_m \times R_m}{I_s} \qquad (8\text{-}2)$$

And since

$$I = I_m + I_s \qquad (5\text{-}2)$$

by transposing,

$$I_s = I - I_m \qquad (8\text{-}3)$$

By substituting this value of I_s in formula (8-2), we obtain

Formula

$$R_s = \frac{I_m \times R_m}{I - I_m} \qquad (8\text{-}4)$$

In this formula, the resistance of the meter must be known, and it is usually obtainable from the manufacturer.

Example 8-12. A Weston model 430 0–1-ma milliammeter has a resistance of 92 ohms. What shunt is necessary to extend its range up to 50 ma?

Solution:

Given: $I_m = 1$ ma $= 0.001$ amp   Find: $R_s = ?$
         $R_m = 92$ ohms
         $I = 50$ ma $= 0.05$ amp

$$R_s = \frac{I_m \times R_m}{I - I_m} = \frac{0.001 \times 92}{0.05 - 0.001} = \frac{0.092}{0.049} = 1.88 \text{ ohms} \qquad Ans.$$

A simpler formula to extend the range of ammeters may be found by a series of algebraic manipulations on formula (8-4).

$$R_s = \frac{I_m \times R_m}{I - I_m} \tag{8-4}$$

or

$$R_s = R_m \frac{I_m}{I - I_m}$$

Inverting and dividing the multiplier of R_m gives

$$R_s = R_m \div \frac{I - I_m}{I_m}$$

Dividing $I - I_m$ by I_m,

$$R_s = R_m \div \left(\frac{I}{I_m} - 1\right)$$

Now, if we define $\dfrac{I}{I_m}$ as N, the multiplying factor,

$$R_s = R_m \div (N - 1) \tag{8-5}$$

Formula

$$R_s = \frac{R_m}{N - 1} \tag{8-6}$$

where R_s = shunt resistor

R_m = resistance of the meter

N = multiplying factor, or $\dfrac{\text{max new range } (I)}{\text{max old range } (I_m)}$ (8-5)

Example 8-13. A Weston model 433 0–100-ma milliammeter has a resistance of 49 ohms. Find the shunt resistor necessary to extend its range to give maximum deflection at 750 ma.

Solution:

Given: Old range = 100 ma   Find: R_s = ?

New range = 750 ma

R_m = 49 ohms

Multiplying factor $N = \dfrac{\text{max new range}}{\text{max old range}} = \dfrac{750}{100} = 7.5$ (8-5)

$R_s = \dfrac{R_m}{N - 1} = \dfrac{49}{7.5 - 1} = \dfrac{49}{6.5} = 7.5$ ohms   *Ans.* (8-6)

Problems

1. Find the shunt necessary to extend the range of a 0–1-ma milliammeter whose resistance is 27 ohms to read 0–10 ma.

2. A 0–1-ma milliammeter has a resistance of 5 ohms.   What shunt resistor is necessary to give a full-scale reading of 51 ma?

3. Find the shunt needed for the milliammeter of Prob. 2 which will permit full-scale deflection at 0.1 amp.

4. A Weston model 45, 0–100-ma milliammeter has a resistance of 0.5 ohm. Find the shunt needed to extend its range to read 0–300 ma.

5. A Weston model 1, 0–15-ma milliammeter has a resistance of 2.24 ohms. Find the shunt needed to extend its range to read 0–60 ma.

6. Full-scale deflection results when 25 ma flows through an ammeter of 25 ohms resistance.   Find the shunt resistance needed to extend its range to read (*a*) 250 ma, (*b*) 500 ma, and (*c*) 1 amp.

7. A Weston model 45, 0–3-amp ammeter has a resistance of 5 ohms.   Find the shunt needed to extend its range to read 0–75 amp.

8. When the coil current in a meter is 10 ma, the pointer deflects past a full scale of 100 divisions.   If the coil resistance is 15 ohms, find the shunts needed to extend its range to read (*a*) 0–1 amp and (*b*) 0–5 amp.

JOB 8-7: READING AMMETERS OF EXTENDED RANGE

Example 8-14. The range of a 0–100-ma milliammeter was increased to read 0–1 amp.   Find the true current flowing when the meter reads 60 ma.

Solution:

Given: Old range = 100 ma   Find: $I = ?$
   New range = 1 amp = 1,000 ma
    $I_m = 60$ ma

The increase in range was from 100 to 1,000 ma.

$$N = \frac{\text{max new range}}{\text{max old range}} = \frac{1,000}{100} = 10 \qquad (8\text{-}5)$$

Therefore all readings will be increased 10 times, or a reading of 60 ma really means

$$60 \times 10 = 600 \text{ ma or } 0.6 \text{ amp} \qquad Ans.$$

Example 8-15. A model 221-T Triplett 0–1-ma milliammeter has a resistance of 55 ohms.   When it is shunted with a 2-ohm resistor, the meter reads 0.5 ma.   Find the true current.

Solution:

Given: $I_m = 0.5$ ma   Find: $I = ?$
   $R_m = 55$ ohms
   $R_s = 2$ ohms

In this problem we do not know the increase in range and cannot use the method shown in the last example.   However, we can find the shunt current by formula (8-2). The line current I may then be found by formula (5-2).

$$R_s = \frac{I_m \times R_m}{I_s} \qquad (8\text{-}2)$$

$$\frac{2}{1} = \frac{0.5 \times 55}{I_s}$$

$$2 \times I_s = 0.5 \times 55$$

$$I_s = \frac{27.5}{2} = 13.8 \text{ ma}$$

The line current may now be found.

$$I = I_m + I_s = 0.5 + 13.8 = 14.3 \text{ ma} \qquad Ans. \qquad (5\text{-}2)$$

Note: Since the shunt usually carries most of the line current, the shunt current is very often used as the line current.

Problems

1. The range of a 0–1-ma milliammeter was increased to read 0–50 ma. Find the true current when the meter reads 0.3 ma.

2. The range of a 0–0.1-amp ammeter was increased to read 0–1 amp. Find the true current when the meter reads 0.07 amp.

3. A 0–1-ma milliammeter of 25 ohms resistance is used with a 0.25-ohm shunt. What is the true current when the meter reads 0.4 ma?

4. A Weston model 45, 0–3-amp ammeter of 5 ohms resistance is used with a 0.1-ohm shunt. What is the true current when the meter reads 0.6 amp?

5. A 0–1-amp ammeter of 10 ohms resistance is used with a 0.1-ohm shunt. What is the true current when the meter reads 0.7 amp?

6. A 0–10-ma milliammeter of 10 ohms resistance is used with a 0.2-ohm shunt. What is the true current when the meter reads 2 ma?

JOB 8-8: USING VOLTMETERS AS AMMETERS

A voltmeter is really an ammeter with a high resistance connected in series with the moving coil. It can be used as an ammeter if a suitable shunt is connected across it. If a voltmeter is substituted for the ammeter in Fig. 8-15,

$$R_s = \frac{E_s}{I_s} \qquad (2\text{-}1)$$

but since the meter and the shunt are in parallel,

$$E_s = E_m \qquad (5\text{-}1)$$

and
$$R_s = \frac{E_m}{I_s} \qquad (8\text{-}7)$$

and since I is practically equal to I_s, we obtain

Formula

$$R_s = \frac{E_m}{I} \tag{8-8}$$

where R_s = shunt resistor, ohms

E_m = maximum voltage reading, volts

I = line current, amp

Example 8-16. A 0–50-mv millivoltmeter whose resistance is 250 ohms (Weston model 622) is to be used as a 0–0.1-amp ammeter. Find the needed shunt resistor. What is the true current if the meter reads 20 mv when measuring a current?

Solution:

Given: E_m = 50 mv = 0.05 volts   Find: R_s = ?

I = 0.1 amp   True current = ?

Meter reading = 20 mv = 0.02 volt

1. Find the shunt resistor.

$$R_s = \frac{E_m}{I} = \frac{0.05}{0.1} = 0.5 \text{ ohm} \qquad Ans. \tag{8-8}$$

2. Find the true current when the meter reads 20 mv.

Since the entire range of the voltmeter now represents a full-scale current, the true current is equal to some fraction of the full-scale current. Thus,

$$\text{True current} = \frac{\text{actual voltage reading}}{\text{max voltage reading}} \times \text{full-scale current} \tag{8-9}$$

In this problem, since the entire range of 50 mv now represents the full-scale current of 0.1 amp, a reading of 20 mv will represent

$$\text{True current} = \frac{20 \text{ mv}}{50 \text{ mv}} \times 0.1 = \frac{0.2}{5} = 0.04 \text{ amp} \qquad Ans.$$

Problems

1. A 0–30-mv millivoltmeter of 100 ohms resistance is used as a milliammeter with a 0–150-ma range. Find the necessary shunt resistor.

2. Find the shunt resistor needed to change the meter of Prob. 1 into an ammeter with a range of (*a*) 500 ma, (*b*) 750 ma, and (*c*) 1 amp.

3. If the meter of Prob. 1 reads 20 mv, what will be the true current when the meter is shunted for ranges of (*a*) 150 ma, (*b*) 500 ma, (*c*) 750 ma, and (*d*) 1 amp?

4. A Weston model 1, 0–10-mv millivoltmeter of 4 ohms resistance is to be used as an ammeter with ranges of (*a*) 0.2 amp, (*b*) 0.3 amp, and (*c*) 0.6 amp. Find the shunts needed for each range.

5. If the millivoltmeter of Prob. 4 reads 3 mv, what will be the true current indicated on each of the ranges found in Prob. 4?

JOB 8-9: USING AMMETERS AS VOLTMETERS

A voltmeter is a device which is used to measure the difference in electrical pressure across two points in a circuit. To do this, the instrument must be placed in parallel with the portion of the circuit

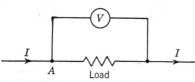

being tested as shown in Fig. 8-16. If the resistance of the voltmeter is low, the current in the line will divide at A and the large current will flow through the moving coil of the meter and burn it out. To avoid this, the resistance of the moving coil is increased by adding a

FIG. 8-16. A voltmeter is always connected in parallel across the ends of the part being tested.

high resistance in *series* with the coil. These resistors are called *multipliers*. Essentially, a voltmeter is really an ammeter with a series resistor. This extra resistance holds down the current to the value required for full-scale deflection when the full-scale voltage is applied to it. For example, suppose we have a 0–1-ma milliam-
meter whose resistance is 50 ohms.
How can we adjust it to read up
to 50 volts?

What we really want is to have
the pointer swing over the complete
scale when 50 volts is applied. At
present, $I = E/R = 50/50 = 1$ amp
or 1,000 ma. But the meter can
safely carry only 1 ma. Evidently
something must be done to prevent
1,000 ma from flowing through a
coil which can handle only 1 ma.
This is accomplished as shown in
Fig. 8-17 by inserting a resistor in

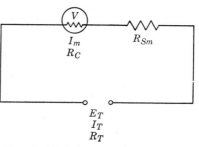

FIG. 8-17. A large resistance R_{sm} is connected in series with the moving coil of a voltmeter in order to reduce the current through it. I_m = meter current, R_c = resistance of moving coil, R_{sm} = resistance of series multiplier, E_t = full-scale voltage desired, I_t = total line current, R_t = total resistance of the series combination.

series with the coil which will reduce the current from 1,000 ma down to the 1 ma required for full-scale deflection. The formula for this series multiplier is derived as follows.

In Fig. 8-17,

$$R_T = \frac{E_T}{I_T} \qquad (4\text{-}7)$$

But in a series circuit,

$$I_T = I_m \qquad (4\text{-}1)$$

Therefore,

$$R_T = \frac{E_T}{I_m}$$

And since

$$R_T = R_c + R_{sm} \qquad (4\text{-}3)$$

$$R_c + R_{sm} = \frac{E_T}{I_m} \qquad (8\text{-}10)$$

However, since R_c is so small in comparison with R_{sm}, it may be neglected. This gives

Formula

$$R_{sm} = \frac{E_T}{I_m} \qquad (8\text{-}11)$$

where R_{sm} = resistance of the series multiplier, ohms

E_T = full-scale voltmeter reading, volts

I_m = ammeter reading, amp

Example 8-17. A 0–1-ma milliammeter of 50 ohms resistance is to read up to 50 volts. (*a*) Find the series multiplier needed. (*b*) What is the voltage when the meter reads 0.6 ma?

Solution:

Given: E_T = 50 volts   Find: R_{sm} = ?

I_m = 1 ma = 0.001 amp E_T = ?

Ammeter reading = I_T = 0.6 ma = 0.0006 amp

a. $R_{sm} = \dfrac{E_T}{I_m} = \dfrac{50}{0.001} = 50{,}000$ ohms   *Ans.*   (8-11)

b. $E_T = I_T \times R_T$ (4-7)

          $E_T = 0.0006 \times 50{,}000 = 30$ volts   *Ans.*

Example 8-18. A 0–25-ma milliammeter of 9 ohms resistance is to read up to 2.5 volts as a voltmeter. (*a*) Find the series resistor needed. (*b*) If the meter reads 15 ma, what is the indicated voltage?

Solution:

Given: E_T = 2.5 volts   Find: R_{sm} = ?

I_m = 25 ma = 0.025 amp E_T = ?

Ammeter reading = I_T = 15 ma = 0.015 amp

a. $R_{sm} = \dfrac{E_T}{I_m} = \dfrac{2.5}{0.025} = 100$ ohms   (8-11)

Up to now, we have been neglecting the resistance of the moving coil because it generally is very small in comparison with the resistance of the series multiplier. However, when the series resistor is fairly close in value to the resistance of the coil, the coil resistance must be taken into account.

$$R_c + R_{sm} = \frac{E_T}{I_m} \qquad (8\text{-}10)$$

Transposing the R_c,

$$R_{sm} = \frac{E_T}{I_m} - R_c \qquad (8\text{-}12)$$

Therefore $\qquad R_{sm} = 100 - 9 = 91$ ohms $\qquad Ans.$

    $b.$ $E_T = I_T \times R_T = 0.015 \times 100 = 1.5$ volts $\qquad Ans.$ (4-7)

Problems

1. What series resistor is needed to change a 0–1-ma milliammeter of 50 ohms resistance into a 0–100-volt voltmeter? What is the true voltage when the meter reads 0.8 ma?

2. What series resistor is needed to change the milliammeter of Prob. 1 into a 0–6-volt voltmeter?

3. The resistance of a meter is 6 ohms and needs 0.01 amp for full-scale deflection. Find the series resistor needed to form a 0–100-volt voltmeter. What is the voltage when the meter reads 0.004 amp?

4. If 0.0075 amp produces a maximum reading on an ammeter, find the series resistor needed to change it into a voltmeter capable of reading up to (a) 15 volts, (b) 30 volts, and (c) 150 volts.

5. The moving coil of a galvanometer has a resistance of 7 ohms. A current of 0.01 amp causes full-scale deflection of the pointer. Find the series resistor needed to give full-scale deflection at (a) 150 volts and (b) 300 volts.

6. A 0–50-ma milliammeter of 10 ohms resistance is to read up to 5 volts as a voltmeter. Find the series resistor needed. If the meter reads 32 ma, what is the voltage indicated by this reading?

JOB 8-10: EXTENDING THE RANGE OF VOLTMETERS

As we learned in the last job, a milliammeter can be converted into a voltmeter capable of reading values of voltage of 50, 100, 300, or 500 volts. The only difference lies in the value of the series resistor connected to the milliammeter. It is possible to use one milliammeter to read all these different ranges if the correct resistances can be placed in the instrument with an arrangement for disconnecting one resistance and connecting another in series. Commercial meters are available which do this by a variety of switching arrangements.

Ohms per Volt. A perfect meter should only test the current but should not use any of the current in the circuit for itself. This is actually impossible, since some current, however small, is needed to operate the meter. The best, or most sensitive, meters, are those which use as little current as possible. The more resistance that can be placed in a meter and still have it read 1 volt, the less the current that is drawn. This means that the meter will use very little current for itself and will have a high sensitivity. Sensitivity is usually expressed as the number of ohms needed to read 1 volt, or the ohms per volt.

Formula

$$\frac{R}{v} = \frac{R_T}{E_T} \qquad (8\text{-}13)$$

where R/v = ohms per volt
$\qquad R_T$ = total meter resistance, ohms
$\qquad E_T$ = maximum scale voltage, volts

Example 8-19. A 50,000-ohm voltmeter reads 50 volts at full scale. What is its sensitivity in ohms per volt?

Solution:

$$\text{Given: } R_T = 50,000 \text{ ohms} \qquad \text{Find: } \frac{R}{v} = ?$$

$$E_T = 50 \text{ volts}$$

$$\frac{R}{v} = \frac{R_T}{E_T} = \frac{50,000}{50} = 1,000 \text{ ohms per volt} \qquad Ans. \qquad (8\text{-}13)$$

Example 8-20. A 0–50-μa meter is to be used as a 0–1-volt voltmeter. Find (a) the needed series resistor and (b) the sensitivity in ohms per volt.

Solution:

$$\text{Given: } E_T = 1 \text{ volt} \qquad\qquad \text{Find: } R_{sm} = ?$$

$$I_m = 50 \ \mu a = 0.00005 \text{ amp} \qquad \frac{R}{v} = ?$$

a. $\qquad R_{sm} = \dfrac{E_T}{I_m} = \dfrac{1}{0.00005} = 20,000 \text{ ohms} \qquad Ans. \qquad (8\text{-}11)$

b. $\qquad \dfrac{R}{v} = \dfrac{R_T}{E_T} = \dfrac{20,000}{1} = 20,000 \text{ ohms per volt} \qquad Ans.$

Example 8-21. A 1,000-ohm-per-volt voltmeter has a range of 0–10 volts. What is the total resistance of the meter?

Solution:

$$\text{Given:} \frac{R}{v} = 1,000 \text{ ohms} \qquad\qquad \text{Find: } R_T = ?$$

$$E_T = 10 \text{ volts}$$

$$\frac{R}{v} = \frac{R_T}{E_T} \tag{8-13}$$

$$1,000 = \frac{R_T}{10}$$

$$R_T = 1,000 \times 10 = 10,000 \text{ ohms} \qquad Ans.$$

Extending the Range of a Voltmeter. As a review, let us take a 0–1-ma milliammeter of 25 ohms resistance and make a voltmeter of 0–150 volts from it. The series resistor is

$$R_{sm} = \frac{E_T}{I_m} = \frac{150}{0.001} = 150,000 \text{ ohms} \tag{8-11}$$

If this 150,000 ohms is placed in series with the moving coil of the milliammeter, we shall have a voltmeter capable of reading values up to 150 volts. Now, suppose we want our voltmeter to read up to 750 instead of only 150 volts? The series resistor needed is

$$R_{sm} = \frac{E_T}{I_m} = \frac{750}{0.001} = 750,000 \text{ ohms} \tag{8-11}$$

But the meter already contains 150,000 ohms. Therefore, to increase the range from 150 up to 750 volts, an additional resistance of

$$750,000 - 150,000 = 600,000 \text{ ohms}$$

must be placed in series with the coil.

. But this method is too long. Perhaps it can be done in a simpler manner. We wanted our meter to read 750 volts (needs 750,000 ohms) instead of 150 volts (needs 150,000 ohms). The 750 volts is 5 times as much as 150 volts, and we therefore need 5 times as much resistance as is in the meter for the 150-volt range. The resistance already in the meter can then be subtracted as before to find the needed additional resistance to up the range to 750 volts. The increase in voltage (the 5 times) represents the multiplying power we desire. Therefore, the series resistor R_s which must be added to extend the range of an existing voltmeter is given by

$$R_s = (\text{multiplying power} \times R_{\text{meter}}) - R_{\text{meter}}$$

Another way to write this is

Formula

$$R_s = (MP - 1) \times R_{\text{meter}} \qquad (8\text{-}14)$$

where R_s = series resistor to be added, ohms

$$MP = \frac{\text{max new voltage}}{\text{max old voltage}} \qquad (8\text{-}15)$$

R_{meter} = resistance of the meter, ohms

Let us use this formula to solve the problem above.

$$MP = \frac{\text{max new voltage}}{\text{max old voltage}} = \frac{750}{150} = 5 \qquad (8\text{-}15)$$

$$R_s = (MP - 1) \times R_m \qquad (8\text{-}14)$$
$$= (5 - 1) \times 150,000 = 4 \times 150,000 = 600,000 \text{ ohms} \qquad Ans.$$

Note: The resistance of the meter must be known in order to use formula (8-14). If it is not given, it may be found by connecting the meter in series with a milliammeter across some voltage within its range as shown in Fig. 8-18. The resistance of the meter may then be found by

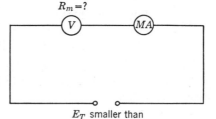

E_T smaller than range of voltmeter

Fig. 8-18. Circuit to find the resistance of a voltmeter.

Formula

$$R_m = \frac{\text{voltmeter reading (volts)}}{\text{ammeter reading (amp)}} \qquad (8\text{-}16)$$

Example 8-22. A 0–10-volt 10,000-ohm voltmeter is to be extended to read 100 volts. What additional series resistance is needed?

Solution:

Given: Max new voltage = 100 volts   Find: R_s = ?
        Max old voltage = 10 volts
        R_{meter} = 10,000 ohms

$$MP = \frac{\text{max new voltage}}{\text{max old voltage}} = \frac{100}{10} = 10 \qquad (8\text{-}15)$$

$$R_s = (MP - 1) \times R_m \qquad (8\text{-}14)$$
$$= (10 - 1) \times 10,000 = 9 \times 10,000 = 90,000 \text{ ohms} \qquad Ans.$$

Example 8-23. A 1,000-ohm-per-volt 0–10-volt voltmeter is to be extended to read 0–100 volts. What is the needed series resistance?

Solution:

$$\text{Given:} \frac{R}{v} = 1,000 \text{ ohms} \qquad \text{Find: } R_s = ?$$

Max new voltage = 100 volts
Max old voltage = 10 volts

Before we can find the series resistance, we must know the resistance of the meter and the multiplying power.

$$\frac{R}{v} = \frac{R_T}{E_T} \qquad (8\text{-}13)$$

$$1,000 = \frac{R_T}{10}$$

$$R_T = 10 \times 1,000 = 10,000 \text{ ohms}$$
$$R_m = 10,000 \text{ ohms} \qquad Ans.$$

$$MP = \frac{\text{max new voltage}}{\text{max old voltage}} = \frac{100}{10} = 10 \qquad Ans. \qquad (8\text{-}15)$$

$$R_s = (MP - 1) \times R_m \qquad\qquad (8\text{-}14)$$
$$= (10 - 1) \times 10,000 = 9 \times 10,000 = 90,000 \text{ ohms} \qquad Ans.$$

Example 8-24. A 0–10-volt voltmeter of 1,000 ohms resistance is extended to read 100 volts. Find the true voltage when the meter reads 5.5 volts.

Solution:

$$\text{Given: } R_m = 1,000 \text{ ohms} \qquad \text{Find: True voltage} = ?$$
Max new voltage = 100 volts
Max old voltage = 10 volts
Meter reading = 5.5 volts

$$MP = \frac{\text{max new voltage}}{\text{max old voltage}} = \frac{100}{10} = 10 \qquad (8\text{-}15)$$

Therefore all readings will be increased 10 times, or a reading of 5.5 volts means

$$5.5 \times 10 = 55 \text{ volts} \qquad Ans.$$

Problems

1. A 1,000-ohm-per-volt 0–10-volt voltmeter is to be extended to read 300 volts. Find (*a*) the series resistor needed and (*b*) the true voltage when the meter reads 5.6 volts.

2. A 0–7.5-mv millivoltmeter whose resistance is 1 ohm is to be extended to read 15 volts. Find (*a*) the series resistor needed and (*b*) the true voltage when the meter reads 6 mv.

3. A 0–50-mv millivoltmeter of 5 ohms resistance is to be extended to read up to 30 volts. Find (*a*) the series resistor needed and (*b*) the true voltage when the meter reads 36 mv.

4. A 0–100-volt voltmeter of 12,000 ohms resistance is to read up to 300 volts. Find the multiplying resistor needed.

5. A voltmeter with a full-scale deflection of 150 volts has a resistance of 17,000 ohms. Find the external series resistance necessary to extend it to read (a) 300 volts and (b) 600 volts.

6. A 1,000-ohm-per-volt 0–1-volt voltmeter is to be extended to read up to 100 volts. Find (a) the series resistor needed and (b) the true voltage when the meter reads 0.7 volt.

7. If the current taken by a 5,000-ohm meter is 1 ma, find the series resistor needed to extend its range to read up to (a) 50 volts, (b) 100 volts, and (c) 150 volts. *Hint:* Find E of the meter by $E = I \times R$.

8. Find the series resistor to be used with a 15,000-ohm voltmeter in order to have its readings multiplied by 5.

JOB 8-11: REVIEW OF METERS

Extending the Range of an Ammeter. Ammeters may be used to measure currents larger than their full-scale deflections by connecting appropriate shunts in parallel with the meter. The value of this shunt resistor may be found by the following formulas:

$$R_s = \frac{I_m \times R_m}{I_s} \qquad (8\text{-}2)$$

$$R_s = \frac{I_m \times R_m}{I - I_m} \qquad (8\text{-}4)$$

$$R_s = \frac{R_m}{N - 1} \qquad (8\text{-}6)$$

where R_s = resistance of the shunt, ohms
I_s = current in the shunt, amp
R_m = resistance of the meter, ohms
I_m = current in the meter, amp
I = line current to be measured, amp
N = multiplying factor which indicates the number of times that the range of the meter is increased

$$N = \frac{\text{max new range}}{\text{max old range}} \qquad (8\text{-}5)$$

Reading Ammeters of Extended Range

1. If the multiplying factor N is known, the true current is equal to the actual reading multiplied by N.

$$\text{True reading} = \text{actual reading} \times N \qquad (8\text{-}17)$$

2. If N is unknown,

a. Find the shunt current by

$$R_s = \frac{I_m \times R_m}{I_s} \qquad (8\text{-}2)$$

b. Find the true current by

$$I = I_m + I_s \qquad (5\text{-}2)$$

Using Voltmeters as Ammeters. A voltmeter may be used as an ammeter by connecting appropriate shunts in parallel with the voltmeter. The value of the shunt resistor is

$$R_s = \frac{E_m}{I} \qquad (8\text{-}8)$$

where R_s = shunt resistor, ohms

E_m = maximum voltage reading, volts

I = maximum line current, amp

Reading Voltmeters Used as Ammeters. The true current may be found by using formula (8-9).

$$\text{True current} = \frac{\text{actual voltage reading}}{\text{max voltage reading}} \times \text{full-scale current} \qquad (8\text{-}9)$$

Using Ammeters as Voltmeters. An ammeter may be used as a voltmeter by placing it in series with appropriate series multiplier resistors. The value of the multiplier resistor is

$$R_{sm} = \frac{E_T}{I_m} \qquad (8\text{-}11)$$

where R_{sm} = resistance of the series multiplier, ohms

E_T = maximum voltage reading, volts

I_m = maximum ammeter reading, amp

In most instances, the resistance of the series multiplier is much larger than the resistance of the moving coil R_c, and so the coil resistance may be neglected. If the coil resistance is 5 per cent or more of the series multiplier resistance, it must be subtracted from the value of E_T/I_m to get the true series multiplier resistance as given by the formula

$$R_{sm} = \frac{E_T}{I_m} - R_c \qquad (8\text{-}12)$$

Reading Ammeters Used as Voltmeters. The true voltage may be found by using formula (4-7).

$$E_T = I_T \times R_T$$

where E_T = true voltage, volts

I_T = actual ammeter reading, amp

R_T = total resistance of the meter = $R_{sm} + R_c$

Extending the Range of Voltmeters.   The range of a voltmeter may be extended by placing it in series with the appropriate series multiplier resistor.

$$R_s = (MP - 1) \times R_{\text{meter}} \qquad (8\text{-}14)$$

where R_s = series resistor to be added, ohms

R_{meter} = resistance of meter, ohms

$$MP = \frac{\text{max new voltage}}{\text{max old voltage}} \qquad (8\text{-}15)$$

Meter Sensitivity.   The sensitivity of a meter is expressed as its resistance in ohms for every volt measured on its scale.   For the same reading of 1 volt, the meter with the larger resistance will draw less current for itself and therefore give more accurate measurements.

$$\frac{R}{v} = \frac{R_T}{E_T} \qquad (8\text{-}13)$$

where R/v = sensitivity, ohms per volt

R_T = total meter resistance, ohms

E_T = maximum scale voltage, volts

Finding the Total Resistance of the Meter

1. Use formula (8-13) to find R_T of the meter.

2. Connect the voltmeter in series with an ammeter across some voltage within its range.   The meter resistance is given by

$$R_m = \frac{\text{voltmeter reading (volts)}}{\text{ammeter reading (amp)}} \qquad (8\text{-}16)$$

Problems

1. A 0–2-ma milliammeter has a resistance of 18 ohms.   Find the parallel shunt resistor which will permit measurements of currents up to 200 ma.

2. The range of a 12-ohm 0–5-ma milliammeter was increased to read 0–50 ma.   Find the true current when the meter reads 4.5 ma.

3. A 0–1-ma milliammeter of 20 ohms resistance is used with a 0.2-ohm shunt in parallel.   Find the true current when the meter reads 0.6 ma.

4. A 0–100-mv millivoltmeter of 40 ohms resistance (Weston model 1) is to be used as an ammeter with a 0–250-ma range.   Find the required shunt resistor.

5. A 0–30-mv millivoltmeter of 100 ohms resistance is to be used as a milliammeter with a 0–180-ma range.   Find (a) the required shunt resistor

and (*b*) the true current when the meter reads (1) 10 mv, (2) 18 mv, and (3) 25 mv.

6. What series resistor is needed to convert a 12-ohm 0–5-ma milliammeter into a 0–50-volt voltmeter?

7. A 0–50-ma milliammeter of 27 ohms resistance is to be converted to read 0–5 volts as a voltmeter. Find the needed series resistor.

8. A 10,000-ohm voltmeter reads 100 volts at full-scale deflection. Find its sensitivity in ohms per volt.

9. A Weston model 5 d-c voltmeter has a sensitivity of 100 ohms per volt and a range of 0–15 volts. Find the total resistance of the meter.

10. A 0–30-volt voltmeter is to be extended to read 150 volts. If the resistance of the meter is 3,000 ohms, find (*a*) the sensitivity, (*b*) the series resistor needed, and (*c*) the true voltage when the meter reads 12 volts.

11. A 100-ohm-per-volt 0–7.5-volt voltmeter is to be extended to read 0–30 volts. Find (*a*) the series multiplier needed and (*b*) the true voltage when the meter reads 3.2 volts.

12. If the current taken by a 1,000-ohm meter is 15 ma, find (*a*) the voltage indicated by the full-scale deflection, (*b*) the sensitivity in ohms per volt, and (*c*) the series multiplier resistor needed to extend the range to read (1) 120 volts and (2) 180 volts.

13. The resistance of a 0–15-ma milliammeter is 3.2 ohms. Find the parallel shunt required to extend the range to 0–100 ma.

14. The range of an 18-ohm 0–3-ma milliammeter was increased to read up to 50 ma. Find the true current when the meter reads 1.7 ma.

15. A 0–0.1-amp ammeter of 1-ohm resistance is to read up to 150 volts as a voltmeter. Find the series resistor needed to make the conversion.

Test—Meters

1. A 0–5-ma milliammeter has a resistance of 12 ohms. Find the shunt resistor which must be connected in parallel in order to increase the range up to 75 ma.

2. The range of a 0–1-ma milliammeter was increased to 0–50 ma. Find the true current when the meter reads 0.65 ma.

3. A 0–5-ma milliammeter of 15 ohms resistance is to be used as a voltmeter with a 0–120-volt range. Find the additional series resistance needed to extend the range of the meter.

4. A 0–10-volt voltmeter of 1,000 ohms resistance is to be extended to read up to 100 volts. Find (*a*) the needed series multiplier resistor and (*b*) the true voltage when the meter reads 5.8 volts.

5. A 1,000-ohm-per-volt 0–25-volt voltmeter is to be extended to read up to 200 volts. Find (*a*) the needed series multiplier resistor and (*b*) the true voltage when the meter reads 13.5 volts.

JOB 8-12: VOLTAGE DIVIDERS

The filter circuit of a radio receiver is designed to smooth out the d-c voltage delivered from the rectifier tube. This voltage may be

300 volts.   However, although some circuits in the receiver may require these 300 volts, other tubes and circuits may need only 180 or only 90 volts.   These different voltages may be obtained by placing a large resistor across the filter output as shown in Fig. 8-19 and tapping the resistor at various points.   This resistor is called a *voltage divider*.

The total voltage of 300 volts appears across points 1 and 4.   If the resistor is divided into three equal parts by taps at points 2 and 3,

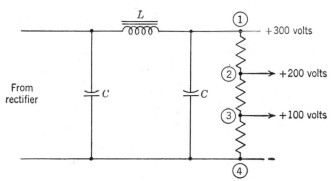

FIG. 8-19. A power-supply voltage divider.

at point 2, which is one-third of the resistor, one-third of the total voltage ($\frac{1}{3} \times 300 = 100$) has been used up.   Therefore only

$$300 - 100 = 200 \text{ volts}$$

will be available at point 2.   At point 3, which is two-thirds of the resistor, two-thirds of the 300 volts ($\frac{2}{3} \times 300 = 200$) has been used up and at point 3 only $300 - 200 = 100$ volts will be available. This will all be true only if the current in all parts of the voltage divider is the same current.   However, the different voltages must be available at different currents, and so the calculations for a working voltage divider are a bit more complicated.

Example 8-25.   Calculate the resistances for the sections of a voltage divider which is to deliver 40 ma at 300 volts, 30 ma at 180 volts, and 20 ma at 90 volts.

Solution: The diagram for the circuit is shown in Fig. 8-20.

1. Determine the current distribution.

Some current will always flow through the voltage divider even when there is no load on it.   This current is called the *bleeder current*.   The bleeder current may be assumed to be the difference between 90 per cent of the current rating of the power transformer and the total cur-

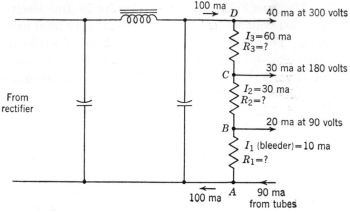

Fig. 8-20

rent drawn by the receiver. In this problem, the receiver needs $40 + 30 + 20$, or 90 ma, and the transformer is rated at 110 ma.

$$90 \text{ per cent of } 110 \text{ ma} = 0.90 \times 110 = 99 \text{ ma}$$
$$\text{Bleeder} = 99 - 90 = 9 \text{ ma or } 10 \text{ ma approximately}$$

At D:

$$I_3 = I \text{ from rectifier} - \text{current to load}$$
$$I_3 = 100 - 40 = 60 \text{ ma}$$

At C:

$$I_2 = I_3 - \text{current to load}$$
$$I_2 = 60 - 30 = 30 \text{ ma}$$

At B:

$$I_1 = I_2 - \text{current to load}$$
$$I_1 = 30 - 20 = 10 \text{ ma}$$

At A:

$$\text{Return from loads} = 40 + 30 + 20 = 90 \text{ ma}$$
$$I \text{ to filter} = \text{bleeder current } I_1 + \text{load current}$$
$$I \text{ to filter} = 10 + 90 = 100 \text{ ma}$$

2. Find the sectional resistances.

For R_3: The voltage drop from D to $C = 300 - 180 = 120$ volts.

$$E_3 = I_3 \times R_3 \qquad\qquad (4\text{-}6)$$
$$120 = 0.06 \times R_3$$
$$R_3 = \frac{120}{0.06} = 2{,}000 \text{ ohms} \qquad Ans.$$

For R_2: The voltage drop from C to $B = 180 - 90 = 90$ volts.

$$E_2 = I_2 \times R_2 \qquad\qquad (4\text{-}5)$$
$$90 = 0.03 \times R_2$$
$$R_2 = \frac{90}{0.03} = 3{,}000 \text{ ohms} \qquad Ans.$$

For R_1: The voltage drop from B to $A = 90 - 0 = 90$ volts.

$$E_1 = I_1 \times R_1 \qquad\qquad (4\text{-}4)$$
$$90 = 0.01 \times R_1$$
$$R_1 = \frac{90}{0.01} = 9{,}000 \text{ ohms} \qquad Ans.$$

Problems

1. Find the resistance of the sections R_1, R_2, and R_3 of the voltage divider shown in Fig. 8-21a.

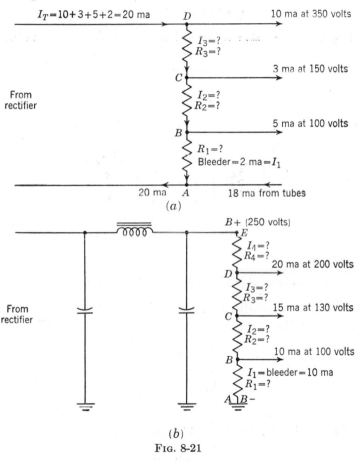

(a)

(b)

FIG. 8-21

2. Find the resistance of the sections R_1, R_2, R_3, and R_4 of the voltage divider shown in Fig. 8-21b. *Hint:* Find the current distribution starting from point A and working up to point E.

3. A power supply is to deliver 45 ma at 150 volts, 30 ma at 100 volts, and 10 ma at 50 volts. Assuming a bleeder current of 5 ma, calculate the resistance of the sections of the voltage divider needed.

4. Design a voltage divider to deliver 70 ma at 350 volts, 40 ma at 250 volts, and 20 ma at 100 volts if the power supply transformer is rated at 155 ma and operates at 90 per cent of its rated value.

5. A power supply is to deliver 60 ma at 250 volts, 5 ma at 100 volts, and 2 ma at 50 volts.   The transformer is rated at 80 ma and operates at 90 per cent of its rated value.   Design a voltage divider to deliver the required currents and voltages.

JOB 8-13: RESISTANCE MEASUREMENT BY THE VOLTAGE-COMPARISON METHOD

In Fig. 8-22, the value of the unknown resistor R_x may be found by

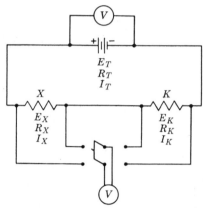

Fig. 8-22. Voltage-comparison method of measuring resistance. X = unknown resistance, K = known standard resistance, R_t = total resistance.

connecting it in series with a known standard resistance R_k and measuring the voltage drops across each.

$$E_x = I_x \times R_x \qquad (4\text{-}4)$$
$$E_k = I_k \times R_k \qquad (4\text{-}5)$$
$$E_T = I_T \times R_T \qquad (4\text{-}7)$$
$$I_T = I_x = I_k \qquad (4\text{-}1)$$

Dividing Eq. (4-4) by Eq. (4-5), and canceling out the equal currents— $I_x = I_k$,

$$\frac{E_x = \overset{1}{\cancel{I_x}} \times R_x}{E_k = \underset{1}{\cancel{I_k}} \times R_k}$$

which gives

$$\frac{E_x}{E_k} = \frac{R_x}{R_k} \qquad (8\text{-}18)$$

Similarly, by dividing Eq. (4-4) by Eq. (4-7),

$$\frac{E_x}{E_T} = \frac{R_x}{R_T} \tag{8-19}$$

These formulas mean that in a series circuit, the voltage across any resistance depends on the value of the resistance—a large voltage appearing across a large resistance and a small voltage appearing across a small resistance. This is discussed in greater detail in Job 11-2.

Example 8-26. Using Fig. 8-22, find the value of the unknown resistance K if the known resistance $R_k = 1,000$ ohms, $E_x = 100$ volts, and $E_k = 25$ volts.

Solution:

Given: $R_k = 1,000$ ohms   Find: $R_x = ?$
$E_x = 100$ volts
$E_k = 25$ volts

$$\frac{E_x}{E_k} = \frac{R_x}{R_k} \tag{8-18}$$

$$\frac{100}{25} = \frac{R_x}{1,000}$$

$$25 \times R_x = 100 \times 1,000$$

$$R_x = \frac{100,000}{25} = 4,000 \text{ ohms} \qquad Ans.$$

Example 8-27. The horizontal hold-control circuit of the RCA television chassis KCS77D is essentially that shown in Fig. 8-23.

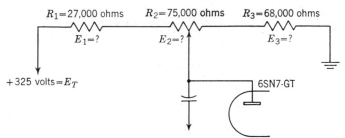

FIG. 8-23. A horizontal hold-control circuit in a television receiver.

Find (*a*) the voltage drop across the 27,000-ohm resistor, (*b*) the voltage drop across the 75,000-ohm resistor, and (*c*) the voltage drop across the 68,000-ohm resistor.

Solution:

a. Find the total resistance of the circuit.

$$R_T = R_1 + R_2 + R_3 \tag{4-3}$$
$$R_T = 27,000 + 75,000 + 68,000 = 170,000 \text{ ohms} \qquad Ans.$$

Find E_1.

$$\frac{E_1}{E_T} = \frac{R_1}{R_T} \tag{8-19}$$

$$\frac{E_1}{325} = \frac{27,000}{170,000}$$

$$\frac{E_1}{325} = \frac{27}{170}$$

$$170 \times E_1 = 325 \times 27$$

$$E_1 = \frac{8,775}{170} = 51.6 \text{ volts} \qquad Ans.$$

b. Find E_2.

$$\frac{E_1}{E_2} = \frac{R_1}{R_2} \tag{8-18}$$

$$\frac{51.6}{E_2} = \frac{27,000}{75,000}$$

$$27 \times E_2 = 51.6 \times 75$$

$$E_2 = \frac{3,870}{27} = 143.3 \text{ volts} \qquad Ans.$$

c. Find E_3.

$$\frac{E_1}{E_3} = \frac{R_1}{R_3} \tag{8-18}$$

$$\frac{51.6}{E_3} = \frac{27,000}{68,000}$$

$$27 \times E_3 = 51.6 \times 68$$

$$E_3 = \frac{3,508.8}{27} = 129.9 \text{ volts} \qquad Ans.$$

Problems

In Probs. 1 to 6, R_k and R_x are connected in series. Find the missing values in each problem.

Problem	R_k	E_k	E_x	R_x	E_T
1	500	10	25	?	
2	50	15.5	70.2	?	
3	10	36.4	40.3	?	
4	100	15	?	250	
5	1,000	?	?	2,000	100 volts
6	15,000	?	?	20,000	120 volts

7. The horizontal hold-control circuit of the Muntz television chassis 17B1 uses a circuit similar to that shown in Fig. 8-23. If $R_1 = 22,000$ ohms, $R_2 = 50,000$ ohms, and $R_3 = 100,000$ ohms, find (a) E_1, (b) E_2, and (c) E_3 if $E_T = 200$ volts.

8. The RCA-Victor model 730 TV1 uses a picture-control circuit as shown in Fig. 8-24. Find the voltage drop across R_1 and R_2.

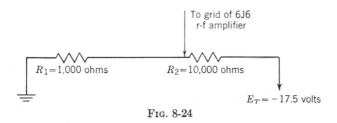

To grid of 6J6
r-f amplifier

$R_1 = 1,000$ ohms $R_2 = 10,000$ ohms

$E_T = -17.5$ volts

FIG. 8-24

9. The Arvin television chassis TE 359 uses a brightness-control circuit essentially as shown in Fig. 8-25. Find the voltage between ground and point A.

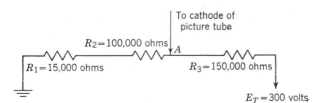

To cathode of
picture tube

$R_2 = 100,000$ ohms

A

$R_1 = 15,000$ ohms $R_3 = 150,000$ ohms

$E_T = 300$ volts

FIG. 8-25. A brightness-control circuit in a television receiver.

10. The Crosley television chassis 466 uses a brightness-control circuit similar to that shown in Fig. 8-25. If R_T equals 5 Megohms and E_T equals 145 volts, find the cathode voltage when the potentiometer arm has covered (a) 1 Megohm and (b) 3.5 Megohms.

JOB 8-14: RESISTANCE MEASUREMENT USING THE WHEATSTONE BRIDGE

The Wheatstone bridge is a device for obtaining accurate measurements of resistance. A diagrammatic sketch of the circuit is shown in Fig. 8-26. The resistors R_1, R_2, R_3, and R_x are arranged in two parallel branches. R_1, R_2, and R_3 are variable *known* resistors, and R_x is the *unknown* resistance. A galvanometer G is connected across the two branches between points B and D. A battery supplies the total current I_T.

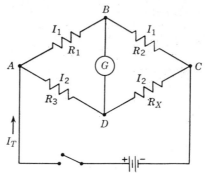

FIG. 8-26. The Wheatstone bridge circuit.

Operation of the Bridge

1. When the circuit is closed, a current I_T will flow through the circuit which divides at point A, current I_1 flowing through the branch ABC (R_1 and R_2) and current I_2 flowing through the branch ADC (R_3 and R_x).

2. The variable resistors are adjusted until the galvanometer indicates no deflection. R_1 and R_2 are usually fixed at some convenient ratio, and then R_3 is varied until the galvanometer reads zero.

3. When there is no deflection of the galvanometer, it indicates that there is no current flowing between points B and D and therefore B and D are at the same voltage level. Under these conditions, we find that

Voltage across AB = voltage across AD or $I_1 \times R_1 = I_2 \times R_3$
Voltage across BC = voltage across DC or $I_1 \times R_2 = I_2 \times R_x$

Dividing one equation by the other gives us the fundamental equation for the Wheatstone bridge.

$$\frac{I_1 \times R_1}{I_1 \times R_2} = \frac{I_2 \times R_3}{I_2 \times R_x}$$

Canceling out the currents I_1 and I_2, we obtain

Formula

$$\frac{R_1}{R_2} = \frac{R_3}{R_x} \qquad\qquad (8\text{-}20)$$

Example 8-28. When a Wheatstone bridge was used, the following readings were obtained: $R_1 = 1,000$ ohms, $R_2 = 10,000$ ohms, and $R_3 = 67.4$ ohms. Find the unknown resistance.

Solution:

Given: $R_1 = 1,000$ ohms   Find: $R_x = ?$
$R_2 = 10,000$ ohms
$R_3 = 67.4$ ohms

$$\frac{R_1}{R_2} = \frac{R_3}{R_x} \qquad\qquad (8\text{-}20)$$

$$\frac{1,000}{10,000} = \frac{67.4}{R_x}$$

$$\frac{1}{10} = \frac{67.4}{R_x}$$

$$R_x = 67.4 \times 10 = 674 \text{ ohms} \qquad Ans.$$

Problems

Find the value of R_x for each problem.

Problem	R_1	R_2	R_3	R_x
1	1,000	10,000	84.3	?
2	10,000	1,000	952.7	?
3	100	10	60.4	?
4	10	1	175.3	?
5	1	10	128.9	?
6	5,000	10,000	823.7	?
7	100	1,000	46.5	?
8	1,000	100	9.16	?
9	10	1	1.6	?
10	1	10	35.79	?

Test—Voltage Dividers and Resistance Measurement

1. In a voltage divider similar to that shown in Fig. 8-21*a*, the loads are 15 ma at 300 volts at *D*, 10 ma at 175 volts at *C*, 5 ma at 100 volts at *B*, and the bleeder current is 2 ma. Find R_3, R_2, and R_1.

2. A 500- and a 700-ohm resistor are connected in series across 120 volts. Find the voltage drop across the 700-ohm resistor.

3. Two resistors are connected in series. If $R_1 = 100$ ohms, $E_1 = 125$ volts, and $E_2 = 500$ volts, find R_2.

4. In a diagram similar to that shown in Fig. 8-25, $R_1 = 30,000$ ohms, $R_2 = 50,000$ ohms, and $R_3 = 160,000$ ohms. If the total voltage is $E_T = 270$ volts, find the voltage between ground and point *A*.

5. When a Wheatstone bridge was used, the following readings were obtained: $R_1 = 100$ ohms, $R_2 = 1,000$ ohms, and $R_3 = 148$ ohms. Find R_x.

CHAPTER 9

EFFICIENCY

JOB 9-1: CHECK-UP ON PER CENT

The efficiency of electrical machinery is expressed as a per cent. The concept of per cent is used throughout the fields of electricity, radio, and television to describe and compare electrical effects. Can you solve the following problems which use per cent? If you have difficulty with any of these problems, turn to Job 9-2, which follows.

Problems

1. What is the possible error in a resistor marked 1,000 ohms if the indicated error (tolerance) is 10 per cent?

2. A solenoid exerts a pull of 0.9 lb at its rated voltage. What pull is exerted at 85 per cent of its rated voltage?

3. A 15-amp fuse carried a 15 per cent overload for 3 sec. What current flowed through the fuse during this time?

4. The plate voltage on a tube might normally vary up to 10 per cent of the rated value. Is a voltage of 200 volts within the normal variation if the rated voltage is 230 volts?

5. The peak voltage of an a-c wave is 141 per cent of the a-c meter reading. Find the peak voltage if the meter reads 50 volts.

6. What is the efficiency of a motor if it uses 20 units of energy and delivers 18 units of energy?

7. What is the efficiency of a transmission line if the power supplied is 4,500 watts and the power delivered is 4,200 watts?

8. A transformer has an efficiency of 96 per cent. If the transformer uses 60 watts, what power will it deliver?

9. The National Electrical Code specifies a maximum of 2 per cent voltage drop in a house line. What is the minimum voltage at a load if the supply voltage is 120 volts?

10. A television mechanic bought $125 worth of tubes at a 35 per cent discount. What did he pay for the tubes?

11. If he was also allowed 2 per cent discount for payment within 10 days, what was his actual cost?

12. A radio mechanic charged the list price of $2.25 for a tube. If the tube cost him $1.80, what was his per cent of profit?

13. A television mechanic estimated that his overhead expenses equaled 20 per cent of his cost. If he charges the list price of $4 for an item, what is the most that he should pay for it?

14. Some storage batteries are shipped dry and filled with electrolyte by the seller. In making up a batch of electrolyte to contain 40 per cent acid, how much acid should be used to make 32 oz of electrolyte?

15. What per cent of the 250 volts rated voltage is a tube receiving if it receives only 225 volts?

JOB 9-2: BRUSH-UP ON PER CENT

The words *per cent* are used to indicate some portion of 100. A mark of 92 per cent on an examination indicates that the student got 92 points out of a possible 100 points. This may also be written as a decimal fraction (0.92) or as a common fraction ($9\frac{2}{100}$), both of which are read as 92 *hundredths*. A per cent indicated by a per cent sign (%) cannot be used in a calculation until it has been changed into an equivalent decimal fraction.

Changing Per Cents to Decimals. Since 92 per cent means $9\frac{2}{100}$, the change to a decimal is made by dividing 92 by 100. This is easily accomplished by moving the decimal point two places to the left as shown in Job 7-6.

Rule: To change a per cent into a decimal, move the decimal point two places to the left and drop the per cent sign.

Example 9-1. Change the following per cents into decimals.

Solution:

$$32\% = 32.\% = 0.32 \qquad Ans.$$
$$8\% = 8.\% = 0.08 \qquad Ans.$$
$$16\tfrac{1}{2}\% = 16.5\% = 0.165 \qquad Ans.$$

Problems

Change the following per cents into decimals:

1. 38%	5. 4%	9. 125%	13. 62.5%	16. 0.9%
2. 60%	6. 26.4%	10. 0.5%	14. 1%	17. 2.25%
3. 6%	7. 3.6%	11. 16⅔%	15. 12.5%	18. 5½%
4. 19%	8. 100%	12. ¾%		

Changing Decimals into Per Cents. To change a decimal into a per cent is to reverse the process of changing a per cent into a decimal.

Rule: To change a decimal into a per cent, move the decimal point two places to the right and add a per cent sign.

Example 9-2.   Change the following decimals into per cents:

Solution:

$$0.20 = 20.\% = 20\% \quad Ans.$$
$$0.06 = 6.\% = 6\% \quad Ans.$$
$$0.125 = 12.5\% \quad Ans.$$
$$1.1 = 110.\% = 110\% \quad Ans.$$
$$2 = 2.00 = 200.\% = 200\% \quad Ans.$$

Problems

Express the following decimals as per cents:

1. 0.50	**4.** 0.075	**7.** 1.00	**10.** 0.092	**13.** 0.7
2. 0.04	**5.** 1.45	**8.** 0.87	**11.** 0.222	**14.** 3
3. 0.2	**6.** 0.008	**9.** 0.625	**12.** 0.15	**15.** 0.055

Changing Common Fractions to Per Cents

Rule: To change a common fraction to a per cent, express the fraction as a decimal; then move the decimal point two places to the right and add a per cent sign.

The decimal equivalents for many of the common fractions may be found in Table 2-1 on page 42.

Example 9-3.   Express the following fractions as per cents.

Solution:

$$\frac{3}{4} = 0.75 = 75\% \quad Ans.$$
$$\frac{1}{2} = 0.50 = 50\% \quad Ans.$$
$$\frac{5}{8} = 0.625 = 62.5\% \quad Ans.$$

If the fraction is not on the decimal equivalent chart, change the fraction into a decimal by dividing the numerator by the denominator as shown in Job 2-8.

Example 9-4.   Express $\frac{8}{25}$ as a per cent.

Solution:

$$\frac{8}{25} = 25\overline{\smash{\big)}\,8.00} \quad \begin{array}{r} 0.32 = 32\% \quad Ans. \\ \end{array}$$

$$\begin{array}{r} 0.32 = 32\% \quad Ans. \\ 25)\overline{8.00} \\ -7\,5 \\ \hline 50 \\ -50 \\ \hline 0 \end{array}$$

Problems

Express the following common fractions as per cents:

1. $\frac{1}{4}$	5. $\frac{5}{8}$	9. $\frac{3}{6}$	13. $\frac{2}{3}$	17. $\frac{16}{48}$
2. $\frac{3}{8}$	6. $\frac{3}{16}$	10. $\frac{9}{10}$	14. $\frac{5}{6}$	18. $\frac{12}{30}$
3. $\frac{2}{5}$	7. $\frac{3}{10}$	11. $\frac{13}{20}$	15. $\frac{5}{11}$	19. $\frac{2}{9}$
4. $\frac{4}{5}$	8. $\frac{3}{5}$	12. $\frac{3}{32}$	16. $\frac{3}{7}$	20. $\frac{13}{15}$

Using Per Cent in Problems

There are three parts to every problem involving per cent.

1. The **base** B is the entire amount.
2. The **rate** R is the per cent of the base.
3. The **part** P is the portion of the base.

These three parts are combined in the following

Formula

$$B \times R = P \qquad (9\text{-}1)$$

Finding the Part

Example 9-5. How much is 20 per cent of $80?

Solution:

Given: $B = \$80$ Find: $P = ?$
$R = 20\% = 0.20$

$$B \times R = P \qquad (9\text{-}1)$$
$$80 \times 0.20 = P$$
$$P = \$16 \quad Ans.$$

Example 9-6. What is the profit on an article costing $30 if it is sold at a profit of 15 per cent?

Solution:

Given: $B = \$30$ Find: $P = ?$
$R = 15\% = 0.15$

$$B \times R = P \qquad (9\text{-}1)$$
$$30 \times 0.15 = P$$
$$P = \$4.50 \quad Ans.$$

Example 9-7. The voltage lost in a line supplying a motor is 5 per cent of the generator voltage of 220 volts. Find (*a*) the voltage lost and (*b*) the voltage supplied to the motor.

Solution:

Given: E_G = base B = 220 volts   Find: E_l = part P = ?
          $R = 5\% = 0.05$ E_L = ?

a. $B \times R = P$ (9-1)
                          $220 \times 0.05 = P$
                                   $P = 11$ volts
                                   $E_l = 11$ volts   *Ans.*

b. $E_L = E_G - E_l$ (6-3)
                          $E_L = 220 - 11 = 209$ volts   *Ans.*

Problems

1. How much is 22 per cent of 150?

2. How much is 6 per cent of $500?

3. How much is 2.5 per cent of $300?

4. What is the amount of sales tax on an order of $7.50 if the tax rate is 3 per cent?

5. A television benchman earned $95 per week. He received an increase of 15 per cent. Find the amount of the increase.

6. A radio mechanic used 30 per cent of a 1,000-ft roll of push-back wire. How many feet of wire did he use?

7. A 15-amp fuse carried a 15 per cent overload for 2 sec. What current flowed through the fuse during this time?

8. What is the possible error in a 500-ohm resistor if it is marked with a silver band indicating only 10 per cent accuracy?

9. The effective value of an a-c wave is 70.7 per cent of the peak value. What is the effective voltage of a wave which reaches a peak of 165 volts?

10. On a television screen, 6 per cent of the 525 horizontal lines are blanked out by vertical blanking. How many lines are blanked out?

11. Out of a lot of 200 radio tubes, $2\frac{1}{2}$ per cent were rejected as being defective. How many were rejected?

12. The voltage drop in a line supplied by a 220-volt generator is 2 per cent of the generator voltage. Find the voltage drop and the voltage supplied to the load.

13. How many watts of power are lost in a transformer rated at 250 watts if 3 per cent of the energy is lost as heat?

14. What is the interest for 1 year at $2\frac{1}{2}$ per cent on $125?

15. If you are allowed a discount of 15 per cent on a bill amounting to $127.85, how much is the discount?

Finding the Rate

Example 9-8.   20 is what per cent of 80?

Solution:

                    Given: $B = 80$ Find: R = ?
                              $P = 20$

$$B \times R = P \tag{9-1}$$
$$80 \times R = 20$$
$$R = \tfrac{20}{80} = \tfrac{1}{4} = 0.25 = 25\% \qquad Ans.$$

Example 9-9. $\tfrac{1}{2}$ is what per cent of 4?

Solution:

Given: $B = 4$ Find: $R = ?$
$$P = \tfrac{1}{2}$$

$$B \times R = P \tag{9-1}$$
$$4 \times R = \tfrac{1}{2}$$
$$R = \tfrac{1}{2} \div 4$$
$$R = \tfrac{1}{2} \times \tfrac{1}{4} = \tfrac{1}{8} = 0.125 = 12.5\% \qquad Ans.$$

Example 9-10. A man earns \$120 per week. If he saves \$10 per week, what per cent of his wages does he save?

Solution:

Given: $B = \$120$ Find: $R =$ per cent saved $= ?$
$$P = \text{part saved} = \$10$$

$$B \times R = P \tag{9-1}$$
$$120 \times R = 10$$
$$R = \tfrac{10}{120} = \tfrac{1}{12} = 0.083 = 8.3\% \qquad Ans.$$

Problems

1. 30 is what per cent of 120?
2. 30 is what per cent of 80?
3. What per cent of 60 is 24?
4. What per cent of 85 is 12?
5. What per cent of 25 is 0.5?
6. What per cent of 30 is 40?
7. 150 is what per cent of 100?
8. 24.5 is what per cent of 70?
9. What per cent of $25\tfrac{1}{2}$ is $8\tfrac{1}{2}$?
10. What per cent of 18.5 is 3.5?
11. A discount of \$2 was given on a bill of \$16. Find the rate of discount.
12. If three tubes out of a lot of 90 tubes are defective, what per cent are defective?
13. If 100 ft of a 250-ft roll of wire has been used, what per cent has been used?
14. A signal generator costing \$65 was sold at a loss of \$25. Find the rate of loss.
15. In transmitting 50 hp by a belt system, 1.2 hp was lost due to slippage. What per cent of the power was lost?
16. A team played 18 games and won 15 of them. What per cent of the games played did they win?

17. An electrician used 40 ft of BX cable from a 200-ft-long coil.   What per cent did he use?

18. A man earning $80 per week received an increase of $2.50 per week. Find the per cent of increase.

19. The voltage loss in a supply line is 5.5 volts.   If the generator voltage is 110 volts, find the rate of loss.

20. A 15-amp fuse carried 18 amp for 2 sec.   What was the per cent of overload?

Finding the Base

Example 9-11.   5 is 25 per cent of what number?

Solution:

Given: $P = 5$ Find: $B = ?$
$\qquad R = 25\% = 0.25$

$$B \times R = P \qquad\qquad\qquad (9\text{-}1)$$
$$B \times 0.25 = 5$$
$$B = \frac{5}{0.25} = 20 \qquad Ans.$$

Example 9-12.   A mechanic is able to save $18.50 each week.   This amount is equal to 12½ per cent of his weekly wages.   How much does he earn each week?

Solution:

Given: $P =$ amount saved $= \$18.50$ Find: $B =$ total wages $= ?$
$\qquad R =$ per cent saved $= 12\frac{1}{2}\% = 0.125$

$$B \times R = P \qquad\qquad\qquad (9\text{-}1)$$
$$B \times 0.125 = 18.50$$
$$B = \frac{18.50}{0.125} = \$148 \qquad Ans.$$

Problems

1. 10 is 50 per cent of what number?

2. 20 is 4 per cent of what number?

3. 16 is 40 per cent of what number?

4. 25 is 2.5 per cent of what number?

5. 70 is 3½ per cent of what number?

6. The voltage loss in a line is 3 volts.   If this is 2 per cent of the generator voltage, what is the generator voltage?

7. A mechanic received a 15 per cent increase in his wages amounting to $12.30.   What were his wages before the increase?

8. A motor has an output of 5 hp.   This amount is 85 per cent of the power put into the motor.   Calculate the power input.

9. A fuse carried 16.5 amp.   This was 110 per cent of the fuse rating. What is the fuse rating?

10. What must be the generator voltage if only 98 per cent of the generator voltage is delivered to a 117-volt line?

Review of Per Cent Problems

Rule: To change a per cent into a decimal, move the decimal point two places to the left and drop the per cent sign.

Rule: To change a decimal into a per cent, move the decimal point two places to the right and add a per cent sign.

Rule: To change a common fraction into a per cent, express the fraction as a decimal; then move the decimal point two places to the right and add a per cent sign.

All per cent problems contain three parts:

1. The base B is the entire amount.
2. The rate R is a per cent of the base.
3. The part P is the portion of the base.

The relationship among these parts is given by a formula:

$$B \times R = P \tag{9-1}$$

Problems

1. Change the following per cents to decimals: (*a*) 62%, (*b*) 3%, (*c*) 5.6%, (*d*) 0.8%, (*e*) 116%, (*f*) 4½%, and (*g*) 6¼%.

2. Change the following decimals to per cents: (*a*) 0.4, (*b*) 0.08, (*c*) 0.6, (*d*) 2.00, (*e*) 0.625, (*f*) 0.045, and (*g*) 5.

3. Change the following fractions to per cents: (*a*) ¾, (*b*) ⅗, (*c*) ¾, (*d*) ⅗₀, (*e*) ⅗₃, (*f*) ⅙, and (*g*) ²⁴⁄₅₂.

4. What is 18 per cent of 96?

5. How much is 4.5 per cent of $2,000?

6. 20 is what per cent of 120?

7. What per cent of 30 is 12?

8. 8 is 40 per cent of what number?

9. How much is 3¼ per cent of $1,500?

10. 10 is 2½ per cent of what number?

11. What per cent of 38.4 is 8?

12. How much is 0.6 per cent of 75?

13. In this transmission of 6 hp by a belt system, 0.09 hp was lost owing to slippage. What per cent was lost?

14. The plate voltage on a radio tube may vary up to 10 per cent of its rated value and still be satisfactory. A tube rated at 200 volts has a plate voltage of 185 volts. Is this within the normal variation?

15. Of the 60 men in a shop, 80 per cent got production bonuses. How many men got a bonus?

16. If only a 2 per cent voltage drop is permitted in a line, what is the maximum loss in voltage at the end of a line supplied by a 120-volt source? What is the voltage at the end of the line?

17. A man received 150 per cent of his hourly wage for every hour that he worked above 40 hr.   If he worked 50 hr in a certain week, at a base rate of $2 per hour, what was his overtime pay?   What was his total salary?   How much was withheld from his salary for social security at a 2 per cent tax rate?

18. A man earning $85 per week received an increase of 8 per cent.   Find the amount of the increase and his new salary.

19. Grid bias resistors usually have a wattage rating about 80 per cent higher than the calculated wattage.   What should be the wattage rating of a grid bias resistor using 0.5 watts?

20. The cost of rewinding an armature is $34.   If the electrician wishes to make a profit of 20 per cent, at what price must he bill the customer?

Test—Per Cent

1. Change each of the following to a per cent: (*a*) 3.75, (*b*) 0.68, (*c*) 0.007, and (*d*) 1½.

2. Change each of the following per cents to decimals: (*a*) 1.5%, (*b*) 8%, (*c*) 35%, and (*d*) 37½%.

3. A radio mechanic bought $85 worth of tubes at a 25 per cent discount.   What was the amount of the discount?   How much did he pay?

4. What per cent of the power taken by a transformer is delivered if it takes 200 watts and delivers 190 watts?

5. The effective value of an a-c wave is 70.7 per cent of its peak value.   What is the peak value of an a-c wave if the effective value is 110 volts?

JOB 9-3: CONVERSION FACTORS FOR ELECTRICAL AND MECHANICAL POWER

A *motor* is a device which uses electrical power and converts this power into the mechanical power of a rotating shaft.   The electrical power supplied to a motor is measured in watts or kilowatts; the mechanical power delivered by a motor is measured in horsepower (hp).   One horsepower is equivalent to 746 watts of electrical power. For most calculations, it is sufficiently accurate to consider 1 hp equal to 750 watts.

A *generator* is a device which uses mechanical power and converts this power into electrical power.   The mechanical power supplied to a generator is measured in horsepower; the electrical power delivered by a generator is measured in watts or kilowatts.

Tables of Conversion Factors.   Tables 9-1 and 9-2 are based on the following relationships.

$$1 \text{ kw} = 1{,}000 \text{ watts}$$
$$1 \text{ hp} = 750 \text{ watts}$$

Table 9-1

	To change	Into	Multiply by
1	Kilowatts (kw)	Watts (w)	1,000
2	Horsepower (hp)	Watts (w)	750
3	Kilowatts (kw)	Horsepower (hp)	4/3
4	Horsepower (hp)	Kilowatts (kw)	3/4

Table 9-2

	To change	Into	Divide by
5	Watts (w)	Kilowatts (kw)	1,000
6	Watts (w)	Horsepower (hp)	750

Items 3 and 4 are derived as follows:

Since hp = watts/750 (6) and watts = kw × 1,000 (1), we can substitute (kw × 1,000) for watts in item 6. This gives

$$Hp = \frac{kw \times 1,000}{750}$$

or
$$Hp = kw \times \tfrac{4}{3}$$

Similarly, since kw = watts/1,000 (5) and watts = hp × 750 (2), we can substitute (hp × 750) for watts in item 5. This gives

$$Kw = \frac{hp \times 750}{1,000}$$

or
$$Kw = hp \times \tfrac{3}{4}$$

Example 9-13.

1. 1.5 kw = 1.5 × 1,000 = 1,500 watts   *Ans.*
2. $\frac{1}{2}$ hp = $\frac{1}{2}$ × 750 = 375 watts   *Ans.*
3. $1\frac{1}{2}$ kw = $1\frac{1}{2}$ × $\frac{4}{3}$ = $\frac{3}{2}$ × $\frac{4}{3}$ = 2 hp   *Ans.*
4. $1\frac{1}{2}$ hp = $1\frac{1}{2}$ × $\frac{3}{4}$ = $\frac{3}{2}$ × $\frac{3}{4}$ = $\frac{9}{8}$ = 1.125 kw   *Ans.*
5. 1,800 watts = 1,800 ÷ 1,000 = 1.8 kw   *Ans.*
6. 1,125 watts = 1,125 ÷ 750 = 1.5 hp   *Ans.*

Problems

Change the following units of measurement.

1. 6.5 kw to watts
2. 2 hp to watts
3. 2,300 watts to kilowatts
4. 2,625 watts to horsepower
5. 0.05 kw to watts

6. 1 kw to horsepower
7. 1 hp to kilowatts
8. $1\frac{3}{4}$ kw to horsepower
9. $2\frac{1}{4}$ hp to kilowatts
10. 7.5 kw to horsepower

11. ⅛ hp to kilowatts
12. ¾ hp to watts
13. 4,000 watts to horsepower

14. 4½ hp to kilowatts
15. 10 kw to horsepower
16. 8.75 kw to horsepower

JOB 9-4: EFFICIENCY OF ELECTRICAL APPARATUS

Most machines are designed to do a specific job. A motor takes in electrical energy and delivers mechanical energy in the form of a rotating shaft. If it could change *all* the electrical energy into mechanical energy, it would be said to be 100 per cent efficient. Unfortunately, not all the electrical energy put into the motor appears as mechanical energy at the shaft. Some of the energy is used in overcoming friction, and some appears as heat energy. *No energy is lost*—it merely does not appear at the shaft as *useful* energy. The amount of useful energy (the power output) is therefore always *less* than the energy received by the machine (the power input). This means that the power output is always some fractional part of the power input. This fraction, obtained by dividing the output by the input, is called the *efficiency* of the machine. It is always expressed as a per cent by multiplying the fraction by 100. The efficiency of electrical devices is generally large, ranging from 75 to 98 per cent.

Formula

$$\text{Efficiency} = \frac{\text{output}}{\text{input}} \qquad (9\text{-}2)$$

In this formula, the output and the input must *both* be expressed in the *same units of measurement*. This will ordinarily necessitate a change in the units of measurement, since for a motor,

Output is measured in horsepower.

Input is measured in watts or kilowatts.

For a generator,

Output is measured in watts or kilowatts.

Input is measured in horsepower.

Example 9-14.   Find the efficiency of a motor which receives 4 kw and delivers 4 hp.

Solution:

Given: Output = 4 hp   Find: Per cent eff = ?
          Input = 4 kw

1. Express all measurements in the same kind of units.

$$\text{Output} = 4 \text{ hp} = 4 \times 750 = 3{,}000 \text{ watts}$$
$$\text{Input} = 4 \text{ kw} = 4 \times 1{,}000 = 4{,}000 \text{ watts}$$

2. Find the efficiency.

$$\text{Eff} = \frac{\text{output}}{\text{input}} \tag{9-2}$$

$$\text{Eff} = \frac{3{,}000}{4{,}000} = 0.75 = 75\% \qquad Ans.$$

Example 9-15. A generator receives 7 hp and delivers 20 amp at 230 volts. Find its efficiency.

Solution:

Given: Output $\begin{cases} E = 230 \text{ volts} \\ I = 20 \text{ amp} \end{cases}$ Find: Per cent eff = ?

Input = 7 hp

1. Express all measurements in the same kind of units.

Output: $P = I \times E$ (7-1)
$$P = 20 \times 230 = 4{,}600 \text{ watts}$$

Input: 7 hp $= 7 \times 750 = 5{,}250$ watts

2. Find the efficiency.

$$\text{Eff} = \frac{\text{output}}{\text{input}} \tag{9-2}$$

$$\text{Eff} = \frac{4{,}600}{5{,}250} = 0.876 = 87.6\% \qquad Ans.$$

Problems

1. A motor rated at 2 hp (delivers 2 hp) receives 1.8 kw of energy. Find its efficiency.

2. A motor delivers 3 hp and receives 2.4 kw. Find its efficiency.

3. A radio "power" transformer draws 0.5 kw from a line and delivers 480 watts. Find its efficiency.

4. A filament transformer draws 60 watts and supplies 50 watts to the tube filaments. Find its efficiency.

5. A generator rated at 10 kw (delivers 10 kw) receives 15 hp. Find its efficiency.

6. A generator delivers $1\frac{1}{4}$ kw and receives 2 hp. What is its efficiency?

7. A transmission line receives 230 kw and delivers 210 kw. What is the efficiency of transmission?

8. A shunt motor takes 24 amp at 220 volts and delivers 5 hp. Find the watt output of the motor and its efficiency.

9. A 2-hp motor requires 17 amp at 110 volts. What per cent of the input is delivered at the shaft? What per cent is wasted?

10. A radio "power" transformer draws 1.4 amp from a 117-volt line. What is the efficiency of the transformer if it delivers 235 volts at 0.65 amp?

JOB 9-5: FINDING THE OUTPUT AND INPUT OF ELECTRICAL DEVICES

The formula for the per cent efficiency may be used to find the values of both the output and the input of electrical devices. The per cent efficiency must be expressed as a decimal by moving the decimal point two places to the left.

Finding the Output

Example 9-16. Find the kilowatt output of a generator if it receives 6 hp and operates at an efficiency of 90 per cent.

Solution:

$$\text{Given: Input} = 6 \text{ hp} \qquad\qquad \text{Find: Output} = ?$$
$$\text{Eff} = 90\% = 0.90$$

1. Write formula.

$$\text{Eff} = \frac{\text{output}}{\text{input}} \qquad\qquad (9\text{-}2)$$

2. Substitute.

$$\frac{0.90}{1} = \frac{\text{output}}{6}$$

3. Cross-multiply.

$$\text{Output} = 6 \times 0.90$$

4. Multiply.

$$\text{Output} = 5.4 \text{ hp}$$

But the output of a generator must be measured in kilowatts. Therefore,

$$5.4 \text{ hp} = 5.4 \times \frac{3}{4} = \frac{16.2}{4} = 4.05 \text{ kw} \qquad Ans.$$

Example 9-17. A motor has an efficiency of 87 per cent. If it draws 20 amp from a 220-volt line, what is its hp output?

Solution:

$$\text{Given: Input} \begin{cases} I = 20 \text{ amp} \\ E = 220 \text{ volts} \end{cases} \qquad \text{Find: Output} = ?$$
$$\text{Eff} = 87\% = 0.87$$

1. Find the watt input.

$$P = I \times E \qquad\qquad (7\text{-}1)$$
$$P = 20 \times 220 = 4{,}400 \text{ watts input}$$

2. Find the watt output.

$$\text{Eff} = \frac{\text{output}}{\text{input}} \qquad (9\text{-}2)$$

$$\frac{0.87}{1} = \frac{\text{output}}{4{,}400}$$

$$\text{Output} = 4{,}400 \times 0.87 = 3{,}828 \text{ watts output}$$

But the output of a motor must be measured in horsepower. Therefore,

$$3{,}828 \text{ watts} = 3{,}828 \div 750 = 5.1 \text{ hp} \qquad Ans.$$

Finding the Input

Example 9-18.   How much power is needed to operate a 5-kw generator if its efficiency is 92 per cent?

Solution:

Given: Output = 5 kw   Find: Input = ?
         Eff = 92% = 0.92

$$\text{Eff} = \frac{\text{output}}{\text{input}} \qquad (9\text{-}2)$$

$$\frac{0.92}{1} = \frac{5}{\text{input}}$$

$$0.92 \times \text{input} = 5$$

$$\text{Input} = \frac{5}{0.92} = 5.43 \text{ kw}$$

But the input to a generator is measured in horsepower.   Therefore,

$$5.43 \text{ kw} = 5.43 \times \frac{4}{3} = \frac{21.72}{3} = 7.24 \text{ hp} \qquad Ans.$$

Example 9-19.   How much current is drawn by a 2½-hp motor if it has an efficiency of 90 per cent and operates on 110 volts?

Solution:

Given: Output = 2½ hp   Find: Input I = ?
         Eff = 90% = 0.90
         Input E = 110 volts

1. Find the power input.

$$\text{Eff} = \frac{\text{output}}{\text{input}} \tag{9-2}$$

$$\frac{0.90}{1} = \frac{2.5}{\text{input}}$$

$$0.90 \times \text{input} = 2.5$$

$$\text{Input} = \frac{2.5}{0.90} = 2.78 \text{ hp}$$

But the input to a motor is measured in watts or kilowatts.   Therefore,

$$2.78 \text{ hp} = 2.78 \times 750 = 2,085 \text{ watts} \qquad Ans.$$

2. Find the input current.

$$P = I \times E \tag{7-1}$$
$$2,085 = I \times 110$$
$$I = \frac{2,085}{110} = 19 \text{ amp} \qquad Ans.$$

Problems

1. Find the horsepower output of a motor drawing 3 kw and operating at an efficiency of 90 per cent.

2. An 80 per cent efficient radio "power" transformer delivers 50 watts. Find its power input.

3. Find the horsepower output of a motor drawing 5 amp at 110 volts and operating at an efficiency of 80 per cent.

4. A motor operates at an efficiency of 92 per cent and draws 5.5 amp from a 110-volt line.   Find the horsepower output.

5. A transmission line operating at an efficiency of 98 per cent receives 20 amp at 230 volts.   Find the power delivered.

6. How much power is delivered by a transformer operating at an efficiency of 88 per cent if it draws 0.08 kw?

7. Find the input to a 3-hp motor if its efficiency is 85 per cent.

8. Find the horsepower input to a generator delivering 5 kw at an efficiency of 90 per cent.

9. A generator delivers 20 amp at a voltage of 110 volts.   Find its output in watts.   If it has an efficiency of 90 per cent, find the horsepower input.

10. How much current is drawn by a 2-hp motor if it has an efficiency of 87 per cent and operates at 110 volts?

11. What voltage is necessary to operate a 3-hp motor if it draws 11.37 amp and its efficiency is 90 per cent?

12. Find the kilowatt output of a generator which uses 9 hp and has an operating efficiency of 92 per cent.

JOB 9-6: REVIEW OF CONVERSION FACTORS AND EFFICIENCY

$$1 \text{ kw} = 1,000 \text{ watts}$$
$$1 \text{ hp} = 750 \text{ watts}$$
$$\text{Watts} = \text{kw} \times 1,000$$
$$\text{Watts} = \text{hp} \times 750$$
$$\text{Hp} = \text{kw} \times \tfrac{4}{3}$$
$$\text{Kw} = \text{hp} \times \tfrac{3}{4}$$
$$\text{Kw} = \text{watts} \div 1,000$$
$$\text{Hp} = \text{watts} \div 750$$

The *efficiency* of a machine is the ratio of the power output to the power input and is usually expressed as a per cent.

$$\text{Eff} = \frac{\text{output}}{\text{input}} \qquad (9\text{-}2)$$

Units of Measurement

For a generator:

Output is in kilowatts or watts or volt-amperes.

Input is in horsepower.

For a motor:

Output is in horsepower.

Input is in kilowatts or watts or volt-amperes.

Problems

1. Change (a) 500 watts to kilowatts, (b) 500 watts to horsepower, (c) 1.5 kw to watts, (d) 1.5 hp to watts, (e) 10 kw to horsepower, and (f) 10 hp to kilowatts.

2. Find the efficiency of a 1½-hp induction motor using 1.3 kw of power.

3. Find the efficiency of a generator if it delivers 20 amp at 120 volts and uses 3.5 hp.

4. What is the efficiency of a ¾-hp motor if it draws 5.5 amp from a 110-volt line?

5. Find the horsepower output of a motor drawing 5 amp at 110 volts if it operates at an efficiency of 85 per cent.

6. Find the kilowatt output of a generator which uses 12 hp and operates at an efficiency of 92 per cent.

7. Find the power needed to operate a ¾-hp motor if its efficiency is 90 per cent.

8. How much current is drawn from a 120-volt line by a 3-hp motor if it operates at an efficiency of 87 per cent?

Test—Conversion Factors and Efficiency

1. Change (a) 700 watts to kilowatts, (b) 1¾ hp to watts, (c) 3.6 kw to horsepower, and (d) 8 hp to kilowatts.

2. What is the efficiency of a 2-hp motor which takes 1.8 kw from a 220-volt line?

3. Calculate the horsepower output of a 90 per cent efficient motor if it draws 10 amp from a 220-volt line.

4. How many kilowatts of power are needed to operate a 2½-hp motor if its efficiency at full load is 85%?

5. Find the current drawn from a 110-volt line by a 1-hp motor if its efficiency is 89 per cent.

CHAPTER 10

ELECTRICAL ENERGY

JOB 10-1: FINDING MECHANICAL AND ELECTRICAL ENERGY

One horsepower or one kilowatt represents a certain amount of power. An electric iron which uses 600 watts of power is more expensive to operate than a 60-watt lamp. However, it would cost more to burn the lamp for 20 hr than to use the iron for 1 hr. The *cost* of energy depends not only on how much power is used but also on *how long it is used*. Thus, the light used 60 watts for 20 hr, or $60 \times 20 = 1{,}200$ units of energy. The iron used 600 watts for 1 hr, or $600 \times 1 = 600$ units of energy. The units of energy are the horsepower-hour (hp-hr) and the kilowatthour (kwhr)

Mechanical Energy. One horsepower-hour is the work done in 1 hr by a machine delivering 1 hp.

Formula

$$\text{Hp-hr} = \text{hp} \times \text{hr} \qquad (10\text{-}1)$$

Electrical Energy. One kilowatthour is the work done in 1 hour by a machine using 1 kw.

Formula

$$\text{Kwhr} = \text{kw} \times \text{hr} \qquad (10\text{-}2)$$

Example 10-1. How much work is done by a 5-hp motor which is in operation for 3 hr?

Solution:

$$\text{Hp-hr} = \text{hp} \times \text{hr} \qquad (10\text{-}1)$$
$$\text{Hp-hr} = 5 \times 3$$
$$\text{Work done} = 15 \text{ hp-hr} \qquad Ans.$$

Example 10-2. How much energy is delivered in 3 hr by a generator rated at 10 kw?

235

Solution:

$$\text{Kwhr} = \text{kw} \times \text{hr} \qquad (10\text{-}2)$$
$$\text{Kwhr} = 10 \times 3$$
$$\text{Energy delivered} = 30 \text{ kwhr} \qquad Ans.$$

Example 10-3. How much electrical energy is used in 3 hr by five 60-watt lamps in parallel?

Solution: The diagram for the circuit is shown in Fig. 10-1.

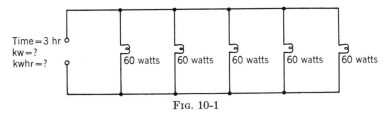

Time = 3 hr
kw = ?
kwhr = ?

60 watts   60 watts   60 watts   60 watts   60 watts

Fig. 10-1

1. Find the total power used.

$$P_T = P_1 + P_2 + P_3 + P_4 + P_5 \qquad (7\text{-}3)$$
$$P_T = 60 + 60 + 60 + 60 + 60 = 300 \text{ watts}$$

2. Change watts to kilowatts.

$$300 \text{ watts} = 300 \div 1{,}000 = 0.3 \text{ kw}$$

3. Find the energy used.

$$\text{Energy used} = \text{kw} \times \text{hr} \qquad (10\text{-}2)$$
$$= 0.3 \times 3 = 0.9 \text{ kwhr} \qquad Ans.$$

Example 10-4. How much energy is drawn from a 110-volt line by two motors in parallel if they draw 4 and 5 amp, respectively? The motors are in operation for 2 hr.

Solution: The diagram for the circuit is shown in Fig. 10-2.

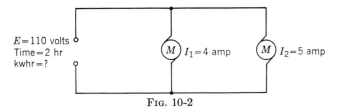

E = 110 volts
Time = 2 hr
kwhr = ?

M $I_1 = 4$ amp M $I_2 = 5$ amp

Fig. 10-2

1. Find the total current drawn.

$$I_T = I_1 + I_2 \qquad (5\text{-}2)$$
$$I_T = 4 + 5 = 9 \text{ amp}$$

2. Find the total power used.

$$P_T = I_T \times E_T \qquad (7\text{-}2)$$
$$P_T = 9 \times 110 = 990 \text{ watts}$$

3. Change watts to kilowatts.

$$990 \text{ watts} = 990 \div 1,000 = 0.99 \text{ kw}$$

4. Find the energy used.

$$\text{Energy} = \text{kw} \times \text{hr} \qquad\qquad (10\text{-}2)$$
$$= 0.99 \times 2 = 1.98 \text{ kwhr} \qquad Ans.$$

Problems

1. Find the work done by a 3-hp motor operating for 6 hr.
2. Find the energy delivered by a 10-kw generator in 8 hr.
3. Find the work done by three 1½-hp motors in 4 hr.
4. How much energy is delivered in 7½ hr by a 40-kw generator?
5. How much electrical energy is used in 2 hr by a bank of six 200-watt lamps?
6. The motor in a washing machine uses about 1,200 watts. How much energy is used by a Laundromat with six washers if they are all in use 10 hr per day for a 6-day week?
7. A radio receiver draws 0.85 amp at 110 volts. If the set is used 4 hr per day, how much energy does it use in 7 days?
8. Seven Christmas-tree lights rated at 15 volts and 0.15 amp are connected in series. If the lights are used for 7 hr per day, how much energy is used per day?
9. A 20-ohm motor drawing 4 amp is in operation for 2 hr. Find the energy used.
10. How much energy is drawn from a 110-volt line by a 22-ohm electric iron in 3 hr?

JOB 10-2: COST OF ELECTRICAL ENERGY

A watthour meter is a meter designed to measure the total electrical *energy* used. These meters are installed by the utility companies near the service entrance of a building to record the energy used. See Job 3-1 for the method of reading meters of this type. The utility company bills the consumer by multiplying the number of units of energy (kwhr) by the cost of 1 kwhr.

Formula

$$\text{Total cost} = \text{kwhr} \times \text{unit cost} \qquad\qquad (10\text{-}3)$$

Example 10-5. A motor uses 5 kw for 6 hr. Find the cost at 5 cents per kilowatthour.

Solution:

Given: Input = 5 kw   Find: Total cost = ?
       Time = 6 hr
       Unit cost = 5¢ per kwhr.

1. Find the energy used.

$$\text{Energy} = \text{kw} \times \text{hr} = 5 \times 6 = 30 \text{ kwhr} \qquad (10\text{-}2)$$

2. Find the total cost.

$$\text{Total cost} = \text{kwhr} \times \text{unit cost} \qquad (10\text{-}3)$$
$$\text{Total cost} = 30 \times 0.05 = \$1.50 \qquad Ans.$$

Example 10-6. A 5-hp motor has an efficiency of 90 per cent. Find the kilowatt input to the motor. What is the cost to run this motor for 2 hr at a cost of 5 cents per kilowatthour?

Solution:

Given: Output = 5 hp   Find: Input = ?
       Eff = 90% = 0.90   Total cost = ?
       Time = 2 hr
       Unit cost = 5¢ per kwhr

1. Find the input.

$$\text{Eff} = \frac{\text{output}}{\text{input}} \qquad (9\text{-}2)$$

$$\frac{0.90}{1} = \frac{5}{\text{input}}$$

$$0.90 \times \text{input} = 5$$

$$\text{Input} = \frac{5}{0.90} = 5.56 \text{ hp}$$

2. Change horsepower to kilowatts.

$$5.56 \text{ hp} = 5.56 \times \frac{3}{4} = \frac{16.68}{4} = 4.17 \text{ kw}$$

3. Find the energy input.

$$\text{Energy} = \text{kw} \times \text{hr} = 4.17 \times 2 = 8.34 \text{ kwhr} \qquad (10\text{-}2)$$

4. Find the total cost.

$$\text{Total cost} = \text{kwhr} \times \text{unit cost} \qquad (10\text{-}3)$$
$$\text{Total cost} = 8.34 \times 0.05 = \$0.42 \qquad Ans.$$

Problems

1. A motor uses 10 kw. At 5 cents per kilowatthour, what is the cost to operate this motor for 3 hr?

2. At 3 cents per kilowatthour, what is the cost of operating a bank of four 25-hp motors for 2 hr?

3. What is the cost of operating a 3-kw electric heater for 6 hr at 6 cents per kilowatthour?

4. What does it cost to operate a 5.5-kw electric range for 3 hr at 5 cents per kilowatthour?

5. An electric clock uses 2 watts of power. What does it cost to operate it for 30 days at 5 cents per kilowatthour?

6. A bank of five 200-watt lamps is connected in parallel. How much will it cost to burn these lamps for 5 hr at 4 cents per kilowatthour?

7. A 3-hp motor has an efficiency of 80 per cent. Find the kilowatt input to the motor. What is the cost to operate this motor for 3 hr at 4 cents per kilowatthour?

Example 10-7. At 5 cents per kilowatthour, how much will it cost to operate a 220-volt 25-amp motor for 4 hr?

Solution:

Given: E = 220 volts   Find: Total cost = ?
I = 25 amp
Time = 4 hr
Unit cost = 5¢ per kwhr

1. Find the power used.

$$P = I \times E \qquad\qquad (7\text{-}1)$$
$$P = 25 \times 220 = 5,500 \text{ watts}$$

2. Change watts to kilowatts.

$$5,500 \text{ watts} = 5,500 \div 1,000 = 5.5 \text{ kw}$$

3. Find the energy used.

$$\text{Energy} = \text{kw} \times \text{hr} \qquad\qquad (10\text{-}2)$$
$$\text{Energy} = 5.5 \times 4 = 22 \text{ kwhr}$$

4. Find the total cost.

$$\text{Total cost} = \text{kwhrs} \times \text{unit cost} \qquad\qquad (10\text{-}3)$$
$$\text{Total cost} = 22 \times 0.05 = \$1.10 \qquad Ans.$$

Problems

1. What is the cost of operating an electric fan for 9 hr at 5 cents per kilowatthour if it draws 0.75 amp from a 110-volt line?

2. A Tungar battery charger uses 15 amp at 110 volts. What is the cost to charge a bank of storage batteries at 5 cents per kilowatthour if it requires 1 hr to charge the batteries?

3. At 7 cents per kilowatthour, what is the cost of running a washing machine for 2 hr if it takes 2.1 amp at 110 volts?

4. What is the cost of operating a radio receiver for 5 hr per day for 1 week at the rate of 4 cents per kilowatthour?   The set draws 0.9 amp from a 110-volt line.

5. An electric refrigerator is in operation about 2 hr per day.   If it draws 3.5 amp at 110 volts, find the cost to operate this refrigerator for 30 days at 5 cents per kilowatthour.

6. An automobile headlight lamp draws 3 amp at 6 volts.   If it is used for 3 hr a day for a year of 300 days, find the cost at 5 cents per kilowatthour. How does this cost compare with the $16 cost of an ordinary automobile storage battery which can be expected to last for 2 years?

Example 10-8.   A 20-ohm neon sign operates on a 110-volt line. Find the cost to operate this sign for 12 hr a day for 1 week at 5 cents per kilowatthour.

Solution: The diagram for the circuit is shown in Fig. 10-3.

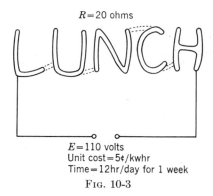

$R=20$ ohms

$E=110$ volts
Unit cost$=5$¢/kwhr
Time$=12$hr/day for 1 week

Fig. 10-3

1. Find the power used.

$$P = \frac{E^2}{R} \tag{7-5}$$

$$P = \frac{110^2}{20} = \frac{\overset{55}{\cancel{110}} \times 11\cancel{0}}{\cancel{20}}$$
$$\qquad\qquad\qquad 1$$
$$= 55 \times 11 = 605 \text{ watts}$$

2. Change watts to kilowatts.

$$605 \text{ watts} = 605 \div 1{,}000 = 0.605 \text{ kw}$$

3. Find the hours of use.

$$1 \text{ week} = 7 \text{ days} \times 12 \text{ hr per day}$$
$$1 \text{ week} = 84 \text{ hr of use}$$

4. Find the energy used.

$$\text{Energy} = \text{kw} \times \text{hr} \qquad (10\text{-}2)$$
$$\text{Energy} = 0.605 \times 84 = 50.82 \text{ kwhr}$$

5. Find the total cost.

$$\text{Total cost} = \text{kwhr} \times \text{unit cost} \qquad (10\text{-}3)$$
$$\text{Total cost} = 50.82 \times 0.05 = \$2.54 \qquad Ans.$$

Example 10-9. A 22-ohm toaster in a cafeteria draws 5 amp. What is the cost to operate this toaster for 3 hr per day for 25 days a month at 5 cents per kilowatthour?

Solution:

Given: $R = 22$ ohms   Find: Total cost = ?
       $I = 5$ amp
Unit cost = 5¢ per kwhr
    Time = 3 hr per day for 25 days

1. Find the power used.

$$P = I^2R \qquad (7\text{-}4)$$
$$P = 5^2 \times 22 = 25 \times 22 = 550 \text{ watts}$$

2. Change watts to kilowatts.

$$550 \text{ watts} = 550 \div 1{,}000 = 0.55 \text{ kw}$$

3. Find the hours of use.

$$25 \text{ days} \times 3 \text{ hr/day} = 75 \text{ hr}$$

4. Find the energy used.

$$\text{Energy} = \text{kw} \times \text{hr} \qquad (10\text{-}2)$$
$$\text{Energy} = 0.55 \times 75 = 41.25 \text{ kwhr}$$

5. Find the total cost.

$$\text{Total cost} = \text{kwhr} \times \text{unit cost} \qquad (10\text{-}3)$$
$$\text{Total cost} = 41.25 \times 0.05 = \$2.06 \qquad Ans.$$

Problems

1. A current of 5 amp is passed through an arc lamp for 2 hr. If the resistance of the lamp is 4 ohms, how much energy has been used? What is the cost at 4 cents per kilowatthour?

2. The resistance of the copper cables connecting a generator to a switchboard is 0.1 ohm, and 2 volts is required to send the full-load current through them. How much energy is expended in the cables in 10 hr? What is the cost at 5 cents per kilowatthour?

3. An electric heater has a resistance of 22 ohms. What does it cost to operate it for 9 hr on a 110-volt line at 5 cents per kilowatthour?

4. A 20-ohm 5-amp motor operates for 5 hr per day. What does it cost per day at 4 cents per kilowatthour?

5. A bank of five 100-watt lamps is in parallel with a motor drawing 4 amp from a 110-volt line. Find the cost to operate the circuit for 4 hours at 5 cents per kilowatthour.

JOB 10-3: COST OF ENERGY TO INDUSTRIAL USERS

Industry does not pay for its electrical energy at the same rate as a residential user. Since a factory uses a much larger amount of energy than a home, the price per kilowatthour decreases as the use increases. In addition, a factory may suddenly need large amounts of energy at any time of day or night, and the utility company must be ready to supply the energy as it is demanded. This means that the utility company must have extra generators standing ready to supply this varying demand, since it cannot store up this energy. To compensate the utility company, industrial users pay a demand charge as well as an energy charge. The maximum demand is measured by maximum-demand meters installed at the factories. Typical rates published by The Consolidated Edison Company of New York, Inc., in October, 1955, are shown in Table 10-1.

Table 10-1. Electric Service Classification No. 2—General
Minimum charge—80 cents per month

Demand charge (per month), kw of max demand	Price per kw	
	Low tension	High tension
For the first 7.................................	Included in energy charge	
For the next 28.................................	$2.50	$2.50
For the next 65.................................	$2.00	$2.00
For the next 900................................	$1.55	$1.45
For the next 19,000.............................	$1.40	$1.30
For excess over 20,000..........................	$1.40	$1.25

Energy charge (per month), kwhr	Price (low- and high-tension service), cents per kwhr
For the first 10......................	80
For the next 190.....................	5.0
For the next 500.....................	3.8
For the next 1,300...................	2.7
For the next 8,000	2.0
For the next 30,000.................	1.5
For the next 60,000.................	1.1
For the next 150,000	1.0
For excess over 250,000.............	0.9

Example 10-10. What is the cost of 12,000 kwhr of low-tension service if the maximum demand was 200 kw during the month?

Solution:

Demand Charge

Total kw remaining	No. kw used	Price per kw	Cost
200	7	No charge	$ 0
193	28	$2.50	70
165	65	$2.00	130
100	100	$1.55	155
Total...	200	.....	$355

Energy Charge

Total kwhr remaining	No. kwhr used	Price per kwhr	Cost
12,000	10	Flat rate	$ 0.80
11,990	190	0.05	9.50
11,800	500	0.038	19.00
11,300	1,300	0.027	35.10
10,000	8,000	0.02	160.00
2,000	2,000	0.015	30.00
Total	12,000	.....	254.40
Demand charge			355.00
Total charge			$609.40 *Ans*

Problems

Find the total cost of energy per month at the industrial rates given in Table 10-1.

Problem	Max kw demand per month	Kwhr used	Type of service
1	100	5,000	Low
2	50	800	Low
3	180	9,200	High
4	500	15,000	Low
5	1,200	42,000	High

JOB 10-4: REVIEW OF ELECTRICAL ENERGY

Rule: The total energy used by a device is equal to the power consumed multiplied by the hours it is in operation.

$$\text{Mechanical energy (hp-hr)} = \text{hp} \times \text{hr} \qquad (10\text{-}1)$$
$$\text{Electrical energy (kwhr)} = \text{kw} \times \text{hr} \qquad (10\text{-}2)$$

Rule: The total cost of electrical energy is equal to the number of kilowatthours of energy multiplied by the cost per kilowatthour.

$$\text{Total cost} = \text{kwhr} \times \text{unit cost} \qquad (10\text{-}3)$$

The total power in an electrical circuit is given by the following formulas:

$$P_T = I_T \times E_T \qquad (7\text{-}2)$$
$$P_T = P_1 + P_2 + P_3 \qquad (7\text{-}3)$$
$$P_T = I^2 R \qquad (7\text{-}4)$$
$$P_T = \frac{E^2}{R} \qquad (7\text{-}5)$$

Problems

1. Find the total work accomplished in 3 hr by a $\frac{1}{2}$-hp motor in parallel with a $\frac{3}{4}$-hp motor.
2. Find the energy delivered in $2\frac{1}{2}$ hr by a generator rated at 8 kw.
3. How much electrical energy is used in 2 hr by two 100-watt lamps and three 75-watt lamps in parallel?
4. How many kilowatthours are used in $2\frac{1}{4}$ hr by a motor drawing 2.6 amp at 24 volts from the secondary of a toy-train transformer?
5. A washing-machine motor draws 4.8 amp at 117 volts. Find the cost to operate the machine for 2 hr per day for 20 days at 5 cents per kilowatthour.
6. How much electrical energy is drawn in 2 hr from a 110-volt line by a 22-ohm iron in parallel with an electric heater drawing 6 amp?
7. At 5 cents per kilowatthour, find the cost to run a 3-hp motor for 3 hr if it operates at an efficiency of 80 per cent.
8. Find the cost to operate a 16-ohm electric heater on a 120-volt line for 5 hr at a rate of 5 cents per kilowatthour.
9. An electric broiler has a resistance of 12 ohms. If it draws 10 amp of current, what does it cost to operate it for $2\frac{1}{2}$ hr at 5 cents per kilowatthour?
10. Two 100-watt lamps are in parallel with a motor drawing 5 amp from a 117-volt line. Find the cost of operation for $3\frac{1}{2}$ hr at 6 cents per kilowatthour.

Test—Cost of Energy

1. How much energy is needed to operate a 2-hp motor for 2 hr if its efficiency is 90 per cent?

2. A motor drawing 6.5 amp at 110 volts is in operation for 3 hr. At 5 cents per kilowatthour, what is the cost?

3. At 5 cents per kilowatthour, what is the cost to operate a 9-ohm electric range drawing 12 amp for 4 hr?

4. An electric drier has a resistance of 11 ohms. At 5 cents per kilowatthour, what is the cost to operate it for 2 hr from a 110-volt line?

CHAPTER 11

RESISTANCE OF WIRE

JOB 11-1: CHECK-UP ON RATIO AND PROPORTION

Many complicated ideas may be expressed quite simply when written in formula form. For example, the rule "In a series circuit, the voltage is directly proportional to the resistance" may be written as $E_1/E_2 = R_1/R_2$. Or "The resistance of a wire is inversely proportional to its area" may be written as $R_1/R_2 = A_2/A_1$. The mathematical concepts of *ratio and proportion* enable us to compare voltages, currents, etc., and to show how they depend on each other. We shall be using these ideas in the next and succeeding jobs. Let us check up on what we know about ratio and proportion. If you have any difficulty with any of the following problems, turn to Job 11-2 which follows.

Problems

1. What is the ratio of 12 to 30 in.?
2. Two pulleys have diameters of 20 and 5 in., respectively. What is the ratio of their diameters?
3. If the number of turns of wire on the primary of a bell-ringing transformer is 360 turns and the secondary has 40 turns, what is the turns ratio of primary to secondary?
4. The power factor (pf) of an a-c circuit is described as the ratio of its resistance R to its impedance Z. Find the pf if $R = 500$ ohms and $Z = 550$ ohms.
5. What is the ratio of 1 hp to 1 kw?
6. A wire 30 ft long has a resistance of 0.02 ohm. If the resistance is directly proportional to the length, find the resistance of 10 ft of this wire.
7. If 60 ft of conduit costs $3.50, how much does 150 ft cost?
8. The ratio of acid to water in the electrolyte of a storage battery is 2:3. If 30 oz of acid is used to prepare a batch of electrolyte, how much water should be mixed with it?
9. In a simple transformer, the voltage is directly proportional to the number of turns. In a simple step-down transformer, the primary has 240

turns and the secondary has 30 turns.   Find the voltage of the secondary if the primary voltage is 120 volts.

10. The resistance of a wire is inversely proportional to its cross-sectional area.   If a wire whose area is 5,200 units has a resistance of 2 ohms, find the resistance of a wire of the same material whose area is 100 units.

11. In a parallel circuit, the current is inversely proportional to the resistance.   Write a formula to state this fact.

12. In a series circuit, the voltage drops are directly proportional to the resistances.   What is the voltage across a 100-ohm resistance if the voltage across a 500-ohm resistance is 10 volts?

JOB 11-2: BRUSH-UP ON RATIO AND PROPORTION

Comparing Quantities.   In our daily lives there are many situations in which we compare quantities.   For example, (1) Mr. Jones is richer than Mr. Smith, (2) Joe is heavier than Jack, (3) a foot is shorter than a yard.   These statements are adequate in most instances, but in scientific work we need more information.   It is not sufficient to say that one resistor is larger than another.   We must know *how much larger* it is.   For example, if resistor A = 40 ohms and resistor B = 20 ohms, by subtraction we could say that A is 20 ohms larger than B.   Using division, we could say that A is twice as large as B. The method of comparing by subtraction is not so useful as the method using division.   For example, in a school election, one class voted 25 for A and 15 for B.   The vote for all classes was 500 for A and 300 for B.   How did the class vote in comparison with the voting for the entire school?   Using the subtraction method, all we can say is that the class voted in *about* the same way as the school, that is, more for A than for B.   However, if we use the method of division,

$$\text{Class vote:}\ \frac{A}{B} = \frac{25}{15} = \frac{5}{3}$$

$$\text{School vote:}\ \frac{A}{B} = \frac{500}{300} = \frac{5}{3}$$

After reducing to lowest terms, we can see that the class voted in *exactly* the same manner as the school.   In the class, voting 25 to 15, for every 5 votes for A, there were 3 votes for B.   In the school, voting 500 to 300, for every 5 votes for A, there were 3 votes for B.

Ratio.   When two quantities are compared by division, the quotient is called the *ratio* of the quantities.   In the example above, the ratio of the vote for A compared with the vote for B is 5 compared with 3.   The ratio of the vote for B compared with the vote for A

is 3 compared with 5.   The ratio of A compared with B may be written as a fraction ($\frac{5}{3}$), using two dots as a ratio sign (5:3), or with words (5 to 3).   In every instance, it means that for every 5 for A there are 3 for B.   It also means that A has $\frac{5}{3}$, or $1\frac{2}{3}$, times as many votes as B or that B has $\frac{3}{5}$ as many votes as A.

Units of a Ratio.   The comparison, or ratio, of **2 yd to 1 ft is** *not* 2 to 1.   This would mean that 2 yd is only twice as large as 1 ft when actually it is 6 times as large.   Therefore, in order to compare two quantities, they must be measured in the *same units* of measurement. Also, the quantities themselves must be of the same *kind*, like two resistances, two voltages, two lengths, or two areas.   Since 2 yd and 1 ft are both lengths, we may compare them by division.

$$\frac{2 \text{ yd}}{1 \text{ ft}} = \frac{6 \cancel{ft}}{1 \cancel{ft}} = \frac{6}{1} = 6:1 = 6 \text{ to } 1$$

Since the units of measurement are identical, they cancel out. Thus, a ratio itself has no units of measurement.

Rule: To find the ratio of two similar quantities
1. Express them in the same units of measurement.
2. Form a fraction using the first quantity as the numerator and the second quantity as the denominator.
3. Reduce to lowest terms.

Example 11-1.   The aspect ratio of a television tube is the ratio of the horizontal length to the vertical width.   Find the aspect ratio of a rectangular tube 20 in. long and 15 in. wide.

Solution:

Given: Length = 20 in.   Find: Aspect ratio = ?
       Width = 15 in.

$$\text{Aspect ratio} = \frac{\text{length}}{\text{width}}$$
$$= {}^{20}\!/_{15} = \frac{4}{3} \text{ or } 4:3 \text{ (read as 4 to 3)}   Ans.$$

Example 11-2.   Find the ratio of 1 mv to 1 volt.

Solution:

Given: The quantities 1 mv and 1 volt   Find: Ratio = ?

$$\text{Ratio} = \frac{1 \text{ mv}}{1 \text{ volt}} = \frac{1 \text{ mv}}{1,000 \text{ mv}} = \frac{1}{1,000} \text{ or } 1:1,000 \text{ (read as 1 to 1,000)}$$

Ans.

Example 11-3.   Find the ratio of 1 hp to 1 kw.

Solution:

Given: The quantities 1 hp and 1 kw   Find: Ratio = ?

If it is difficult to change one unit into the other or vice versa, then change both units into a third unit. Since 1 hp = 750 watts and 1 kw = 1,000 watts,

$$\text{Ratio} = \frac{1 \text{ hp}}{1 \text{ kw}} = \frac{750 \text{ watts}}{1,000 \text{ watts}} = \frac{3}{4} \text{ or } 3:4 \text{ (read as 3 to 4)} \quad Ans.$$

Not all ratios are expressed as fractions. It is sometimes more convenient to express the ratio as a decimal or as a per cent. Also, the *order* in which the quantities are compared is very important. In trigonometry, the ratio of the side *o* to the side *a* is called the tangent ratio, while the ratio of the side *a* to the side *o* is called the cotangent ratio.

Example 11-4. Find the tangent ratio and the cotangent ratio for the triangle shown in Fig. 11-1.

Solution:

Tangent ratio $= \dfrac{o}{a}$

Tangent ratio $= \frac{4}{3} = 1.333$ *Ans.*

Cotangent ratio $= \dfrac{a}{o}$

Cotangent ratio $= \frac{3}{4} = 0.750$ *Ans.*

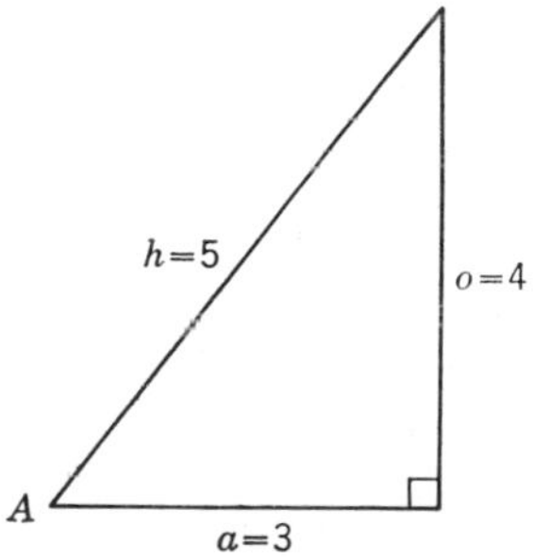

FIG. 11-1

Example 11-5. The power factor (pf) of an a-c circuit is the ratio of its resistance R to its impedance Z. Find the pf of a circuit if R = 2.46 ohms and Z = 30 ohms.

Solution:

Given: R = 2.46 ohms   Find: pf = ?
Z = 30 ohms

$$\text{pf} = \frac{R}{Z} = \frac{2.46}{30} = 0.082$$

Since pf is often expressed as a per cent,

$$\text{pf} = 0.082 \text{ or } 8.2\% \quad Ans.$$

Example 11-6. The efficiency of a motor is the ratio of the output to the input and is described as a per cent. Find the efficiency of a motor whose output is 5 hp and whose input is 4 kw.

Solution:

Given: Output = 5 hp   Find: Eff = ?
       Input = 4 kw

$$\text{Eff} = \frac{\text{output}}{\text{input}} = \frac{5 \text{ hp}}{4 \text{ kw}}$$

$$= \frac{5 \times 750}{4 \times 1,000} = \frac{3,750 \text{ watts}}{4,000 \text{ watts}} = 0.9375$$

$$\text{Eff} = 0.9375 = 93.75\% \qquad Ans.$$

Problems

Find the ratio of the quantities in each problem.

1. 3 to 12 in.   **5.** 3 ft to 18 in.
2. 6 to 2 ft   **6.** 2 kc to 500 cycles
3. 18 to 27 volts   **7.** 0.4 Megohm to 100,000 ohms
4. 105 to 20 turns   **8.** 2 hp to 3 kw

9. In Fig. 11-2, find (*a*) the ratio of D_2 to D_1 and (*b*) the ratio of D_1 to D_2.

10. Find the teeth ratio of two gears if the first has 35 teeth and the second has 30 teeth.

11. In Fig. 11-3, the turns ratio of the

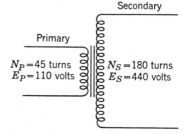

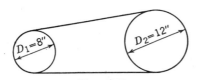

$N_P = 45$ turns $N_S = 180$ turns
$E_P = 110$ volts $E_S = 440$ volts

FIG. 11-2

FIG. 11-3. A step-up transformer.

transformer is the ratio of the number of turns on the primary coil N_p to the number of turns on the secondary coil N_s. Find the turns ratio.

12. In Fig. 11-3, find the ratio of the secondary turns N_s to the primary turns N_p.

13. In Fig. 11-3, find the ratio of the primary voltage E_p to the secondary voltage E_s.

14. If the primary voltage E_p of a transformer is 125 volts and the secondary voltage E_s is 20 volts, find the ratio of E_p to E_s.

15. Find the efficiency of a motor if the output is 2 hp and the input is 1.8 kw.

16. The quality Q of a coil is the ratio of its reactance X to its resistance R. Find the Q of an r-f coil if its reactance is 2,500 ohms and its resistance is 25 ohms.

17. Find the Q of a tuned circuit if $X = 12,000$ ohms and $R = 70$ ohms.

18. In a triangle similar to that shown in Fig. 11-1, the sine is the ratio of *o* to *h*, the cosine is the ratio of *a* to *h*, and the tangent is the ratio of *o* to *a*. Find the value of all three functions if $o = 7$, $a = 24$, and $h = 25$.

19. Find the pf of an a-c circuit if $R = 1,000$ ohms and $Z = 5,000$ ohms.

20. Find the pf of an a-c circuit if $R = 56.8$ ohms and $Z = 65$ ohms.

21. The multiplying power of a meter is the ratio of the new voltage to the old voltage. Find the multiplying power of a voltmeter reading 10 volts if it is extended to read 100 volts.

22. Find the multiplying power of a 150-volt 150,000-ohm voltmeter which has been extended to read 750 volts.

23. What is the ratio of the distance on a drawing to the actual distance if the scale of the drawing is $\frac{1}{4}$ in. equals 1 ft?

24. If 34 oz of acid is mixed with 51 oz of water to make the electrolyte for a storage battery, find (*a*) the ratio of acid to water and (*b*) the ratio of water to acid.

25. A generator rated at 117 volts supplies 115 volts to a motor some distance away. Find (*a*) the line loss in volts, (*b*) the ratio of the line loss to the rated voltage in per cent, and (*c*) the ratio of the load voltage to the rated voltage in per cent.

Proportion. Consider the following statement. If 3 pencils cost 8 cents, then 6 pencils will cost 16 cents. At the given rate, the cost depends only on the number of pencils bought. The more pencils bought, the larger the cost. The fewer pencils bought, the smaller the cost. When two quantities depend on each other, the relationship between them may be stated as a *proportion*.

A proportion is a mathematical statement that two ratios are equal. In our problem, the two quantities are the number of pencils N and the cost C.

First purchase	Second purchase
$N_1 = 3$ pencils	$N_2 = 6$ pencils
$C_1 = 8$ cents	$C_2 = 16$ cents

The ratio of the number of pencils is

$$\frac{N_1}{N_2} = \frac{3}{6} = \frac{1}{2}$$

The ratio of the costs is

$$\frac{C_1}{C_2} = \frac{8}{16} = \frac{1}{2}$$

Since the two ratios are equal, the proportion may be written mathematically as

$$\frac{N_1}{N_2} = \frac{C_1}{C_2}$$

and is an example of a *direct proportion*.

Direct Proportion. When two quantities depend on each other so that one increases as the other increases or one decreases as the other decreases, they are said to be *directly proportional* to each other. Notice that the two ratios are compared in the *same order* so that the items in the first situation (N_1 and C_1) are in the numerator and the items in the second situation (N_2 and C_2) are in the denominator. The proportion may be written as

$$\frac{C_1}{C_2} = \frac{N_1}{N_2} \quad \text{or} \quad \frac{C_2}{C_1} = \frac{N_2}{N_1} \quad \text{or} \quad \frac{N_2}{N_1} = \frac{C_2}{C_1} \quad \text{or} \quad \frac{N_1}{N_2} = \frac{C_1}{C_2}$$

It is unimportant which ratio is written first. However, once the first ratio is written, the second ratio must be written *in the same order*.

Rule: To set up a direct proportion between two variables
1. Make a ratio of one of the variables.
2. Make a ratio of the second variable in the same order.
3. Set the two ratios equal to each other.

Example 11-7. Write as a proportion: The weight of pipe is directly proportional to its length.

Solution:

<table>
<tr><td>First pipe</td><td>Second pipe</td></tr>
<tr><td>Length $= L_1$</td><td>Length $= L_2$</td></tr>
<tr><td>Weight $= W_1$</td><td>Weight $= W_2$</td></tr>
</table>

Since the ratio of the lengths $= L_1/L_2$ and the ratio of the weights $= W_1/W_2$, the proportion may be written as

$$\frac{L_1}{L_2} = \frac{W_1}{W_2} \quad \text{or} \quad \frac{W_1}{W_2} = \frac{L_1}{L_2}$$

or since the ratio of the lengths $= L_2/L_1$ and the ratio of the weights $= W_2/W_1$, the proportion may be written as

$$\frac{L_2}{L_1} = \frac{W_2}{W_1} \quad \text{or} \quad \frac{W_2}{W_1} = \frac{L_2}{L_1}$$

Rule: To solve problems involving direct proportion
1. Set up the proportion.
2. Substitute the values.
3. Solve by cross multiplication.

Example 11-8. In the series circuit shown in Fig. 11-4, the voltage across any resistor is directly proportional to the resistance of the resistor. Find the value of E_2.

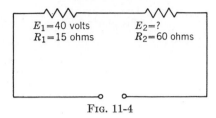

$$E_1 = 40 \text{ volts} \qquad E_2 = ?$$
$$R_1 = 15 \text{ ohms} \qquad R_2 = 60 \text{ ohms}$$

FIG. 11-4

Solution:

1. Set up the direct proportion.

$$\frac{E_1}{E_2} = \frac{R_1}{R_2}$$

2. Substitute numbers,

$$\frac{40}{E_2} = \frac{15}{60}$$

3. Cross-multiply.

$$15 \times E_2 = 40 \times 60$$

4. Simplify.

$$15 \times E_2 = 2{,}400$$

5. Solve for E_2.

$$E_2 = \frac{2{,}400}{15}$$

6. Divide.

$$E_2 = 160 \text{ volts} \qquad Ans.$$

Example 11-9. An automobile can travel 280 miles in 7 hr. At the same rate, how long will it take to travel 200 miles?

Solution: This is a direct proportion, since the distance increases as the time increases and the distance traveled depends on the time.

Given: $D_1 = 280$ miles   Find: $T_2 = ?$
$\qquad\quad T_1 = 7$ hr
$\qquad\quad D_2 = 200$ miles

$$\frac{D_1}{D_2} = \frac{T_1}{T_2}$$

$$\frac{280}{200} = \frac{7}{T_2}$$

$$280 \times T_2 = 7 \times 200$$
$$280 \times T_2 = 1{,}400$$

$$T_2 = \frac{1{,}400}{280} = 5 \text{ hr} \qquad Ans.$$

Problems

1. An 8-ft-long steel beam weighs 2,200 lb. What would be the weight of a similar beam 10 ft long?

2. If 1 gross (144) of resistors costs $2.60, how much do 36 resistors cost?

3. An airplane can travel 2,040 miles in 6 hr. At the same rate, how long would it take the plane to travel 1,530 miles?

4. The shadows cast by vertical poles are directly proportional to the heights of the poles. If a pole 9 ft high casts a shadow 12 ft long, how high is a tree that casts a shadow 36 ft long?

5. The volume of a gas is directly proportional to the temperature. If a gas occupies 100 cu ft at 70°F, what volume will it occupy at 50°F, assuming the pressure to be constant?

6. If 14 lb of cement is used to make 70 lb of concrete, how many pounds of concrete can be made with 30 lb of cement?

7. Using a diagram similar to Fig. 11-4, find R_1 if $E_1 = 20$ volts, $E_2 = 36$ volts, and $R_2 = 1,800$ ohms.

8. If a 500-ft length of wire has a resistance of 30 ohms, find the resistance of an 850-ft length of the same wire. Use the fact that the resistance of identical wires is directly proportional to the length.

9. In the series-circuit grid-bias voltage divider shown in Fig. 11-5, find the value of the bias resistor R_1.

10. In a transformer, the voltage is directly proportional to the number of turns. In a diagram similar to that shown in Fig. 11-3, find the secondary voltage E_s if $N_p = 160$ turns, $E_p = 18$ volts, and $N_s = 400$ turns.

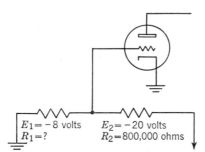

$E_1 = -8$ volts $E_2 = -20$ volts
$R_1 = ?$ $R_2 = 800,000$ ohms

FIG. 11-5. A series-circuit grid-bias voltage divider.

Inverse Proportion. When two gears are meshed as shown in Fig. 11-6, the smaller the gear, the faster it turns. When gear 1 turns once, its 40 teeth must engage 40 teeth on gear 2. Therefore, gear 2 must turn *twice* in order for 40 teeth (2 × 20) to mesh with the 40 teeth on gear 1. When two quantities depend on each other so that one *increases* as the other *decreases* or one *decreases* as the other *increases,* they are said to be *inversely proportional* to each other. This may be written mathematically as

$$\frac{T_1}{T_2} = \frac{S_2}{S_1}$$

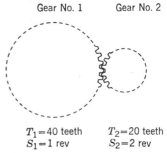

Gear No. 1   Gear No. 2

$T_1 = 40$ teeth $T_2 = 20$ teeth
$S_1 = 1$ rev $S_2 = 2$ rev

FIG. 11-6. The speed is inversely proportional to the number of teeth.

Notice that the two ratios are compared in the *opposite*, or *inverse*, order. The proportion will be correct regardless of which ratio is written first *provided* the second ratio is written in the *opposite order*. Thus, the proportion may be written as

$$\frac{T_1}{T_2} = \frac{S_2}{S_1} \quad \text{or} \quad \frac{T_2}{T_1} = \frac{S_1}{S_2} \quad \text{or} \quad \frac{S_1}{S_2} = \frac{T_2}{T_1} \quad \text{or} \quad \frac{S_2}{S_1} = \frac{T_1}{T_2}$$

Rule: To set up an inverse proportion between two variables
1. Make a ratio of one variable.
2. Make a ratio of the second variable in the opposite order.
3. Set the two ratios equal to each other.

Example 11-10. Write as a proportion: "The speeds of pulleys are inversely proportional to their diameters."

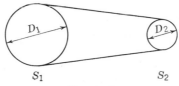

FIG. 11-7

Solution: The diagram for the problem is shown in Fig. 11-7.

$$\frac{D_1}{D_2} = \frac{S_2}{S_1} \quad \text{or} \quad \frac{S_1}{S_2} = \frac{D_2}{D_1} \quad \text{or} \quad \frac{D_2}{D_1} = \frac{S_1}{S_2} \quad \text{or} \quad \frac{S_2}{S_1} = \frac{D_1}{D_2}$$

Rule: To solve problems involving inverse proportion
1. Set up the proportion.
2. Substitute the values.
3. Solve by cross multiplication.

Example 11-11. The resistance of a length of wire is inversely proportional to its cross-sectional area. A certain copper wire has a resistance of 32 ohms and a cross-sectional area of 20 units. Find the resistance of another wire of the same length whose area is 100 units.

Solution:

Given: $R_1 = 32$ ohms   Find: $R_2 = ?$
$$A_1 = 20$$
$$A_2 = 100$$

$$\frac{R_1}{R_2} = \frac{A_2}{A_1}$$
$$\frac{32}{R_2} = \frac{100}{20}$$
$$100R_2 = 32 \times 20$$
$$R_2 = {}^{640}\!/_{100} = 6.4 \text{ ohms} \quad Ans.$$

Example 11-12.   In a parallel circuit, the currents are inversely proportional to the resistances.   In the circuit shown in Fig. 11-8, find I_2.

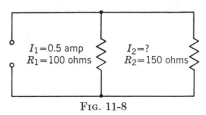

$I_1 = 0.5$ amp
$R_1 = 100$ ohms

$I_2 = ?$
$R_2 = 150$ ohms

Fig. 11-8

Solution:

$$\frac{R_1}{R_2} = \frac{I_2}{I_1}$$

$$\frac{100}{150} = \frac{I_2}{0.5}$$

$$150 \times I_2 = 0.5 \times 100$$

$$150 I_2 = 50$$

$$I_2 = {}^{50}\!/_{150} = 0.33 \text{ amp} \qquad Ans.$$

Problems

The speeds of pulleys are inversely proportional to their diameters.   Using Fig. 11-7,

1. Find D_1 if $S_1 = 40$ rpm, $S_2 = 100$ rpm, and $D_2 = 2$ in.
2. Find S_1 if $D_1 = 5$ in., $D_2 = 6$ in., and $S_2 = 120$ rpm.

The resistance of a wire is inversely proportional to its cross-sectional area.

3. Find R_2 if $A_1 = 200$, $R_1 = 50$ ohms, and $A_2 = 150$.
4. Find A_2 if $A_1 = 200$, $R_1 = 50$ ohms, and $R_2 = 10$ ohms.
5. Find A_1 if $R_1 = 20$ ohms, $A_2 = 10,000$, and $R_2 = 1$ ohm.
6. Find R_1 if $A_1 = 30$, $A_2 = 600$, and $R_2 = 16$ ohms.

In a parallel circuit, the currents are inversely proportional to the resistances.   Using a diagram similar to Fig. 11-8,

7. Find I_1 if $I_2 = 0.06$ amp, $R_1 = 30$ ohms, and $R_2 = 40$ ohms.
8. Find R_2 if $I_1 = 2$ amp, $I_2 = 4.5$ amp, and $R_1 = 90$ ohms.
9. Find R_1 if $I_1 = 2.25$ amp, $I_2 = 3.5$ amp, and $R_2 = 0.6$ ohm.

In a transformer, the currents in the primary and secondary coils are inversely proportional to the voltages.   Using a diagram similar to that shown in Fig. 11-3,

10. Find E_s if $E_p = 120$ volts, $I_p = 5$ amp, and $I_s = 2$ amp.
11. Find I_p if $E_p = 120$ volts, $E_s = 15$ volts, and $I_s = 2$ amp.
12. Find I_s if $E_p = 120$ volts, $I_p = 4$ amp, and $E_s = 6$ volts.

JOB 11-3: REVIEW OF RATIO AND PROPORTION

A *ratio* is the comparison of two quantities of the same kind.

A ratio is indicated by the division of the quantities.

A ratio may be written as (1) 8 to 2, (2) 8:2, or (3) $\frac{8}{2}$ and is always read as "8 to 2."

The two quantities of a ratio must always be measured in the same units of measurement.

A *proportion* is a mathematical statement that two ratios are equal.

In a *direct proportion*, the two quantities increase or decrease together. This is indicated by comparing the two ratios in the *same order*. Thus, if A is directly proportional to B,

$$\frac{A_1}{A_2} = \frac{B_1}{B_2} \quad \text{or} \quad \frac{B_1}{B_2} = \frac{A_1}{A_2} \quad \text{or} \quad \frac{A_2}{A_1} = \frac{B_2}{B_1} \quad \text{or} \quad \frac{B_2}{B_1} = \frac{A_2}{A_1}$$

In an *inverse proportion*, as one quantity increases, the other decreases, and vice versa. This is indicated by comparing the two ratios in the *opposite order*. Thus, if C is inversely proportional to D,

$$\frac{C_1}{C_2} = \frac{D_2}{D_1} \quad \text{or} \quad \frac{D_2}{D_1} = \frac{C_1}{C_2} \quad \text{or} \quad \frac{C_2}{C_1} = \frac{D_1}{D_2} \quad \text{or} \quad \frac{D_1}{D_2} = \frac{C_2}{C_1}$$

Problems

1. Find the ratio of (*a*) 6 to 18 in., (*b*) 1 ft to 2 yd, (*c*) 100 ma to 1 amp, (*d*) 500 cycles to 0.8 kc, and (*e*) 4 hp to 4 kw.

2. In a series circuit, the voltage across a resistance is directly proportional to the resistance. Using a circuit similar to that shown in Fig. 11-4, find R_1 if $E_1 = 90$ volts, $E_1 = 18$ volts, and $R_2 = 80$ ohms.

In Probs. 3 to 6, A is directly proportional to B.

3. Find B_2 if $A_1 = 15$, $A_2 = 6$, and $B_1 = 90$.

4. Find B_1 if $A_1 = 35$, $A_2 = 45$, and $B_2 = 63$.

5. Find A_2 if $A_1 = 27$, $B_1 = 3$, and $B_2 = 8$.

6. Find A_1 if $A_2 = 56$, $B_1 = 4$, and $B_2 = 7$.

In a parallel circuit similar to that shown in Fig. 11-8, the current in each branch is inversely proportional to the resistance.

7. Find I_1 if $I_2 = 0.4$ amp, $R_1 = 100$ ohms, and $R_2 = 150$ ohms.

8. Find I_2 if $I_1 = 1.8$ amp, $R_1 = 225$ ohms, and $R_2 = 75$ ohms.

In a transformer, the currents in the primary and secondary coils are inversely proportional to the voltages. Using a diagram similar to that shown in Fig. 11-3,

9. Find E_p if $E_s = 2,200$ volts, $I_p = 50$ amp, and $I_s = 2.5$ amp.

10. Find I_p if $E_p = 24$ volts, $E_s = 120$ volts, and $I_s = 0.2$ amp.

Test—Ratio and Proportion

1. Find the ratio of (*a*) 5 dimes to 3 nickels, (*b*) 18 in. to 2 yd, (*c*) 3 kw to 8 hp, (*d*) 400 mv to 2 volts, and (*e*) 2 hr to 15 min.

2. *a*. A baseball team won 30 games and lost 20 games. What is the ratio of the games won to the games played?

b. In a radio class, 20 boys passed and 5 boys failed. What is the ratio of the boys passing to the total number of boys? Express this ratio as a per cent.

c. A radio "power" transformer draws 1.2 amp from a 120-volt line and delivers 175 volts at 0.8 amp. Find the ratio of the power output to the power input.

d. If 1 ma flows through a milliammeter and 99 ma flows through its shunt, find the ratio of the meter current to the line current.

3. In a transformer, the voltage is directly proportional to the number of turns. In a diagram similar to that shown in Fig. 11-3, find the number of turns on the secondary N_s if $N_p = 200$ turns, $E_p = 20$ volts, and $E_s = 50$ volts.

4. In a parallel circuit similar to that shown in Fig. 11-8, the current in each branch is inversely proportional to the resistance. Find R_2 if $I_1 = 0.3$ amp, $I_2 = 1.05$ amp, and $R_1 = 490$ ohms.

JOB 11-4: THE AMERICAN WIRE GAGE TABLE

Wires are manufactured in standard sizes which are listed in Table 11-1 and are known as the American Wire Gage (AWG). It has been found that calculations involving these wires may be simplified by expressing their diameters and cross-sectional areas in new units of measurement.

Mils.   The diameter of wires is expressed in terms of *mils* instead of inches.

$$1,000 \text{ mils} = 1 \text{ in.} \qquad \text{or} \qquad 1 \text{ mil} = \frac{1}{1,000} \text{ in.}$$

Changing Units

To change inches to mils: Multiply the number of inches by 1,000.

To change mils to inches: Divide the number of mils by 1,000.

Example 11-13.   A wire has a diameter of 0.162 in. Change the diameter to mils and find the AWG number.

Solution:
$$0.162 \text{ in.} = 0.162 \times 1,000 = 162 \text{ mils} \qquad Ans.$$

In the second column of the AWG table marked "Diameter, mils," read down until you find 162 mils. Read to the left to the column marked "AWG No." to find No. 6 wire.   *Ans.*

Example 11-14.   A wire has a diameter of $\frac{1}{8}$ in. Change the diameter to mils and find the AWG number.

Solution:
$$\frac{1}{8} = 0.125 \text{ in.}$$
$$0.125 \text{ in.} = 0.125 \times 1,000 = 125 \text{ mils} \qquad Ans.$$

Table 11-1. American Wire Gage Table
Resistance of bare annealed copper wire at 20°C (68°F)

AWG No.	Diameter, mils, d	Area, cir mils, d^2	Ohms per 1,000 ft
0000	460.0	211,600	0.0490
000	409.6	167,800	0.0618
00	364.8	133,100	0.0779
0	324.9	105,500	0.0983
1	289.3	83,690	0.1239
2	257.6	66,360	0.1563
3	229.4	52,630	0.1970
4	204.3	41,740	0.2485
5	181.9	33,100	0.3133
6	162.0	26,250	0.3951
7	144.3	20,820	0.4982
8	128.5	16,510	0.6282
9	114.4	13,090	0.7921
10	101.9	10,380	0.9989
11	90.74	8,234	1.260
12	80.81	6,530	1.588
13	71.96	5,178	2.003
14	64.08	4,107	2.525
15	57.07	3,257	3.184
16	50.82	2,583	4.016
17	45.26	2,048	5.064
18	40.30	1,624	6.385
19	35.89	1,288	8.051
20	31.96	1,022	10.15
21	28.46	810.1	12.80
22	25.35	642.4	16.14
23	22.57	509.5	20.36
24	20.10	404.0	25.67
25	17.90	320.4	32.37
26	15.94	254.1	40.81
27	14.20	201.5	51.47
28	12.64	159.8	64.90
29	11.26	126.7	81.83
30	10.03	100.5	103.2
31	8.928	79.70	130.1
32	7.950	63.21	164.1
33	7.080	50.13	206.9
34	6.305	39.75	260.9
35	5.615	31.52	329.0
36	5.000	25.00	414.8
37	4.453	19.83	523.1
38	3.965	15.72	659.6
39	3.531	12.47	831.8
40	3.145	9.888	1,049

In the second column, read down until you find the number closest to 125. This number is 128.5. Read to the left to the first column to find No. 8 wire.   *Ans.*

Example 11-15. Express the diameter of No. 18 wire in mils and inches.

Solution: Read down in the first column until you find No. 18. Read to the right to the second column to find 40.30 mils.

$$40.30 \text{ mils} = 40.30 \div 1,000 = 0.0403 \text{ in.}   Ans.$$

Problems

Using Table 11-1, find the missing values in the following problems.

Problem	Gage No.	Diameter, mils	Diameter, in.
1	?	28.46	?
2	10	?	?
3	?	?	¼
4	?	?	0.05082
5	?	?	$\dfrac{162}{1,000}$
6	?	204.3	?
7	14	?	?
8	12	?	?
9	?	40.30	?
10	?	?	¹⁄₁₆

Circular Mils. The circular mil (cir mil) is the unit of area which is used to measure the cross-sectional area of wires. The circular-mil area is used rather than the ordinary units of area because of the ease of obtaining the circular-mil area when the diameter is given in mils.

Rule: To obtain the circular-mil area of a wire, express the diameter in mils and then square the resulting number.

Formula

$$A = D_m{}^2 \tag{11-1}$$

where A = area, cir mils

D_m = diameter, mils

Example 11-16. Find the circular-mil area A of No. 12 wire.

Solution: Read across to the right from No. 12 in the first column to find the circular-mil area in column 3.

$$\text{Area of No. 12 wire} = 6,530 \text{ cir mils}   Ans.$$

Example 11-17. Find the circular-mil area A of a wire whose diameter is 0.005 in.

Solution:

$$0.005 \text{ in.} = 0.005 \times 1,000 = 5 \text{ mils} = D_m$$
$$A = D_m{}^2 \qquad (11\text{-}1)$$
$$A = 5^2 = 25 \text{ cir mils} \qquad Ans.$$

Rule: To obtain the diameter of a wire in mils, find the square root of the circular-mil area.

Formula

$$D_m = \sqrt{\text{cir mil}} \qquad (11\text{-}2)$$

Example 11-18. Find the diameter of a wire whose cross-sectional area is 25,000 cir mils.

Solution:

$$D_m = \sqrt{\text{cir mil}} \qquad (11\text{-}2)$$
$$D_m = \sqrt{25,000} = 158 \text{ mils} \qquad Ans.$$

(Review Job 7-9 on square root.)
If the diameter is wanted in inches,

$$158 \text{ mils} = \frac{158}{1,000} = 0.158 \text{ in.} \qquad Ans.$$

Problems

Find the missing values in the following problems:

Problem	Diameter, in.	Diameter, mils	Area, cir mils
1	?	10	?
2	0.05	?	?
3	?	?	4,096
4	?	60	?
5	0.032	?	?
6	?	?	9,500
7	?	87.2	?
8	¼	?	?
9	?	?	30,000
10	0.102	?	?

JOB 11-5: RESISTANCE OF WIRES OF DIFFERENT MATERIALS

All materials differ in their atomic structure and therefore in their ability to resist the flow of an electric current. The measure of the ability of a specific material to resist the flow of electricity is called its *specific resistance*.

The *specific resistance K* of a material is the resistance offered by a wire of this material which is 1 ft long with a diameter of 1 mil. The specific resistances of different materials are given in Table 11-2.

Table 11-2. Specific Resistance of Materials in Ohms per Mil-foot at 20°C

Material	K	Material	K
Silver......................	9.7	Tantalum...................	93.3
Copper......................	10.4	German silver (18%)........	200
Gold........................	14.7	Monel metal..............	253
Aluminum...................	17.0	Manganin.................	265
Tungsten....................	34.0	Magnesium	276
Brass.......................	43.0	Constantan	295
Iron (pure).................	60.0	Nichrome	600
Tin.........................	69.0	Nickel	947

Rule: The resistance of a wire is directly proportional to the specific resistance of the material.

Formula

$$\frac{R_1}{R_2} = \frac{K_1}{K_2} \tag{11-3}$$

where R_1 and K_1 = resistance and specific resistance of a wire of one material, respectively

R_2 and K_2 = resistance and specific resistance of a wire of another material, respectively

Example 11-19. A copper wire has a resistance of 5 ohms. What is the resistance of a nichrome wire of the same length and cross-sectional area?

Solution:

Given: Copper wire, $R_1 = 5$ ohms   Find: R_2 of nichrome = ?
$K_1 = 10.4$
Nichrome wire, $K_2 = 600$

$$\frac{R_1}{R_2} = \frac{K_1}{K_2} \tag{11-3}$$

$$\frac{5}{R_2} = \frac{10.4}{600}$$

$$10.4R_2 = 5 \times 600$$

$$10.4R_2 = 3{,}000$$

$$R_2 = \frac{3{,}000}{10.4} = 288 \text{ ohms} \quad Ans.$$

Problems

1. A copper wire has a resistance of 12 ohms.   What is the resistance of an aluminum wire of the same length and diameter?

2. A tungsten wire has a resistance of 40 ohms.   What is the resistance of a nichrome wire of the same length and diameter?

3. A copper wire has a resistance of 2.5 ohms.   What is the resistance of a manganin wire of the same length and diameter?

4. A nichrome wire has a resistance of 125 ohms.   What is the resistance of an iron wire of the same length and diameter?

JOB 11-6: RESISTANCE OF WIRES OF DIFFERENT LENGTHS

Consider two wires of the same material and diameter but of different lengths.   A length of wire may be considered to be made of a large number of small lengths all connected in series.   The total resistance of the length of wire is then equal to the sum of the resistances of all the small lengths.   Therefore, the longer the wire, the greater its resistance.

Rule: The resistance of a wire is directly proportional to its length.

Formula

$$\frac{R_1}{R_2} = \frac{L_1}{L_2} \tag{11-4}$$

where R_1 and L_1 = resistance and length of the first wire, respectively

R_2 and L_2 = resistance and length of the second wire, respectively

Example 11-20.   If 1,000 ft of No. 16 copper wire has a resistance of 4 ohms, find the resistance of 1,800 ft of the same wire.

Solution:

Given: R_1 = 4 ohms   Find: R_2 = ?

L_1 = 1,000 ft

L_2 = 1,800 ft

$$\frac{R_1}{R_2} = \frac{L_1}{L_2} \tag{11-4}$$

$$\frac{4}{R_2} = \frac{1,000}{1,800}$$

$$1,000R_2 = 1,800 \times 4$$

$$1,000R_2 = 7,200$$

$$R_2 = \frac{7,200}{1,000} = 7.2 \text{ ohms} \qquad Ans.$$

Example 11-21.   Find the resistance of 700 ft of No. 20 copper wire. What current flows through the wire when there is a voltage drop of 14.2 volts across the ends of the wire?

Solution:

      Given: L = 700 ft of No. 20 copper wire.   Find: R = ?
             E = 14.2 volts I = ?

1. Find the resistance of No. 20 copper wire.

From the Table 11-1, No. 20 wire has a resistance of 10.15 ohms per 1,000 ft.

2. Find the resistance of 700 ft of this wire.

$$\frac{R_1}{R_2} = \frac{L_1}{L_2} \qquad\qquad (11\text{-}4)$$

$$\frac{10.15}{R_2} = \frac{10\cancel{0}\cancel{0}}{70\cancel{0}}$$

$$10R_2 = 7 \times 10.15$$

$$R_2 = \frac{71.05}{10} = 7.105 \text{ ohms} = 7.1 \text{ ohms} \qquad Ans.$$

3. Find the current.

$$E = IR \qquad\qquad (2\text{-}1)$$

$$14.2 = I \times 7.1$$

$$I = \frac{14.2}{7.1} = 2 \text{ amp} \qquad Ans.$$

Problems

1. If 1,000 ft of No. 12 copper wire has a resistance of 1.6 ohms, find the resistance of 2,300 ft of this wire.

2. Find the resistance of 800 ft of No. 16 copper wire.

3. Find the resistance of 400 ft of No. 20 copper wire.

4. What is the resistance of the primary coil of a transformer if it is wound with 600 ft of No. 20 copper wire?

5. The coil of an electromagnet is wound with 300 ft of No. 16 copper wire. What is the resistance of the coil?   What current will be drawn from a 6-volt battery?

6. The coil of an outboard motor is wound with 100 ft of No. 18 copper wire.   What current will it draw from a 6-volt battery?

7. The four field windings of a motor are connected in series.   If each winding uses 50 ft of No. 32 copper wire, find the total resistance of the field windings.   What current is drawn when the motor is used on a 110-volt line?

8. Find the resistance of a two-wire service line 100 ft long if No. 8 copper wire is used.

9. What is the resistance of a telephone line 1 mile long if No. 18 copper wire is used?   What is the voltage drop across this line if the current is 200 ma?

10. Find the resistance of 10 ft of No. 22 copper wire. What is the resistance of the same length of No. 22 nichrome wire? If this nichrome wire is used as the resistance element in an electric furnace, what current is drawn from a 110-volt line?

JOB 11-7: RESISTANCE OF WIRES OF DIFFERENT AREAS

The flow of electricity in a wire is very similar to the flow of water in a pipe. A large-diameter pipe can carry more water than a small-diameter pipe. Similarly, a large-diameter wire can carry more current than a small-diameter wire. But the ability of a wire to carry a large current means that its resistance is small. Thus, a large-diameter wire has a small resistance while a small-diameter wire has a large resistance. As we have learned, when two quantities depend on each other so that one increases as the other decreases, and vice versa, the relationship is called an *inverse ratio*.

Rule: The resistance of a wire is inversely proportional to its cross-sectional area.

Formula

$$\frac{R_1}{R_2} = \frac{A_2}{A_1} \tag{11-5}$$

where R_1 and A_1 = resistance and area of the first wire, respectively
R_2 and A_2 = resistance and area of the second wire, respectively

Example 11-22. A wire has a resistance of 20 ohms and a cross-sectional area of 320 cir mils. Find the resistance of the same length of wire with an area of 800 cir mils.

Solution:

Given: $R_1 = 20$ ohms   Find: $R_2 = ?$
$A_1 = 320$ cir mils
$A_2 = 800$ cir mils

$$\frac{R_1}{R_2} = \frac{A_2}{A_1} \tag{11-5}$$

$$\frac{20}{R_2} = \frac{800}{320}$$

$$800R_2 = 320 \times 20$$

$$R_2 = \frac{6,400}{800} = 8 \text{ ohms} \qquad Ans.$$

Example 11-23. A certain length of No. 36 copper wire has a resistance of 200 ohms. Find the resistance of the same length of No. 30 wire.

Solution:

Given: First wire: No. 36 = 200 ohms = R_1 Find: R_2 = ?
       Second wire: No. 30

1. From the table, find the circular-mil area of each wire.

A_1 of No. 36 = 25 cir mils
A_2 of No. 30 = 100 cir mils   (approx)

2. Set up the inverse ratio.

$$\frac{R_1}{R_2} = \frac{A_2}{A_1} \tag{11-5}$$

$$\frac{200}{R_2} = \frac{100}{25}$$

$$100R_2 = 200 \times 25$$

$$R_2 = \frac{5{,}000}{100} = 50 \text{ ohms} \qquad Ans.$$

Problems

1. If R_1 = 21 ohms, A_1 = 10,000 cir mils, and A_2 = 4,000 cir mils, find R_2.

2. A wire has a resistance of 30 ohms and a cross-sectional area of 100 cir mils. Find the resistance of the same length of a wire whose area is 320 cir mils.

3. A certain length of No. 30 wire has a resistance of 50 ohms. Find the resistance of the same length of No. 40 wire.

4. A certain length of No. 36 wire has a resistance of 1.5 ohms. Find the resistance of the same length of No. 34 wire.

5. A certain length of No. 12 wire has a resistance of 3.2 ohms. Find the resistance of the same length of No. 18 wire.

JOB 11-8: RESISTANCE OF WIRES OF ANY DIAMETER, ANY LENGTH, OR ANY MATERIAL

In the last three jobs we learned that

1. The resistance is directly proportional to the specific resistance K of the material.

2. The resistance is directly proportional to the length L.

3. The resistance is inversely proportional to the area A.

These three concepts may be combined into one rule.

Rule: The resistance R of a wire is equal to the specific resistance K multiplied by the length in feet L, and divided by the circular-mil area of the wire A.

Formula

$$R = \frac{K \times L}{A} \qquad (11\text{-}6)$$

where R = resistance of wire, ohms

K = specific resistance for a particular material

L = length of the wire, ft

A = area of the wire, cir mils

Example 11-24. Find the resistance of a tungsten wire 10 ft long whose diameter is 0.005 in.

Solution:

Given: Tungsten $K = 34$ Find: $R = ?$

$L = 10$ ft

$D = 0.005$ in.

1. Change the diameter to mils.

$$0.005 \text{ in.} = 0.005 \times 1,000 = 5 \text{ mils}$$

2. Find the circular-mil area.

$$A = D_m{}^2 = 5^2 = 25 \text{ cir mils} \qquad (11\text{-}1)$$

3. Find the resistance of the wire.

$$R = \frac{K \times L}{A} \qquad (11\text{-}6)$$

$$R = \frac{34 \times 10}{25} = \frac{340}{25} = 13.6 \text{ ohms} \qquad Ans.$$

Example 11-25. An electric heater is made with a heating element of 4 ft of No. 30 nichrome wire. (*a*) What is the resistance of the heating coil? (*b*) What current will it draw from a 120-volt line? (*c*) How much power will it use?

Solution: The diagram for the problem is shown in Fig. 11-9.

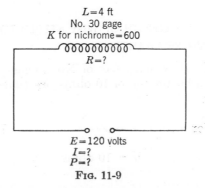

L = 4 ft

No. 30 gage

K for nichrome = 600

R = ?

E = 120 volts

I = ?

P = ?

Fɪɢ. 11-9

a. 1. Find the circular-mil area.   From Table 11-1,

No. 30 = 100.5 cir mils = 100 cir mils   (approx)

2. Find the resistance of the coil.

$$R = \frac{K \times L}{A} \tag{11-6}$$

$$R = \frac{600 \times 4}{100} = \frac{2,400}{100} = 24 \text{ ohms} \quad Ans.$$

b. Find the current drawn.

$$E = IR \tag{2-1}$$
$$120 = I \times 24$$
$$I = {}^{120}\!/_{24} = 5 \text{ amp} \quad Ans.$$

c. Find the power used.

$$P = I \times E \tag{7-1}$$
$$P = 5 \times 120 = 600 \text{ watts} \quad Ans.$$

Problems

1. Find the resistance of a 0.1-in.-diameter copper wire which is 100 ft long.

2. Find the resistance of 150 ft of No. 32 copper wire.

3. Find the resistance of 10 ft of ⅛-in.-diameter silver wire.

4. What is the resistance of 20 ft of No. 20 gage manganin wire?   What current will flow through the wire if the voltage is 6 volts?

5. Find the resistance of 30 ft of No. 24 iron wire.   What current will flow through the wire if it is used as a resistance element across 110 volts? What is the power used?

6. What is the resistance of ½ ft of No. 40 nichrome wire?

7. A winding made of 400 ft of No. 30 copper wire is placed across 6 volts. Find (*a*) the current drawn and (*b*) the power used.

8. Find the resistance of 200 ft of copper annunciator wire whose diameter is 0.04 in.

JOB 11-9: FINDING THE LENGTH OF WIRE NEEDED TO MAKE A CERTAIN RESISTANCE

Example 11-26.   How many feet of No. 20 gage nichrome wire are required to make a heater coil of 10 ohms resistance?

Solution:

Given: *K* for nichrome = 600   Find: *L* = ?
            Gage = No. 20
            R = 10 ohms

1. Find the circular-mil area.   From Table 11-1, for No. 20 gage,

$$A = 1,022 \text{ cir mils}$$

2. Find the length of the wire.

$$R = \frac{K \times L}{A} \tag{11-6}$$

$$\frac{10}{1} = \frac{600 \times L}{1,022}$$

$$600L = 1,022 \times 10$$

$$L = \frac{10,220}{600} = 17.03 \text{ ft} \qquad Ans.$$

Example 11-27.   How much resistance must be placed in series with a 50-volt 50-ohm lamp in order to operate it from a 110-volt line? How many feet of No. 18 German silver wire are required to make this limiting resistor?

Solution: The diagram for the circuit is shown in Fig. 11-10.

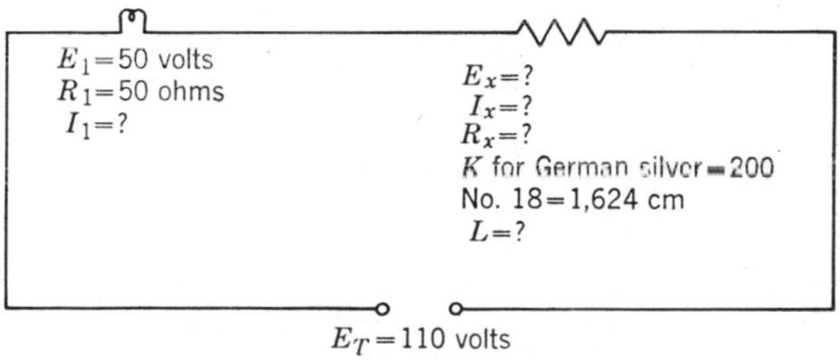

$E_1 = 50$ volts
$R_1 = 50$ ohms
$I_1 = ?$

$E_x = ?$
$I_x = ?$
$R_x = ?$
K for German silver $= 200$
No. $18 = 1,624$ cm
$L = ?$

$E_T = 110$ volts

FIG. 11-10

1. Find the series current.

$$E_1 = I_1 \times R_1 \tag{4-4}$$
$$50 = I_1 \times 50$$
$$I_1 = \frac{50}{50} = 1 \text{ amp}$$

Therefore,

$$I_x = I_1 = 1 \text{ amp} \tag{4-1}$$

2. Find E_x.

$$E_T = E_1 + E_x \tag{4-2}$$
$$110 = 50 + E_x$$
$$E_x = 110 - 50 = 60 \text{ volts}$$

3. Find R_x.

$$E_x = I_x \times R_x \tag{4-5}$$
$$60 = 1 \times R_x$$
$$R_x = 60 \text{ ohms} \qquad Ans.$$

4. Find the length of wire needed to make a 60-ohm resistor.

$$R = \frac{K \times L}{A} \qquad\qquad (11\text{-}6)$$

$$\frac{60}{1} = \frac{200 \times L}{1,624}$$

$$200L = 1,624 \times 60$$

$$L = \frac{97,440}{200} = 487.2 \text{ ft} \qquad Ans.$$

Problems

1. What is the resistance of an aluminum wire 200 ft long if its circular-mil area is 2,000?

2. What is the resistance of a 100-ft-long constantan wire if its diameter is 80 mils?

3. How many feet of 0.01-in.-diameter copper wire are required to make a resistance of 10 ohms?

4. A 0.02-in.-diameter nichrome wire is used for the coils of an electric heater. If the resistance of the coils is to be 18 ohms, how many feet of wire are needed? What are the current and power drawn when the heater is used on a 110-volt line?

5. How many feet of No. 28 copper wire are needed to make an ammeter shunt of 0.2 ohms?

6. What would be the length of the wire in Prob. 5 if manganin wire were used instead of copper?

7. A subway-car heater is made of No. 24 iron wire. It is to operate on 550 volts and 10 amp. How many feet of wire are needed to make the heater?

8. What resistance must be inserted in series with the heater of a 2A3 tube in order to operate it from two dry cells connected in series? The tube takes 2.5 volts at 2.5 amp. What length of No. 20 iron wire is needed to make the resistance?

9. Which of the following has the greater resistance: (a) 50 ft of No. 20 iron wire or (b) 10 ft of No. 18 nichrome wire?

JOB 11-10: FINDING THE DIAMETER OF WIRE NEEDED TO MAKE A CERTAIN RESISTANCE

Example 11-28. What must be the diameter and gage No. of a nichrome heating element 40 ft long if the resistance is to be 20 ohms?

Solution:

Given: K for nichrome = 600   Find: D = ?
$\qquad\qquad R$ = 20 ohms   Gage No. = ?
$\qquad\qquad L$ = 40 ft

1. Find the required circular-mil area.

$$R = \frac{K \times L}{A} \qquad (11\text{-}6)$$

$$\frac{20}{1} = \frac{600 \times 40}{A}$$

$$20A = 24,000$$

$$A = \frac{24,000}{20} = 1,200 \text{ cir mils}$$

Find the diameter in mils.

$$D_m = \sqrt{\text{cir mil}} \qquad (11\text{-}2)$$
$$D_m = \sqrt{1,200} = 34.6 \text{ mils} \qquad Ans.$$

3. Find the gage number. This may be found by looking up the table for either the diameter of 34.6 mils or the area of 1,200 cir mils.

No. 18 = 40.3 mils   No. 18 = 1,624 cir mils
  ?   = 34.6 mils   ?   = 1,200 cir mils
No. 19 = 35.89 mils   No. 19 = 1,288 cir mils

Using either method, the closest gage number is No. 19. However, common practice is always to use the smaller gage number so as to select a wire of smaller resistance and larger current-carrying ability. Therefore, use No. 18 wire.   *Ans.*

Example 11-29. Find the size of copper wire to be used in a two-wire system 100 ft long if the total resistance of the system is to be 1.3 ohms.

Solution: The diagram for the problem is shown in Fig. 11-11.

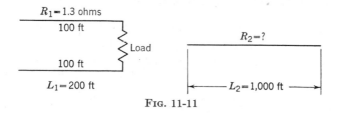

Fig. 11-11

When the wire is made of copper, we can use the Table 11-1 to simplify our calculations. If we can find the resistance per 1,000 ft, we can look up the table to find the wire which has this resistance. The total length L_1 of the two-wire system equals $2 \times 100 = 200$ ft.

Find the resistance per 1,000 ft.

$$\frac{R_1}{R_2} = \frac{L_1}{L_2} \qquad\qquad (11\text{-}4)$$

$$\frac{1.3}{R_2} = \frac{200}{1,000}$$

$$200R_2 = 1.3 \times 1,000$$

$$R_2 = \frac{1,300}{200} = 6.5 \text{ ohms per 1,000 ft}$$

In column 4 of Table 11-1, the next *smaller* resistance per 1,000 ft is 6.385 ohms.   Reading to the left to column 1, we find the gage number to be No. 18.   *Ans.*

Problems

1. What diameter of constantan wire should be used to make a coil of 10 ohms resistance if only 3 ft of wire is used?

2. What must be the diameter of an aluminum wire 2,000 ft long if its resistance is to be 3 ohms?

3. What must be the diameter of an iron wire 40 ft long if the resistance is to be 50 ohms?

4. What size of copper wire should be used for a single line 200 ft long if the allowable resistance is 1 ohm?

5. What diameter of copper wire should be used for a two-wire system 500 ft long if the total resistance is not to exceed 10 ohms?

6. The heating coil of an electric heater using 4 ft of nichrome wire is to have a resistance of 24 ohms.   What gage wire should be used?

7. A rheostat is to be wound with 500 ft of German silver wire to produce a resistance of 60 ohms.   What gage wire should be used?

JOB 11-11: REVIEW OF RESISTANCE OF WIRES

A *mil* is the unit used to measure the diameter of round wires.

A *mil* is equal to one-thousandth of an inch.

A *circular mil* (cir mil) is the unit of area used to measure the cross-sectional area of wires.

Formulas

$$\text{Mils} = \text{inches} \times 1,000$$

$$\text{Inches} = \text{mils} \div 1,000$$

$$A = D_m{}^2 \qquad\qquad (11\text{-}1)$$

$$D_m = \sqrt{\text{cir mil}} \qquad\qquad (11\text{-}2)$$

where A = area of the wire, cir mils
$\quad D_m$ = diameter of the wire, mils

The specific resistance K of a wire is the resistance of a wire 1 ft long with a diameter of 1 mil. The specific resistance of different materials is given in Table 11-2.

The resistance of a wire is directly proportional to its specific resistance.

$$\frac{R_1}{R_2} = \frac{K_1}{K_2} \qquad (11\text{-}3)$$

The resistance of a wire is directly proportional to its length.

$$\frac{R_1}{R_2} = \frac{L_1}{L_2} \qquad (11\text{-}4)$$

The resistance of a wire is inversely proportional to its area.

$$\frac{R_1}{R_2} = \frac{A_2}{A_1} \qquad (11\text{-}5)$$

The general formula for the resistance of any wire is

$$R = \frac{K \times L}{A} \qquad (11\text{-}6)$$

where R = resistance of the wire, ohms
$\quad K$ = specific resistance of the material
$\quad L$ = length of the wire, ft
$\quad A$ = area of the wire, cir mils

Problems

1. Find the diameter in mils and gage number of the wires whose diameters are (a) 0.025 in., (b) 0.102 in., (c) ⅛ in., and (d) 128/1,000 in.

2. Find the area in circular mils of wires whose diameters are (a) 15 mils, (b) 40 mils, (c) 0.01 in., and (d) 0.204 in.

3. A constantan wire has a resistance of 50 ohms. What is the resistance of a manganin wire of the same length and area?

4. Find the resistance of a two-wire line 500 ft long using No. 20 copper wire. Find the voltage drop across this line if the current is 150 ma.

5. A length of No. 12 copper wire has a resistance of 3.6 ohms. What is the resistance of the same length of No. 8 wire?

6. Find the resistance of 6 in. of No. 20 nichrome wire.

7. A resistance element designed to operate at 110 volts and 6 amp is to be made of No. 30 nichrome wire. Find the length of wire needed.

8. What diameter of iron wire 12 ft long is needed to make a resistance of 80 ohms?

Test—Resistance of Wires

1. A copper wire has a resistance of 0.4 ohm. What is the resistance of a nichrome wire of the same length and cross-sectional area?

2. A winding made of 100 ft of No. 26 iron wire is placed across 10 volts. Find (*a*) the resistance of the circuit, (*b*) the current, and (*c*) the power dissipated.

3. A resistance element for an electric enameling kiln is designed to operate at 120 volts and 12 amp. How many feet of nichrome wire 0.01 in. in diameter are needed to make the required resistance?

4. What diameter of copper wire should be used for a two-wire system 125 ft long if the total resistance of the line is not to exceed 8 ohms? Give the answer in mils and inches.

CHAPTER 12

SIZE OF WIRING

JOB 12-1: MAXIMUM CURRENT-CARRYING CAPACITY OF WIRES

Heat is produced whenever a current flows in a wire. The larger the current, the greater the amount of heat that is produced. This heat must be given up to the surrounding atmosphere, or the wire may get hot enough to burst into flame.

The heat produced in a wire depends not only on the current but also on the resistance to that flow of current. Thick wires, because of their low resistance, can carry more current than thin wires before they dangerously overheat. But exactly how many amperes can be safely carried by a particular wire? Can a No. 20 wire carry 30 amp, or is a No. 12 or larger wire required? Many tests have been made by the National Board of Fire Underwriters to determine the largest current which may be safely carried by wires of different sizes and different insulation. The National Electrical Code has set forth these values as shown in Table 12-1. This table gives the *maximum* current permitted in any size wire insulated as indicated.

Using the Table of Allowable Current Capacities

Example 12-1. What is the largest current that may be safely carried by No. 12 rubber-covered wire?

Solution:

1. Locate No. 12 wire in column I.
2. Read across to the right to column V for rubber-covered wire.
3. The answer (20 amp) means that No. 12 rubber-covered wire should never be permitted to carry more than 20 amp.   *Ans.*

Example 12-2. What is the allowable current-carrying capacity of No. 14 varnished-cambric-insulated wire?

Solution:

1. Locate No. 14 wire in column I.
2. Read across to the right to column VI for varnished-cambric-insulated wire.
3. The answer is 25 amp.

Example 12-3. What is the smallest rubber-covered wire that should be used to carry 16 amp?

Solution:

1. Read down column V for rubber-covered wire until you find a number *larger* than 16 amp. This will be 20 amp.
2. Read to the left until you get to column I. No. 12 gage is the smallest wire that can be used. *Ans.*

Example 12-4. What gage wire should be used if the circular-mil area required is 3,000 cir mils?

Solution:

1. Read down column III until you get to the number which is *just larger* than 3,000 cir mils. This number is 4,107 cir mils.
2. Read to the left until you get to column I. No. 14 gage is the smallest wire that may be used. *Ans.*

Example 12-5. What gage wire should be used if the resistance required is 0.5 ohm per 1,000 ft?

Solution:

1. Read down column IV until you get to a number which is *just smaller* than 0.5 ohm. This number is 0.395 ohm.
2. Read to the left until you get to column I. No. 6 gage is the smallest wire that may be used. *Ans.*

Example 12-6. Find the voltage drop along 1,000 ft of No. 10 rubber-covered wire if it is carrying its maximum current.

Solution:

1. Find the maximum current for No. 10 rubber-covered wire. This is 30 amp.
2. Find the resistance per 1,000 ft of No. 10 rubber-covered wire. Read across to the right from No. 10 in column I to find 0.999 ohm in column IV.
3. Find the voltage drop.

$$E = IR \qquad\qquad (2\text{-}1)$$
$$E = 30 \times 0.999 = 29.97 \text{ volts} \qquad Ans.$$

Table 12-1. Table of Allowable Current-carrying Capacities of Copper Conductors
National Electrical Code, 1953

AWG No.	Diameter, mils	Cross section, cir mils	Resistance, ohms per 1,000 ft	Allowable carrying capacity, amp		
				Rubber-covered, Type RH	Varnished cambric, type V	Asbestos, type A
(I)	(II)	(III)	(IV)	(V)	(VI)	(VII)
14	64.1	4,107	2.53	15	25	30
12	80.8	6,530	1.59	20	30	40
10	101.9	10,380	0.999	30	40	55
8	128.5	16,510	0.628	45	50	70
6	162.0	26,250	0.395	65	70	95
4	204.3	41,740	0.249	85	00	120
3	229.4	52,630	0.197	100	105	145
2	257.6	66,370	0.156	115	120	165
1	289.3	83,690	0.124	130	140	190
0	325	105,500	0.0983	150	155	225
00	364.8	133,100	0.0779	175	185	250
000	409.6	167,800	0.0618	200	210	285
0000	460	211,600	0.0490	230	235	340

Summary. Always choose the wire

1. Which can carry *more* current than is required.
2. Which has the *larger* circular-mil area.
3. Which has the *smaller* resistance.

Problems

1. What is the maximum current that may be safely carried by No. 8 varnished-cambric-insulated wire?

2. What is the smallest rubber-covered wire that should be used to carry 50 amp?

3. What gage wire should be used if the circular-mil area required is 18,000 cir mils?

4. What gage wire should be used if the required resistance is not to exceed 0.91 ohm per 1,000 ft?

5. Find the voltage drop along 1,000 ft of No. 8 varnished-cambric-insulated wire when it is carrying its maximum current.

6. What is the smallest varnished-cambric-insulated wire that should be used to carry 62 amp safely?

7. What is the resistance per foot of the smallest rubber-covered wire that should be used to carry 66 amp safely?

8. What size of asbestos-covered wire should be used to carry 42 amp safely?

9. What size of wire should be used if the circular-mil area required is 42,000 cir mils?

10. What is the diameter in mils and inches of the smallest rubber-covered wire that can be used to carry 80 amp safely?

JOB 12-2: FINDING THE MINIMUM SIZE OF WIRE TO SUPPLY A GIVEN LOAD

The minimum size of wire that may be used in any installation depends on two factors: (1) the total current load and (2) the voltage drop in the wire. In this job we shall determine the size of wire needed to carry the given current. In the next job, we shall take the voltage drop into consideration.

Procedure

1. Determine the total current load.
2. Consult the table to find the smallest wire to carry this load.

Example 12-7. What is the smallest size of varnished-cambric-insulated wire that is needed to supply a bank of 50 lamps in parallel if each lamp draws 0.75 amp?

Solution:

Given: 50 lamps in parallel
I per lamp $= 0.75$ amp
Find: Minimum size varnished-cambric-insulated wire $= ?$

1. Find the total current load.

$$I_T = I \text{ per lamp} \times \text{No. of lamps}$$
$$I_T = 0.75 \times 50 = 37.5 \text{ amp.}$$

2. Find the gage number to handle 37.5 amp.
 a. Read down column VI until you get to the first number *larger* than 37.5. This number is 40 amp.
 b. Read to the left from 40 amp until you get to column I, where we read the gage number as No. 10.   *Ans.*

Example 12-8. What is the smallest size of rubber-covered wire that may be used to supply two 10-ohm heating elements operated in parallel from a 220-volt line?

Solution:

Given: $R_1 = 10$ ohms
$R_2 = 10$ ohms
$E_T = 220$ volts
Find: Smallest size of rubber-covered wire $= ?$

1. Find the total resistance.

$$R_T = \frac{R}{N} = \frac{10}{2} = 5 \text{ ohms} \qquad (5\text{-}4)$$

2. Find the total current.

$$I_T = \frac{E_T}{R_T} = \frac{220}{5} = 44 \text{ amp} \qquad (4\text{-}7)$$

3. Find the gage number to handle 44 amp.

a. Read down column V until you get to the first number *larger* than 44 amp.   This number is 45 amp.

b. Read to the left from 45 amp until you get to column I, where we read the gage number as No. 8.   *Ans.*

Example 12-9.   What is the smallest size of slow-burning weather-proof cable that may be used to carry current to a 10-hp motor from a 100-volt source?

Solution:

Given: $P = 10$ hp   Find: Smallest size of slow-burning cable = ?
        $E = 100$ volts

1. Find the watts of power to be delivered by the cable.   Assume an input to the motor equal to 110 per cent of the rated hp.

Input hp = 1.1 × 10 = 11 hp
Watts = hp × 750 = 11 × 750 = 8,250 watts

2. Find the current drawn.

$$P = I \times E \qquad (7\text{-}1)$$
$$8,250 = I \times 100$$
$$I = \frac{8,250}{100} = 82.5 \text{ amp}$$

3. Find the gage number to handle 82.5 amp.   *Note:* For any wire other than rubber-covered or varnished-cambric-insulated wire, use the data for asbestos-covered wire in column VII.

a. Read down column VII until you get to the first number *larger* than 82.5 amp.   This number is 95 amp.

b. Read to the left from 95 amp until you get to column I, where we read the gage number as No. 6.   *Ans.*

Problems

1. What is the minimum size of rubber-covered wire that may be used to supply a load of 60 lamps each drawing 0.91 amp?

2. What is the minimum size of asbestos-covered wire that may be used to supply a load of three 5-ohm electric ovens operated in parallel from a 110-volt line?

3. What is the minimum size of varnished-cambric-covered wire that may be used to supply a load of thirty 200-watt lamps and twenty 100-watt lamps if they are all operated in parallel from the same 110-volt line?

4. A 30-hp motor is to be used on a 220-volt line. If the efficiency of the motor is 90 per cent, what is the smallest size of varnished-cambric-covered wire that may be used?

5. A 220-volt generator supplies motors drawing 5, 10, and 12 kw of power. What is the minimum size of rubber-covered wire that may be used?

JOB 12-3: FINDING THE SIZE OF WIRE NEEDED TO PREVENT EXCESSIVE VOLTAGE DROPS

A wire not only must be able to carry a current without overheating but must also be able to carry this current without too many volts being used up in the wire itself. If the voltage drop in the line is too large, the voltage available at the load will be too small for proper operation of the load. For example, a 117-volt generator is used to supply current to a bank of lamps some distance away. If the supply line should use up 17 volts in supplying this current, then only 100 volts would be available at the lamps and they would be dim. Not only that, but the loss in the line represents wasted power and a very inefficient system. To cover this, the National Electrical Code stipulates that the voltage drop in a line must not be more than 2 per cent of the rated voltage for lighting purposes and not more than 5 per cent of the rated voltage for power installations.

Example 12-10. A bank of lamps draws 32 amp from a 117-volt source 300 ft away. Find the smallest gage of rubber-covered wire that may be safely used.

Solution: The diagram for the circuit is shown in Fig. 12-1.

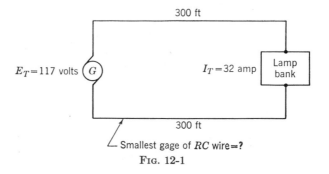

$$E_T = 117 \text{ volts}$$

$$I_T = 32 \text{ amp}$$

Lamp bank

300 ft

300 ft

Smallest gage of *RC* wire = ?

Fig. 12-1

1. Find the allowable voltage drop. For lighting purposes, the Code permits only a 2 per cent drop.   Therefore,

Allowable drop = 2% of 117 = 0.02 × 117 = 2.34 volts

2. Find the line resistance for this drop.

$$E_l = I_l \times R_l \qquad\qquad (6\text{-}1)$$
$$2.34 = 32 \times R_l$$
$$R_l = \frac{2.34}{32} = 0.0731 \text{ ohm}$$

3. Find the circular-mil area of the wire that has this resistance. Since there are two wires, $L = 2 \times 300 = 600$ ft.   Also, the K for copper is 10.4.

$$R = \frac{K \times L}{A} \qquad\qquad (11\text{-}6)$$
$$\frac{0.0731}{1} = \frac{10.4 \times 600}{A}$$
$$0.0731 \times A = 10.4 \times 600$$
$$0.0731A = 6{,}240$$
$$A = \frac{6{,}240}{0.0731} = 85{,}300 \text{ cir mils}$$

4. Find the gage number of the wire whose circular-mil area is *larger* than 85,360 cir mils.

   a. Read down column III until you get to a number *just larger* than 85,360.   This number is 105,500.

   b. Read across to the left to find gage No. 0 in column I.   *Ans.*

Example 12-11.   A bank of lathes is operated by individual motors in a machine shop.   The motors draw a total of 60 amp at 110 volts from the distributing panel box.   What size of rubber-covered wire is required for the two-wire line between the panel box and the switchboard located 100 ft away if the switchboard voltage is 115 volts?

Solution: The diagram for the circuit is shown in Fig. 12-2.

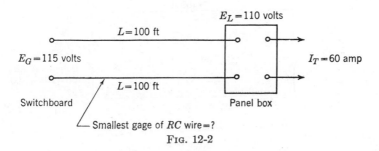

$E_L = 110$ volts

$L = 100$ ft

$E_G = 115$ volts

$I_T = 60$ amp

$L = 100$ ft

Switchboard   Panel box

Smallest gage of *RC* wire = ?

Fig. 12-2

1. Find the line drop between the switchboard and the panel box.

$$E_G = E_l + E_L \qquad (6\text{-}2)$$
$$115 = E_l + 110$$
$$E_l = 115 - 110 = 5 \text{ volts}$$

2. Find the line resistance for this drop.

$$E_l = I_l \times R_l \qquad (6\text{-}1)$$
$$5 = 60 \times R_l$$
$$R_l = \frac{5}{60} = 0.0833 \text{ ohm}$$

3. Find the circular-mil area of the wire that has this resistance. Since there are two wires, $L = 2 \times 100 = 200$ ft.

$$R = \frac{K \times L}{A} \qquad (11\text{-}6)$$
$$\frac{0.0833}{1} = \frac{10.4 \times 200}{A}$$
$$0.0833A = 10.4 \times 200$$
$$A = \frac{2,080}{0.0833} = 25,000 \text{ cir mils}$$

4. Find the gage number of the wire whose circular-mil area is *larger* than 25,000 cir mils.

   a. Read down column III until you get to a number *just larger* than 25,000 cir mils. This number is 26,250.

   b. Read across to the left to find gage No. 6 in column I. This No. 6 wire can safely carry the 60 amp without overheating, since its maximum current-carrying capacity is 65 amp as found in column V for rubber-covered wire. *Ans.*

Example 12-12. A 10-hp motor is operated at an efficiency of 90 per cent from a 232-volt source 100 ft away. What is the minimum size of slow-burning insulated wire that may be used for the line supplying the motor?

Solution: The diagram for the circuit is shown in Fig. 12-3.

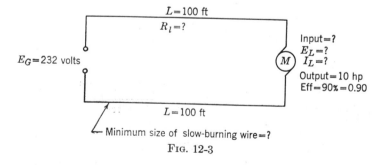

$L = 100$ ft
$R_l = ?$

$E_G = 232$ volts

Input $= ?$
$E_L = ?$
$I_L = ?$

Output $= 10$ hp
Eff $= 90\% = 0.90$

$L = 100$ ft

Minimum size of slow-burning wire $= ?$

Fig. 12-3

1. Find the allowable voltage drop. For power installations, the Code permits a 5 per cent drop. Therefore,

E_l = allowable drop = 5% of 232 = 0.05 × 232 = 11.6 volts

2. Find the voltage at the motor load.

$$E_L = E_G - E_l \qquad (6\text{-}3)$$
$$E_L = 232 - 11.6 = 220.4 \text{ volts}$$

3. Find the input to the motor.

$$\text{Eff} = \frac{\text{output}}{\text{input}} \qquad (9\text{-}2)$$

$$\frac{0.90}{1} = \frac{10 \times 750}{\text{input}}$$

$$0.00 \text{ input} = 7,500$$

$$\text{Input} = \frac{7,500}{0.90} = 8,333 \text{ watts}$$

4. Find the current drawn.

$$P_L = I_L \times E_L \qquad (7\text{-}1)$$
$$8,333 = I_L \times 220.4$$

$$I_L = \frac{8,333}{220.4} = 37.8 \text{ amp}$$

5. Find the resistance of the line wires. Since $I_l = I_L$,

$$E_l = I_l \times R_l \qquad (6\text{-}1)$$
$$11.6 = 37.8 \times R_l$$

$$R_l = \frac{11.6}{37.8} = 0.3069 \text{ ohm}$$

6. Find the circular-mil area of the wire that has this resistance. Since there are two wires, $L = 2 \times 100 = 200$ ft.

$$R = \frac{K \times L}{A} \qquad (11\text{-}6)$$

$$\frac{0.3069}{1} = \frac{10.4 \times 200}{A}$$

$$0.3069A = 10.4 \times 200$$

$$A = \frac{2,080}{0.3069} = 6,777 \text{ cir mils}$$

7. Find the gage number of the wire whose circular-mil area is *larger* than 6,777 cir mils.

a. Read down column III until you get to a number *just larger* than 6,777 cir mils. This number is 10,380.

b. Read across to the left to find gage No. 10 in column I. This No. 10 wire can safely carry the required 37.8 amp without overheating, since its maximum current-carrying capacity is 55 amp as found in column VII for slow-burning wire. *Ans.*

Problems

1. What is the minimum size of rubber-covered wire that may be used to carry 40 amp if the allowable voltage drop is 10 volts per 1,000 ft of wire?

2. A 50-ft two-wire extension line is to carry 30 amp with a voltage drop of only 5 volts. What is the smallest size of weatherproof cable that may be used?

3. A bank of lamps draws 90 amp from a 110-volt line. What size of rubber-covered wire should be used if the voltage drop along 150 ft of the two-wire system must not exceed 3 volts?

4. A bank of lamps draws 50 amp from a 117-volt source 40 ft away. Find the smallest gage rubber-covered wire that may be used for this two-wire system if the voltage drop must not exceed 2 per cent of the voltage at the source.

5. A 20-kw motor load is 100 ft from a 230-volt source. If the allowable voltage drop is 5 per cent, what is the smallest size of varnished-cambric-covered wire that may be used?

6. A load 400 ft from a generator requires 80 amp. The generator voltage is 115.6 volts, and the load requires 110 volts. What is the smallest size of rubber-covered wire that may be used?

7. A 10-hp motor is located 20 ft from a 225-volt generator. What is the smallest size of slow-burning wire that may be used?

8. A 10-hp motor operates at an efficiency of 85 per cent at a distance of 100 ft from a 122-volt generator. What is the smallest size of varnished-cambric-covered wire that may be used?

9. A generator supplies 5.5 kw at 125 volts to a motor 500 ft away. The motor delivers 6.3 hp at an efficiency of 90 per cent. Find (*a*) the watt input to the motor, (*b*) the watts lost in the line, (*c*) the current delivered to the line, (*d*) the voltage drop in the line, and (*e*) the smallest size of rubber-covered wire that may be used.

10. Calculate the smallest size of weatherproof wire required to conduct current to one hundred 220-ohm lamps in parallel which are located 125 ft from a generator delivering 112 volts. The lamps must receive 110 volts.

JOB 12-4: AREAS OF PLANE FIGURES

In our next job we shall calculate the size of entrance wires to small houses. Part of the calculation involves finding the floor area of the house. These areas are generally in the form of squares, rectangles, triangles, or parts of circles.

A *square* (Fig. 12-4) is a figure with four *equal* sides and four right angles in the corners.

A *rectangle* (Fig. 12-5) is a four-sided figure whose opposite sides are equal and parallel with four right angles in the corners.

A *triangle* (Fig. 12-6) is a three-sided figure.

A *circle* (Fig. 12-7) is a figure every point of which is the same distance from a fixed point called the center. The *radius* of a circle is the distance from the center to the outside of the circle. The *diameter* of the circle is the distance across the circle through the center.

The *area* of a figure is the amount of *surface* contained within its boundaries. Areas are measured by the number of *unit surfaces* contained in the figure.

Units of Area. A square inch (sq in.) is the amount of surface contained within a square which is one inch long on all four sides. A square foot (sq ft) is the amount of surface contained within a square which is one foot long on all four sides.

In order to calculate the area of a figure by the following formulas, be sure to express all lengths in the *same* units of measurement.

Formulas

Area of a Square. In Fig. 12-4,

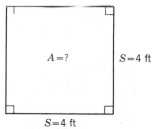

$A=?$ $S=4$ ft

$S=4$ ft

FIG. 12-4. A square.

$$A = S \times S \quad \text{or} \quad A = S^2 \quad\quad (12\text{-}1)$$

where A = area, square units
S = side of square

Example 12-13. Find the area of the square shown in Fig. 12-4.

Solution:

$$A = S^2 \quad\quad\quad (12\text{-}1)$$
$$A = 4^2 = 4 \times 4 = 16 \text{ sq ft} \quad Ans.$$

Area of a Rectangle.   In Fig. 12-5,

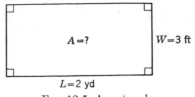

FIG. 12-5. A rectangle.

$$A = L \times W \hspace{3cm} (12\text{-}2)$$

where A = area, square units
   L = length
   W = width

Example 12-14.   Find the area of the rectangle shown in Fig. 12-5.

Solution:

1. Since all measurements must be in the same units, we must change 2 yd into the equivalent number of feet.

$$L = 2 \text{ yd} = 2 \times 3 = 6 \text{ ft}$$

2. Find the area.

$$A = L \times W \hspace{3cm} (12\text{-}2)$$
$$A = 6 \times 3 = 18 \text{ sq ft} \hspace{1cm} Ans.$$

Area of a Triangle.   In Fig. 12-6,

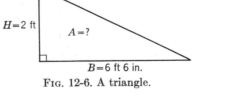

FIG. 12-6. A triangle.

$$A = \tfrac{1}{2} \times B \times H \hspace{3cm} (12\text{-}3)$$

where A = area, square units
   B = base
   H = height

Example 12-15.   Find the area of the triangle shown in Fig. 12-6.

Solution:

1. Change the measurement of the base into feet.

$$B = 6 \text{ ft } 6 \text{ in.} = 6\tfrac{6}{12} \text{ ft} = 6\tfrac{1}{2} \text{ ft}$$

2. Find the area.

$$A = \tfrac{1}{2} \times B \times H \qquad\qquad (12\text{-}3)$$
$$A = \tfrac{1}{2} \times 6\tfrac{1}{2} \times 2$$
$$A = \tfrac{1}{2} \times \tfrac{13}{2} \times 2 = 6\tfrac{1}{2} \text{ sq ft} \qquad Ans.$$

Area of a Circle.   In Fig. 12-7,

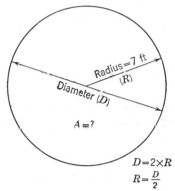

FIG. 12-7. A circle.

$$A = \pi R^2 \qquad\qquad (12\text{-}4)$$

or since $\pi = \tfrac{22}{7}$

$$A = \tfrac{22}{7} \times R^2 \qquad\qquad (12\text{-}5)$$

where A = area, square units
R = radius

Example 12-16.   Find the area of the circle shown in Fig. 12-7.

Solution:

$$A = \tfrac{22}{7} \times R^2 \qquad\qquad (12\text{-}5)$$
$$A = \tfrac{22}{7} \times 7^2 = \tfrac{22}{7} \times 49 = 154 \text{ sq ft} \qquad Ans.$$

Problems

Find the area in each problem.

Prob-lem	Type of figure	L	W	B	H	Radius	S
1	Square	....	....	...	.....	.....	8 ft
2	Rectangle	14 ft	9 ft				
3	Triangle	....	....	12 ft	10 ft		
4	Circle	....	....	...	....	14 ft	
5	Rectangle	11 ft 6 in.	9 ft				
6	Triangle	....	....	14 ft	9 ft 8 in.		
7	Circle	....	....	...	....	7 ft 6 in.	
8	Rectangle	18 ft 4 in.	11 ft 6 in.				

JOB 12-5: DETERMINING ENTRANCE-WIRE SIZES FOR SMALL HOUSES

The size of the entrance wire depends on the total power that will be used in the house. The total power requirements are those for (1) lighting, (2) normal household appliances, (3) electric ranges and heating devices, and (4) motors.

The National Electrical Code specifies the following wattages:

1. For lighting purposes, a minimum of 2 watts per square foot of floor area.

2. For normal household appliances, a blanket 1,500 watts is added to the total wattage.

3. Electric ranges are calculated at only 80 per cent of the maximum wattage, since all heating elements will probably not be used at the same time.

4. The wattages for motors are calculated above their rated wattage because of the ordinarily low power factor and the possibility of overloading. The standard wattages are given below.

$$\frac{1}{6} \text{ hp} = 500 \text{ watts}$$
$$\frac{1}{4} \text{ hp} = 750 \text{ watts}$$
$$\frac{1}{3} \text{ hp} = 900 \text{ watts}$$
$$\frac{1}{2} \text{ hp} = 1,100 \text{ watts}$$
$$\frac{3}{4} \text{ hp} = 1,400 \text{ watts}$$
$$1 \text{ hp} = 1,600 \text{ watts}$$

Oil-burner motors are calculated at 100 per cent of the rated wattage. Home workshop motors are calculated at 50 per cent of the rated wattage.

Procedure

1. Find the total wattage required.
2. Assume a 230-volt entrance voltage.
3. Determine the current requirements.
4. Find the size of entrance wire.

Example 12-17. Find the size of entrance wire required for a house with a floor area in the shape of a rectangle measuring 50 by 40 ft and including a $\frac{1}{4}$-hp oil-burner motor.

Solution:

Given: Floor area $\begin{cases} L = 50 \text{ ft} \\ W = 40 \text{ ft} \end{cases}$ Find: Size of entrance wire = ?

$\frac{1}{4}$-hp motor

1. Find the area of the house.

$$A = L \times W = 50 \times 40 = 2,000 \text{ sq ft} \qquad (12\text{-}2)$$

2. Find the total wattage required.

    a. Lighting, at 2 watts per sq ft = 2 × 2,000 = 4,000
    b. Appliances, at a blanket 1,500   = 1,500
                                             Total = 5,500 watts

Section 2203 of the National Electrical Code specifies that the first 3,000 watts are being used 100 per cent of the time but only 35 per cent of the remaining wattage is in use at the same time. Therefore, the basis for the service wire is as follows.

	Per cent of time in use		*Actual watts*
First 3,000 watts	×	100	= 3,000
5,500 − 3,000 = 2,500	×	35	= 875
¼-hp motor (750 watts)	×	100	= 750
		Total =	4,625 watts

3. Find the total current demand.

$$P = I \times E \qquad\qquad (7\text{-}1)$$
$$4,625 = I \times 230$$
$$I = \frac{4,625}{230} = 20.1 \text{ amp}$$

4. Find the minimum size of wire needed. Since the service wire is usually a rubber-covered wire brought in through some kind of conduit, we read down column V of Table 12-1 until we get to a number just larger than 20.1 amp. This number is 30 amp. Reading across to the left to column I will give us No. 10 wire. However, in Section 2304a, the Code demands the use of No. 6 wire as the very minimum unless there are more than two branch circuits, in which case No. 8 wire is permitted. Since motors are always wired on a separate branch circuit, the house will have more than two branches and the No. 8 wire should be used. *Ans.*

Example 12-18. Find the size of entrance wire required for the house shown in Fig. 12-8. Include a 6,000-watt electric range, a ¼-hp oil-burner motor, and two ⅙-hp home workshop motors.

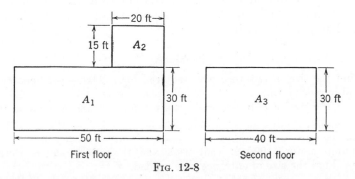

FIG. 12-8

Solution:

> Given: Electric range = 6,000 watts
> ¼-hp motor (750 watts)
> Two ⅙-hp motors (500 watts each)
> Find: Size of entrance wire = ?

1. Find the floor area of the house.

First floor		*Second floor*	
$A_1 = L \times W$	$A_2 = L \times W$	$A_3 = L \times W$	(12-2)
$A_1 = 50 \times 30$	$A_2 = 20 \times 15$	$A_3 = 40 \times 30$	
$A_1 = 1,500$ sq ft	$A_2 = 300$ sq ft	$A_3 = 1,200$ sq ft	

Total area = 1,500 + 300 + 1,200 = 3,000 sq ft

2. Find the total wattage required.

   a. Lighting, at 2 watts per sq ft = 2 × 3,000 = 6,000
   b. Appliances, at a blanket 1,500   = 1,500

Total = 7,500 watts

Item		*Per cent of time in use*		*Actual watts*
First 3,000 watts	×	100	=	3,000
7,500 − 3,000 = 4,500	×	35	=	1,575
6,000-watt range	×	80	=	4,800
¼-hp motor (750 watts)	×	100	=	750
Two ⅙-hp shop motors (2 × 500 = 1,000)	×	50	=	500

Total = 10,625 watts

3. Find the total current demand.

$$P = I \times E \qquad\qquad (7\text{-}1)$$
$$10,625 = I \times 230$$
$$I = \frac{10,625}{230} = 46.2 \text{ amp}$$

4. Find the minimum gage number of rubber-covered wire. Read down column V of Table 12-1 until you get to a number just larger than 46.2 amp. This number is 65 amp. Read across to the left to column I to get No. 6 wire. *Ans.*

Problems

1. Find the size of entrance wire required for a 3,000-sq-ft house with a ¼-hp oil-burner motor.

2. Find the size of entrance wire required for a 3,500-sq-ft house with a ¼-hp oil-burner motor and a 2-kw water heater rated at 100 per cent use.

3. The house shown in Fig. 12-9 includes a ¼-hp oil-burner motor, a ½-hp water-pump motor (100 per cent use), and three ⅙-hp home workshop motors. Find the size of entrance wire needed.

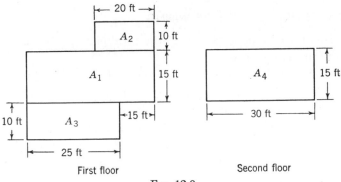

FIG. 12-9

4. The house shown in Fig. 12-10 includes a ¼-hp oil-burner motor, a ½ hp water-pump motor, a 7-kw electric range, and a 1-kw electric water heater. Find the size of entrance wire needed.

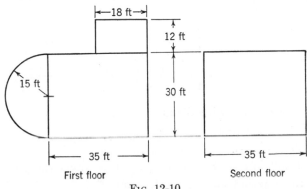

FIG. 12-10

5. A large guest house at a summer resort has a floor plan as shown in Fig. 12-11. It includes the following items: ten 0.8-kw electric heaters, two 8-kw electric ranges, two ⅓-hp washing-machine motors, a 4-kw water heater, and three ⅙-hp motors for the workshop. The heaters and washing machines are rated at 75 per cent use. Find the size of entrance wire.

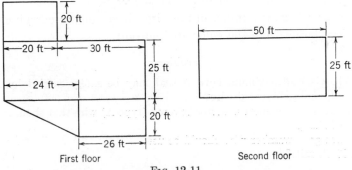

FIG. 12-11

JOB 12-6: REVIEW OF SIZE OF WIRING

The size of a wire depends on (1) the total current load and (2) the voltage drop in the wires.

To find the smallest wire that may be used in a given job

1. Find the total current drawn by the load.
2. Find the voltage drop in the supply wires.
3. Find the maximum resistance of the line wires.
4. Find the circular-mil area of the required wire.
5. Look up Table 12-1 to find the wire which has the next larger circular-mil area.
6. Look up the table to find the wire which can carry *more* current than that required by the load.
7. Choose the larger of the two wires found in steps 5 and 6.

Areas

Square:	$A = S^2$	(12-1)
Rectangle:	$A = L \times W$	(12-2)
Triangle:	$A = \frac{1}{2} \times B \times H$	(12-3)
Circle:	$A = \frac{22}{7} \times R^2$	(12-5)

Determining Entrance-wire Sizes

1. Find the floor area.
2. Double the area to get the wattage for lighting.
3. Add 1,500 watts for general appliances to get the gross wattage.
4. The total actual wattage is the sum of
   a. First 3,000 watts at 100 per cent.
   b. Remaining wattage at 35 per cent.
   c. Motors and hot-water heaters at 100 per cent.
   d. Electric ranges at 80 per cent.
   e. Workshop motors at 50 per cent.
5. Find the total current drawn at 230 volts.
6. Select the gage number of the wire whose current-carrying capacity is just larger than the calculated current.

Problems

1. What is the maximum current that may be safely carried by No. 10 varnished-cambric-covered wire?

2. What is the smallest asbestos-covered (type A) wire that should be used to carry 56 amp?

3. What gage number wire should be used if the circular mil area required is 52,000 cir mils?

4. What is the diameter in mils of the smallest rubber-covered wire that should be used to carry 22 amp?

5. What size of varnished-cambric-insulated wire is needed to supply a 5-hp motor operating at an efficiency of 90 per cent from a 220-volt line?

6. What size of rubber-covered wire is needed to supply a bank of ten 200-watt lamps and two ½-hp motors connected in parallel across a 110-volt line?

7. Find the size of rubber-covered wire needed to supply two 8-ohm heaters in parallel across 122 volts.

8. What is the smallest gage of rubber-covered wire that may be used to carry a current of 32 amp if the allowable voltage drop is 6 volts per 1,000 ft of wire?

9. A 50-amp 112-volt load is located 200 ft from a switch-board delivering 115 volts. Find the smallest varnished-cambric-covered wire that may be safely used in this two-wire system.

10. A lamp bank draws 60 amp from a 230-volt source 500 ft away. Assuming a maximum voltage drop of 2 per cent, what is the smallest rubber-covered wire that may be used?

11. A 5-hp motor operates at an efficiency of 87 per cent at a distance of 50 ft from a 232-volt source. Find the smallest size of rubber-covered wire that may be safely used.

12. A house has a floor area of 2,600 sq ft. It contains a 4-kw electric range, a ¼-hp washing-machine motor (40 per cent use), a ¼-hp oil-burner motor, a 1-kw hot-water heater, and a ⅓-hp home workshop motor. Find the size of the entrance wire.

Test—Size of Wiring

1. *a.* What is the maximum current that may be safely carried by No. 12 weatherproof cable?

b. What is the smallest rubber-covered wire that should be used to carry 31 amp?

c. What gage number wire should be used if the circular-mil area required is 17,000 cir mils?

d. What is the diameter in mils of the smallest varnished-cambric-insulated wire that should be used to carry 27 amp?

2. What size of rubber-covered wire should be used to supply a bank of six 150-watt lamps and a ¾-hp motor connected in parallel across a 120-volt line?

3. A 15-kw motor load is located 75 ft from a 230-volt source. If the allowable voltage drop is 5 per cent, what is the smallest rubber-covered wire that may be used?

4. A house has a floor area of 2,000 sq ft. It contains a 2.5-kw electric range, a ¼-hp washing-machine motor (40 per cent use), a ¼-hp oil-burner motor, and a 1.5-kw hot-water heater. Find the size of entrance wire required.

CHAPTER 13

TRIGONOMETRY FOR ALTERNATING-CURRENT ELECTRICITY

JOB 13-1: TRIGONOMETRIC FUNCTIONS OF A RIGHT TRIANGLE

Trigonometry is the study of the relationships that exist among the sides and angles of a triangle. These relationships will form a basic mathematical tool used in the solution of a-c electrical problems.

Angles. An angle is a figure formed when two lines meet at a point. In Fig. 13-1, the lines OA and OC are the sides of the angle. They meet at the point O, which is the vertex of the angle.

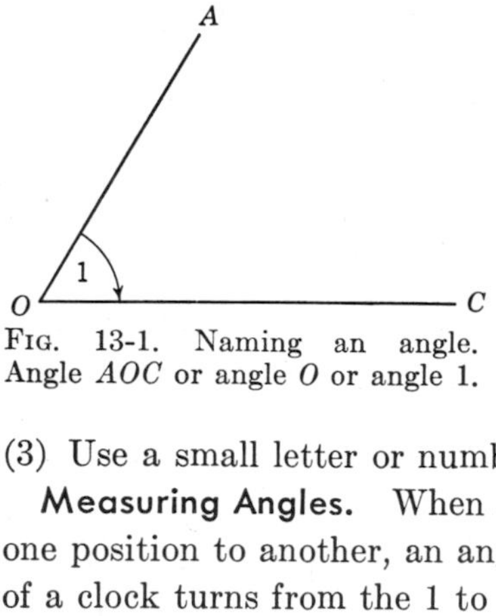

FIG. 13-1. Naming an angle. Angle AOC or angle O or angle 1.

Naming Angles. The angle shown in Fig. 13-1 may be named in three ways. (1) Use three capital letters, setting them down in order from one end of the angle to the other. Thus the angle may be named $\angle AOC$ or $\angle COA$. (2) Use only the capital letter at the vertex of the angle, as $\angle O$. (3) Use a small letter or number inside the angle, as $\angle 1$.

Measuring Angles. When a straight line *turns* about a point from one position to another, an angle is formed. When the minute hand of a clock turns from the 1 to the 3, the hand has turned through an angle approximately equal to $\angle AOC$. An angle is measured *by the amount of rotation of a line about a fixed point*. The end of the minute hand of a clock describes a circle as it revolves around the dial. The circumference of this circle is divided into 60 parts. In Fig. 13-2a, the angle formed by a rotation through $\frac{1}{60}$ part of the circle is called one minute. In ordinary angular measurement, a circle is divided into 360 parts as shown in Fig. 13-2b. The angle formed by a rotation through $\frac{1}{360}$ part of the circle is called one degree ($1°$).

A *right angle* is an angle formed by a rotation through one-fourth of a circle, as ∠*ABC* in Fig. 13-3. Since a complete circle contains 360°, a right angle contains ¼ × 360, or 90°.

An *acute angle* is an angle containing *less* than 90°, as ∠*AOC* in Fig. 13-1.

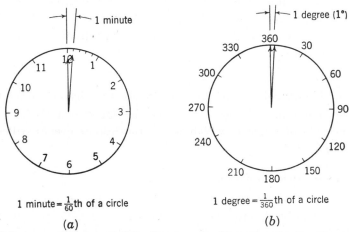

1 minute = $\frac{1}{60}$th of a circle   1 degree = $\frac{1}{360}$th of a circle

(a)   (b)

Fig. 13-2. An angle is measured by the amount of rotation of a line about a fixed point.

Triangles. A triangle is a closed plane figure of three sides. Triangles are named by naming the three vertices of the triangle using capital letters. The letters are then given in order around the triangle. Thus in Fig. 13-3, the triangle is named △*ACB* or △*CBA* or △*BAC* or △*ABC* or △*BCA* or △*CAB*.

A *right triangle* is a triangle which contains a right angle, as △*ABC* in Fig. 13-3. The little square at ∠*B* is used to indicate a right angle.

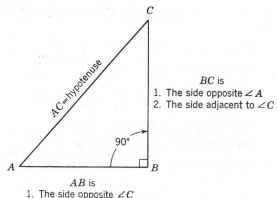

BC is
1. The side opposite ∠*A*
2. The side adjacent to ∠*C*

AB is
1. The side opposite ∠*C*
2. The side adjacent to ∠*A*

Fig. 13-3. Naming the sides of a right triangle.

Naming the Sides of a Right Triangle. In trigonometry, the sides of a right triangle are named depending on which of the *acute* angles are used. In Fig. 13-3,

For angle A:

1. The side opposite the right angle is called the *hypotenuse* (AC).

2. The side opposite angle A is called the *opposite side* (BC).

3. The side of angle A which is *not* the hypotenuse is called the *adjacent side* (AB).

For angle C:

1. The side opposite the right angle is called the hypotenuse (AC).

2. The side opposite angle C is called the opposite side (AB).

3. The side of angle C which is *not* the hypotenuse is called the *adjacent side* (BC).

The Trigonometric Formulas

The Tangent of an Angle. In addition to degrees, the size of an angle may also be described in terms of the lengths of the sides of a right triangle formed from the angle. Refer to Fig. 3-4, in which each space represents one unit of length. From various points on one side of angle A, lines have been drawn making right angles with the other side. These lines have formed the right triangles ABE, ACF, and ADG. Notice that all these triangles contain the same angle A.

	In ABE	In ACF	In ADG
Hypotenuse $= AB =$	5	$AC =$ 10	$AD =$ 12.5
Side opposite $\angle A = BE =$	3	$CF =$ 6	$DG =$ 7.5
Side adjacent $\angle A = AE =$	4	$AF =$ 8	$AG =$ 10

In each triangle, let us divide the side opposite $\angle A$ by the side adjacent to $\angle A$.

In $\triangle ABE$, $\quad \dfrac{\text{side opposite } \angle A}{\text{side adjacent } \angle A} = \dfrac{BE}{AE} = \dfrac{3}{4} = 0.75$

In $\triangle ACF$, $\quad \dfrac{\text{side opposite } \angle A}{\text{side adjacent } \angle A} = \dfrac{CF}{AF} = \dfrac{6}{8} = 0.75$

In $\triangle ADG$, $\quad \dfrac{\text{side opposite } \angle A}{\text{side adjacent } \angle A} = \dfrac{DG}{AG} = \dfrac{7.5}{10} = 0.75$

Notice that this particular division of the opposite side by the adjacent side always resulted in the same answer *regardless* of the size of the triangle. This is true because all the triangles contain the same angle A. The ratio of these sides remains constant because they all describe the same angle A. This constant number describes the size of angle A and is called the *tangent of angle A*. Therefore, if the tangent of an unknown angle were calculated to be 0.75, then the angle would be equal to angle A, or about 37°. If the angle changes, then the number for the tangent of the angle will also change. However, the tangent of every angle is a specific number which never changes. These numbers are found in Table 13-1.

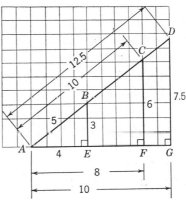

Rule: The tangent of an angle =

$$\frac{\text{side opposite the angle}}{\text{side adjacent to the angle}}.$$

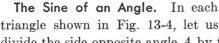

Formula

$$\tan \angle = \frac{o}{a} \qquad (13\text{-}1)$$

FIG. 13-4. Diagram used to obtain the trigonometric formulas.

The Sine of an Angle. In each triangle shown in Fig. 13-4, let us divide the side opposite angle A by the side called the hypotenuse.

In $\triangle ABE$, $\dfrac{\text{side opposite } \angle A}{\text{hypotenuse}} = \dfrac{BE}{AB} = \dfrac{3}{5} = 0.6$

In $\triangle ACF$, $\dfrac{\text{side opposite } \angle A}{\text{hypotenuse}} = \dfrac{CF}{AC} = \dfrac{6}{10} = 0.6$

In $\triangle ADG$, $\dfrac{\text{side opposite } \angle A}{\text{hypotenuse}} = \dfrac{DG}{AD} = \dfrac{7.5}{12.5} = 0.6$

Once again, the resulting quotients are fixed regardless of the size of the triangles. This number is called the *sine of angle A* and is *another* way to describe the size of the angle. If the angle changes, then the number for the sine of the angle will also change. However, the sine of every angle is a specific number which never changes. These numbers are also found in Table 13-1.

Rule: The sine of an angle = $\dfrac{\text{side opposite the angle}}{\text{hypotenuse}}.$

Formula

$$\sin \angle = \frac{o}{h} \qquad (13\text{-}2)$$

The Cosine of an Angle. In each triangle shown in Fig. 13-4, let us divide the side adjacent to the angle A by the hypotenuse.

In $\triangle ABE$, $\dfrac{\text{side adjacent } \angle A}{\text{hypotenuse}} = \dfrac{AE}{AB} = \dfrac{4}{5} = 0.8$

In $\triangle ACF$, $\dfrac{\text{side adjacent } \angle A}{\text{hypotenuse}} = \dfrac{AF}{AC} = \dfrac{8}{10} = 0.8$

In $\triangle ADG$, $\dfrac{\text{side adjacent } \angle A}{\text{hypotenuse}} = \dfrac{AG}{AD} = \dfrac{10}{12.5} = 0.8$

Here, too, the resulting quotients are fixed regardless of the size of the triangles. This number is called the *cosine of angle A* and is a third way to describe the size of the angle. If the angle changes, then the number for the cosine of the angle will also change. However, the cosine of every angle is a specific number which never changes. These numbers are found in Table 13-1.

Rule: The cosine of an angle $= \dfrac{\text{side adjacent to the angle}}{\text{hypotenuse}}$.

Formula

$$\cos \angle = \frac{a}{h} \tag{13-3}$$

Example 13-1.   Find the sine, cosine, and tangent of $\angle A$ in the triangle shown in Fig. 13-5.

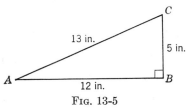

FIG. 13-5

Solution:

1. Name the sides using $\angle A$ as the reference angle.

Hypotenuse $= AC = 13$ in.
Opposite side $= BC = 5$ in.
Adjacent side $= AB = 12$ in.

2. Find the values of the three functions.

$\sin \angle A = \dfrac{o}{h}$ $\cos \angle A = \dfrac{a}{h}$ $\tan \angle A = \dfrac{o}{a}$

$\sin \angle A = \frac{5}{13}$ $\cos \angle A = \frac{12}{13}$ $\tan \angle A = \frac{5}{12}$

$\sin \angle A = 0.384$ $\cos \angle A = 0.923$ $\tan \angle A = 0.417$ *Ans.*

Example 13-2.   Find the sine, cosine, and tangent of $\angle B$ in the triangle shown in Fig. 13-6.

Solution:

1. Name the sides, using $\angle B$ as the reference angle.

Hypotenuse $= BD = 65$ in.
Opposite side $= CD = 33$ in.
Adjacent side $= BC = 56$ in.

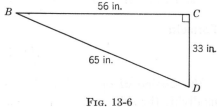

FIG. 13-6

2. Find the values of the three functions.

$$\sin \angle B = \frac{o}{h} \qquad\qquad \cos \angle B = \frac{a}{h} \qquad\qquad \tan \angle B = \frac{o}{a}$$

$$\sin \angle B = \tfrac{33}{65} \qquad\qquad \cos \angle B = \tfrac{56}{65} \qquad\qquad \tan \angle B = \tfrac{33}{56}$$

$$\sin \angle B = 0.5077 \qquad \cos \angle B = 0.8615 \qquad \tan \angle B = 0.5893 \qquad Ans.$$

Problems

Calculate the sine, cosine, and tangent of the angles named in each problem below.

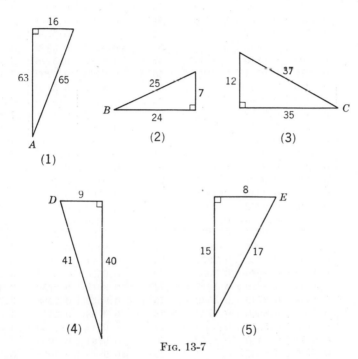

Fig. 13-7

JOB 13-2: USING THE TABLE OF TRIGONOMETRIC FUNCTIONS

Since the values of the trigonometric functions of an angle never change, it is possible to set these values down in a table such as is shown in Table 13-1.

Example 13-3. Find the value of sin 50°.

Solution: Follow down the column marked "Angle" until you reach 50°. Read across to the right to find the number 0.7660 in the sine column. Therefore,

$$\sin 50° = 0.7660 \qquad Ans.$$

Table 13-1. Values of the Trigonometric Functions

Angle	sin	cos	tan	Angle	sin	cos	tan
0°	0.0000	1.0000	0.0000	46°	0.7193	0.6947	1.0355
1°	0.0175	0.9998	0.0175	47°	0.7314	0.6820	1.0724
2°	0.0349	0.9994	0.0349	48°	0.7431	0.6691	1.1106
3°	0.0523	0.9986	0.0524	49°	0.7547	0.6561	1.1504
4°	0.0698	0.9976	0.0699	50°	0.7660	0.6428	1.1918
5°	0.0872	0.9962	0.0875	51°	0.7771	0.6293	1.2349
6°	0.1045	0.9945	0.1051	52°	0.7880	0.6157	1.2799
7°	0.1219	0.9925	0.1228	53°	0.7986	0.6018	1.3270
8°	0.1392	0.9903	0.1405	54°	0.8090	0.5878	1.3764
9°	0.1564	0.9877	0.1584	55°	0.8192	0.5736	1.4281
10°	0.1736	0.9848	0.1763	56°	0.8290	0.5592	1.4826
11°	0.1908	0.9816	0.1944	57°	0.8387	0.5446	1.5399
12°	0.2079	0.9781	0.2126	58°	0.8480	0.5299	1.6003
13°	0.2250	0.9744	0.2309	59°	0.8572	0.5150	1.6643
14°	0.2419	0.9703	0.2493	60°	0.8660	0.5000	1.7321
15°	0.2588	0.9659	0.2679	61°	0.8746	0.4848	1.8040
16°	0.2756	0.9613	0.2867	62°	0.8829	0.4695	1.8807
17°	0.2924	0.9563	0.3057	63°	0.8910	0.4540	1.9626
18°	0.3090	0.9511	0.3249	64°	0.8988	0.4384	2.0503
19°	0.3256	0.9455	0.3443	65°	0.9063	0.4226	2.1445
20°	0.3420	0.9397	0.3640	66°	0.9135	0.4067	2.2460
21°	0.3584	0.9336	0.3839	67°	0.9205	0.3907	2.3559
22°	0.3746	0.9272	0.4040	68°	0.9272	0.3746	2.4751
23°	0.3907	0.9205	0.4245	69°	0.9336	0.3584	2 6051
24°	0.4067	0.9135	0.4452	70°	0.9397	0.3420	2.7475
25°	0.4226	0.9063	0.4663	71°	0.9455	0.3256	2.9042
26°	0.4384	0.8988	0.4877	72°	0.9511	0.3090	3.0777
27°	0.4540	0.8910	0.5095	73°	0.9563	0.2924	3.2709
28°	0.4695	0.8829	0.5317	74°	0.9613	0.2756	3.4874
29°	0.4848	0.8746	0.5543	75°	0.9659	0.2588	3.7321
30°	0.5000	0.8660	0.5774	76°	0.9703	0.2419	4.0108
31°	0.5150	0.8572	0.6009	77°	0.9744	0.2250	4.3315
32°	0.5299	0.8480	0.6249	78°	0.9781	0.2079	4.7046
33°	0.5446	0.8387	0.6494	79°	0.9816	0.1908	5.1446
34°	0.5592	0.8290	0.6745	80°	0.9848	0.1736	5.6713
35°	0.5736	0.8192	0.7002	81°	0.9877	0.1564	6.3138
36°	0.5878	0.8090	0.7265	82°	0.9903	0.1392	7.1154
37°	0.6018	0.7986	0.7536	83°	0.9925	0.1219	8.1443
38°	0.6157	0.7880	0.7813	84°	0.9945	0.1045	9.5144
39°	0.6293	0.7771	0.8098	85°	0.9962	0.0872	11.4300
40°	0.6428	0.7660	0.8391	86°	0.9976	0.0698	14.3010
41°	0.6561	0.7547	0.8693	87°	0.9986	0.0523	19.0810
42°	0.6691	0.7431	0.9004	88°	0.9994	0.0349	28.6360
43°	0.6820	0.7314	0.9325	89°	0.9998	0.0175	57.2900
44°	0.6947	0.7193	0.9657	90°	1.0000	0.0000	
45°	0.7071	0.7071	1.0000				

Example 13-4.   Find the value of tan 30°.

Solution: Follow down the column marked "Angle" until you get to 30°.   Read across to the right to find the number 0.5774 in the tangent column.   Therefore,

$$\tan 30° = 0.5774 \qquad Ans.$$

Finding the Angle When the Function Is Given

Example 13-5.   Find $\angle A$ if cos $A = 0.7314$.

Solution: Follow down the column marked "cos" until you find the number 0.7314.   Read across to the left to find 43° in the column marked "Angle."   Therefore,

$$\angle A = 43° \qquad Ans.$$

Example 13-6.   Find $\angle B$ if tan $B = 1.8807$.

Solution: Follow down the column marked "tan" until you find the number 1.8807.   Read across to the left to find 62° in the column marked "Angle."   Therefore,

$$\angle B = 62° \qquad Ans.$$

Problems

Find the number of degrees in each angle.

1. tan $A = 0.3249$	**4.** cos $D = 0.9877$	**7.** tan $G = 0.5774$
2. sin $B = 0.6428$	**5.** sin $E = 0.5000$	**8.** cos $H = 0.7071$
3. cos $C = 0.1736$	**6.** tan $F = 1.0724$	**9.** sin $J = 0.8660$

Finding the Angle When the Function Is Not in the Table

Example 13-7.   Find $\angle A$ if tan $A = 0.5120$.

Solution: The number 0.5120 is not in the table under the column "tan" but lies between 0.5095 (27°) and 0.5317 (28°).   Choose the number closest to 0.5120.

$$\begin{array}{l} \tan 27 = 0.5095 \\ \tan A = 0.5120 \\ \tan 28 = 0.5317 \end{array} \left. \begin{array}{l} \\ \\ \end{array} \right\} \begin{array}{l} \text{difference} = 0.0025 \\ \\ \text{difference} = 0.0197 \end{array}$$

The smaller difference indicates the closer number.   Therefore,

$$\angle A = 27° \qquad Ans.$$

Problems

Find the number of degrees in each angle correct to the nearest degree.

1. tan $A = 0.2700$	**4.** sin $D = 0.2350$	**7.** tan $G = 0.2783$
2. cos $B = 0.7500$	**5.** cos $E = 0.4172$	**8.** cos $H = 0.1645$
3. sin $C = 0.8500$	**6.** tan $F = 1.9120$	**9.** sin $J = 0.7250$

JOB 13-3: FINDING THE ACUTE ANGLES OF A RIGHT TRIANGLE

In order to find the value of an angle in any problem, it is only necessary to find the number for the sine *or* the cosine *or* the tangent of the angle. If we know *any one* of these values, we can determine the angle by finding the number in the appropriate column of the table.

Example 13-8. Find $\angle A$ and $\angle B$ in the triangle of Fig. 13-8.

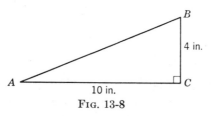

B

4 in.

A

10 in.

C

Fig. 13-8

Solution:

1. Name the sides which have values, using $\angle A$ as the reference angle.

4 in. = the side *opposite* $\angle A$
10 in. = the side *adjacent* $\angle A$

2. Choose the trigonometric formula which uses the *opposite* and *adjacent* sides.

$$\tan A = \frac{o}{a} = \frac{4}{10} = 0.4000 \qquad (13\text{-}1)$$

3. Find the number in the tangent table closest to 0.4000.

$$\angle A = 22° \text{ (nearest angle)} \qquad Ans.$$

4. Since the two acute angles of any right triangle always total 90°,

$$\angle B = 90° - \angle A \qquad (13\text{-}4)$$
$$\angle B = 90° - 22° = 68° \qquad Ans.$$

Example 13-9. The phase angle in an a-c circuit may be represented by $\angle\theta$ (angle theta) as shown in Fig. 13-9. Find $\angle\theta$ and $\angle B$.

Solution:

1. Name the sides which have values, using $\angle\theta$ as the reference angle.

100 ohms = hypotenuse
90 ohms = side adjacent $\angle\theta$

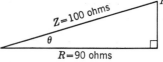

$Z = 100$ ohms

B

θ

$R = 90$ ohms

Fig. 13-9. The angle theta (θ) is the phase angle in an inductive a-c circuit.

2. Choose the trigonometric formula which uses the adjacent side and the hypotenuse.

$$\cos \theta = \frac{a}{h} = \frac{90}{100} = 0.9000 \qquad (13\text{-}3)$$

3. Find the number in the cosine table closest to 0.9000.

$$\angle\theta = 25° \text{ (nearest angle)} \qquad Ans.$$

4. Since the two acute angles of a right triangle always total 90°,

$$\angle B = 90° - \angle \theta \qquad\qquad (13\text{-}4)$$
$$\angle B = 90° - 25° = 65° \qquad Ans.$$

Problems

1. Find $\angle A$ and $\angle B$ in the right triangle shown in Fig. 13-10.

Using Fig. 13-10, find $\angle A$ and $\angle B$ if

2. $AC = 100$ ft and $BC = 70$ ft.
3. $BC = 4$ in. and $AB = 8$ in.
4. $BC = 40$ ohms and $AC = 25$ ohms.
5. $AC = 200$ ohms and $AB = 350$ ohms.
6. $BC = 300$ watts and $AB = 1,000$ watts.
7. $AC = 600$ ohms and $AB = 960$ ohms.
8. $BC = 7.5$ volts and $AC = 12.5$ volts.
9. $BC = 12.4$ amp and $AB = 67.8$ amp.
10. $AC = 62.5$ ohms and $BC = 100$ ohms.

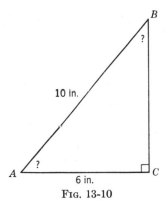

Fig. 13-10

JOB 13-4: FINDING THE SIDES OF A RIGHT TRIANGLE

Example 13-10. Find (*a*) side BC and (*b*) $\angle B$ of the right triangle shown in Fig. 13-11.

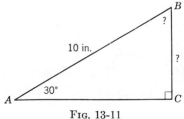

Fig. 13-11

Solution:

a. Find the side BC.

   1. Select the angle to be used ($\angle A = 30°$).
   2. Select the side to be found (BC).
   3. Select one other side whose value is known ($AB = 10$ in.).

4. Name these two sides.

$$BC = \text{side } opposite\ \angle A$$
$$10 \text{ in.} = AB = hypotenuse$$

5. Select the correct trigonometric formula. It will be the formula that uses these two sides—the *opposite* and the *hypotenuse*. Only the *sine* formula uses the *opposite* side and the *hypotenuse*.

$$\sin A = \frac{o}{h} \qquad\qquad (13\text{-}2)$$

$$\sin 30° = \frac{BC}{10}$$

From Table 13-1, the sin 30° = 0.5000.   Therefore,

$$\frac{0.5000}{1} = \frac{BC}{10}$$

$$BC = 0.5000 \times 10 = 5 \text{ in.} \qquad Ans.$$

b. Find ∠B.

$$\angle B = 90° - \angle A \qquad\qquad (13\text{-}4)$$
$$\angle B = 90° - 30° = 60° \qquad Ans.$$

Example 13-11.   Find side BC in the right triangle shown in Fig. 13-12.

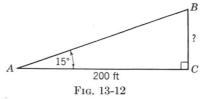
Fig. 13-12

Solution: Find the side BC.
1. Select the angle to be used ($\angle A = 15°$).
2. Select the side to be found (BC).
3. Select one other side whose value is known ($AC = 200$ ft).

4. Name these two sides.

$$BC = \text{the side } opposite \ \angle A$$
$$200 \text{ ft} = AC = \text{the side } adjacent \ \angle A$$

5. Select the correct trigonometric formula.   It will be the formula that uses these two sides—the *opposite* and the *adjacent*.   Only the tangent formula uses the *opposite* side and the *adjacent* side.

$$\tan A = \frac{o}{a} \qquad\qquad (13\text{-}1)$$

$$\tan 15° = \frac{BC}{200}$$

From Table 13-1, the tan 15° = 0.2679.   Therefore,

$$\frac{0.2679}{1} = \frac{BC}{200}$$
$$BC = 0.2679 \times 200 = 53.58 \text{ ft} \qquad Ans.$$

Example 13-12.   The relationship among the impedance Z, the resistance R, and the capacitive reactance X_C of an a-c circuit is shown in Fig. 13-13.   Find the impedance.
Solution: Find the impedance Z represented by side AB.

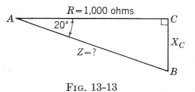
Fig. 13-13

1. Select the angle to be used ($\angle A = 20°$).
2. Select the side to be found (AB).
3. Select one other side whose value is known ($AC = 1,000$ ohms).

4. Name these two sides.

$$AB = hypotenuse$$
$$1,000 \text{ ohms} = AC = \text{side } adjacent \angle A$$

5. Select the correct trigonometric formula.   It will be the formula that uses these two sides—the *adjacent* and the *hypotenuse*.   Only the cosine formula uses the *adjacent* side and the *hypotenuse*.

$$\cos A = \frac{a}{h} \qquad\qquad (13\text{-}3)$$

$$\cos 20° = \frac{1,000}{AB}$$

From Table 13-1, the cos 20° = 0.9397.   Therefore,

$$\frac{0.9397}{1} = \frac{1,000}{AB}$$
$$AB \times 0.9397 = 1,000$$
$$AB = \frac{1,000}{0.9397} = 1,064 \text{ ohms}$$
$$\text{Impedance } Z = 1,064 \text{ ohms} \qquad Ans.$$

Problems

Use the triangle shown in Fig. 13-11 for the following problems.
1. Find AC and $\angle B$ if $AB = 20$ in. and $\angle A = 60°$.
2. Find BC and $\angle B$ if $AB = 26$ ft and $\angle A = 40°$.
3. Find AC and $\angle A$ if $BC = 75$ ft and $\angle B = 50°$.
4. Find AC and $\angle B$ if $AB = 400$ watts and $\angle A = 28°$.
5. Find AB and $\angle B$ if $BC = 75.5$ ohms and $\angle A = 30°$.
6. Find AB and $\angle B$ if $AC = 30$ ohms and $\angle A = 25°$.
7. Find BC and $\angle A$ if $AC = 500$ ft and $\angle B = 28°$.
8. Find AC and $\angle A$ if $AB = 36.8$ in. and $\angle B = 35°$.
9. Find BC and $\angle B$ if $AB = 475$ ohms and $\angle A = 15°$.
10. Find AC and $\angle A$ if $AB = 92.8$ volts and $\angle B = 15°$.

JOB 13-5: REVIEW OF TRIGONOMETRY

Formulas

1. Tangent of an angle $= \dfrac{\text{opposite side}}{\text{adjacent side}}$.

$$\tan \angle = \frac{o}{a} \qquad\qquad (13\text{-}1)$$

2. Sine of an angle $= \dfrac{\text{opposite side}}{\text{hypotenuse}}$.

$$\sin \angle = \frac{o}{h} \qquad\qquad (13\text{-}2)$$

3. Cosine of an angle $= \dfrac{\text{adjacent side}}{\text{hypotenuse}}$.

$$\cos \angle = \frac{a}{h} \qquad\qquad (13\text{-}3)$$

4. The sum of the two acute angles of a right triangle equals 90°.

$$\angle A + \angle B = 90° \qquad\qquad (13\text{-}4)$$

Procedure for Finding Angles in a Right Triangle

1. Name the sides which have values, using the angle to be found as the reference angle.
2. Choose the trigonometric formula which uses these sides.
3. Substitute values, and divide.
4. Find the number in the table closest to this quotient. Be certain to look in the column indicated by step 2.
5. Find the angle in the angle column corresponding to this number.
6. Use formula (13-4) to find the other acute angle.

Procedure for Finding Sides in a Right Triangle

1. Select the angle to be used.
2. Select the side to be found.
3. Select one other side whose value is known.
4. Name these two sides.
5. Select the correct trigonometric formula which uses these sides.
6. Substitute values, using Table 13-1.
7. Solve the equation.

Problems

Find the value of the following functions.

1. $\sin 36°$.   **2.** $\cos 78°$.   **3.** $\tan 69°$.   **4.** $\sin 52°$.   **5.** $\cos 25°$.

Find angle A, correct to the nearest degree.

6. $\sin A = 0.5878$ **9.** $\cos A = 0.9800$ **12.** $\tan A = 0.1340$
7. $\cos A = 0.4226$ **10.** $\sin A = 0.7200$ **13.** $\cos A = 0.2868$
8. $\tan A = 5.7500$ **11.** $\tan A = 0.3113$ **14.** $\sin A = 0.7240$

Use the triangle shown in Fig. 13-11 for the following problems:

15. Find $\angle A$ if $BC = 30$ and $AC = 40$.

16. Find $\angle B$ if $AC = 50$ and $AB = 100$.

17. Find $\angle B$ if $BC = 25$ and $AB = 75$.

18. Find $\angle A$ if $BC = 16$ and $AB = 65$.

19. Find $\angle B$ if $AC = 22.5$ and $BC = 14$.

20. Find $\angle A$ if $AC = 4.5$ and $AB = 20.5$.

21. Find BC if $AB = 2,200$ watts and $\angle A = 25°$.

22. Find AC if $AB = 600$ watts and $\angle A = 8°$.

23. Find AB if $BC = 28.6$ and $\angle B = 42°$.

24. Find AB if $AC = 9.3$ ohms and $\angle A = 34°$.

25. Find BC if $AC = 750$ ohms and $\angle A = 48°$.

26. Find AC if $BC = 17.6$ ft and $\angle B = 60°$.

27. Find AC if $AB = 4,000$ watts and $\angle B = 45°$.

28. Find BC if $AB = 2,500$ watts and $\angle A = 15°$.

29. Find AB if $BC = 142$ volts and $\angle A = 37°$.

30. Find AC if $AB = 85.8$ ohms and $\angle A = 83°$.

Test—Trigonometry

1. Find angle A, correct to the nearest degree, if (a) $\sin A = 0.7416$, (b) $\tan A = 0.9150$, and (c) $\cos A = 0.3333$.

Use a diagram similar to Fig. 13-11 for the problems 2 to 5.

2. Find $\angle B$ and $\angle A$ if $BC = 20$ and $AB = 45$.

3. Find BC if $AB = 100$ and $\angle A = 40°$.

4. Find AC if $BC = 60$ and $\angle A = 75°$.

5. Find AB if $BC = 30$ and $\angle A = 30°$.

CHAPTER 14

INTRODUCTION TO A-C ELECTRICITY

JOB 14-1: POSITIVE AND NEGATIVE NUMBERS

Many of the calculations, graphs, and tables used to solve problems in a-c circuits require an understanding of positive and negative numbers. These numbers, commonly called *signed* numbers, are used to indicate *opposite* amounts, such as a *gain or a loss* in voltage, an *increase or a decrease* in loudness, or currents that flow in *opposite directions*.

Writing Positive and Negative Numbers. In our daily conversations we often indicate opposite quantities by pairs of words such as north or south, up or down, gain or loss, and win or lose. In our electrical work, it is much easier to indicate opposite quantities by the use of the plus sign (+) or the minus sign (−). For example, 5° above zero may be written as +5° and 5° below zero may be written as −5°. A current in one direction is written as +10 amp but as −10 amp if the flow is in the opposite direction. Numbers preceded by a minus sign are called *negative numbers*. The minus sign must always be written before a negative number. If no sign is written before a number, the quantity is understood to be a positive number. Signed numbers are usually written to agree with the following system. Gains, increases, directions to the right or upward are written as positive (+). Losses, decreases, directions to the left or downward are written as negative (−).

Problems

Write the following quantities as signed numbers:
1. A loss of $3.
2. A temperature of 8° below zero.
3. 23° north latitude.
4. 70° east longitude.
5. An increase in loudness of 2 decibels (db).

6. A drop of 10° in temperature.

7. Ten miles per hour slower.

8. Eight paces to the right.

9. Five blocks downtown.

10. Twenty feet below sea level.

11. If the voltage of the ground is considered to be zero volts, indicate a voltage of 4 volts below ground.

12. Indicate a grid bias of 2 volts below ground.

Addition of Signed Numbers

Rule: To add two positive numbers, add the numbers and place the plus sign before the sum.

Example 14-1. A gain of 7 plus a gain of 3 equals a gain of 10 may be indicated as

$$(+7) + (+3) = +10 \qquad Ans.$$

Rule: To add two negative numbers, add the numbers and place the minus sign before the sum.

Example 14-2. A loss of 5 plus a loss of 2 equals a loss of 7 may be indicated as

$$(-5) + (-2) = -7 \qquad Ans.$$

Rule: To add two numbers of *different* sign, *subtract* the numbers and place the sign of the larger before the answer.

Example 14-3. A gain of 7 plus a loss of 3 equals a total gain of 4 may be indicated as

$$(+7) + (-3) = +4 \qquad Ans.$$

Example 14-4. A loss of 9 plus a gain of 4 equals a total loss of 5 may be indicated as

$$(-9) + (+4) = -5 \qquad Ans.$$

Problems

Add the signed numbers indicated in each problem.

1. $(+3) + (+9)$	10. $\begin{array}{r} +18 \\ +14 \\ \hline \end{array}$	14. $\begin{array}{r} -47 \\ -23 \\ \hline \end{array}$
2. $(-6) + (-5)$		
3. $(+8) + (-2)$	11. $\begin{array}{r} -26 \\ +12 \\ \hline \end{array}$	15. $\begin{array}{r} -75 \\ +23 \\ \hline \end{array}$
4. $(-10) + (+3)$		
5. $(-12) + (-5)$	12. $\begin{array}{r} +36 \\ -14 \\ \hline \end{array}$	16. $\begin{array}{r} -8.2 \\ +11.6 \\ \hline \end{array}$
6. $(+16) + (+3)$		
7. $(+18) + (-11)$	13. $\begin{array}{r} -6 \\ +22 \\ \hline \end{array}$	17. $\begin{array}{r} -10.5 \\ +12.4 \\ \hline \end{array}$
8. $(-21) + (+9)$		
9. $(-8) + (-9)$		

18. -16.8
$\underline{+7}$

19. $(-\tfrac{1}{4}) + (+\tfrac{1}{2})$

20. $(+\tfrac{5}{8}) + (-\tfrac{1}{4})$

21. $(-\tfrac{1}{2}) + (-\tfrac{1}{3})$

22. $-16\tfrac{7}{8}$
$\underline{+8\tfrac{3}{4}}$

23. $+3\tfrac{9}{16}$
$\underline{-9\tfrac{1}{4}}$

24. $-15\tfrac{3}{4}$
$\underline{+28\tfrac{1}{2}}$

25. A 12SK7 tube is to operate with a grid bias of -3 volts. What is the voltage on the grid when the a-c signal input to the grid is (a) 3 volts, (b) 2 volts, (c) 1 volt, (d) -1 volt, (e) -2 volts?

JOB 14-2: GRAPHS

In Fig. 14-1, the current that flows through the resistor depends on the voltage that is applied across the ends of the resistor. If the voltage changes, then the current will also change. Let us prepare a table of values of different voltages and the resulting currents using Ohm's law.

Voltage E	Resistance R	Current I
0	10	0
20	10	2
40	10	4
60	10	6
80	10	8
100	10	10

Quantities like voltages and currents whose values may change are called *variables*. An *independent variable*, like voltage, is one whose value is changed in order to observe the effect on another *dependent variable*, like the current. Tables of information like the above are fairly easy to understand and interpret. A glance at the data tells us that the current will double if the voltage is doubled. However, as the information given in a table becomes more complicated, it becomes more difficult to understand and interpret. The relationships between the two variables may be made more evident by presenting the data in the form of a picture, or *graph*.

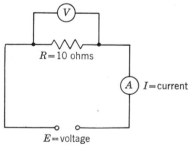

Fig. 14-1. Changes in the independent variable (voltage) cause corresponding changes in the dependent variable (current).

A graph is a picture that shows the effect of one variable on another. Graphs are used throughout the electronics industry to present information in simple form, to describe the operation of circuits, and to illustrate relationships that cannot be shown by data presented in tabular form.

The Scale of a Graph. Graphs are drawn on paper ruled with uniformly spaced horizontal and vertical lines. Every fifth line or every

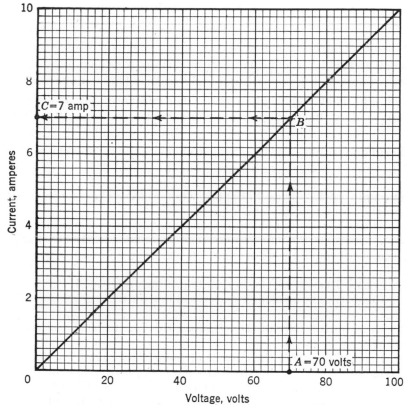

FIG. 14-2. The current through a 10-ohm resistor depends on the voltage across it.

tenth line may be heavier than the rest in order to make it easier to read the graph. Figure 14-2, which shows the graph of the data in the foregoing table, is drawn on paper ruled 10 boxes to the inch. The two heavy lines at right angles to each other are the *base lines*, or *reference lines*. The horizontal line, or *abscissa*, is generally used to describe the independent variable, while the vertical base line, or *ordinate*, is used for the dependent variable. The value of each box along each base line must be indicated on the graph. This is called the *scale* for that variable. The highest value of the variable will determine the scale to be used.

For the voltage or abscissa: If we had 100 boxes, we could make each box equal to 1 volt and indicate the scale up to 100 volts. However, only 50 boxes are available. Therefore, in order to show 100 volts, each box must have a value of 100 ÷ 50, or 2 volts for every box. Only every tenth box is numbered in order to keep the graph neat and uncluttered.

For the current or ordinate: The vertical current scale need not be the same as the horizontal scale. Actually, since the highest value of current that must be indicated is only 10 amp, we would have a graph only 5 boxes high if we used the same scale. This would cramp the graph and make it difficult to read. Since 50 boxes are available, in order to show 10 amp, each box must have a value of 10 ÷ 50, or 0.2 amp for each box. Only every tenth box is numbered.

Reading Graphs. As one variable changes, the corresponding value of the other variable may be read from the graph.

Example 14-5. Using Fig. 14-2, what is the value of the current when the voltage is 70 volts?

Solution: Notice that this information is not included in the table. Without a graph, the information could be obtained only by substitution in the formula for Ohm's law. To get the information from the graph,

1. Locate 70 volts on the horizontal voltage scale at A.
2. Read straight up along this vertical line until the graph is reached at B.
3. Read horizontally to the left along this line to reach the vertical current scale at C.
4. Read the value of the current at point C as 7 amp.   *Ans.*

Example 14-6. If a constant voltage is applied across the ends of different resistors, the resulting current may be calculated by Ohm's law. This information may then be shown as a graph such as Fig. 14-3, in which a constant voltage of 10 volts was applied across different resistances. Using this graph, find the current when the resistance is (*a*) 5 ohms and (*b*) 7 ohms.

Solution:

    a. 1. Locate 5 ohms at A on the horizontal resistance scale.
       2. Read straight up to the graph at B.
       3. Read horizontally to the left to reach the vertical current scale at C.
       4. Read the value of the current at point C as 2 amp.   *Ans.*

b. 1. Locate 7 ohms at *D* on the horizontal resistance scale.

2. Read straight up to the graph at *E*.

3. Read horizontally to the left to reach the vertical current scale at *F*.

4. Read the value of the current at point *F* as slightly more than 1.4 amp.   *Ans.*

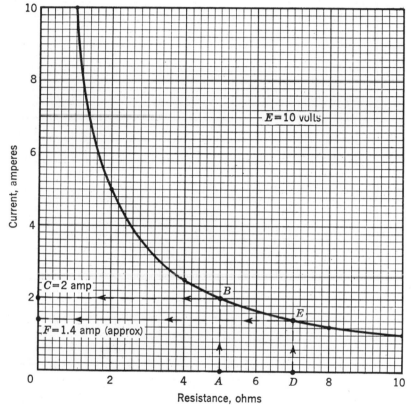

Fɪɢ. 14-3. The relationship between current and resistance at a constant voltage.

Plotting Graphs

Example 14-7.   In determining the characteristic curve of a 6J5 tube at 0 volts grid bias, the voltage on the plate E_p was varied and the corresponding plate current I_p was measured.   The data obtained is shown in the following table.   Plot the graph.

Point No..................	1	2	3	4	5	6
Plate voltage E_p, volts......	20	30	40	60	80	100
Plate current I_p, ma........	1.0	1.5	2.7	5.5	8.2	11.1

Solution: The finished curve is shown in Fig. 14-4.

1. Draw two base lines at right angles to each other.

2. Label the horizontal line as the plate voltage in volts and the vertical line as the plate current in milliamperes.

3. Select appropriate scales for each. Since the maximum voltage is 100 volts, we can use 1 box to represent 2 volts. This will require

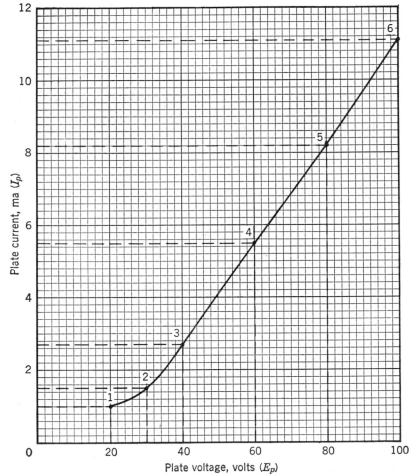

FIG. 14-4. E_p-I_p curve for a 6J5 tube at 0 volts grid bias.

$100 \div 2$, or 50 boxes. Number every tenth box. On the current scale, to show at least 12 ma, we can use 5 boxes to represent 1 ma, which will require $5 \times 12 = 60$ boxes. Each box will then represent 0.2 ma. Number every tenth box.

4. Plot the individual points. To locate point 1, find 20 volts on the horizontal scale. Draw a light line straight up. Now find the corresponding current (1.0 ma) on the vertical scale. Draw a light

line straight across.   These two lines will intersect at point 1.   In the same manner, plot points 2 to 6.   Notice that our choice of values for the current scale makes it easy to locate tenths of a milliampere.   Each box represents 0.2 ma, and half a box represents 0.1 ma.

5. Draw a smooth curve through the points.   If all the points do not fall on this smooth curve, draw the curve so that there are as many points over the line as under it.

Graphs with Positive and Negative Values.

Many graphs have negative as well as positive values to be considered, and these values must be located on the graph.   To do this, the two base lines are extended as shown in Fig. 14-5 to form the horizontal axis X-X' and the vertical axis Y-Y'.   The two axes meet at the *origin O*.   Values along the X axis measured to the *right* of Y-Y' are *positive;* values measured to the *left* of Y-Y' are *negative.*   Values along the Y axis measured *upward* from X-X' are *positive;* values *downward* from X-X' are *negative.*   For example, in Fig. 14-5, the points are located depend-

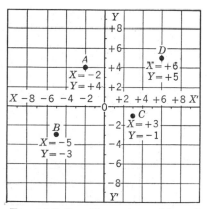

Fig. 14-5. Locating points with positive and negative coordinates.

ing on the values of X and Y.   These values are called the coordinates of the point.   All points are located starting from the origin O.   To locate point A, move two units to the *left* along the X axis, since $X = -2$.   Then move four units *up* along this line, since $Y = +4$. To locate point B, move five units to the *left* along the X axis, since $X = -5$.   Then move three units *down* along this line, since $Y = -3$. To locate point C, move three units to the *right* along the X axis, since $X = +3$.   Then move one unit *down* along this line, since $Y = -1$. To locate point D, move six units to the *right* along the X axis, since $X = +6$.   Then move five units *up* along this line, since $Y = +5$.

Example 14-8.   For a constant plate voltage, the plate current will change when the grid voltage changes.   Plot the $E_g I_p$ curve of a tube from the following data.

Grid voltage, volts.....	−3.0	−2.5	−2	−1.5	−1.0	−0.5	0	0.5	1.0
Plate current, ma......	0.1	0.3	0.6	1.5	2.4	3.3	4.3	5.1	6.0
Point number..........	1	2	3	4	5	6	7	8	9

Solution: The curve is shown in Fig. 14-6.   Each box along the grid voltage or X axis is worth 0.2 volt.   Each box along the plate current or Y axis is worth 0.2 ma.

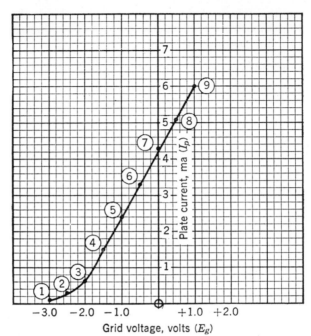

FIG. 14-6. An E_g-I_p curve.   At a constant plate voltage, the plate current depends on the grid voltage.

Problems

1. Figure 14-7 is a graph showing the current taken by an incandescent lamp at various voltages.   Find the current taken at the following voltages: (*a*) 30 volts, (*b*) 45 volts, (*c*) 50 volts, (*d*) 65 volts, (*e*) 80 volts, (*f*) 100 volts, and (*g*) 120 volts.

2. Figure 14-8 is a graph showing the resistance in ohms per 1,000 ft of copper wires of various diameters.   Referring to Table 11-1 for the diameter in mils of the gage numbers, find the resistance per 1,000 ft of (*a*) No. 0, (*b*) No. 4, (*c*) No. 6, (*d*) No. 8, (*e*) No. 10, and (*f*) No. 12.   Find the resistance per 1,000 ft of wires whose diameters are (*g*) 150 mils, (*h*) 220 mils, (*i*) 250 mils, and (*j*) 0.3 in.

Plot a graph for each of the following problems:

3. The volume of a cube when the side is changed.

Side, in...............	0	1	2	3	4	5
Volume, cu in..........	0	1	8	27	64	125

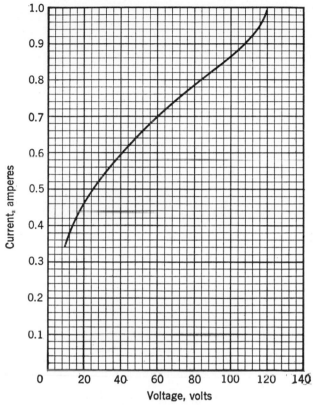

FIG. 14-7. Current taken by an incandescent lamp at various voltages.

4. The power used by a 100-ohm resistor carrying different currents.

Current, amp.....	0.1	0.2	0.3	0.4	0.5	0.6	0.7	0.8	0.9	1.0
Power, watts......	1	4	9	16	25	36	49	64	81	100

5. In an inductive circuit, the current does not rise to its Ohm's law value instantaneously. The growth of the current in a certain coil is shown by the following data. Plot the curve.

Time, sec......	0	0.1	0.2	0.3	0.4	0.5	0.6	0.7	0.8	0.9	1.0
Current, amp..	0	4.2	6.6	8.0	8.9	9.3	9.6	9.8	9.9	10	10

6. The plate voltage E_p against the plate current I_p for a 6C5 tube at a grid bias of -2 volts.

E_p, volts...	30	50	75	100	125	150	175	200
I_p, ma.....	0	1.1	2.9	4.9	7.3	10	13.0	16.2

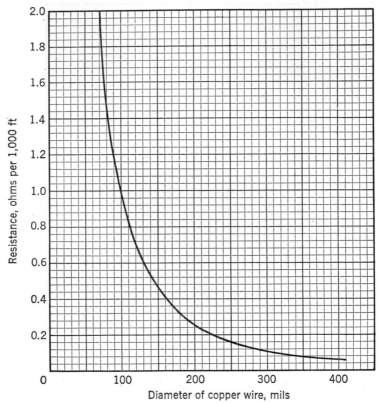

FIG. 14-8. Graph of a portion of the AWG Table 11-1.

7. The inductive reactance of a 0.01-henry coil at different frequencies.

Frequency, cps.............	60	100	250	500	1,000
Inductive reactance, ohms.......	3.7	6.3	15.7	31.4	62.8

8. The capacitive reactance for a 4-μf capacitor at different frequencies.

Frequency, cps...................	25	50	60	120	240
Capacitive reactance, ohms........	1,590	795	663	331	166

9. The grid voltage E_g against the plate current I_p for a 6J5 tube at a plate voltage of 280 volts.

E_g, volts......	-16	-15	-14	-13	-12	-11	-10	-9	-8
I_p, ma........	0.2	0.7	1.4	2.2	3.6	5.3	7.3	10.0	13.1

10. The sine of an angle against the number of degrees in the angle.

Angle, deg..........	0	30	45	60	90	120	135
Sine of the angle.....	0	0.5	0.7	0.86	1.0	0.86	0.7

Angle, deg...........	150	180	210	225	240	270	300
Sine of the angle.......	0.5	0	−0.5	−0.7	−0.86	−1.0	−0.86

Angle, deg................	315	330	360
Sine of the angle...........	−0.7	−0.5	0

JOB 14-3: THE GENERATION OF AN A-C VOLTAGE

Magnetism. The phenomenon of magnetism was discovered about 100 B.C. when it was observed that a peculiar stone had the property of attracting bits of iron to it. This natural magnet was called a *lodestone*. The lodestone was used to create other magnets artificially by stroking pieces of iron with it.

Magnetic Poles. Every magnet has two points opposite each other which attract pieces of iron best. These points are called the *poles* of the magnet: the north pole and the south pole. Just as similar electrical charges repel each other and opposite charges attract each other, similar magnetic poles repel each other and unlike poles attract each other.

A magnet evidently attracts a bit of iron because of some force that exists around the magnet. This force is called the magnetic field. Although it is invisible to the naked eye, it can be shown to exist by its effect on bits of iron. Place a sheet of glass or some other nonmagnetic material over a bar magnet as shown in Fig. 14-9. Sprinkle some iron filings over the glass, and tap it gently. The filings will fall back into a definite pattern which describes the field of force around the magnet. The field evidently seems to be made up of *lines* of force which appear to leave the magnet at the north pole, travel through the air around the magnet, and continue through the magnet to the north pole to form a *closed loop* of force. The stronger the magnet, the greater the number of lines of force and the larger the area covered by the field.

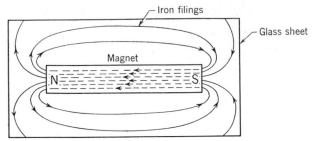

FIG. 14-9. The iron filings indicate the pattern of the lines of force around a bar magnet.

Electromagnetism. In 1819, Hans Christian Oersted, a Danish physicist, discovered that a field of magnetic force exists around a wire carrying an electric current. In Fig. 14-10, a wire is passed through a piece of cardboard and connected through a switch to a dry cell. With the switch open (no current flowing), sprinkle iron filings on the cardboard and tap it gently. The filings will fall back haphazardly. Now close the switch, which will permit a current to

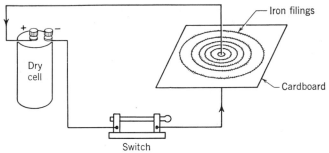

FIG. 14-10. A circular pattern of magnetic force exists around a wire carrying an electric current.

flow in the wire. Tap the cardboard again. This time, the magnetic effect of the current in the wire will cause the filings to fall back into a definite pattern of concentric circles with the wire as the center of the circles. Every section of the wire has this field of force around it in a plane perpendicular to the wire as shown in Fig. 14-11.

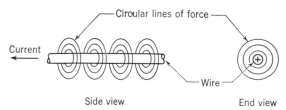

FIG. 14-11. The circular fields of force around a wire carrying a current are in planes which are perpendicular to the wire.

The Strength of the Magnetic Field. The ability of the magnetic field to attract bits of iron depends on the number of lines of force present. The strength of the magnetic field around a wire carrying a current depends on the current, since it is the current that produces the field. The greater the current, the greater the strength of the

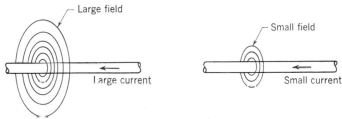

Fig. 14-12. The strength of the magnetic field around a wire carrying a current depends on the amount of current.

field. A large current will produce many lines of force extending far from the wire, while a small current will produce only a few lines close to the wire as shown in Fig. 14-12.

Electromagnetic Induction. Michael Faraday is credited with the discovery, in 1831, of the basic principle underlying the operation of a-c machinery. Simply stated, he discovered that if a conductor "cut across" lines of magnetic force, or if lines of force "cut across" a

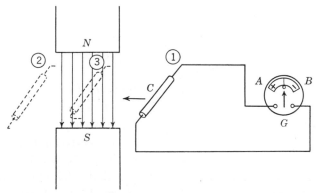

Fig. 14-13. When a conductor cuts lines of force, an emf is induced in the conductor. The direction in which the conductor cuts the lines determines the direction of the induced emf.

conductor, an electromotive force or voltage would be induced across the ends of the conductor. Figure 14-13 represents a magnet with its lines of force streaming from the north to the south pole. A conductor C, which can be moved between the poles, is connected to a galvanometer, which is a very sensitive meter used to indicate the presence of an electromotive force. When the conductor is stationary, the galvanometer indicates zero emf. If the wire is *moved about outside* the magnetic field at position 1, the galvanometer will still indicate zero. However, if the conductor is moved to the *left* to position 2, so that it *cuts across the lines of magnetic force,* the galvanometer pointer will deflect to *A*. This indicates that an emf was induced in the conductor because lines of force were "cut." Upon reaching position 2, the galvanometer pointer swung back to zero because no lines of force were being cut. Now move the conductor to the *right* through the lines of force back to position 1. During this *movement,* the pointer will deflect to *B*, indicating that an emf has again been induced in the wire, but in the *opposite direction.* If the wire is held *stationary* in the middle of the field of force at position 3,

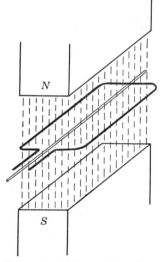

FIG. 14-14. The rotating loop cuts the lines of force to produce an alternating emf.

the galvanometer reads zero. If the conductor is moved up or down *parallel* to the lines of force so that *none are cut,* no emf will be induced. From experiments similar to these, Faraday deduced the following:

1. When lines of force are cut by a conductor or lines of force cut a conductor, an emf is induced in the conductor.

2. There must be a relative *motion* between the conductor and the lines of force in order to induce an emf.

3. Changing the direction of the cutting will change the direction of the induced emf.

Generating an Alternating EMF. Since a voltage is induced in a conductor when lines of force are cut, the amount of the induced emf depends on the number of lines cut in a unit time. In order to induce an emf of 1 volt, a conductor must cut 100,000,000 lines of force per second. To obtain this great number of "cuttings," the conductor is formed into a loop and rotated on an axis at great speed as shown in Fig. 14-14. The two sides of the loop become individual conductors in series, each side of the loop cutting lines of force and inducing twice the voltage that a single conductor would induce. In commercial generators, the number of "cuttings" and the resulting emf are increased by (1) increasing the number of lines of force by using more magnets or stronger electromagnets, (2) using more conductors or loops, (3) rotating the loops faster.

Let us follow a single conductor as it rotates at a uniform speed through a uniformly distributed field of force. In Fig. 14-15, the lines *AD*, *BE*, and *CF* are all equal to *OC* and represent the direction in which the conductor is moving at points *A*, *B*, and *C*, respectively. At *A*, the conductor is moving parallel to the lines of force. No lines of force are cut, and zero volts are induced. At *C*, the conductor has rotated through 90° and is moving in the direction *CF*. This

motion is directly across the lines of force and produces the maximum number of cuttings and the maximum voltage E_{max}. This maximum voltage may be represented by the distance *CF*. Since *OC* is equal to *CF*, the maximum voltage may be represented by the radius of the circle *OC*. At *B*, the conductor has rotated through some angle θ and is moving in the direction shown by *BE*. This motion from *B* to *E* may be considered to be made of a motion from *B* to *G* and then from *G* to *E*. However, only one of these motions is useful in cutting lines of force. The motion *GE* is parallel to the lines of force and produces no cuttings. Therefore, the distance *BG* represents the total cut-

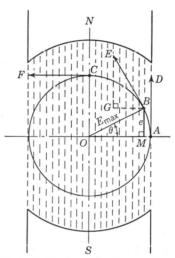

FIG. 14-15. A conductor rotating at a constant speed through a uniform magnetic field.

tings produced by the motion *BE*. *BG* therefore represents the voltage produced at the instant that the conductor is passing through point *B*. It can be shown by geometry that *BG* = *BM*. Thus, the vertical line drawn from the conductor at any instant perpendicular to the base represents the voltage induced in the conductor at that instant. The voltage at any instant of time evidently depends on the position of the conductor at that instant and is known as the instantaneous voltage *e*.

Summary

1. Only that part of the motion of a conductor directly across the field cuts lines and produces voltage.

2. The number of lines cut and the voltage produced are zero at 0° and increase to a maximum at 90°.

3. The vertical distance drawn from the conductor at any point to the horizontal base line represents the voltage produced at the instant that the conductor is passing through that point.

The complete picture of the voltage produced by a rotating conductor may now be drawn. Draw a circle, and divide the circumference into 12 parts, each 30° apart, as shown in Fig. 14-16. A horizontal base line is drawn as shown and labeled in degrees to correspond to the positions of the conductor. The vertical distances represent the voltages produced. As the conductor rotates, the vertical distance at each point is drawn at the corresponding point on the graph. Notice that the motion from 0 to 180° was to the *left*. The motion from 180 to 360° was to the *right* and produced a voltage

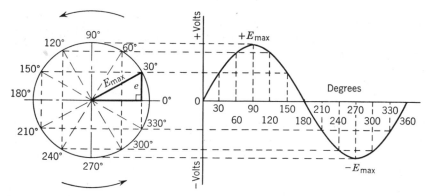

FIG. 14-16. The voltage wave produced by a conductor rotating at a constant speed through a uniform field of force.

in the *opposite* direction. This is indicated by *negative* voltages drawn *below* the base line. This graph gives a complete picture of all the changes in voltage during one complete rotation.

1. At 0°, the emf is 0 volts.

2. At 90°, the emf is the greatest and is known as $+E_{max}$.

3. At 180°, the emf is again 0 volts. The direction of the rotation and voltage changes at this point.

4. At 270°, the emf is again a maximum, but in the *opposite* direction, and is known as $-E_{max}$.

5. At 360°, the emf is 0 volts.

6. The voltage passes twice through both the zero value and the maximum value during the cycle.

7. The maximum voltages are equal in value but are of opposite sign.

8. The instantaneous voltage means the voltage at any instant during an a-c cycle. The symbol is e.

The Sine Wave. Consider the triangle OBM in Fig. 14-15. OB is a radius of the circle and is equal to the maximum voltage E_{max}. BM

is the instantaneous voltage at any angle θ (theta), given as e. By trigonometry,

$$\sin \theta = \frac{e}{E_{\text{max}}} \qquad (14\text{-}1)$$

or
$$e = E_{\text{max}} \times \sin \theta \qquad (14\text{-}2)$$

This formula says that the value of the voltage at any instant depends on the maximum voltage and the *sine of the angle at that instant.* If the maximum voltage is 1 volt,

$$e = 1 \times \sin \theta$$

or
$$e = \sin \theta \qquad (14\text{-}3)$$

We can now plot a graph of the changes in the voltage as a conductor rotates in a circle through a uniform field at a constant speed. Figure 14-17 shows the graph obtained by plotting the angles against the

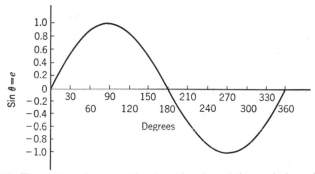

FIG. 14-17. The voltage is proportional to the sine of the angle in a sine wave.

values of the sine of the angles. Compare this curve with the curve of Fig. 14-16. They are identical. Most commercial generators are designed to produce alternating waves of this type. They are called sine waves because the voltage at any instant is proportional to the sine of the angle at that instant.

Cycle, Frequency. An alternating wave may be an a-c voltage or an alternating current. During one *cycle*, the wave will pass through a complete series of positive and negative values. In one cycle, as shown in Fig. 14-18, an a-c voltage starts at 0°, rises to a positive maximum at 90°, and falls to zero at 180°; then *reverses its polarity,* rises to a negative maximum at 270°, and falls to zero at 360°. An alternating current starts at 0°, rises to a positive maximum at 90°, and falls to zero at 180°; then *reverses its direction,* rises to a negative maximum at 270°, and falls to zero at 360°.

Each cycle of an a-c wave may be repeated over and over. The frequency f of an a-c wave means the number of complete cycles that occur *in one second*. In the United States the standard frequency for light and power is 60 cycles per second (60 cps). Audio frequencies range between 30 and 15,000 cps. Radio and television frequencies range between 15,000 and 890,000,000 cps.

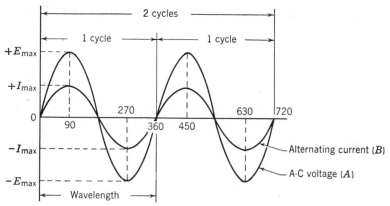

FIG. 14-18. A cycle describes all the changes of voltage or current during a rotation of 360°.

Wavelength. The distance traveled by an a-c wave during one complete cycle is called its *wavelength*. Its symbol is the Greek letter lambda λ. This distance may be expressed in any convenient unit of length. However, since most scientific work uses the metric system, the wavelength is usually measured in terms of *meters*. One meter is equal to 39.37 in.

The speed of radio waves is the same as the speed of light, or 186,000 miles per second. This speed may be expressed in the metric system in terms of meters per second. Since 1 mile = 5,280 ft,

$$
\begin{aligned}
186{,}000 \text{ miles} &= 186{,}000 \times 5{,}280 \; \textit{feet} \\
&= 186{,}000 \times 5{,}280 \times 12 \; \textit{inches} \\
&= \frac{186{,}000 \times 5{,}280 \times 12}{39.37} \; \textit{meters} \\
&= 300{,}000{,}000 \; \textit{meters}
\end{aligned}
$$

Therefore, the speed of a radio wave may be expressed as 300,000,000 meters per second.

If we divide the speed in meters per second by the frequency in cycles per second, the units of time will cancel out as shown below.

$$
\frac{\text{Meters}}{\text{Second}} \div \frac{\text{cycles}}{\text{second}}
$$

Inverting and multiplying,

$$\frac{\text{Meters}}{\underset{1}{\cancel{\text{second}}}} \times \frac{\overset{1}{\cancel{\text{second}}}}{\text{cycles}} = \frac{\text{meters}}{\text{cycle}}$$

The number of meters per cycle is the wavelength.

Formula

$$\lambda = \frac{300,000,000}{f} \tag{14-4}$$

where λ = wavelength, meters
f = frequency, cps

If the frequency is expressed in kilocycles per second,

$$\lambda = \frac{300,000}{f} \tag{14-5}$$

where λ = wavelength, meters
f = frequency, kc per second

Example 14-9. What is the wavelength of radio station WCBS, which broadcasts at a frequency of 880 kc per second?

Solution:

Given: Station WCBS   Find: λ = ?
f = 880 kc

$$\lambda = \frac{300,000}{f} \tag{14-5}$$

$$\lambda = \frac{300,000}{880} = 340.9 \text{ meters} \qquad Ans.$$

Example 14-10. What is the frequency of a radio wave if its wavelength is equal to 297 meters? What New York City station broadcasts at this frequency?

Solution:

Given: λ = 297 meters   Find: f = ?
                                 Name of New York station = ?

$$\lambda = \frac{300,000}{f} \tag{14-5}$$

$$297 = \frac{300,000}{f}$$

$$297 \times f = 300,000$$

$$f = \frac{300,000}{297} = 1,010 \text{ kc} \qquad Ans.$$

The station is WINS.

Summary

A magnet attracts bits of iron or steel. A magnet has a north and a south pole. Like poles repel; unlike poles attract. A magnetic field composed of closed loops of lines of force exists around a magnet.

A field of magnetic force exists around a wire that carries an electric current. The strength of the field is directly proportional to the strength of the current.

Electromagnetic Induction. When there is a mutual cutting of lines of force by a conductor, or vice versa, an emf is induced in the conductor. The direction of the induced voltage depends on the direction of the motion of the conductor.

Generating a Sine Wave EMF. An emf will be induced in a conductor if it is rotated at a constant speed through a uniform field of force. The amount of voltage induced depends on the number of lines of force which are cut per second. The number of "cuttings" and the voltage at any instant depend on the position of the conductor at that instant and are proportional to the sine of the angle at that instant. The voltage will rise and fall and change polarity at regular intervals of time. Such a wave is called an alternating wave or a-c wave. An alternating-current wave is one which changes in amount and *direction* at regular intervals of time.

A *cycle* of an a-c wave is a record of all the changes that occur during a *single* rotation from 0 to 360°.

The *frequency* of an a-c wave is the number of complete cycles that occur in one second. The symbol is f.

The *wavelength* of an a-c wave is the distance traveled by the wave during one complete cycle. The symbol is λ.

JOB 14-4: INSTANTANEOUS VALUES, MAXIMUM VALUES, AND PHASE ANGLES OF AN A-C WAVE

Since alternating waves or voltage and current change in amount and direction at regular intervals, voltage or current at any instant of time must be calculated. These values are called the *instantaneous values*. For example, in Fig. 14-15, when the conductor has rotated through some angle θ to reach point B, the instantaneous value is indicated by the vertical line BM. The radius of the circle OB indicates the maximum value of the wave. By trigonometry, we obtain

Formulas

$$\sin \theta = \frac{e}{E_{\max}} \qquad (14\text{-}1)$$

or
$$e = E_{\max} \times \sin \theta \qquad (14\text{-}2)$$

If this changing voltage wave is impressed across a resistance, each instantaneous voltage e will produce its own value of instantaneous current i. Thus, as shown in Fig. 14-18, the a-c voltage wave A produced the a-c wave B. This current wave will have the same frequency as the voltage wave which produced it. Using this current wave, we obtain

Formulas

$$\sin \theta = \frac{i}{I_{max}} \qquad (14\text{-}6)$$

or
$$i = I_{max} \times \sin \theta \qquad (14\text{-}7)$$

Example 14-11. An a-c voltage has a maximum value of 170 volts. Find the instantaneous voltage at 30°.

Solution.

$$\text{Given: } E_{max} = 170 \text{ volts} \qquad \text{Find: } e = ?$$
$$\theta = 30°$$

$$e = E_{max} \times \sin \theta \qquad (14\text{-}2)$$
$$e = 170 \times \sin 30° = 170 \times 0.5000 = 85 \text{ volts} \qquad Ans.$$

Example 14-12. An a-c wave has a maximum value of 100 ma. Find the instantaneous current at 70°.

Solution:

$$\text{Given: } I_{max} = 100 \text{ ma} \qquad \text{Find: } i = ?$$
$$\theta = 70°$$

$$i = I_{max} \times \sin \theta \qquad (14\text{-}7)$$
$$i = 100 \times \sin 70° = 100 \times 0.9397 = 93.97 \text{ ma} \qquad Ans.$$

Maximum Values. The maximum value of an a-c voltage (E_{max}) or an alternating current (I_{max}) is reached twice during each cycle. The positive maximums occur at 90°, and the negative maximums occur at 270°. By solving Eqs. (14-2) and (14-7) for the E_{max} and I_{max} we obtain the following formulas:

Formulas

$$E_{max} = \frac{e}{\sin \theta} \qquad (14\text{-}8)$$

$$I_{max} = \frac{i}{\sin \theta} \qquad (14\text{-}9)$$

Example 14-13. An alternating current has a value of 77.8 amp at 45°. Find the maximum value at 90° and at 270°.

Solution:

$$\text{Given: } i = 77.8 \text{ amp} \qquad \text{Find: } +I_{max} = ?$$
$$\theta = 45° \qquad\qquad\qquad -I_{max} = ?$$

$$I_{max} = \frac{i}{\sin \theta} = \frac{77.8}{\sin 45°} = \frac{77.8}{0.7071} = +110 \text{ amp at } 90° \quad (14\text{-}9)$$
$$I_{max} = -110 \text{ amp at } 270° \qquad Ans.$$

Example 14-14. An a-c voltage wave has an instantaneous value of 70 volts at 30°. (*a*) Find the maximum value of the wave. (*b*) Can this wave be impressed across a capacitor whose breakdown voltage is 125 volts?

Solution:

$$\text{Given: } e = 70 \text{ volts} \qquad \text{Find: } E_{max} = ?$$
$$\theta = 30°$$

a. $E_{max} = \dfrac{e}{\sin \theta} = \dfrac{70}{\sin 30°} = \dfrac{70}{0.5000} = 140 \text{ volts} \qquad Ans.$

b. No, since 140 volts is larger than the breakdown voltage of 125 volts.   *Ans.*

Phase Angles. The phase angle θ or phase of an a-c cycle refers to the value of the electrical angle at any point during the cycle. These angles may be found by solving formula (14-1) or (14-6).

Example 14-15. An a-c voltage wave has a maximum value of 155.5 volts. Find the phase angle at which the instantaneous voltage is 110 volts.

Solution:

$$\text{Given: } E_{max} = 155.5 \text{ volts} \qquad \text{Find: } \theta = ?$$
$$e = 110 \text{ volts}$$

$$\sin \theta = \frac{e}{E_{max}} = \frac{110}{155.5} = 0.7074 \qquad (14\text{-}1)$$
$$\theta = 45° \qquad Ans.$$

Problems

1. What is the wavelength of an a-c wave whose frequency is 30,000 cps?
2. Find the frequency of a carrier wave whose wavelength is 600 meters.
3. Find the instantaneous voltage at 50° in a wave whose maximum value is 165 volts.
4. Find the maximum value of an a-c wave if the instantaneous voltage is 50 volts at 35°.
5. Find the phase angle at which an instantaneous voltage of 72 volts appears in a wave whose maximum value is 250 volts.
6. Find the instantaneous current at 85° in a wave whose maximum value is 26 amp.

7. Find the maximum value of an a-c wave if the instantaneous current is 9 amp at 12°.

8. Find the phase angle at which an instantaneous current of 3.5 amp appears in a wave whose maximum value is 20 amp.

9. The maximum current of the current wave of a transmitter is 10 amp. At what instant (angle) will the instantaneous current be (a) 5 amp, (b) 6 amp, and (c) 8.66 amp?

10. The maximum voltage of an a-c wave is 100 volts. Find the instantaneous voltage at (a) 0°, (b) 15°, (c) 30°, (d) 45°, (e) 60°, (f) 75°, and (g) 90°. (h) What is the average of these voltages?

JOB 14-5: EFFECTIVE VALUE OF AN A-C WAVE

An alternating current is a current that is continually changing in amount and direction. In Fig. 14-19, the current starts at 0 amp at

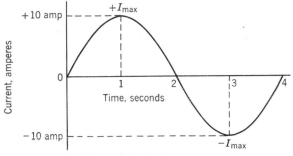

FIG. 14-19. An a-c wave.

0 time. After 1 sec, it reaches 10 amp but drops down to 0 after 2 sec. At this point, the current reverses its direction and increases negatively to 10 amp at 3 sec, after which it drops down to 0 after 4 sec. The *average* current during these 4 sec equals (0 + 10 + 0 − 10 + 0) divided by 5, or 0 amp. Obviously, even though the average of all the currents is zero, this a-c wave can be effective in running a motor or lighting a lamp. But how many amperes are actually flowing? If an a-c ammeter is used to measure this current, it will read 7.07 amp. This meter reading is called the *effective value* of all the changes that occur during one cycle of the wave.

One of the effects of the passage of any electrical current through a resistance, whether it be alternating or direct, is the production of heat. To determine the *worth*, or *effectiveness*, of an a-c wave, we must compare its effect with the effect of a direct current.

Rule: If an a-c wave produces as much heat as 1 amp of direct current, we say that the a-c wave is as effective as 1 amp of direct current.

Thus, as in Fig. 14-20, an a-c wave may start at zero and pass through many values of current up to a maximum of 10 amp, continuing to fall to zero, change direction, rise to a negative maximum of 10 amp, and fall to zero again.   If the *effect* of all these changes is to produce only as much heat as 7.07 amp of direct current would produce, then the wave is said to have an *effective* value of only 7.07 amp. The effective value of any current wave may be calculated by averaging the *heating* effects of the many individual instantaneous currents.

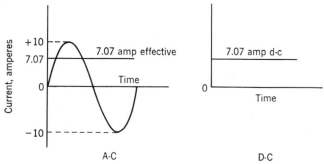

FIG. 14-20. Effective values of alternating and direct currents.

Since $P = I^2R$, the heating effect on any resistance depends on the *square* of the current.   Thus,

$$I_{dc}^2 = \text{average of } i^2$$

by taking the square root of both sides,

$$I_{dc} = \sqrt{i_{av}^2}$$

Since the effective alternating current is to have the same heating effect as the direct current,

$$I_{ac} = I_{dc} = \sqrt{i_{av}^2}$$

This equation says that the effective value of an a-c wave is equal to the square root of the average (mean) of the squares of the instantaneous currents.   For this reason it is sometimes called the rms value (root mean square).   This gives us a method for calculating the effective value of any a-c wave.   One quarter of a cycle is divided into a number of equal parts, and the instantaneous currents are calculated at each point.   These currents are squared, and the average found.   The square root of this average is equal to the effective value of the wave. The results of many calculations for waves of different maximums indicate that the effective value of a sine-wave current is always 0.707 times the maximum value of the wave.

Formula

$$I = 0.707 \times I_{max} \qquad (14\text{-}10)$$

where I = effective value of an a-c wave

I_{max} = maximum value of an a-c wave

Since alternating currents are the result of a-c voltages, the effective values of a voltage wave have an identical relation to the maximum voltages.

Formula

$$E = 0.707 \times E_{max} \qquad (14\text{-}11)$$

where E = effective value of an a-c voltage wave

E_{max} = maximum value of an a-c voltage wave

Notice that the effective values are written as I and E, with no subscripts. Alternating-current meters are designed and calibrated to indicate these effective values. Unless otherwise specified, a value of an alternating current or a-c voltage always means the effective value.

Formulas (14-10) and (14-11) may be transformed to obtain formulas for the I_{max} and the E_{max}.

$$I = 0.707 \times I_{max}$$

or
$$I_{max} = \frac{I}{0.707}$$

Formula

$$I_{max} = 1.414 \times I \qquad (14\text{-}12)$$

Similarly
$$E = 0.707 \times E_{max}$$

or
$$E_{max} = \frac{E}{0.707}$$

Formula

$$E_{max} = 1.414 \times E \qquad (14\text{-}13)$$

Thus, an effective voltage of 120 volts is the effective voltage of a wave whose maximum equals $1.414 \times 120 = 170$ volts. This means that if an electric heater were used on a 120-volt a-c line, it would produce only as much heat as would be produced on a 120-volt d-c line, even though the a-c line reaches the maximum of 170 volts twice in each cycle.

Example 14-16.   An alternating current has a maximum value of 50 amp.   Find (*a*) the effective current and (*b*) the instantaneous current at 10°.

Solution:

$$\text{Given: } I_{max} = 50 \text{ amp} \qquad \text{Find: } I = ?$$
$$\theta = 10° \qquad\qquad\qquad i = ?$$

a.
$$I = 0.707 \times I_{max} \qquad\qquad (14\text{-}10)$$
$$I = 0.707 \times 50 = 35.35 \text{ amp} \qquad Ans.$$

b.
$$i = I_{max} \times \sin \theta \qquad\qquad (14\text{-}7)$$
$$i = 50 \times \sin 10°$$
$$i = 50 \times 0.1736 = 8.68 \text{ amp} \qquad Ans.$$

Example 14-17.   An a-c voltage wave has an effective value of 110 volts.   Find (*a*) the maximum value and (*b*) the instantaneous value at 40°.

Solution:

$$\text{Given: } E = 110 \text{ volts} \qquad \text{Find: } E_{max} = ?$$
$$\theta = 40° \qquad\qquad\qquad e = ?$$

a. $E_{max} = 1.414 \times E = 1.414 \times 110 = 155 \text{ volts} \qquad Ans.$

b.
$$e = E_{max} \times \sin \theta \qquad\qquad (14\text{-}2)$$
$$e = 155 \times \sin 40°$$
$$e = 155 \times 0.6428 = 99.6 \text{ volts} \qquad Ans.$$

Example 14-18.   An a-c wave has an instantaneous value of 12.95 amp at 15°.   Find (*a*) the maximum value and (*b*) the effective value.

Solution:

$$\text{Given: } i = 12.95 \text{ amp} \qquad \text{Find: } I_{max} = ?$$
$$\theta = 15° \qquad\qquad\qquad I = ?$$

a.
$$I_{max} = \frac{i}{\sin \theta} \qquad\qquad (14\text{-}9)$$
$$I_{max} = \frac{12.95}{\sin 15°} = \frac{12.95}{0.2588} = 50 \text{ amp} \qquad Ans.$$

b. $I = 0.707 \times I_{max} = 0.707 \times 50 = 35.35 \text{ amp} \qquad Ans.$

Problems

Find the values indicated in each problem.

Problem	Maximum value	Effective value	Phase angle	Instantaneous value
1	35 amp	?	30°	?
2	456 volts	?	40°	?
3	?	440 volts	50°	?
4	?	25 amp	60°	?
5	155 volts	?	30°	?
6	10 amp	?	45°	?
7	?	110 volts	65°	?
8	?	20 amp	75°	?
9	?	?	50°	26.81 amp
10	?	?	15°	120.3 volts
11	100 volts	?	?	43.84 volts
12	20 amp	?	?	5.5 amp

13. A sine wave has an instantaneous value of 10 volts at 30°. What is its value at 60°?

14. What must be the minimum breakdown voltage rating of a capacitor in order to use it on a 110-volt a-c line?

Test—A-C Waves

1. Using the following data, plot a graph showing the current taken by an incandescent lamp at different voltages.

Voltage, volts.........	10	20	30	40	50	60	70	80	90	100	110
Current, amp.........	0.17	0.24	0.30	0.37	0.44	0.50	0.57	0.64	0.71	0.76	0.84

2. An a-c wave has a maximum value of 300 volts. Find the effective value and the instantaneous value at 30°.

3. An a-c wave has an effective value of 50 ma. Find the maximum value and the instantaneous value at 60°.

4. An a-c wave reaches an instantaneous value of 40 volts at 18°. Find the maximum and the effective value of the wave.

5. An a-c wave has a maximum value of 200 volts. Find the angle at which the voltage is 165.8 volts. What is the effective value?

CHAPTER 15

INDUCTANCE AND TRANSFORMERS

JOB 15-1: INDUCTANCE OF A COIL

Basic Ideas. In Chap. 14 we learned the following:

1. A field of force exists around a wire carrying a current.

2. This field has the form of concentric circles around the wire, in planes perpendicular to the wire, and with the wire at the center of the circles.

3. The strength of the field depends on the current. Large currents produce large fields; small currents produce small fields.

4. When lines of force cut across a conductor, a voltage is induced in the conductor.

Effect of Inductance

Experiment 1. Connect a 20-volt source of direct current across a *straight* wire whose resistance is 10 ohms as shown in Fig. 15-1a. When the switch is closed, the direct current

$$I = \frac{E}{R} = \frac{20}{10} = 2 \text{ amp}$$

will flow. This current will produce *stationary* lines of force perpendicular to the wire. No cuttings can occur, and therefore no voltage is induced in the wire.

Experiment 2. Remove the 20-volt d-c source from the circuit of Fig. 15-1a, and replace it with a 20-volt a-c source as in Fig. 15-1b. When the switch is closed, the alternating current

$$I = \frac{E}{R} = \frac{20}{10} = 2 \text{ amp}$$

will flow. This current will produce lines of force that move *out* from the wire as the alternating current increases and collapse *back* toward the wire as the current decreases.   The field expands and contracts with the variations in the current.   However, since the lines of force are perpendicular to the wire, no lines of force can cut the wire and no voltage is induced in the wire.

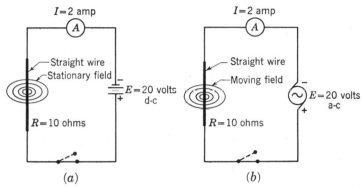

(a)   (b)

Fig. 15-1. (a) Direct current through a straight wire produces 2 amp.   (b) Alternating current through a straight wire produces the same 2 amp.

Experiment 3.   Remove the 10-ohm wire, and *twist it into a coil.* The resistance of the wire will still be 10 ohms.   Replace the 20-volt a-c source with a 20-volt d-c source as shown in Fig. 15-2a.   When the switch is closed, the direct current

$$I = \frac{E}{R} = \frac{20}{10} = 2 \text{ amp}$$

will flow.   This current will produce *stationary* lines of force perpendicular to the wire.   Since the field is stationary, there can be no relative *motion* between the lines and the wire; therefore no cuttings can occur and no voltage is induced in the wire.

Experiment 4.   Remove the 20-volt d-c source from the circuit of Fig. 15-2a, and replace it with the 20-volt a-c source as shown in Fig. 15-2b.   When the switch is closed, the alternating current

$$I = \frac{E}{R} = \frac{20}{10} = 2 \text{ amp}$$

will not flow!   Actually it might be only 1.9 amp.   This is what happened.   The alternating current produced an expanding and collapsing field of force as in Experiment 2, but *because the wire was twisted into a coil, the moving lines of force could cut the turns of the coil.* These cuttings induced a voltage in the coil *and in a direction so as to oppose the original voltage.*   For this reason it is called a *back emf.*

If the back emf is 1 volt, then the voltage available to force the current through the 10-ohm resistance is only $20 - 1 = 19$ volts. The current will therefore be

$$I = \frac{E}{R} = \frac{19}{10} = 1.9 \text{ amp.}$$

Notice that this back emf can occur only when a *coil* is carrying a *changing* current.

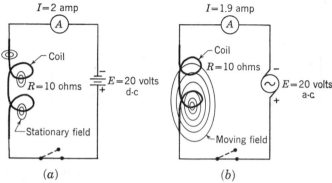

Fig. 15-2. (*a*) Direct current through a coil produces 2 amp. (*b*) Alternating current through a coil *reduces* the current to 1.9 amp.

Inductance. The inductance of a coil is a measure of its ability to produce a back emf when an a-c voltage is impressed across it. If the voltage and resulting current are *increasing*, the induced emf will be in a direction so as to *reduce* the increase. If the voltage and resulting current are *decreasing*, the induced emf will be in a direction so as to *increase* the current. The net effect of inductance is to slow down the speed at which any change occurs. The symbol for inductance is L.

The Unit of Inductance. The back emf induced in a coil depends on the number of "cuttings" of lines of force by conductors. A rapidly changing current will induce a larger back emf than a slowly changing current because the former will produce more cuttings in the same time. In order to compare two coils, we must pass the same kind of current through both and observe the back emf generated in each. If this same current induces 1 volt of back emf in coil A and 2 volts of back emf in coil B, then coil B would have twice the inductance of coil A. This enables us to define the unit of inductance.

Definition. If a current changing at the uniform rate of 1 amp per second induces a back emf of 1 volt, then the inductance is 1 henry.

Rule: The inductance of a circuit is equal to the average number of volts of back emf divided by the rate of change of current.

Formula

$$L = E_{av} \div \frac{\Delta I}{t} \tag{15-1}$$

where L = inductance, henrys

E_{av} = average back emf, volts

ΔI = the *change* in the current, amp (ΔI is read as "delta I")

t = time for this change, sec

Example 15-1. Find the inductance in a circuit if an average of 6. volts of back emf is induced when the current drops from 10 to 2 amp in 0.01 sec.

Solution:

Given: E_{av} = 6 volts   Find: L = ?
ΔI = 10 − 2 = 8 amp
t = 0.01 sec

$$L = E_{av} \div \frac{\Delta I}{t} \tag{15-1}$$

$$L = 6 \div \frac{8}{0.01}$$

$$L = \frac{6}{1} \times \frac{0.01}{8} = \frac{0.06}{8} = 0.0075 \text{ henry} \qquad Ans.$$

Rule: The average back emf in an inductive circuit is equal to the inductance multiplied by the rate of change of current.

Formula

$$E_{av} = L \times \frac{\Delta I}{t} \tag{15-2}$$

Example 15-2. Find the average back emf induced in a filter choke of 20-henry inductance if the current changes at the rate of 5.5 amp per second.

Solution:

Given: L = 20 henrys   Find: E_{av} = ?
ΔI = 5.5 amp
t = 1 sec

$$E_{av} = L \times \frac{\Delta I}{t} \tag{15-2}$$

$$E_{av} = 20 \times \frac{5.5}{1} = \frac{110}{1} = 110 \text{ volts} \qquad Ans.$$

Problems

1. What is the inductance of a circuit if 3 volts average back emf is induced by a current changing at the rate of 200 amp per second?

2. What is the inductance of a coil if an average of 5 volts of back emf is induced by a current which changes from 8 amp to zero in 0.1 sec?

3. A choke coil in the high-voltage supply of a television receiver has an inductance of 6 henrys. Find the average back emf induced in the coil if the current changes at the rate of 2.5 amp per second.

4. The inductance of an r-f choke in a radio receiver is 50 μh. Find the average induced voltage if the current through the coil changes at the rate of 1,000 amp per second.

5. A loudspeaker coil has an inductance of 0.1 henry and carries a current that changes at the rate of 0.3 amp in 0.001 sec. Find the average back voltage induced in the coil.

6. The fourth picture i-f coil in the RCA 630 television chassis has an inductance of 120 μh. What is the average back emf induced in the coil if the current changes at the rate of 0.007 amp in 0.01 μsec?

JOB 15-2: REACTANCE OF A COIL

When an a-c voltage is impressed across a coil,

1. The a-c voltage will produce an alternating current.

2. When a current flows in a wire, lines of force are produced around the wire.

Expanding field of force

Contracting field of force

FIG. 15-3. An alternating current produces a *moving* field of force which cuts the wires forming the turns of the coil.

3. Large currents produce many lines of force; small currents produce only a few lines of force.

4. As the current changes, the number of lines of force will change. The field of force will seem to expand and contract as the current increases and decreases as shown in Fig. 15-3.

5. As the field expands and contracts, the lines of force must cut across the wires which form the turns of the coil.

6. These "cuttings" induce an emf in the coil.

7. This emf acts in a direction so as to oppose the original voltage and is called a "back emf."

8. The effect of this back emf is to reduce the original voltage impressed on the coil. The net effect will be to reduce the current below that which would flow if there were no cuttings or back emf.

9. In this sense, the back emf is acting as a resistance in reducing the current.

10. Actually, it is extremely convenient to consider the current-reducing effect of a back emf as a number of ohms of effective resistance. However, since a back emf is not actually a resistance but merely *acts* as a resistance, we use the term *reactance* to describe this effect. The *reactance* of a coil is the number of ohms of resistance which the coil seems to offer as a result of a back emf induced in it. Its symbol is X to differentiate it from the d-c resistance R.

What Factors Affect the Reactance?   (1) If the frequency of the a-c voltage changes, then the number of cuttings and the resulting reactance will change.   (2) If the natural ability of the coil to produce a back emf—its inductance—changes, then the reactance will also change.   The value of the reactance of a coil is therefore proportional to its inductance and the frequency of the a-c circuit in which it is used.   Its actual value may be found by the formula $X_L = 2\pi fL$. Since $2\pi = 2 \times 3.14 = 6.28$, the formula for the reactance of a coil becomes

Formula
$$X_L = 6.28fL \tag{15-3}$$

where X_L = inductive reactance, ohms
   f = frequency, cps
   L = inductance, henrys
   6.28 = constant of proportionality

Example 15-3.   The primary of a power transformer has an inductance of 150 mh.   (*a*) Find its inductive reactance at a frequency of 60 cps.   (*b*) What current will it draw from a 117-volt line?

Solution:

Given: L = 150 mh   Find: X_L = ?
       f = 60 cps I_L = ?
       E = 117 volts

a.   150 mh = 150 ÷ 1,000 = 0.15 henry
            $X_L = 6.28fL$ \hfill (15-3)
            $X_L = 6.28 \times 60 \times 0.15$
            $X_L = 56.6$ ohms   *Ans.*

b. Since the only resistance in the circuit is the inductive reactance, the formula for Ohm's law, $E = IR$, may be rewritten as

$$E_L = I_L \times X_L \qquad (15\text{-}4)$$
$$117 = I_L \times 56.5$$

$$I_L = \frac{117}{56.5} = 2.07 \text{ amp} \qquad Ans.$$

Example 15-4. A 20-mh coil is in a tank circuit operating at a frequency of 1,500 kc. Find its inductive reactance.

Solution:

$$\text{Given: } L = 20 \text{ mh} \qquad \text{Find: } X_L = ?$$
$$f = 1,500 \text{ kc}$$

1. Change units of measurement.

$$20 \text{ mh} = \frac{20}{1,000} \text{ henry}$$
$$1,500 \text{ kc} = 1,500 \times 1,000 \text{ cps}$$

2. Find the inductive reactance.

$$X_L = 6.28fL \qquad (15\text{-}3)$$

$$X_L = 6.28 \times 1,500 \times \cancel{1,000} \times \frac{20}{\cancel{1,000}}$$

$$X_L = 6.28 \times 1,500 \times 20 = 188,400 \text{ ohms} \qquad Ans.$$

Example 15-5. What must be the inductance of a coil in order that it have a reactance of 942 ohms at a frequency of 60 cps?

Solution:

$$\text{Given: } X_L = 942 \text{ ohms} \qquad \text{Find: } L = ?$$
$$f = 60 \text{ cps}$$

$$X_L = 6.28fL \qquad (15\text{-}3)$$
$$942 = 6.28 \times 60 \times L$$
$$942 = 376.8 \times L$$

$$L = \frac{942}{376.8} = 2.5 \text{ henrys} \qquad Ans.$$

Problems

1. Find the inductive reactance of a 10-henry choke coil at (*a*) 100 cps, (*b*) 1 kc, and (*c*) 5,000 cps.

2. A loudspeaker coil of 2-henry inductance is operating at a frequency of 1 kc. Find (*a*) its inductive reactance and (*b*) the current flowing if the voltage across the coil is 40 volts.

$R_{sin} = \dfrac{100\ v}{.01\ r}$ $.001\ r$

$\dfrac{100,000\ \Omega -}{1/100000}$ $\dfrac{10950}{99950}$

$\dfrac{100,000}{1,000000}$ $.0005$

.0005 (80)

8 Ohms

$\dfrac{100v}{.01}$ | 10000 Ω

40v

$\dfrac{.06v\ .01\ r}{}$

$\dfrac{.101}{9}$
.66

$\dfrac{6\ v}{.01\ r}$

10,000
.004

96,000
40v

.004

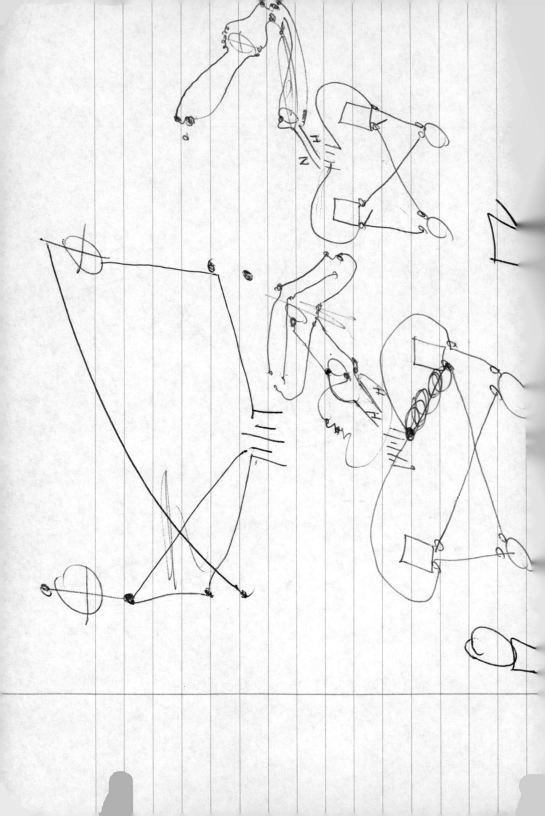

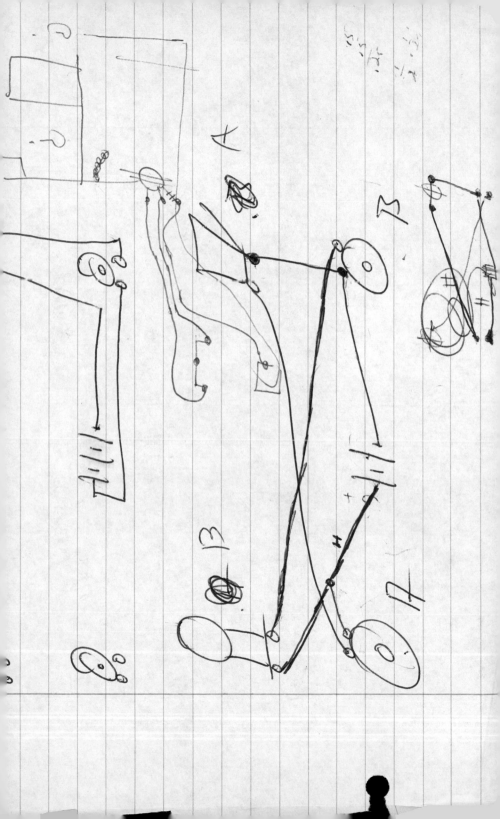

$\dfrac{6v}{.001A}$ $\dfrac{6.000\,\Omega}{)6.000}$

$\dfrac{.8}{X} = \dfrac{1}{100}$ $R_{sm} =$

X = 80   80

0

$\dfrac{.8}{0.08}$

$R_{sm} =$ 10

$.8 = \dfrac{1}{100}$

$E = 100v$

$I m\ .8ma = .0008A$

$\dfrac{125.000\,\Omega}{8\,)100\,0.000}$

50 Ω

3. A 20-henry choke in the filter circuit of a radio receiver operates at the power-supply frequency of 60 cps. Find (*a*) its inductive reactance and (*b*) the current flowing if the voltage across the coil is 150 volts.

4. An r-f choke coil whose inductance is 5.5 mh operates at a frequency of 1,200 kc. Find (*a*) its inductive reactance and (*b*) the current flowing if the voltage across the coil is 41.5 volts.

5. A Miller No. 7825 line filter choke used in a noise-control circuit of a flasher sign has an inductance of 0.6 mh. Find its inductive reactance at a frequency of 10 kc.

6. What must be the inductance of a coil in order that it have a reactance of 1,884 ohms at 60 cps?

7. An antenna circuit has an inductance of 150 μh. What is its reactance to a 1,000-kc signal?

8. An r-f coil in an f-m receiver has an inductance of 100 μh. What is its reactance at 100 Mc?

9. What is the reactance of the 10-mh coil in the high-pass filter shown in Fig. 15-4 to (*a*) a 3,000-cps a-f current and (*b*) a 600-kc r-f current?

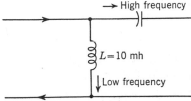

Fig. 15-4. A simple high-pass filter.

10. A 1-mh coil in the primary of an i-f transformer is resonant to 456 kc. Find its inductive reactance at this frequency.

11. A 0.5-mh coil in the oscillator circuit of a continuous-wave transmitter operates at 30 Mc. Find its reactance at this frequency.

12. What must be the inductance of a coil in order that it have a reactance of 10,000 ohms at 600 kc?

JOB 15-3: THE IMPEDANCE OF A COIL

In a "pure" coil, the opposition to the flow of an alternating current is its reactance. Actually, of course, every coil is made of wire which has some resistance. If this resistance is small in comparison with the reactance, it may be neglected, and the total opposition to the flow of current through the coil is equal to its inductive reactance. If the ohmic resistance of the coil is large, it must be added on to the reactance of the coil to obtain the total opposing effect. This total opposition is called the *impedance Z* of the coil. The addition of the ohms of resistance and the ohms of inductive reactance is *not* accomplished by simple addition but by *vector addition*, for reasons which will be explained in Job 17-5.

Rule: The impedance of a coil is the vector sum of the resistance and the reactance.

Formula

$$Z^2 = R^2 + X_L{}^2 \qquad (15\text{-}5)$$

or $$Z = \sqrt{R^2 + X_L{}^2} \qquad (15\text{-}6)$$

where Z = impedance, ohms

R = d-c resistance, ohms

X_L = inductive reactance, ohms

The comparative values of the inductive reactance and the resistance are described by a value called the Q, or "quality," of the coil.

Rule: The Q of a coil is the ratio of its inductive reactance to its resistance.

Formula

$$Q = \frac{X_L}{R} \qquad (15\text{-}7)$$

If the Q of a coil is greater than 5, then the resistance may be neglected in the calculation of the impedance. If the Q is smaller than 5, then the resistance must be added to the reactance by formula (15-6) to obtain the impedance. Also, if the ratio of R/X_L is larger than 5, the reactance may be neglected and the impedance is equal to the resistance.

Example 15-6. A coil has a resistance of 5 ohms and an inductive reactance of 12 ohms at a certain frequency. Find (a) the Q of the coil and (b) the impedance of the coil.

Solution:

Given: R = 5 ohms   Find: Q = ?

X_L = 12 ohms Z = ?

a. $$Q = \frac{X_L}{R} \qquad (15\text{-}7)$$

$$Q = \frac{12}{5} = 2.4 \qquad Ans.$$

b. Since Q is less than 5, the resistance *must* be included in the calculation of the impedance.

$$Z = \sqrt{R^2 + X_L{}^2} \qquad (15\text{-}6)$$

$$= \sqrt{5^2 + 12^2}$$

$$Z = \sqrt{25 + 144} = \sqrt{169} = 13 \text{ ohms} \qquad Ans.$$

Example 15-7. A coil has a resistance of 10 ohms and an inductive reactance of 70 ohms at a certain frequency. Find (a) the Q of the coil and (b) the impedance of the coil. (c) If the resistance is neglected, what is the per cent of error?

Solution:

Given: $R = 10$ ohms   Find: $Q = ?$
        $X_L = 70$ ohms $Z = ?$
                          Per cent of error $= ?$

a.
$$Q = \frac{X_L}{R} = \frac{70}{10} = 7 \qquad Ans. \qquad\qquad (15\text{-}7)$$

b. Since Q is larger than 5, the resistance may be neglected and the impedance is equal to the inductive reactance.

$$Z = 70 \text{ ohms} \qquad Ans.$$

c. If we had included the resistance in the calculation of the impedance,

$$Z = \sqrt{R^2 + X_L^2} \qquad\qquad\qquad (15\text{-}6)$$
$$Z = \sqrt{10^2 + 70^2} = \sqrt{100 + 4{,}900} = \sqrt{5{,}000}$$
$$Z = 70.7 \text{ ohms}$$

The error introduced by not including R is equal to $70.7 - 70 = 0.7$ ohm. The per cent of error is

$$\frac{0.7}{70.7} \times 100 \text{ equals } 0.99 \text{ or 1 per cent}$$

This error is well within the normal human error incurred in merely taking measurements and is therefore unimportant.

Example 15-8. The field coils of a loudspeaker have a resistance of 6,000 ohms and an inductance of 1.592 henrys. Find (*a*) the inductive reactance at 800 cps, (*b*) the Q of the coils, (*c*) the impedance of the coils, and (*d*) the current flowing if the voltage across the coils is 40 volts.

Solution:

Given: $R = 6{,}000$ ohms   Find: $X_L = ?$
        $L = 1.592$ henrys $Q = ?$
        $f = 800$ cps $Z = ?$
        $E = 40$ volts $I = ?$

a. $X_L = 6.28fL = 6.28 \times 800 \times 1.592 = 8{,}000$ ohms   *Ans.*

b. $Q = \dfrac{X_L}{R} = \dfrac{8{,}000}{6{,}000} = 1.33 \qquad Ans. \qquad\qquad (15\text{-}7)$

c. Since Q is less than 5, the resistance *must* be included in the calculation of the impedance.

$$Z = \sqrt{R^2 + X_L^2} \qquad (15\text{-}6)$$
$$Z = \sqrt{6,000^2 + 8,000^2}$$
$$Z = \sqrt{36,000,000 + 64,000,000}$$
$$Z = \sqrt{100,000,000}$$
$$Z = 10,000 \text{ ohms} \qquad Ans.$$

d. Since the total opposition is the impedance, the formula for Ohm's law may be rewritten as

$$E = IZ \qquad (15\text{-}8)$$
$$40 = I \times 10,000$$
$$I = \frac{40}{10,000} = 0.004 \text{ amp} \qquad Ans.$$

Problems

1. Find the Q of a coil if $R = 30$ ohms and $X_L = 120$ ohms.

2. Find the Q of a coil if $X_L = 6,000$ ohms and $R = 1,000$ ohms.

3. Find the Q of a coil at 100 cps if $R = 200$ ohms and $L = 10$ henrys.

4. Find the impedance of a coil if its resistance is 12 ohms and its reactance is 35 ohms.

5. Find (*a*) the Q and (*b*) the impedance of a coil if its resistance is 100 ohms and its reactance is 1,000 ohms.

6. An antenna circuit has an inductance of 30 μh and a resistance of 20 ohms. Find the impedance to a 500-kc signal.

7. A 40-volt emf at a frequency of 1 kc is impressed across a loudspeaker of 5,000 ohms resistance and 1.5 henrys inductance. Find (*a*) the inductive reactance, (*b*) the impedance, and (*c*) the current.

8. A 120-volt 60-cps line is connected across a 10-henry choke coil whose resistance is 400 ohms. Find (*a*) the inductive reactance, (*b*) the Q of the coil, (*c*) the impedance, and (*d*) the current.

9. The primary of an a-f transformer has a resistance of 100 ohms and an inductance of 50 mh. Find (*a*) the inductive reactance at 1 kc and (*b*) the impedance.

10. A 3,000-ohm resistor has an inductance of 10 mh. Find its impedance at (*a*) 500 cps, (*b*) 5 kc, (*c*) 500 kc, and (*d*) 1,500 kc.

11. The primary of an i-f coupling transformer has an inductance of 5 mh and a resistance of 100 ohms. If the voltage across the primary is 10 volts at 456 kc, what is the current flowing in the primary?

12. An a-f amplifier circuit uses an audio choke of 100-mh inductance and 3,000-ohm resistance. Find the impedance to (*a*) 500 cps, (*b*) 1,000 cps, and (*c*) 5,000 cps.

JOB 15-4: MEASURING THE INDUCTANCE OF A COIL

The inductance of a coil may be calculated by the use of several formulas involving specific dimensions of the coil. However, these dimensions are not always easily obtained, and other methods are substituted. One method uses a standard inductance and a circuit similar to the Wheatstone bridge. Another method obtains the resonant frequency of the combination of the coil with a known capacity, and the inductance is calculated from the formula for the resonant frequency given in Job 17-8. In a third method, called the impedance method, an a-c voltage is impressed across the coil and voltage, frequency, and current are measured. The resistance of the coil is obtained by use of an ohmmeter.

Example 15-9. A 120-volt 60-cycle a-c source is placed across a filter choke whose resistance is 300 ohms. If the current drawn is 20 ma, what is the inductance of the coil?

Solution:

$$\text{Given: } E = 120 \text{ volts} \qquad \text{Find: } L = ?$$
$$f = 60 \text{ cps}$$
$$R = 300 \text{ ohms}$$
$$I = 20 \text{ ma} = 0.02 \text{ amp}$$

1. Find the impedance.

$$E = IZ \qquad (15\text{-}8)$$
$$120 = 0.02 \times Z$$
$$Z = \frac{120}{0.02} = 6,000 \text{ ohms} \qquad Ans.$$

2. Find the reactance.

$$R^2 + X_L{}^2 = Z^2 \qquad (15\text{-}5)$$
$$300^2 + X_L{}^2 = 6,000^2$$
$$90,000 + X_L{}^2 = 36,000,000$$
$$X_L{}^2 = 36,000,000 - 90,000$$
$$X_L{}^2 = 35,910,000$$
$$X_L = \sqrt{35,910,000} = 5,992 \text{ ohms} \qquad Ans.$$

3. Find the inductance.

$$X_L = 6.28fL \qquad (15\text{-}3)$$
$$5,992 = 6.28 \times 60 \times L$$
$$5,992 = 376.8 \times L$$
$$L = \frac{5,992}{376.8} = 15.9 \text{ henrys} \qquad Ans.$$

In this last example, the inductive reactance (5,992 ohms) is practically equal to the impedance (6,000 ohms). This is because the resistance (300 ohms) is quite small when compared with the impedance. The disparity in values is emphasized when they are squared

($Z^2 = 36,000,000$ and $R^2 = 90,000$). When the values of the resistance and the impedance are so far apart, it appears that the resistance cannot affect the impedance to any appreciable degree. Therefore, when the resistance is small in comparison with the impedance, it may be neglected completely, making $X_L = Z$. The resistance is small when Z/R is more than 5 as shown in Example 15-10.

Example 15-10. What is the inductance of a coil that draws 30 ma from a 120-volt 60-cycle a-c source? The resistance of the coil is 400 ohms.

Solution:

Given: $I = 30$ ma $= 0.03$ amp   Find: $L = ?$
$E = 120$ volts
$f = 60$ cps
$R = 400$ ohms

1. Find the impedance.

$$E = IZ \tag{15-8}$$
$$120 = 0.03 \times Z$$
$$Z = \frac{120}{0.03} = 4,000 \text{ ohms} \qquad Ans.$$

2. Compare the R and the Z.

$$\frac{Z}{R} = \frac{4,000}{400} = 10$$

Therefore, since Z/R is larger than 5, the resistance is small when compared with the impedance and $X_L = Z$.

3. Find the inductance.

$$X_L = 6.28 \times 60 \times L \tag{15-3}$$
$$4,000 = 376.8 \times L$$
$$L = \frac{4,000}{376.8} = 10.6 \text{ henrys} \qquad Ans.$$

Problems

1. What is the inductance of a coil whose resistance is 200 ohms if it draws 0.1 amp from a 120-volt 60-cycle line?

2. What is the inductance of a coil whose resistance is 500 ohms if it draws 20 ma from a 110-volt 60-cycle line?

3. What is the inductance of a coil whose resistance is 300 ohms if it draws 10 ma from a 50-volt 1,000-cps a-c source?

4. What is the inductance of a coil whose resistance is 200 ohms if it draws 100 ma from a 50-volt 1-kc source?

5. What is the inductance of a coil whose resistance is 50 ohms if it draws 0.55 amp from a 110-volt 60-cycle line?

6. What is the inductance of a coil whose resistance is 100 ohms if it draws 0.4 amp from a 120-volt 100-cps source?

JOB 15-5: REVIEW OF COILS

1. When an a-c voltage is impressed across a coil,

    a. The resulting current is an alternating current.

    b. This changing current produces changing fields of force which cut the wires of the coil.

    c. These cuttings induce a back emf in the coil.

2. The *inductance* of a coil is a measure of its ability to produce a back emf when the current through it is changing. The symbol for inductance is L.

3. Unit of inductance. A coil has an inductance of 1 *henry* if a current changing at the rate of 1 amp per second can induce a back emf of 1 volt in the coil.

4. To calculate inductance

$$L = E_{av} \div \frac{\Delta I}{t} \qquad (15\text{-}1)$$

5. To calculate the average back emf

$$E_{av} = L \times \frac{\Delta I}{t} \qquad (15\text{-}2)$$

6. The reactance of a coil is the opposition of the coil to the passage of a changing current.

$$X_L = 6.28fL \qquad (15\text{-}3)$$

7. The Q of a coil is the comparison of its inductive reactance with its resistance.

$$Q = \frac{X_L}{R} \qquad (15\text{-}7)$$

8. The impedance Z of a coil is the vector sum of its resistance and its reactance. If Q is larger than 5, the resistance may be neglected and $Z = X_L$. If Q is smaller than 5, the resistance must be added to the reactance to find Z.

$$Z^2 = R^2 + X_L{}^2 \qquad (15\text{-}5)$$

or
$$Z = \sqrt{R^2 + X_L{}^2} \qquad (15\text{-}6)$$

9. To measure the inductance of a coil, an a-c voltage is impressed across the coil and the voltage, frequency, and current are measured. The resistance of the coil is measured with an ohmmeter. The inductance is calculated by the following steps.

    a. Find the impedance.

$$E = IZ \tag{15-8}$$

    b. Find the reactance.

$$R^2 + X_L{}^2 = Z^2 \tag{15-5}$$

    c. Find the inductance.

$$X_L = 6.28fL \tag{15-3}$$

    d. If the ratio of Z to R is larger than 5, the resistance may be neglected and $X_L = Z$.

Problems

1. Find the inductance of a coil if 2 volts of back emf is induced in it by a current changing at the rate of 50 amp per second.

2. A coil has an inductance of 5 henrys and carries a current of 0.2 amp. Find the average back emf induced in it if the current is reduced to zero in 0.01 sec.

3. Find the inductive reactance of a 0.2-henry choke coil at (*a*) 100 cps, (*b*) 1,000 cps, (*c*) 10 kc, and (*d*) 100 kc.

4. A 5-volt 100-kc a-c voltage is impressed across an r-f choke whose inductance is 10 mh. Find (*a*) the reactance and (*b*) the current that flows.

5. Find the inductive reactance of a 50-μh coil at a frequency of 10 Mc.

6. What must be the inductance of a coil in order that it have a reactance of 8,000 ohms at 800 cps?

7. Find the Q of a coil if $R = 80$ ohms and $X_L = 4,800$ ohms.

8. Find the impedance of a coil if its resistance is 39 ohms and its reactance is 80 ohms.

9. Find the impedance of a coil to a frequency of 60 cps if its resistance is 30 ohms and its inductance is 0.2 mh.

10. A coil has an inductance of 50 μh and a resistance of 5 ohms. Find (*a*) the reactance to a 500-kc frequency, (*b*) the impedance, and (*c*) the current flowing if the voltage is 3 volts.

11. A coil of 100 ohms resistance draws 100 ma from a 25-volt 60-cycle source. Find its inductance.

12. A coil having a Q of 50 draws 10 ma when connected to a 15-volt 1-kc power supply. Find its inductance.

Test—Coils

1. A coil has an inductance of 10 henrys and carries a current of 100 ma. Find the average back emf induced if the current is reduced to zero in 0.05 sec.

2. A 12-volt 200-kc a-c voltage is

impressed across a coil whose inductance is 30 mh. Find the reactance
and the current in the circuit.

3. Find the impedance of a coil
to a frequency of 1 kc if its resistance is 40 ohms and its inductance
is 30 mh.

4. Find the impedance of a coil
to a frequency of 10 kc if its
resistance is 100 ohms and its
inductance is 0.5 henry .

5. A coil of 400 ohms resistance
draws 50 ma from a 120-volt 60-
cycle line. Find its inductance.

JOB 15-6: INTRODUCTION TO TRANSFORMERS

It is cheaper to transmit electrical energy at high voltages than at
low voltages because of the smaller loss of power in the line at high
voltages. For this reason, the 220 volts that is delivered by an a-c
generator may be stepped up to 2,200 or even 220,000 volts for transmission over long distances. At its destination, the voltage is stepped
down to 240 volts for industrial users and to 120 volts for ordinary
home and power users. The changes in the voltage continue. In
our radio and television receiver, the voltage is changed again to 6.3
volts to operate the tube heaters or to 350 volts for the plate supply
of the tubes. Elsewhere, the 120-volt supply is reduced to 20 volts
to operate a toy train or to 12 volts to operate a door bell. All these
changes in voltage are made by an extremely efficient electrical
device called a *transformer*.

Basic Construction. As shown in Fig. 15-5, a transformer consists
of (1) the *primary coil* which *receives*
energy from an a-c source, (2) the
secondary coil which *delivers* energy to
an a-c load, and (3) a *core* on which the
two coils are wound. The core is
generally of some highly magnetic
material, although cardboard, ceram-
ics, and other nonmagnetic materials
are used for the cores of some radio
and television transformers.

Principle of Operation. An alternating current will flow when an

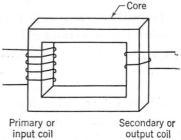

Fig. 15-5. Basic transformer construction.

a-c voltage is applied to the primary coil of a transformer. This
current produces a field of force which changes as the current changes.
The changing magnetic field is carried by the magnetic core to the
secondary coil, where it cuts across the turns of that coil. These
"cuttings" induce a voltage in the secondary coil. In this way, an

a-c voltage in one coil is transferred to another coil, even though there is no electrical connection between them. The number of lines of force available in the primary is determined by the primary voltage and the number of turns on the primary—each turn producing a given number of lines. Now, if there are *many turns on the secondary*, each line of force will cut *many turns* of wire and *induce a high voltage*. If the *secondary contains only a few turns*, there will be few cuttings and a *low induced voltage*. The secondary voltage, then, depends on the number of secondary turns as compared with the number of primary turns. If the secondary has twice as many turns as the primary, the secondary voltage will be twice as large as the primary voltage. If the secondary has half as many turns as the primary, the secondary voltage will be one-half as large as the primary voltage. This is stated as the following rule:

Rule: The voltage on the coils of a transformer is directly proportional to the number of turns on the coils.

Formula

$$\frac{E_p}{E_s} = \frac{N_p}{N_s} \tag{15-9}$$

where E_p = voltage on primary coil

E_s = voltage on secondary coil

N_p = number of turns on primary coil

N_s = number of turns on secondary coil

The ratio E_p/E_s is called the voltage ratio (VR). The ratio N_p/N_s is called the turns ratio (TR). By substituting these terms in formula (15-9), we obtain an equivalent statement.

$$VR = TR \tag{15-10}$$

Nomenclature. A voltage ratio of 1:3 (read as 1 to 3) means that for each volt on the primary, there are 3 volts on the secondary. This is called a "*step-up*" transformer. A step-up transformer *receives a low voltage* on the primary and *delivers a high voltage* from the secondary. A voltage ratio of 3:1 (read as 3 to 1) means that for 3 volts on the primary, there is only 1 volt on the secondary. This is called a "*step-down*" transformer. A step-down transformer *receives a high voltage* on the primary and *delivers a low voltage* from the secondary.

Example 15-11. A bell transformer reduces the primary voltage of 120 volts to the 18 volts delivered by the secondary. If there are

180 turns on the primary and 27 turns on the secondary, find (*a*) the voltage ratio and (*b*) the turns ratio.

Solution: The diagram for the problem is shown in Fig. 15-6.

a. $\text{VR} = \dfrac{E_p}{E_s}$

$\text{VR} = \frac{120}{18} = \frac{20}{3}$ (read as 20 to 3)   *Ans.*

b. $\text{TR} = \dfrac{N_p}{N_s}$

$\text{TR} = \frac{180}{27} = \frac{20}{3}$ (read as 20 to 3)   *Ans.*

Note: The ratios are always expressed in fractional form, even if the fraction can be reduced to a whole number.

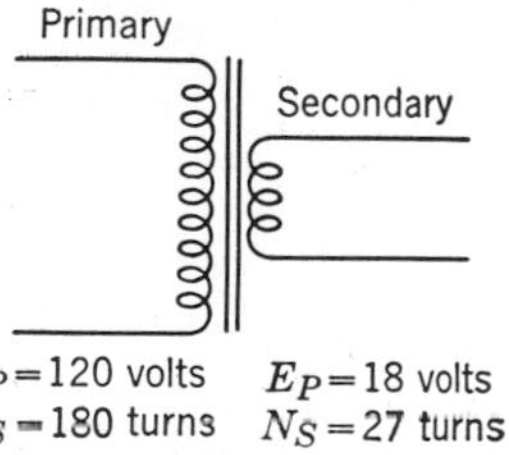

Primary

Secondary

$E_P = 120$ volts $E_P = 18$ volts
$N_S = 180$ turns $N_S = 27$ turns

$VR = ?$
$TR = ?$

Fig. 15-6

Example 15-12.   A radio "power" transformer has 99 turns on the primary and 315 turns on the secondary.   What voltage will it deliver if the primary voltage is 110 volts?

Solution:

Given: $N_p = 99$ turns   Find: $E_s = ?$
$N_s = 315$ turns
$E_p = 110$ volts

$$\frac{E_p}{E_s} = \frac{N_p}{N_s} \tag{15-9}$$

$$\frac{110}{E_s} = \frac{99}{315}$$

$$99E_s = 315 \times 110$$

$$E_s = \frac{315 \times 110}{99} = 350 \text{ volts}   \quad Ans.$$

Example 15-13.   The Stancor P-6011 television plate transformer has a voltage ratio of 11:35.   If the primary has 242 turns, how many turns must be wound on the secondary?

Solution:

Given: VR = 11:35   Find: $N_s = ?$
$N_p = 242$

$$\frac{E_p}{E_s} = \frac{N_p}{N_s} \tag{15-9}$$

but $\dfrac{E_p}{E_s} = \text{VR}$

therefore, $$VR = \frac{N_p}{N_s}$$

$$\frac{11}{35} = \frac{242}{N_s}$$

$$N_s = \frac{242 \times 35}{11} = 770 \text{ turns} \qquad Ans.$$

Problems

1. A filament transformer reduces the 110 volts on the primary to 10 volts on the secondary. Find (*a*) the voltage ratio and (*b*) the turns ratio.

2. The Stancor P-6293 universal-type power transformer steps down the voltage from 120 to 2.5 volts. Find (*a*) the voltage ratio and (*b*) the turns ratio.

3. A Stancor A-4773 transformer whose turns ratio is 1:3 is used as a plate-to-grid coupling transformer in a radio receiver. What is the secondary voltage if the primary voltage is 15 volts?

4. A 24:1 welding transformer has 25 turns on the secondary. How many turns are there on the primary?

5. A UTC LS-185 plate transformer steps up the voltage from 100 to 2,500 volts. If there are 50 turns on the primary, how many turns are on the secondary?

6. A toy-train transformer is connected to a 120-volt 60-cycle source. The secondary has 60 turns and delivers 24 volts. How many turns are on the primary?

7. The secondary coil of a transformer has 100 turns, and the secondary voltage is 5 volts. If the turns ratio is 22:1, find (*a*) the voltage ratio, (*b*) the primary voltage, and (*c*) the primary turns.

8. A step-down transformer is wound with 3,750 turns on the primary and 60 turns on the secondary. What is the delivered voltage if the high-voltage side is 15,000 volts?

9. The 117-volt primary of a transformer has 250 turns. Two secondaries are to be provided to deliver (*a*) 12.6 volts and (*b*) 35 volts. How many turns are needed on each secondary?

10. A power transformer with 100 turns on the primary is to be connected to a 120-volt source of supply. Separate secondary windings are to deliver (*a*) 2.5 volts, (*b*) 6.3 volts, and (*c*) 600 volts. Find the number of turns on each secondary.

JOB 15-7: CURRENT IN A TRANSFORMER

In the modern transformer, the power delivered to the primary is transferred to the secondary with practically no loss. For all practical purposes, the power input to the primary is equal to the power output of the secondary, and the transformer is assumed to operate at an efficiency of 100 per cent. Thus,

$$\text{Power input} = \text{power output} \qquad (15\text{-}11)$$

Since
$$\text{Power input} = E_p \times I_p \qquad (15\text{-}12)$$
and
$$\text{Power output} = E_s \times I_s \qquad (15\text{-}13)$$
$$E_p \times I_p = E_s \times I_s \qquad (15\text{-}14)$$

By dividing both sides of the equation by $E_s \times I_p$ and canceling out identical terms,

$$\frac{E_p \times \overset{1}{\cancel{I_p}}}{E_s \times \underset{1}{\cancel{I_p}}} = \frac{\overset{1}{\cancel{E_s}} \times I_s}{\underset{1}{\cancel{E_s}} \times I_p}$$

we obtain

Formula

$$\frac{E_p}{E_s} = \frac{I_s}{I_p} \qquad (15\text{-}15)$$

This formula indicates that the current ratio in a transformer is *inversely proportional* to the voltage ratio. If the *voltage* ratio *increases*, the *current* ratio will *decrease*. If the *voltage ratio decreases*, the *current* ratio will *increase*.

In addition, since

$$\frac{E_p}{E_s} = \frac{N_p}{N_s}$$

we may substitute $\dfrac{N_p}{N_s}$ for $\dfrac{E_p}{E_s}$ in Eq. (15-15). This gives

Formula

$$\frac{N_p}{N_s} = \frac{I_s}{I_p} \qquad (15\text{-}16)$$

Example 15-14. The Stancor model P-6293 universal-type power transformer delivers 36 watts of power to a rectifier circuit. If the primary voltage is 120 volts, how much current is drawn by the transformer?

Solution:

Given: Power output = 36 watts   Find: $I_p = ?$
$\qquad\qquad E_p = 120$ volts

$$\text{Power input} = \text{power output} \qquad (15\text{-}11)$$
$$E_p \times I_p = \text{power output}$$
$$120 \times I_p = 36$$
$$I_p = \tfrac{36}{120} = 0.6 \text{ amp} \qquad Ans.$$

Example 15-15. The primary of a transformer is connected to a 110-volt 60-cycle line. The secondary delivers 250 volts at 0.1 amp. Find (*a*) the current in the primary and (*b*) the power input to the primary.

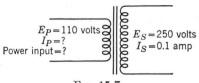

$E_P = 110$ volts
$I_P = ?$
Power input $= ?$

$E_S = 250$ volts
$I_S = 0.1$ amp

Fig. 15-7

Solution: The diagram for the problem is shown in Fig. 15-7.

a.
$$\frac{E_p}{E_s} = \frac{I_s}{I_p} \qquad (15\text{-}15)$$

$$\frac{110}{250} = \frac{0.1}{I_p}$$

$$110 \times I_p = 250 \times 0.1$$
$$I_p = \tfrac{25}{110} = 0.227 \text{ amp} \qquad Ans.$$

b. Power input $= E_p \times I_p = 110 \times 0.227 = 24.97$ watts   *Ans.*

Example 15-16. A bell transformer with 300 turns on the primary and 45 turns on the secondary draws 0.3 amp from the 110-volt line. Find (*a*) the current delivered by the secondary, (*b*) the voltage delivered by the secondary, and (*c*) the power delivered by the secondary.

Solution:

Given: $N_p = 300$ turns   Find: $I_s = ?$
$N_s = 45$ turns $E_s = ?$
$I_p = 0.3$ amp   Power output $= ?$
$E_p = 110$ volts

a.
$$\frac{N_p}{N_s} = \frac{I_s}{I_p} \qquad (15\text{-}16)$$

$$\frac{300}{45} = \frac{I_s}{0.3}$$

$$45 \times I_s = 300 \times 0.3$$
$$I_s = \tfrac{90}{45} = 2 \text{ amp} \qquad Ans.$$

b.
$$\frac{E_p}{E_s} = \frac{N_p}{N_s} \qquad (15\text{-}9)$$

$$\frac{110}{E_s} = \frac{300}{45}$$

$$300 \times E_s = 110 \times 45$$
$$E_s = \frac{4,950}{300} = 16.5 \text{ volts} \qquad Ans.$$

c. Power output $= E_s \times I_s = 16.5 \times 2 = 33$ watts   *Ans.*

Example 15-17. A 120:24-volt transformer draws 1.5 amp. Find the secondary current.

Solution:

Given: VR = 120:24   Find: I_s = ?

I_p = 1.5 amp

$$\frac{E_p}{E_s} = \frac{I_s}{I_p} \tag{15-15}$$

but

$$\frac{E_p}{E_s} = VR = \frac{120}{24}$$

$$\frac{120}{24} = \frac{I_s}{1.5}$$

$$24 \times I_s = 120 \times 1.5$$

$$I_s = \frac{180}{24} = 7.5 \text{ amp} \qquad Ans.$$

Problems

1. A bell transformer draws 20 watts from a line. What is the secondary current if the secondary voltage is 10 volts?

2. A Thermador model 5A6086 power transformer delivers 22.5 watts of power. If the primary voltage is 112.5 volts, how much current is drawn by the primary?

3. A 120-volt 60-cycle line supplies power to a Stancor model P-6297 universal-type transformer. If the secondary delivers 480 volts at 0.04 amp, find (a) the primary current and (b) the power input.

4. A bell transformer with 240 turns on the primary and 30 turns on the secondary draws 0.25 amp from a 120-volt line. Find (a) the secondary current, (b) the secondary voltage, and (c) the secondary power.

5. A transformer is wound with 2,200 turns on the primary and 150 turns on the secondary. (a) If it delivers 2 amp, what is the primary current? (b) If the primary voltage is 110 volts, what is the secondary voltage?

6. A 230:110-volt step-down transformer in a stage-lighting circuit draws 10 amp from the line. Find the current delivered.

7. A 120:8-volt transformer draws 1.2 amp. Find I_s.

8. A filament transformer delivers 1.5 amp at 6.3 volts. If E_p is 110 volts, find (a) I_p and (b) the power input.

9. A transformer with 2,400 turns on the primary and 480 turns on the secondary draws 8.5 amp from a 230-volt line. Find (a) I_s, (b) E_s, and (c) the power output.

10. A transformer has 120 turns on the primary and 1,500 turns on the secondary. (a) If it delivers 0.4 amp, what is the primary current? (b) If the primary voltage is 120 volts, what is the secondary voltage?

11. A 9:2 step-down transformer draws 1.8 amp. Find the I_s.

12. A substation transformer reduces the voltage from the transmission-line voltage of 150,000 to 4,400 volts. If the transmission line carries 15 amp, what current will the transformer deliver?

JOB 15-8: EFFICIENCY OF A TRANSFORMER

In Job 9-4 we learned that the efficiency of an electrical machine is equal to the ratio of the power output to the power input. This ratio is expressed as a per cent by multiplying it by 100. In general, the efficiency of any device is the ratio of its output to its input and describes the effectiveness of the device in utilizing the energy supplied to it. Thus, a transformer which delivers *all* the power put into it would have an efficiency of 100 per cent. In the last job, we assumed that the transformers had an efficiency of 100 per cent and delivered all the energy that they received. Actually, because of copper and core losses, the efficiency of even the best transformer is less than 100 per cent.

Formula

$$\text{Eff} = \frac{\text{power output}}{\text{power input}} \qquad (9\text{-}2)$$

Example 15-18. A plate transformer draws 30 watts from a 117-volt line and delivers 300 volts at 90 ma. Find its per cent efficiency.

Solution:

Given: Power input = 30 watts   Find: Per cent eff = ?
$\qquad E_s = 300$ volts
$\qquad I_s = 90$ ma = 0.09 amp

$$\text{Eff} = \frac{\text{power output}}{\text{power input}} \qquad (9\text{-}2)$$

$$\text{Eff} = \frac{300 \times 0.09}{30}$$

$$\text{Eff} = \tfrac{27}{30} = 0.9 = 90\% \qquad Ans.$$

Example 15-19. A transformer that draws 90 watts from the line operates at an efficiency of 95 per cent and delivers 40 volts from the secondary. Find (*a*) the watts delivered and (*b*) the secondary current.

Solution:

Given: Power input = 90 watts   Find: Power output = ?
$\qquad$ Eff = 95% = 0.95 I_s = ?
$\qquad E_s = 40$ volts

a.
$$Eff = \frac{power\ output}{power\ input} \qquad (9\text{-}2)$$

$$0.95 = \frac{power\ output}{90}$$

Power output = $90 \times 0.95 = 85.5$ watts   *Ans.*

b.
$$Power\ output = E_s \times I_s \qquad (15\text{-}13)$$
$$85.5 = 40 \times I_s$$

$$I_s = \frac{85.5}{40} = 2.14\ amp \qquad Ans.$$

Example 15-20. A transformer whose efficiency is 80 per cent draws its power from a 120-volt line. If it delivers 192 watts, find (*a*) the power input and (*b*) the primary current.

Solution:

Given: Eff = $80\% = 0.80$ Find: Power input = ?
$E_p = 120$ volts $I_p = ?$
Power output = 192 watts

a.
$$Eff = \frac{power\ output}{power\ input} \qquad (9\text{-}2)$$

$$0.80 = \frac{192}{power\ input}$$

$$Power\ input = \frac{192}{0.80} = 240\ watts \qquad Ans.$$

b.
$$Power\ input = E_p \times I_p \qquad (15\text{-}12)$$
$$240 = 120 \times I_p$$
$$I_p = \tfrac{240}{120} = 2\ amp \qquad Ans.$$

Problems

1. What is the efficiency of a transformer if it draws 800 watts and delivers 700 watts?

2. A toy transformer draws 150 watts from a 110-volt line and delivers 24 volts at 5 amp. Find its efficiency.

3. A transformer draws 1.5 amp at 120 volts and delivers 7 amp at 24 volts. Find (*a*) the power input, (*b*) the power output, and (*c*) the efficiency.

4. A radio power transformer draws 96 watts and delivers 420 volts at 200 ma. Find (*a*) the efficiency and (*b*) the primary current if the primary voltage is 120 volts.

5. In Fig. 15-8, an impedance-matching transformer couples a power tube delivering 4.2 watts to a voice coil which receives 3.36 watts. Find its efficiency.

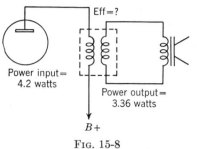

Power input =
4.2 watts

Power output =
3.36 watts

$B+$

FIG. 15-8

6. A transformer that draws 1,000 watts from a 230-volt line operates at an efficiency of 92 per cent and delivers 50 volts. Find (*a*) the watts delivered and (*b*) the secondary current.

7. A transformer that delivers 10,000 watts at an efficiency of 96 per cent draws its power from a 2,000-volt line. Find (*a*) the power input and (*b*) the primary current.

8. A transformer delivers 750 volts at 120 ma at an efficiency of 90 per cent. If the primary current is 0.8 amp, find (*a*) the power input and (*b*) the primary voltage.

9. The three secondary coils of a radio transformer deliver 100 ma at 350 volts, 2 amp at 2.5 volts, and 1.2 amp at 12.6 volts. What is the efficiency of the transformer if it draws 60 watts from the 117-volt line?

JOB 15-9: IMPEDANCE-MATCHING TRANSFORMERS

The maximum transfer of energy from one circuit to another will occur when the impedances of the two circuits are equal or matched. If the two circuits have unequal impedances, a coupling transformer

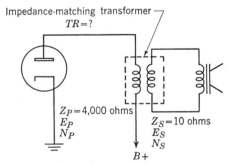

Impedance-matching transformer
$TR = ?$

$Z_P = 4{,}000$ ohms
E_P
N_P

$Z_S = 10$ ohms
E_S
N_S

$B+$

FIG. 15-9. An impedance-matching transformer is used to couple the output tube to the voice coil of the loudspeaker.

may be used as an intermediate impedance-changing device between the two circuits. In Fig. 15-9, the output of a radio power tube is used to operate the voice coil of a loudspeaker. The output of the tube cannot be connected directly to the voice coil because the impedance of the tube circuit is 4,000 ohms and the impedance of the voice coil is only 10 ohms. The circuits may be *matched* by a transformer with an appropriate turns ratio whose value depends on the values of the impedances involved. In Fig. 15-9,

$$\frac{N_p}{N_s} = \frac{E_p}{E_s} \quad \text{and} \quad \frac{N_p}{N_s} = \frac{I_s}{I_p}$$

By multiplying the two equations,

$$\frac{N_p}{N_s} \times \frac{N_p}{N_s} = \frac{E_p}{E_s} \times \frac{I_s}{I_p}$$

or

$$\left(\frac{N_p}{N_s}\right)^2 = \frac{E_p}{I_p} \times \frac{I_s}{E_s}$$

but $E_p/I_p = Z_p$ and $I_s/E_s = 1/Z_s$; therefore

$$\left(\frac{N_p}{N_s}\right)^2 = \frac{Z_p}{Z_s} \tag{15-17}$$

By taking the square root of both sides we obtain

Formula

$$\frac{N_p}{N_s} = \sqrt{\frac{Z_p}{Z_s}} \tag{15-18}$$

where N_p = number of turns on primary
   N_s = number of turns on secondary
   Z_p = impedance of primary, ohms
   Z_s = impedance of secondary, ohms

Example 15-21. Find the turns ratio of the transformer shown in Fig. 15-9.

Solution:

$$\frac{N_p}{N_s} = \sqrt{\frac{Z_p}{Z_s}} = \sqrt{\frac{4,000}{10}} = \sqrt{400} \tag{15-18}$$
$$\frac{N_p}{N_s} = \frac{20}{1} \quad Ans.$$

Example 15-22. The output from a 25L6 beam-power amplifier is to be matched to a 13.9-ohm voice coil. Find the required turns ratio.

Solution:

Given: 25L6 power tube   Find: $\dfrac{N_p}{N_s} = ?$
   Z_s = 13.9 ohms

From the tube manual, the recommended load resistance for a 25L6 tube is 2,000 ohms. Therefore, $Z_p = 2,000$ ohms.

$$\frac{N_p}{N_s} = \sqrt{\frac{Z_p}{Z_s}} = \sqrt{\frac{2,000}{13.9}} = \sqrt{144} \qquad (15\text{-}18)$$

$$\frac{N_p}{N_s} = \frac{12}{1} \qquad Ans.$$

The tube is connected to the primary ($N_p = 12$), and the voice coil is connected to the secondary ($N_s = 1$).

Example 15-23.   A carbon microphone whose impedance is 20 ohms is to be coupled to a grid circuit whose impedance is 72,000 ohms. Find the turns ratio of the coupling transformer.

Solution:

$$\text{Given: } Z_p = 20 \text{ ohms} \qquad \text{Find: } \frac{N_p}{N_s} = \text{?}$$
$$Z_s = 72,000 \text{ ohms}$$

When coupling from a low impedance to a high impedance, it is best to find the turns ratio by comparing N_s with N_p.   This can be done by inverting both sides of formula (15-18).

$$\frac{N_s}{N_p} = \sqrt{\frac{Z_s}{Z_p}} = \sqrt{\frac{72,000}{20}} = \sqrt{3,600} = 60 \qquad (15\text{-}19)$$

$$\frac{N_s}{N_p} = \frac{60}{1} \qquad \text{or} \qquad \frac{N_p}{N_s} = \frac{1}{60} \qquad Ans.$$

Thus, the microphone is connected to the primary ($N_p = 1$) and the grid is connected to the secondary ($N_s = 60$).

Example 15-24.   A 1:20 step-up transformer is used to match a microphone with a grid circuit impedance of 40,000 ohms.   Find the impedance of the microphone.

Solution:

$$\text{Given: } \frac{N_p}{N_s} = \frac{1}{20} \qquad \text{Find: } Z_p = \text{?}$$
$$Z_s = 40,000 \text{ ohms}$$

$$\left(\frac{N_p}{N_s}\right)^2 = \frac{Z_p}{Z_s} \qquad (15\text{-}17)$$

$$\left(\frac{1}{20}\right)^2 = \frac{Z_p}{40,000}$$

$$\frac{1}{400} = \frac{Z_p}{40,000}$$

$$Z_p = \frac{40,000}{400} = 100 \text{ ohms} \qquad Ans.$$

Problems

1. Find the turns ratio of a transformer used to match a 1,600-ohm load to a 4-ohm load.

2. Find the turns ratio of a transformer used to match a 60-ohm load to a 540-ohm line.

3. The impedance of the output circuit of a power stage is 8,000 ohms. What is the turns ratio of a transformer used to transfer the power to a 500-ohm line supplying a public-address system?

4. The 7B5 power tube in the Motorola model 55F11 radio receiver requires a load impedance of 9,000 ohms. Find the turns ratio of the transformer needed to feed into a 10-ohm voice coil.

5. Find the turns ratio of a microphone transformer required to couple a 20-ohm microphone to a 500-ohm line.

6. Find the turns ratio of a microphone transformer required to couple a 20-ohm microphone to a grid circuit of 50,000 ohms impedance.

7. A 55:1 output transformer is used to match an output tube to a 4-ohm voice coil. Find the impedance of the output circuit.

8. Two 6F6 tubes in push-pull working into a load impedance of 14,000 ohms are to have their output matched to an 8-ohm voice coil. Find the required turns ratio.

9. Find the turns ratio of a Stancor model A-8101 transformer which is used to match a 500-ohm line to an 8-ohm voice coil.

10. The 3Q4 beam-power tube in the Emerson model 505 three-way portable requires a load impedance of 10,000 ohms. Find the turns ratio of the transformer needed to match this load to a 5-ohm voice coil.

11. Find the turns ratio of the transformer used to match a 6L6 beam-power output tube to a 500-ohm line supplying a distant auditorium loud-speaker. The tube requires a 4,200-ohm impedance.

12. Find the turns ratio of the transformer needed to match a 50-ohm Amperite model PGL dynamic microphone to a 500-ohm line.

JOB 15-10: REVIEW OF TRANSFORMERS

1. A transformer transmits energy from one circuit to another by means of electromagnetic induction between two coils.

2. The *primary* coil is connected to the source of supply. The *secondary* coil is connected to the load.

3. A step-up transformer increases the voltage and decreases the current. A step-down transformer decreases the voltage and increases the current.

4. The turns ratio of a transformer is the comparison (by division) of the number of turns on the primary with the number of turns on the secondary.

$$TR = \frac{N_p}{N_s}$$

The voltage ratio of a transformer is the comparison (by division) of the voltage on the primary with the voltage on the secondary.

$$VR = \frac{E_p}{E_s}$$

5. In a 100 per cent efficient transformer

a.   Power input = power output   (15-11)

b.   Power input = $E_p \times I_p$ (15-12)

c.   Power output = $E_s \times I_s$ (15-13)

d. The voltage is directly proportional to the number of turns.

$$\frac{E_p}{E_s} = \frac{N_p}{N_s} \qquad (15\text{-}9)$$

e. The voltage is inversely proportional to the current.

$$\frac{E_p}{E_s} = \frac{I_s}{I_p} \qquad (15\text{-}15)$$

f. The number of turns is inversely proportional to the current.

$$\frac{N_p}{N_s} = \frac{I_s}{I_p} \qquad (15\text{-}16)$$

6. The efficiency of a transformer is the ratio of the power output to the power input and is expressed as a per cent.

$$Eff = \frac{\text{power output}}{\text{power input}} \qquad (9\text{-}2)$$

7. Impedance-matching transformers permit transfer of power between loads of different impedance. The turns ratio of such transformers is given by the formulas below:

$$\left(\frac{N_p}{N_s}\right)^2 = \frac{Z_p}{Z_s} \qquad (15\text{-}17)$$

or

$$\frac{N_p}{N_s} = \sqrt{\frac{Z_p}{Z_s}} \qquad (15\text{-}18)$$

Problems

1. A bell transformer reduces the voltage from 120 to 15 volts. If there are 22 turns on the secondary, find (a) the number of turns on the primary and (b) the turns ratio.

2. If the turns ratio of a transformer is 20:3, find the primary voltage if the secondary voltage is 24 volts.

3. The 110-volt primary of a transformer has 500 turns. Two secondaries are to be provided to deliver (a) 22 volts and (b) 5 volts. How many turns are needed for each secondary?

4. A radio power transformer delivers 50 watts of power. If the primary voltage is 110 volts, find the primary current.

5. A transformer connected to a 120-volt 60-cycle line delivers 750 volts at 200 ma. Find (a) the primary current and (b) the power drawn by the primary.

6. A 5:1 transformer draws 0.5 amp from a 120-volt line. Find (a) the secondary current, (b) the secondary voltage, and (c) the power output.

7. A filament transformer delivers 1.2 amp at 6.3 volts. If the primary voltage is 120 volts, find (a) I_p and (b) the power input.

8. A transformer with 1,500 turns on the primary and 375 turns on the secondary draws 3.5 amp from a 115-volt line. Find (a) the secondary current, (b) the secondary voltage, and (c) the power output.

9. A plate transformer draws 250 ma from a 120-volt line and delivers 80 ma at 350 volts. Find its efficiency.

10. A transformer drawing 150 watts from the line operates at an efficiency of 90 per cent and delivers 50 volts. Find (a) the power delivered and (b) the secondary current.

11. The 50B5 power tube in the Emerson model 642 radio receiver requires a load impedance of 2,500 ohms. Find the turns ratio of the transformer needed to match this load to the 5-ohm voice coil.

12. A 1:30 step-up transformer is used to match a 50-ohm microphone to a grid circuit. Find the impedance of the grid circuit.

Test—Transformers

1. The Stancor model P-6165 rectifier filament transformer has a voltage ratio of 24:1. If the primary has 312 turns, how many turns must be wound on the secondary?

2. A bell transformer with 180 turns on the primary and 27 turns on the secondary draws 0.2 amp from a 120-volt line. Find (a) the secondary current and (b) the secondary voltage.

3. A transformer whose efficiency is 90 per cent draws its power from a 120-volt line. If it delivers 180 watts, find (a) the power input and (b) the primary current.

4. The load impedance of a 50L6 beam-power tube is 2,000 ohms. Find the turns ratio of the transformer needed to couple this impedance to a 3.5-ohm voice coil.

5. A UTC model 0-1 step-up transformer has a turns ratio of 1:10. It is used to couple a 500-ohm line to a grid circuit. Find the impedance of the grid circuit.

CHAPTER 16

CAPACITANCE

JOB 16-1: INTRODUCTION TO CAPACITANCE

What Is a Capacitor? A capacitor, or "condenser," is formed whenever two pieces of metal are separated by a thin layer of insulating material. To form a capacitor of any appreciable value, however, the area of the metal pieces must be quite large and the thickness of the insulating material, or *dielectric*, must be quite small.

What Does a Capacitor Do? A capacitor is an electrical storehouse. When we wish to store up electricity for a little while, we

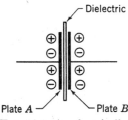

FIG. 16-1. An electrically neutral capacitor.

"charge" the capacitor. When we "discharge" a capacitor, we draw the electrons from it to operate some device. The two plates of the capacitor shown in Fig. 16-1 are electrically neutral, since there are as many protons as electrons on each plate. The capacitor has no "charge." Now let us connect a battery across the plates as shown in Fig. 16-2a. When the switch is closed (Fig. 16-2b), the positive side of the battery pulls electrons from plate A of the capacitor and deposits them on the plate B. Electrons will continue to flow from A to B until the number of electrons on plate B exert a force equal to the electromotive force of the battery. The capacitor is now charged. It will remain in this condition even if the battery is removed as shown in Fig. 16-3a. This is a condition of extreme unbalance, and the electrons on plate B will attempt to return to plate A if they can. The resistance of the dielectric and the surrounding air prevents this from happening, although some electrons do manage to "leak" off plate B and return to plate A. However, if a conductor is placed across the plates as in Fig. 16-3b, then the electrons find an easy path back to plate A and they will return in a rush, thus "discharging"

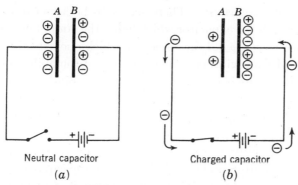

Neutral capacitor   Charged capacitor

(a)   (b)

FIG. 16-2. A charged capacitor has an excess of electrons on one plate.

the capacitor. There are many uses for capacitors such as in tuning circuits, filter circuits, coupling circuits, bypasses for alternating currents of high frequency, and blocking devices in audio circuits. In

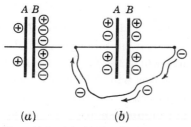

(a)   (b)

FIG. 16-3. (a) A charged capacitor has more electrons on one plate than on the other. (b) Discharging a capacitor.

each application, the capacitor operates by storing up electrons and discharging them at the proper time. Capacitors may not be used in d-c circuits, since the dielectric of the capacitor acts to present an open circuit. Current will flow in an a-c circuit containing a capacitor as shown in Fig. 16-4. During the positive half of the a-c cycle, the electrons travel through the lamp and pile up on plate A of the capacitor. During this time, electrons are drawn off plate B of the capacitor by the a-c source. During the negative half of the cycle, the direction of the electron flow is reversed. The capacitor discharges through the lamp; the source pulls the electrons from plate A and piles them up on plate B. This action continues with each reversal

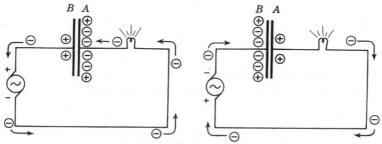

FIG. 16-4. Electron flow around a capacitor in an a-c circuit.

of the alternating current.   There seems to be a continuous flow of electrons through the capacitor which lights the lamp, but it is actually a flow of electrons *around* the capacitor which operates the lamp.

Meaning of Capacitance.   The measure of the ability of a capacitor to hold electrons is called its capacitance.   Since an electron is so small, and since there are so many of them, the *coulomb* is used as the measure of electrical quantity.   In Job 1-1 we learned that a coulomb is equal to approximately 6 billion billion electrons.   The word "capacity" generally means the quantity that a certain thing can hold and is a definite number.   For example, the capacity of an office-building elevator may be 15 people—which is a definite number. Yet during the "rush hours," as many as 20 people may be crammed into the car.   Does this mean that the capacity of the car has changed? Not at all!   It simply means that 15 people can enter the car under normal conditions but, when the pressure of the crowd increases, many more people will be pressed into the car.   The increase in pressure has increased the ability of the car to hold people.   Similarly with a capacitor.   A capacitor may hold a certain number of coulombs of electricity, but if the pressure or voltage which forced the electrons onto the plates is increased, then the capacitor will hold many more electrons than before.   If the number of electrons on the plates can be changed by changing the pressure, what number shall we use as the capacity of the capacitor?   It has been agreed that the capacitance of a capacitor be defined as the number of coulombs of electricity that may be placed on the plates by a pressure of 1 volt.   If 1 coulomb is held on the plates by a pressure of 1 volt, then the capacity is called 1 farad.   If 4 coulombs may be held by 4 volts, then 1 coulomb may be held by 1 volt and the capacity will still be 1 farad.   But if 4 coulombs may be held by only 2 volts, then 2 coulombs will be held by 1 volt and the capacity will be 2 farads.   From this, we can get a formula to find the capacity of a capacitor.

Formula

$$C = \frac{Q}{E} \tag{16-1}$$

where C = capacitance, farads

Q = number of electrons on plates, coulombs

E = voltage across the plates, volts

Example 16-1.   What is the capacity of a capacitor which can hold 0.0005 coulomb under a pressure of 100 volts?

Solution:

Given: $Q = 0.0005$ coulomb   Find: $C = ?$
$E = 100$ volts

$$C = \frac{Q}{E} = \frac{0.0005}{100} = 0.000005 \text{ farad} \qquad (16\text{-}1)$$

It is very inconvenient to discuss capacities in terms of farads, since a farad is such a tremendous unit of measurement. Always change units of capacity into microfarads (μf) or micromicrofarads ($\mu\mu$f). See Job 8-1 for methods of changing units of measurement. Therefore, 0.000005 farad $= 5\mu$f.   *Ans.*

Example 16-2. How many coulombs of electricity can he held on the plates of a 20-μf capacitor by a pressure of 100 volts?

Solution:

Given: $C = 20\ \mu$f $= 0.00002$ farad   Find: $Q = ?$
$E = 100$ volts

$$C = \frac{Q}{E} \qquad (16\text{-}1)$$

$$\frac{0.00002}{1} = \frac{Q}{100}$$

$$Q = 0.00002 \times 100$$
$$Q = 0.002 \text{ coulomb} \qquad Ans.$$

Example 16-3. What voltage is necessary to obtain a charge of 0.0004 coulomb on the plates of a 5-μf capacitor?

Solution:

Given: $Q = 0.0004$ coulomb   Find: $E = ?$
$C = 5\ \mu$f $= 0.000005$ farad

$$C = \frac{Q}{E} \qquad (16\text{-}1)$$

$$\frac{0.000005}{1} = \frac{0.0004}{E}$$
$$0.000005 \times E = 0.0004$$
$$E = \frac{0.0004}{0.000005} = \frac{400}{5} = 80 \text{ volts} \qquad Ans.$$

Problems

1. What is the capacitance of a capacitor if it absorbs 0.0001 coulomb when placed across a 100-volt line? Express the answer in farads and microfarads.

2. What is the capacitance of the grid-leak capacitor shown in Fig. 16-5?

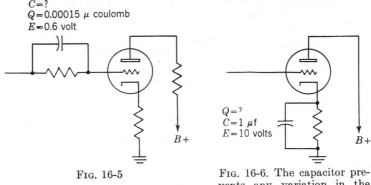

$C = ?$
$Q = 0.00015 \mu$ coulomb
$E = 0.6$ volt

$Q = ?$
$C = 1 \mu f$
$E = 10$ volts

$B+$

$B+$

FIG. 16-5

FIG. 16-6. The capacitor prevents any variation in the cathode bias voltage.

3. How many coulombs of electricity are held on the plates of a 16-μf filter capacitor which operates at 250 volts?

4. How many coulombs are held on the plates of a 1-μf cathode bypass capacitor if the voltage drop across it is 10 volts as shown in Fig. 16-6?

5. What is the voltage across a 2.5-μf bridge circuit capacitor if it holds 150 microcoulombs?

6. What is the voltage across a 0.00035-μf parallel plate-tuning capacitor if it holds 0.000049 microcoulomb?

7. In a diagram similar to that shown in Fig. 16-5, if a 2-Megohm grid leak passes 0.2 μa, what is the voltage drop across it? How many coulombs will be held on the plates of the grid-leak capacitor if its capacitance is 0.0002 μf?

8. What is the capacity of the coupling capacitor in the a-f amplifier section shown in Fig. 16-7?

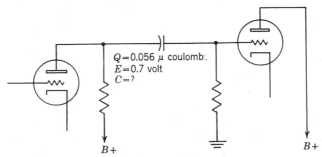

$Q = 0.056 \mu$ coulomb
$E = 0.7$ volt
$C = ?$

$B+$

$B+$

FIG. 16-7. A resistance-coupled a-f amplifier.

JOB 16-2: CAPACITORS IN PARALLEL

In the last job we learned that the capacity depends on the number of coulombs that can be held on the plates by a pressure of 1 volt.   A capacitor that can hold 3 coulombs will have three times the capacity of another that can hold only 1 coulomb if the same voltage is applied to both. What is it about a capacitor that enables one to hold more electrons than another? Obviously, the electrons must be held somewhere, and they are usually distributed on the surface of the capacitor plates. If the area of the plates is large, then many electrons can be placed on the large area, but if the plates are small in area, then only a few electrons can be held there and the capacity will be small. The capacitance of a capacitor depends on this plate area and also on the thickness of the dielectric. The larger the plate area, the larger the capacity. The *thinner* the dielectric, the *larger* the capacity.

What Is the Effect of Placing Capacitors in Parallel? In Fig. 16-8, C_1 and C_2 are connected in parallel. Since plate A and plate B are

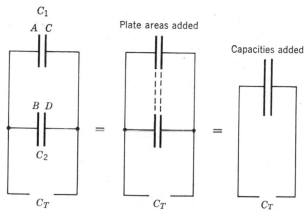

FIG. 16-8. When capacitors are in parallel, the plate areas are added and the total capacitance C_T equals the sum of the individual capacitances.

both connected together, the effect is the same as if we had one big plate whose area is equal to the sum of plates A and B. Similarly, plates C and D on the other side are connected together to form one large plate equal to the sum of C and D. Since the capacity increases as we increase the plate area, we get the capacity of the combination by adding the capacities of the individual capacitors.

Formula

$$C_T = C_1 + C_2 + C_3 + \cdots + \text{etc.} \qquad (16\text{-}2)$$

where C_T = total capacity
C_1, C_2, C_3, etc. = capacities of the individual capacitors
All capacitances must be measured in the same units.

Working Voltage. There is a limit to the voltage that may be applied across any capacitor. If too large a voltage is applied, it will overcome the resistance of the dielectric and a current will be forced through it from one plate to the other, sometimes burning a hole in the dielectric. In this event, a short circuit exists and the capacitor must be discarded. This applies only to mica or waxed-paper capacitors. If the dielectric is air, the "short" disappears as soon as the voltage is removed. The maximum voltage that may be applied to a capacitor is known as the *working voltage* and must never be exceeded.

Example 16-4. A 0.00035-μf tuning capacitor is in parallel with a trimmer capacitor of 0.000075 μf. What is the total capacity?

Solution: The diagram for the circuit is shown in Fig. 16-9.

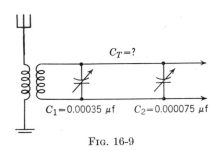

FIG. 16-9

$$C_T = C_1 + C_2 \qquad (16\text{-}2)$$
$$C_T = 0.00035 + 0.000075$$
$$C_T = 0.000425 \ \mu f \qquad Ans.$$

Note: Remember to keep the decimal points in line when adding.

Example 16-5. What is the total capacity and working voltage of a 0.0005-μf 50-volt capacitor, a 0.015-μf 100-volt capacitor, and a 0.00025-μf 100-volt capacitor when they are connected in parallel?

Solution: The total capacity is the sum of the capacities:

$$
\begin{array}{r}
0.0005 \\
0.015 \\
0.00025 \\
\hline
C_T = 0.01575 \ \mu f \qquad Ans.
\end{array}
$$

Just as a chain is only as strong as its weakest link, the working voltage of a group of parallel capacitors is only as great as the *smallest* working voltage. Therefore, the working voltage of the combination is only 50 volts.   *Ans.*

Example 16-6. A capacitor of 0.00035 μf is in parallel with a second capacitor which holds a charge of 0.000005 coulomb at 100 volts. What is the total capacity of the group?

Solution:

Given: $C_1 = 0.00035 \ \mu f$ Find: $C_T = ?$
$\quad\quad\quad Q_2 = 0.000005$ coulomb
$\quad\quad\quad E_3 = 100$ volts

1. Find C_2.

$$C_2 = \frac{Q_2}{E_2} \tag{16-1}$$

$$C_2 = \frac{0.000005}{100} = 0.00000005 \text{ farad}$$

2. Change farads into microfarads.

$$0.00000005 \text{ farad} = 0.00000005 \times 10^6 = 0.05 \ \mu f$$

3. Find the total capacity.

$$C_T = C_1 + C_2 = 0.00035 + 0.05 - 0.05035 \ \mu f \qquad Ans.$$

Problems

1. A capacitor in a tuning circuit has a capacity of 0.00032 μf. When the stage is aligned, the trimmer capacitor in parallel with it is adjusted to a capacity of 0.000053 μf. What is the total capacity of the combination?

2. A mechanic has the following capacitors available: 0.0003-μf 75-volt, 0.00025-μf 50-volt, 0.0002-μf 50-volt, 0.00015-μf 75-volt, and 0.00005-μf 75-volt. Which of these should he arrange in parallel to form a combination with a capacity of 0.0005 μf and 75 volts working voltage?

3. What is the total capacity in parallel of the following capacitors: 35 $\mu\mu f$, 0.005 μf, and 0.00003 μf?

4. A capacitor of 0.0003-μf capacity is connected in parallel with a 0.000005-farad capacitor. What is the total capacity?

5. What is the total capacity of a 25-$\mu\mu f$, a 0.00006-μf, and a 0.00000003-farad capacitor?

6. A capacitor of 0.003 μf is in parallel with another which holds a charge of 0.000004 coulomb at 200 volts. What is the total capacity?

7. What amount of capacity must be added in parallel with a 0.00055-μf capacitor in order to get a total capacity of 0.0007 μf?

8. What is the total capacity in parallel of two capacitors if they are charged at 120 volts with 0.00006 and 0.0001728 coulomb, respectively?

JOB 16-3: CAPACITORS IN SERIES

It has been found that the thicker the dielectric, or the greater the distance between the plates, the smaller the capacity. If we were to combine capacities so that the effective distance between the plates was increased, then the resulting capacity would necessarily be less than before.

What Is the Effect of Placing Capacitors in Series? In Fig. 16-10, capacitors C_1 and C_2 are connected in series. When a voltage is impressed on this combination, electrons are drawn from plate A

and deposited on plate D. The charges on plates B and C are equal and opposite and therefore neutralize each other. In this event, they may be considered to be eliminated and the combination replaced by a single capacitor whose dielectric thickness is equal to the sum of the dielectric thicknesses of the original capacitors. Thus the effect of a series combination is to increase the dielectric thickness and therefore to decrease the capacitance.

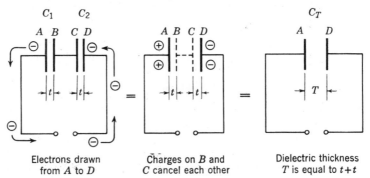

Electrons drawn   Charges on B and   Dielectric thickness
from A to D C cancel each other T is equal to $t+t$

FIG. 16-10. Capacitors in series increase the total dielectric thickness and decrease the total capacitance.

Formula

$$\frac{1}{C_T} = \frac{1}{C_1} + \frac{1}{C_2} + \frac{1}{C_3} + \cdots \text{ etc.} \qquad (16\text{-}3)$$

All capacities must be measured in the same units.

Notice the similarity between this formula and the formula for resistances in parallel given in Job 5-7 as formula (5-3). The similarity is continued through the formula for the total resistance in parallel of a number of equal resistors given in the same job as formula (5-4). For equal capacitors in *series*, we have

Formula

$$C_T = \frac{C}{N} \qquad (16\text{-}4)$$

where C_T = total capacity
C = capacity of one of the equal capacitors
N = number of equal capacitors

Working Voltage. Within limits, the total voltage that may be applied across a group of capacitors in series is equal to the sum of the working voltages of the individual capacitors.

Example 16-7. A 4-, a 5-, and a 10-μf capacitor are connected in series. Find the total capacity.

Solution: Review Job 5-4 on Addition of Fractions.

$$\frac{1}{C_T} = \frac{1}{C_1} + \frac{1}{C_2} + \frac{1}{C_3} \qquad (16\text{-}3)$$

$$\frac{1}{C_T} = \frac{1}{4} + \frac{1}{5} + \frac{1}{10}$$

$$\frac{1}{C_T} = \frac{11}{20}$$

$$11 \times C_T = 20$$

$$C_T = \tfrac{20}{11} = 1.818 \ \mu\text{f} \qquad Ans.$$

Example 16-8. A simplified diagram of a voltage doubler is shown in Fig. 16-11. The a-c line voltage charges first one and then the other capacitor as the polarity of the line alternates. Since the capacitors are in series, the total voltage to the load is twice the line voltage. What is the total capacity and working voltage of the capacitor combination if C_1 and C_2 are both 30-μf 200-volt capacitors?

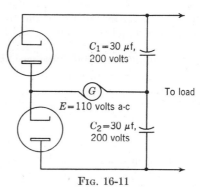

$C_1 = 30 \ \mu\text{f},$ 200 volts

To load

$E = 110$ volts a-c

$C_2 = 30 \ \mu\text{f},$ 200 volts

Fig. 16-11

Solution:

$$C_T = \frac{C}{N} = \frac{30}{2} = 15 \ \mu\text{f} \qquad Ans. \qquad (16\text{-}4)$$

Working voltage $= 200 + 200 = 400$ volts   *Ans.*

Example 16-9. The frequency which beats against the incoming frequency in the superheterodyne receiver is produced by an oscillator circuit. The Colpitts oscillator shown in Fig. 16-12 controls the frequency of oscillation by changing the total series capacitance of the

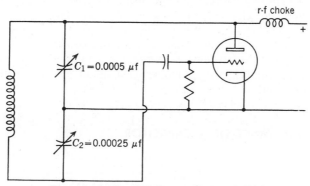

r-f choke

$C_1 = 0.0005 \ \mu\text{f}$

$C_2 = 0.00025 \ \mu\text{f}$

Fig. 16-12. The Colpitts oscillator circuit.

two capacitors.   What is the total capacity of the group if $C_1 = 0.0005$ μf and $C_2 = 0.00025$ μf?

Solution: When only two capacitors are in series, we can use a formula very similar to the formula for finding the total resistance of two resistors in parallel.

Formula

$$C_T = \frac{C_1 \times C_2}{C_1 + C_2} \tag{16-5}$$

In this formula, all the measurements must be in the same units. Since it is easier to use whole numbers than decimals in the formula, all measurements are changed into micromicrofarads.

$$C_1 = 0.0005 \ \mu f = 0.0005 \times 10^6 = 500 \ \mu\mu f$$
$$C_2 = 0.00025 \ \mu f = 0.00025 \times 10^6 = 250 \ \mu\mu f$$
$$C_T = \frac{500 \times 250}{500 + 250} = \frac{125,000}{750} = 167 \ \mu\mu f \qquad Ans.$$

Problems

1. Capacitors of 3, 4, and 6μf are connected in series.   What is their total capacity?

2. What is the total capacity and working voltage of a voltage doubler similar to that shown in Fig. 16-11 if the circuit uses two 40-μf 175-volt capacitors?

3. Find the total capacity of the series capacitors in a Colpitts oscillator similar to that shown in Fig. 16-12 if $C_1 = 0.0004$ μf and $C_2 = 0.00002$ μf.

4. A 25Z5 rectifier uses two 16-μf capacitors in series in a voltage doubler. Find the total capacity of the group.

5. What is the range of total capacities available in an oscillator circuit which uses a tuning capacitor of a 35- to 350-μμf range in series with a padder capacitor set at 300 μμf?

6. In some vibrator power supplies operating from a storage battery, a pair of "buffer" capacitors are placed across the secondary of the transformer to reduce the voltage peaks.   What is the total capacity and working voltage of a pair of 0.0075-μf 800-volt buffer capacitors in series?

7. Find the total capacity of a 6-, a 10-, and a 15-μf capacitor in series.

8. What is the total capacity of a 0.00000002-farad, a 0.04-μf, and a 60,000-μμf capacitor in series?

JOB 16-4: REACTANCE OF A CAPACITOR

We learned in Job 16-1, that as a capacitor is charged, electrons are drawn from one plate and deposited on the other.   As more and more electrons accumulate on the second plate, they begin to act as an opposing voltage which attempts to stop the flow of electrons just as a resistor would do. This opposing effect is called the *reactance* of the capacitor and is measured in ohms.

What Factors Determine the Reactance?

1. The size of the capacitor is one factor. The larger the capacitor, the greater the number of electrons that may be accumulated on its plates. However, because the plate area is large, the electrons do not accumulate in one spot but spread out over the entire area of the plate and do not impede the flow of new electrons on to the plate. Therefore, a large capacitor offers a small reactance. If the capacity was small, as in a capacitor with a small plate area, the electrons could not spread out and would attempt to stop the flow of electrons coming to the plate. Therefore, a small capacitor offers a large reactance. The reactance is therefore *inversely* proportional to the capacitance.

2. If an a-c voltage is impressed across the capacitor, electrons are accumulated first on one plate and then on the other. If the frequency of the changes in polarity is low, the time available to accumulate electrons will be large. This means that a large number of electrons will be able to accumulate, which will result in a large opposing effect, or a large reactance. If the frequency is high, the time available to accumulate electrons will be small. This means that there will be only a few electrons on the plates, which will result in only a small opposing effect, or a small reactance. The reactance is therefore *inversely* proportional to the frequency.

3. A special constant of proportionality is necessary to change the current-reducing effect of the electron accumulation into ohms of reactance. This number is 2π. The formula for the capacitive reactance is

$$X_c = \frac{1}{2\pi f C}$$

with C measured in farads. If the capacitance is measured in microfarads,

$$X_c = \frac{1}{2 \times 3.14 \times f \times (C/1,000,000)} = \frac{1,000,000}{6.28 \times f \times C}$$

Formula

$$X_c = \frac{159,000}{f \times C} \tag{16-6}$$

where X_c = capacitive reactance, ohms

f = frequency, cps

C = capacity, μf

Note: The larger the capacity, the smaller the reactance. The larger the frequency, the smaller the reactance.

Example 16-10. The cathode resistor for a 6V6 beam-power amplifier is bypassed with a 10-μf capacitor so as to eliminate any variation in the cathode bias. What is the reactance of this capacitor to a 0.4-kc audio frequency? If the voltage across this capacitor is 13 volts, what current will flow?

Solution: The diagram for the circuit is shown in Fig. 16-13.

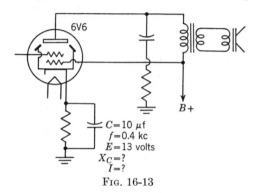

$C = 10\ \mu f$
$f = 0.4$ kc
$E = 13$ volts
$X_C = ?$
$I = ?$

Fig. 16-13

1. Change all units into the required units of measurement.

$$\text{Frequency} = 0.4 \text{ kc} = 0.4 \times 1{,}000 = 400 \text{ cps}$$

2. Find the capacitive reactance.

$$X_c = \frac{159{,}000}{f \times C} \qquad (16\text{-}6)$$

$$X_c = \frac{159{,}000}{400 \times 10} = \frac{159}{4} = 40 \text{ ohms} \qquad (\text{approx}) \qquad Ans.$$

3. Find the current. Since the only opposition to the flow of current around the capacitor is its reactance, the formula for Ohm's law, $E = IR$, may be rewritten as

$$E_c = I_c \times X_c \qquad (16\text{-}7)$$
$$13 = I_c \times 40$$
$$I_c = \tfrac{13}{40} = 0.325 \text{ amp} \qquad Ans.$$

Example 16-11. Find the capacitive reactance of a 0.00035-μf tuning capacitor in parallel with a 0.00015-μf trimmer capacitor at a frequency of 600 kc.

Solution: The diagram for the circuit is shown in Fig. 16-14.

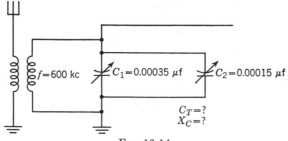

FIG. 16-14

1. Find the total capacity.

$$C_T = C_1 + C_2 = 0.00035 + 0.00015 = 0.0005 \ \mu f \qquad Ans.$$

2. Change to required units.

$$600 \ \text{kc} = 600 \times 1,000 = 600,000 \ \text{cps}$$

3. Find the capacitive reactance.

$$X_c = \frac{159,000}{f \times C} = \frac{159,000}{600,000 \times 0.0005} = \frac{159,000}{300} = 530 \ \text{ohms} \qquad Ans.$$

Example 16-12. A capacitor is formed whenever two metal pieces are separated by a dielectric. A capacitor formed by two wires of a circuit or two turns of a coil, produces a *distributed capacity.* This is extremely undesirable, because even a very small distributed capacity can transfer energy from one circuit to another at radio frequencies, since the reactance at radio frequencies is very small. This unwanted transfer of energy represents wasted power. What is the current lost through a distributed capacity of 10 $\mu\mu f$ formed by two parallel wires, one of which carries a 1,000-kc current? The difference in potential between the wires is 1 volt.

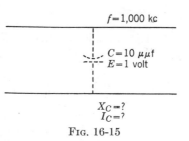

FIG. 16-15

Solution: The diagram of the circuit is shown in Fig. 16-15.

1. Change the measurements to the required units.

$$1,000 \ \text{kc} = 1,000 \times 1,000 = 1,000,000 \ \text{cps}$$
$$10 \ \mu\mu f = 10 \div 10^6 = 0.00001 \ \mu f$$

2. Find the capacitive reactance.

$$X_c = \frac{159,000}{f \times C} = \frac{159,000}{1,000,000 \times 0.00001} = \frac{159,000}{1} = 159,000 \ \text{ohms}$$

3. Find the current.

$$E_c = I_c \times X_c \qquad (16\text{-}7)$$
$$1 = I_c \times 159{,}000$$
$$I_c = \frac{1}{159{,}000} = 0.000062 \text{ amp}$$
$$I_c = 0.062 \text{ ma} \qquad Ans.$$

Example 16-13. Find the size of filter capacitor necessary to provide a capacitive reactance of 159 ohms at a frequency of 60 cps. *Solution:* The diagram for the circuit is shown in Fig. 16-16.

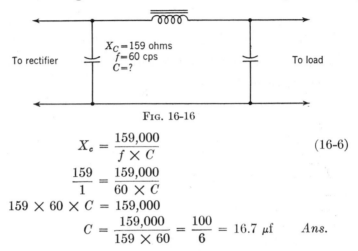

To rectifier

$X_C = 159$ ohms
$f = 60$ cps
$C = ?$

To load

FIG. 16-16

$$X_c = \frac{159{,}000}{f \times C} \qquad (16\text{-}6)$$
$$\frac{159}{1} = \frac{159{,}000}{60 \times C}$$
$$159 \times 60 \times C = 159{,}000$$
$$C = \frac{159{,}000}{159 \times 60} = \frac{100}{6} = 16.7 \ \mu\text{f} \qquad Ans.$$

Use the commercially available 16-μf 500-volt capacitor.

Problems

1. The cathode resistor for a 6J5 class A amplifier is bypassed with a 0.1-μf capacitor. Find its reactance to frequencies of (a) 50 cps, (b) 2 kc, and (c) 500 kc.

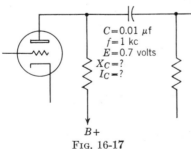

$C = 0.01$ μf
$f = 1$ kc
$E = 0.7$ volts
$X_C = ?$
$I_C = ?$

$B+$

FIG. 16-17

2. What is the reactance of a 0.0003-μf grid-leak capacitor at (a) 30 kc, (b) 100 kc, and (c) 800 kc?

3. What is the reactance of an oscillator capacitor of 0.0004 μf to a frequency of 456 kc?

4. What is the reactance of a 0.01-μf coupling capacitor to an audio frequency of 1 kc? What current will flow if the voltage across the capacitor is 0.7 volts as shown in Fig. 16-17?

5. A 0.00035-μf tuning capacitor is in parallel with a 0.00005-μf trimmer capacitor. Find the total capacity of the combination and its reactance to a frequency of 100 kc.

6. Find the capacitance required for a power triode bypass capacitor if the reactance should be 200 ohms at 600 kc.

7. Find the capacitive reactance between two wires if the stray capacitance between them is 8 $\mu\mu$f and one wire carries a radio frequency of 1,500 kc.

8. A 6J7 acting as a self-biased detector has its cathode resistor bypassed by a 4-μf capacitor. What is the reactance of the capacitor to the 500-cps a-f current?

9. What is the reactance of a 0.005-μf blocking capacitor at a frequency of 1,010 kc?

10. In the RCA model 648PV television receiver, the 6BA6 first sound i-f tube has its cathode resistor bypassed with a 0.25-μf capacitor. What is its reactance to a frequency of 21.25 Mc?

11. In a simple diode-detector circuit, the cathode load resistance is bypassed with a 100-$\mu\mu$f capacitor. What is its reactance to (a) 1,500 kc, (b) 1,000 kc, and (c) 500 kc?

12. Find the bypass capacitor required for a 6C5 tube, used as a self-biased detector if it is to have a reactance of 850 ohms at 500 cps.

JOB 16-5: IMPEDANCE OF A CAPACITOR

In the last job, the opposition to the flow of current offered by a capacitor was considered to be its reactance. Actually, however, it is impossible to obtain a circuit which contains only reactance. The plates of the capacitor and its connecting leads all have some resistance. The *impedance* is the total opposition to the flow of current and is equal to the *vector sum* of the resistance and the reactance. The symbol for the impedance is Z. The complete explanation of impedance and the derivation of the formula are given in Job 17-6.

Formula

$$Z = \sqrt{R^2 + X_c^2} \qquad\qquad (16\text{-}8)$$

where Z = impedance, ohms
R = resistance, ohms
X_c = capacitive reactance, ohms

Example 16-14. Find the impedance of a capacitor if its reactance is 40 ohms and its resistance is 30 ohms.

Solution:

$$\text{Given: } X_c = 40 \text{ ohms} \qquad \text{Find: } Z = ?$$
$$R = 30 \text{ ohms}$$

$$Z = \sqrt{R^2 + X_c^2} \qquad\qquad (16\text{-}8)$$
$$Z = \sqrt{30^2 + 40^2}$$
$$Z = \sqrt{900 + 1,600} = \sqrt{2,500} = 50 \text{ ohms} \qquad Ans.$$

Example 16-15. Find the impedance offered by a 10-μf filter capacitor to a 60-cps frequency if its resistance is 50 ohms.

Solution:

$$\text{Given: } C = 10 \ \mu\text{f} \qquad\qquad \text{Find: } Z = \ ?$$
$$f = 60 \text{ cps}$$
$$R = 50 \text{ ohms}$$

1. Find the capacitive reactance.

$$X_c = \frac{159,000}{f \times C} = \frac{159,000}{60 \times 10} = \frac{1,590}{6} = 265 \text{ ohms} \qquad Ans. \quad (16\text{-}6)$$

2. Find the impedance.

$$Z = \sqrt{R^2 + X_c^2} = \sqrt{50^2 + 265^2} = \sqrt{2,500 + 70,225}$$
$$= \sqrt{72,725} = 270 \text{ ohms} \qquad Ans.$$

Problems

1. Find the impedance of a capacitor if its reactance is 40 ohms and its resistance is 9 ohms.

2. Find the impedance of a capacitor if its reactance is 24 ohms and its resistance is 7 ohms.

3. Using Fig. 16-18, find the impedance of a coupling capacitor circuit to an audio frequency of 1 kc if the capacity is 0.01 μf and the resistance of the circuit is 3,000 ohms.

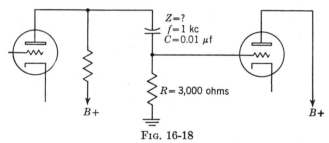

Fig. 16-18

4. Find the impedance of the tone-control circuit shown in Fig. 16-19.

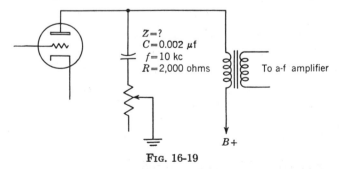

Fig. 16-19

5. What is the total impedance of the circuit in Fig. 16-19 if $f = 5$ kc, $C = 0.01$ μf, and $R = 10,000$ ohms?

6. A 3,000-ohm resistor is in series with a 0.02-μf capacitance. Find the impedance at (a) 500 kc, (b) 5 kc, and (c) 500 cps.

JOB 16-6: MEASUREMENT OF CAPACITY

Voltmeter-Ammeter Method. The circuit used to measure the capacitance of a capacitor is shown in Fig. 16-20. The voltmeter measures the voltage across the capacitor, and the ammeter measures the current in the circuit. Since the resistance of the capacitor is so very small when compared with its reactance, we can neglect it in this situation.

Example 16-16. Find the capacity of the capacitor shown in Fig. 16-20.

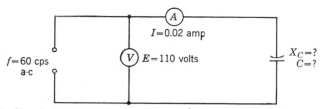

Fig. 10-20. Circuit for measuring capacitance by the voltmeter-ammeter method.

Solution:

1. Find the capacitive reactance.

$$E_c = I_c \times X_c \qquad (16\text{-}7)$$
$$110 = 0.02 \times X_c$$
$$X_c = \frac{110}{0.02} = 5,500 \text{ ohms} \qquad Ans.$$

2. Find the capacity.

$$X_c = \frac{159,000}{f \times C} \qquad (16\text{-}6)$$
$$\frac{5,500}{1} = \frac{159,000}{60 \times C}$$
$$5,500 \times 60 \times C = 159,000$$
$$C = \frac{159,000}{33,000} = 0.482 \text{ }\mu\text{f} \qquad Ans.$$

Problems

Find the capacity of each capacitor if the measurements obtained by the voltmeter-ammeter method are given below.

Problem	E	I	f
1	110 volts	0.11 amp	60 cps
2	110 volts	0.5 amp	60 cps
3	18 volts	20 ma	60 cps
4	50 volts	10 ma	25 cps
5	318 mv	20 ma	1 kc

Bridge Method. An adaptation of the Wheatstone bridge may be

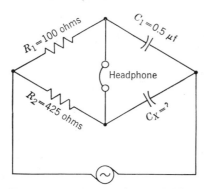

used to measure the capacitance of an unknown capacitor. In the circuit shown in Fig. 16-21, R_1 and R_2 are variable resistors, C_1 is a known capacitance, and C_x is the unknown capacitance. A headphone is used instead of a galvanometer, and a source of alternating current is used instead of a battery. In operating the bridge, R_1 and R_2 are adjusted until there is no sound in the headphone. At this point we may use

FIG. 16-21. A capacitance bridge circuit.

Formula

$$\frac{R_1}{R_2} = \frac{C_x}{C_1} \qquad (16\text{-}9)$$

The main difference between the capacity bridge and the Wheatstone bridge is that in the capacity bridge the resistance is *inversely proportional* to the capacitance.

Example 16-17. No sound is heard in the headphone of the circuit shown in Fig. 16-21 when $R_1 = 100$ ohms, $R_2 = 425$ ohms, and $C_1 = 0.5$ μf. Find C_x.

Solution:

$$\frac{R_1}{R_2} = \frac{C_x}{C_1} \qquad (16\text{-}9)$$

$$\frac{100}{425} = \frac{C_x}{0.5}$$

$$425 \times C_x = 100 \times 0.5$$

$$C_x = \tfrac{50}{425} = 0.117 \ \mu\text{f} \qquad Ans.$$

Problems

Using a capacity bridge, the following measurements were taken. Find the unknown capacitance in each problem.

Problem	R_1, ohms	R_2, ohms	C_1, μf
1	100	250	0.6
2	1	3.2	2.5
3	100	750	0.05
4	453	10	0.2

Using a Capacity Bridge to Locate Breaks in Cables. The distributed capacity that exists between two wires may be used to locate a break in a length of cable. Suppose an actual break occurs in one of a pair of cables. The capacity of the broken cable will depend on the length of the cable out to the break, whereas the capacity of the unbroken cable depends on its total length. In other words, the capacity is directly proportional to the length of the cable.

$$\frac{L_2}{L_1} = \frac{C_x}{C_1} \qquad (16\text{-}10)$$

where L_2 — length of cable up to break

$L_1 =$ length of unbroken cable

$C_x =$ capacity of cable up to break

$C_1 =$ capacity of full length of unbroken cable

When the bridge is used, an adjoining pair of good wires are used as the capacity C_1 and the capacity of the pair of wires out to the break is C_x. R_1 and R_2 are adjusted until there is no sound in the headphone. The circuit is shown in Fig. 16-22.

The formula for the bridge is

$$\frac{R_1}{R_2} = \frac{C_x}{C_1} \qquad (16\text{-}9)$$

Also, $\qquad \dfrac{L_2}{L_1} = \dfrac{C_x}{C_1} \qquad (16\text{-}10)$

Therefore, we can set R_1/R_2 equal to L_2/L_1, since they are both equal to C_x/C_1. This will give

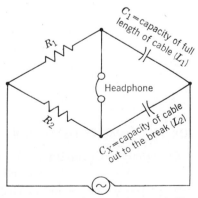

FIG. 16-22. A capacitance bridge used to locate a break in a cable.

Formula

$$\frac{R_1}{R_2} = \frac{L_2}{L_1} \tag{16-11}$$

where R_1 and R_2 are variable resistances, ohms

L_2 = length to break in cable, ft

L_1 = length of unbroken cable, ft

Example 16-18. If a capacity bridge is used to locate a cable break, a balance is obtained (indicated by no sound in the headphone) when R_1 = 10 ohms and R_2 = 25 ohms. The full length of the unbroken pair of wires is 4,000 ft. Find the length out to the break.

Solution:

$$\text{Given: } R_1 = 10 \text{ ohms} \qquad \text{Find: } L_2 = ?$$
$$R_2 = 25 \text{ ohms}$$
$$L_1 = 4,000 \text{ ft}$$

$$\frac{R_1}{R_2} = \frac{L_2}{L_1} \tag{16-11}$$

$$\frac{10}{25} = \frac{L_2}{4,000}$$

$$25 \times L_2 = 4,000 \times 10$$

$$L_2 = \frac{40,000}{25} = 1,600 \text{ ft} \qquad Ans.$$

Problems

Using a capacity bridge, the following measurements were taken to determine the length out to a break in a cable. Find the length out to the break in each problem.

Problem	R_1, ohms	R_2, ohms	L_1, ft
1	10	50	2,000
2	100	150	3,000
3	100	120	1,500
4	10	42	1,100

JOB 16-7: TIME CONSTANTS IN RC CIRCUITS

Charging a Capacitor. A perfect capacitor, that is, one without any resistance, may be charged almost instantaneously. Any resistance in the capacitor or its circuit will increase the time required to charge it.

The Time Constant. When a capacitor is charged, the charge on it will increase from zero through 10, 20, etc., up to 100 per cent of the applied voltage. The time required to charge a capacitive circuit up to 63.2 per cent of the applied voltage is called the *time constant* of the circuit.

Formula

$$t = CR \qquad (16\text{-}12)$$

where t = time for voltage across capacitor to reach 63.2 per cent of applied voltage, sec
C = capacity of the circuit, farads
R = resistance of the circuit, ohms

Example 16-19. What is the time constant for a cathode bias circuit for a 6J7 tube using a 4-μf capacitor and a 10,000-ohm resistor in parallel?

Solution:

Given: C = 4 μf = 0.000004 farad   Find: t = ?
$\qquad\quad R$ = 10,000 ohms

$\qquad t = CR \qquad\qquad\qquad\qquad\qquad\qquad (16\text{-}12)$
$\qquad t = 0.000004 \times 10,000 = 0.04$ sec   *Ans.*

Time Required for Any Per Cent of Charge. The time required for the voltage across an RC circuit to reach values other than 63.2 per cent of the applied voltage is given by the following formula.

Formula

$$T = k \times RC \qquad (16\text{-}13)$$

where T = time to reach any per cent of charge, sec
R = resistance of the circuit, ohms
C = capacity of the circuit, farads
k = values as given in Table 16-1, column I

Example 16-20. A 4-μf capacitor and a 10,000-ohm resistor are connected in parallel across 10 volts. (*a*) Find the time required to charge the capacitor to 33 per cent of the applied voltage. (*b*) What will be the voltage after 3 time constants?

Solution:

Given: Find:
  E = 10 volts T = ?
  C = 4 μf = 0.000004 farad E after 3 time constants = ?
  R = 10,000 ohms
  Per cent of applied voltage = 33%

a. From Table 16-1, column II, next to 33 per cent, find k = 0.4 time constant in column I.

$$T = k \times RC \qquad (16\text{-}13)$$
$$T = 0.4 \times 10,000 \times 0.000004$$
$$T = 0.016 \text{ sec} \qquad Ans.$$

b. From the table, under column II, the voltage after 3 time constants equals 95 per cent of the maximum applied voltage. Therefore,

$$E = 0.95 \times 10 = 9.5 \text{ volts} \qquad Ans.$$

Table 16-1. Universal Time Constants

Time constants k (I)	Per cent of maximum applied voltage		Time constants k (I)	Per cent of maximum applied voltage	
	Charging (II)	Discharging (III)		Charging (II)	Discharging (III)
0	0	100	0.3	25.9	74.1
0.001	0.1	99.9	0.4	33.0	67.0
0.002	0.2	99.8	0.5	39.3	60.7
0.003	0.3	99.7	0.6	45.1	54.9
0.004	0.4	99.6	0.7	50.3	49.7
0.005	0.5	99.5	0.8	55.1	44.9
0.006	0.6	99.4	0.9	59.3	40.7
0.007	0.7	99.3	1.0	63.2	36.8
0.008	0.8	99.2	1.2	69.9	30.1
0.009	0.9	99.1	1.4	75.3	24.7
0.01	1	99	1.6	79.8	20.2
0.02	2	98	1.8	83.5	16.5
0.03	3	97	2.0	86.5	13.5
0.04	4	96	2.5	91.8	8.2
0.05	5	95	3.0	95.0	5.0
0.06	6	94	3.5	97.0	3.0
0.07	7	93	4.0	98.2	1.8
0.08	8	92	4.5	98.9	1.1
0.09	9	91	5.0	99.3	0.7
0.1	9.5	90.5	5.5	99.6	0.4
0.15	14.0	86	6.0	99.8	0.2
0.2	18.1	81.9	7.0	99.9	0.1

Discharging a Capacitor. Any resistance in the circuit of a capacitor will increase the time required for the capacitor to discharge completely. When a capacitor is discharged, the charge will decrease from 100 through 90, 80, etc., down to 0 per cent of the original voltage. The time required to discharge 63.2 per cent of the original voltage requires 1 time constant. Thus, in 1 time constant, the voltage remaining on the capacitor equals 100 − 63.2, or 36.8 per cent of the original voltage. The time required for the voltage across an RC circuit to reach values other than 36.8 per cent of the original voltage is given by formula (16-13), where k equals values as given in Table 16-1, column III (Discharging).

Example 16-21. A 0.02-μf capacitor and a 5-Megohm resistor are connected in parallel across 100 volts. After the capacitor is fully charged, (a) find the time required to discharge the capacitor to 50 volts. (b) What voltage will remain on the capacitor after 2 time constants?

Solution:

$$\text{Given: } C = 0.02 \ \mu\text{f} = 0.00000002 \text{ farad}$$
$$R = 5 \text{ Megohms} = 5,000,000 \text{ ohms}$$
$$E = 100 \text{ volts}$$
$$\text{Find: } T \text{ to reach 50 v} = \ ?$$
$$E \text{ after 2 time constants} = \ ?$$

a. When the capacitor is discharged to 50 volts, the per cent of the original maximum value remaining on the capacitor equals

$$\tfrac{50}{100} \times 100 = 50 \text{ per cent}$$

For a charge of 50 per cent, from Table 16-1, column III (Discharging), k equals approximately 0.7

$$T = k \times RC \qquad\qquad (16\text{-}13)$$
$$T = 0.7 \times 5,000,000 \times 0.00000002$$
$$T = 0.07 \text{ sec} \qquad Ans.$$

b. From Table 16-1, column III, the voltage remaining after 2 time constants equals 13.5 per cent of the original maximum voltage. Therefore,

$$E = 0.135 \times 100 = 13.5 \text{ volts} \qquad Ans.$$

Problems

1. A 1,500-ohm resistor and a 0.06-μf capacitor are connected in parallel across 250 volts. Find the time required to charge the capacitor to (a) 14 per cent, (b) 45 per cent, (c) 70 per cent, and (d) 95 per cent of the applied voltage. What will the voltage be after (e) 0.5 time constant, (f) 1.4 time constants, and (g) 4.5 time constants?

2. A 500-ohm resistor and a 0.02-μf capacitor are connected in parallel across 120 volts. Find the time required to charge the capacitor to (a) 2 per cent, (b) 18 per cent, (c) 55 per cent, and (d) 97 per cent of the applied voltage. What will the voltage be after (e) 0.01 time constant, (f) 0.6 time constant, and (g) 3.5 time constants?

3. A 0.5-Megohm resistor and a 16-μf capacitor are connected in parallel across 400 volts. After the capacitor is completely charged, find the time to discharge the capacitor to (a) 368 volts, (b) 219.6 volts, (c) 20 volts, and (d) 4.4 volts. What will the voltage be after (e) 0.009 time constant, (f) 0.5 time constant, and (g) 5.5 time constants?

4. A 1.5-Megohm resistor and a 0.006-μf capacitor are connected in parallel across 900 volts. After the capacitor is completely charged, find the time to discharge it to (a) 819 volts, (b) 603 volts, (c) 448 volts, and (d) 6.3 volts. What will the voltage be after (e) 0.03 time constant, (f) 0.6 time constant, (g) 1.2 time constants, and (h) 5 time constants?

Voltage Fluctuation in RC Filter Circuits. The half-wave rectifier shown in Fig. 16-23 changes the 60-cps a-c wave into a pulsing d-c wave

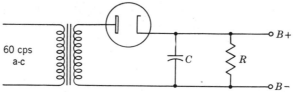

60 cps a-c

C R $B+$ $B-$

FIG. 16-23. A simple RC filter circuit for a half-wave rectifier.

consisting of 60 pulses per second. This pulsing direct current charges the capacitor. During the time between the pulses, the capacitor attempts to discharge through the resistor. The per cent of the charge on the capacitor which is actually discharged during the time between pulses is called the voltage fluctuation. If this per cent of drop in voltage is small, the filter will maintain a practically constant voltage. This per cent of drop in voltage is called the per cent of *ripple voltage*. The lower the per cent of ripple voltage, the better the filter.

Example 16-22. In Fig. 16-23, what is the per cent of ripple voltage if $C = 16$ μf and $R = 10,000$ ohms?

Solution:

Given: $C = 16$ μf $= 0.000016$ farad   Find: Per cent ripple $= ?$
        $R = 10,000$ ohms

1. Find the time between pulses. In a half-wave rectifier, the 60-cps a-c wave is reduced to 60 d-c pulses per second. The time between the pulses is therefore equal to $\frac{1}{60}$ or 0.0167 sec.

2. Express this time in terms of the number of time constants k.

$$T = k \times RC \tag{16-13}$$
$$0.0167 = k \times 10,000 \times 0.000016$$
$$0.0167 = 0.16k$$

$$k = \frac{0.0167}{0.16} = 0.104 \text{ time constant}$$

3. Find the per cent of ripple. From Table 16-1, column I, for k equal to 0.104, the per cent of the voltage *remaining* is found in column III and is equal to 90.5 per cent. Therefore, in the 0.0167 sec between pulses, the capacitor *discharged* $100 - 90.5$, or 9.5 per cent of its charge. This means that the ripple voltage equals 9.5 per cent. *Ans.*

Example 16-23. Find the per cent of ripple voltage across the resistor shown in Fig. 16-24.

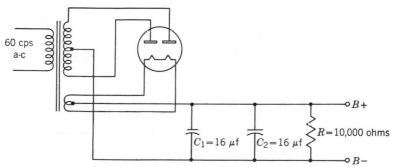

Fig. 16-24. A full-wave diode rectifier and filter circuit.

Solution:

1. Find the time between pulses. In a full-wave rectifier, the 60-cps a-c wave is reduced to 120 d-c pulses per second. The time between the pulses is therefore equal to $\frac{1}{120}$ or 0.0083 sec.

2. Express this time in terms of the number of time constants k. In order to use formula (16-13), the total capacity must be known. Since C_1 and C_2 are in parallel,

$$C_T = C_1 + C_2 \tag{16-2}$$
$$C_T = 16 + 16 = 32 \ \mu f = 0.000032 \text{ farad}$$

$$T = k \times RC \tag{16-13}$$
$$0.0083 = k \times 10,000 \times 0.000032$$
$$0.0083 = 0.32k$$

$$k = \frac{0.0083}{0.32} = 0.026 \text{ time constant}$$

3. Find the per cent of ripple. From Table 16-1, column I, for k equal to 0.026, the per cent of the voltage *remaining* is found in column III, and is equal to 97.5 per cent. Therefore, in the 0.0083 sec between pulses, the capacitor *discharged* 100 − 97.5 or 2.5 per cent of its charge. This means that the ripple voltage equals 2.5 per cent. *Ans.*

Problems

Find the per cent of ripple using the circuits indicated.

Problem	Figure	C_1, μf	C_2, μf	R
1	16-23	40	...	5,000 ohms
2	16-24	20	20	10,000 ohms
3	16-23	10	...	0.04 Megohm
4	16-24	8	8	50,000 ohms
5	16-23	40	...	2,000 ohms
6	16-24	15	15	8,000 ohms

Finding the Capacitance or Resistance Needed to Obtain a Given Per Cent of Ripple

Example 16-24. A half-wave rectifier RC filter circuit using a 20,000-ohm resistor requires a 5 per cent ripple. Find the required capacitance.

Solution:

Given: Half-wave rectifier   Find: $C = ?$
$R = 20,000$ ohms
Per cent ripple $= 5\%$

1. Find the time between pulses. In a half-wave rectifier, the time between pulses equals 0.0167 sec.
2. Find k for a 5 per cent ripple. Since the per cent of ripple is the difference between 100 per cent and the per cent of charge *remaining*, this difference may be found directly in column II of Table 16-1. Therefore, next to 5 per cent in column II, read k equal to 0.05 in column I.
3. Find the required capacitance.

$$T = k \times RC \qquad\qquad (16\text{-}13)$$
$$0.0167 = 0.05 \times 20,000 \times C$$
$$0.0167 = 1,000C$$
$$C = \frac{0.0167}{1,000} = 0.0000167 \text{ farad}$$
$$C = 16.7 \ \mu\text{f} \qquad Ans.$$

Example 16-25. A full-wave rectifier RC filter circuit using a 30-μf capacitance requires a 2 per cent ripple. Find the required resistance.

Solution:

Given: Full-wave rectifier   Find: $R = ?$
$\qquad C = 30 \ \mu f = 0.00003$ farad
$\qquad$ Per cent ripple $= 2\%$

1. Find the time between pulses. In a full-wave rectifier, the time between pulses equals 0.0083 sec.
2. Find k for a 2 per cent ripple. Next to 2 per cent in column II, read k equal to 0.02 in column I.
3. Find the required resistance.

$$T = k \times RC \qquad\qquad (16\text{-}13)$$
$$0.0083 = 0.02 \times R \times 0.00003$$
$$0.0083 = 0.0000006R$$
$$R = \frac{0.0083}{0.0000006} = 13{,}830 \text{ ohms} \qquad Ans.$$

Problems

Find the required capacitance or resistance for each problem.

Problem	Type of rectifier	Per cent ripple required	R, ohms	C, μf
1	Half-wave	5	167,000	?
2	Half-wave	8	?	20
3	Full-wave	7	20,000	?
4	Full-wave	1	?	40
5	Half-wave	0.6	?	10

JOB 16-8: REVIEW OF CAPACITANCE

A capacitor is made of two metallic plates separated by an insulating material, or dielectric.

A capacitor is used to store up an electrical charge.

The capacitance of a capacitor is a measure of its ability to store up electrons.

The capacitance *increases* if the *plate area increases* or the *dielectric thickness decreases*.

The working voltage is the largest voltage that may be placed across a capacitor before it breaks down. The working voltage in parallel is the working voltage of the weakest capacitor. The working voltage in series is the sum of the working voltages of the series capacitors.

A *farad* is the capacity of a capacitor which can hold 1 coulomb of electricity on its plates under a pressure of 1 volt.

The *reactance* of a capacitor is the opposition offered by the capacitor to the passage of an alternating current. The reactance decreases as the frequency and capacity increase.

Distributed, or "stray," capacity is the capacity formed when two wires run close together or when any two metal parts are separated by a thin insulating material.

Formulas

Capacitance:

$$C = \frac{Q}{E} \tag{16-1}$$

where C = capacity, farads
Q = charge, coulombs
E = voltage, volts

Capacitors in parallel:

$$C_T = C_1 + C_2 + C_3 \tag{16-2}$$

where C_T = total capacity
C_1, C_2, C_3 are the individual capacities, all measured in the same units.

Capacitors in series:

$$\frac{1}{C_T} = \frac{1}{C_1} + \frac{1}{C_2} + \frac{1}{C_3} \tag{16-3}$$

where C_T = total capacity
C_1, C_2, C_3 are the individual capacities, all measured in the same units

Equal capacitors in series:

$$C_T = \frac{C}{N} \tag{16-4}$$

where C_T = total capacity
C = capacity of one of the equal capacitors
N = number of equal capacitors

Two capacitors in series:

$$C_T = \frac{C_1 \times C_2}{C_1 + C_2} \tag{16-5}$$

where C_T = total capacity

C_1 and C_2 are the individual capacities, all measured in the same units

Reactance of a capacitor:

$$X_c = \frac{159,000}{f \times C} \qquad (16\text{-}6)$$

where X_c = reactance, ohms

f = frequency, cps

C = capacity, μf

Impedance of a capacitor:

$$Z = \sqrt{R^2 + X_c^2} \qquad (16\text{-}8)$$

where Z = impedance, ohms

R = resistance, ohms

X_c = reactance, ohms

Capacitor bridge:

$$\frac{R_1}{R_2} = \frac{C_x}{C_1} \qquad (16\text{-}9)$$

where R_1 and R_2 are variable resistances, ohms

C_x = unknown capacity, μf

C_1 = known capacity, μf

Using a capacity bridge to locate cable breaks:

$$\frac{R_1}{R_2} = \frac{L_2}{L_1} \qquad (16\text{-}11)$$

where R_1 and R_2 are variable resistances, ohms

L_1 = length of unbroken cable, ft

L_2 = length to break in cable, ft

Time constant for an RC circuit:

$$t = CR \qquad (16\text{-}12)$$

where t = time for voltage across capacitor to reach 63.2% of applied voltage, sec

C = capacity of circuit, farads

R = resistance of circuit, ohms

Time required to obtain any per cent of charge:

$$T = k \times RC \qquad (16\text{-}13)$$

where T = time to reach any per cent of charge, sec

R = resistance of circuit, ohms

C = capacity of circuit, farads

k = values as given in column I of Table 16-1

Problems

1. What is the capacity of a coupling capacitor if its plates hold 0.00558 coulomb when the voltage across the capacitor is 0.62 volt?

2. How many coulombs are held on the plates of an 8-μf capacitor in a 280-volt filter circuit?

3. Find the total capacity in parallel of a 0.0035-μf, a 0.00000004-farad, and a 6,200-$\mu\mu$f capacitor.

4. What amount of capacity must be added in parallel to a 0.00035-μf capacitor to obtain a total capacity of 0.00115 μf?

5. Find the total capacity in series of a 3-, a 6-, and an 8-μf capacitor.

6. What is the total capacity and working voltage of two 25-μf 180-volt capacitors used in a voltage multiplier?

7. What is the total capacity of the capacitors in a Colpitts oscillator similar to Fig. 16-12 if $C_1 = 0.0004$ μf and $C_2 = 0.00035$ μf.

8. An oscillator circuit contains a 0.00035- and a 0.00025-μf capacitor in series. Find the total capacity.

9. Find the reactance of an 0.8-μf bypass capacitor to a frequency of 1.5 kc.

10. Find the reactance of a 0.0003-μf tuning capacitor to a frequency of 1,350 kc.

11. Find the impedance of a capacitor if its reactance is 40 ohms and its resistance is 20 ohms.

12. Find the impedance of a capacitive circuit to a 2-kc audio frequency if the resistance is 2,000 ohms and the capacity is 0.02 μf.

13. What capacity is necessary to provide a reactance of 318 ohms at a frequency of 600 kc?

14. What cathode bypass capacitor is needed to provide a reactance of 1,000 ohms at an audio frequency of 500 cps?

15. In finding the capacity of a capacitor by the voltmeter-ammeter method, the current was 0.004 amp and the voltage was 110 volts at 60 cps. Find the capacity.

16. Using a capacity bridge to locate a cable break, a balance was obtained when $R_1 = 10$ ohms, $R_2 = 45$ ohms, and the full length of an unbroken pair of wires used in the test was 2,500 ft. Find the distance to the break in the cable.

17. What is the time constant of an automatic-volume-control filter circuit that uses a 1-Megohm resistor and a 0.5-μf capacitor?

18. Find the time required to charge the capacitor in Prob. 17 to approximately 50 per cent of the applied voltage.

19. A 1,000-ohm resistor and a 0.25-μf capacitor are connected in parallel across 200 volts. Find (*a*) the time required to charge the capacitor to 150 volts and (*b*) the voltage after 2 time constants.

20. After the capacitor in Prob. 19 is fully charged to 200 volts, find the time to discharge the capacitor to 100 volts.

21. Using a circuit similar to Fig. 16-23, what is the per cent of ripple voltage if $C = 40$ μf and $R = 5,050$ ohms?

22. A full-wave rectifier RC filter circuit using a 40-μf capacitor requires a 5 per cent ripple. Find the required resistance.

Test—Capacitance

1. Find the total capacity in parallel of a 0.00025-μf and a 750-$\mu\mu$f capacitor.

2. Find the total capacity in series of a 4-, an 8-, and a 12-μf capacitor.

3. Find the impedance of a capacitive circuit to a 10-kc frequency if its resistance is 400 ohms and its capacitance is 0.0318 μf.

4. In finding the capacity of a capacitor by the voltmeter-ammeter method, the current was 0.03 amp and the voltage was 120 volts at 25 cps. Find the capacity.

5. Using a capacity bridge to locate a cable break, a balance was obtained when $R_1 = 50$ ohms, $R_2 = 120$ ohms, and the full length of an unbroken pair of wires was 6,000 ft. Find the length to the break in the cable.

6. A half-wave rectifier filter circuit using a 30,000-ohm resistor requires a 9 per cent ripple. Find the required capacitance.

7. Find the time required to charge the capacitor of Prob. 6 to 14 per cent of the applied voltage.

CHAPTER 17

SERIES A-C CIRCUITS

JOB 17-1: ALTERNATING-CURRENT CIRCUITS CONTAINING ONLY RESISTANCE

As we have learned, an a-c voltage consists of a number of different instantaneous voltages, each instant of time giving rise to a different value of voltage. If this voltage is impressed across a resistor, each instantaneous voltage will cause an instantaneous current to flow at that time. The increasing and decreasing voltages and currents are shown in Fig. 17-1. The current that flows as a result of an a-c volt-

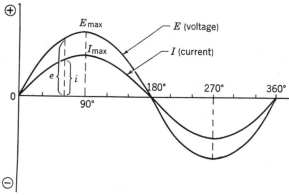

Fig. 17-1. The voltage and current are in phase in a purely resistive circuit.

age will be an alternating current with the same frequency as the a-c voltage. The voltage and the current both start at zero and rise to their maximum values, reaching them at the same instant. The voltage and current continue to rise and fall in step with each other throughout the entire cycle. We say that the voltage and current are "in phase" or "in step" with each other. It is difficult to draw these curves whenever we wish to indicate this or any other condition, and so we shall use a method in which the voltage and current are indicated by straight lines drawn to a definite length and in a definite direction.

Vectors. A vector is a straight line having a definite length and *direction*. Vectors are commonly used to show the amount and *direction* of a quantity like a 10-lb force which acts straight up. We shall use vectors to show the amount and *time* at which a voltage or current is acting. Vectors which are drawn in the *same direction* will indicate that they are happening at the *same time*. Vectors which are drawn in *different directions* will indicate that they are happening at *different times*.

In a circuit containing only resistance, we have seen that the voltage and current occur at the *same time*, or are in phase. To indicate this condition by means of vectors, all that is necessary is to draw the vectors for the voltage and the current in the *same direction*. The values of each are indicated by the *length* of the vector. When vectors are drawn in the same direction, the angle between the vectors is 0°. This angle is called the phase angle and is denoted by the Greek letter theta (θ).

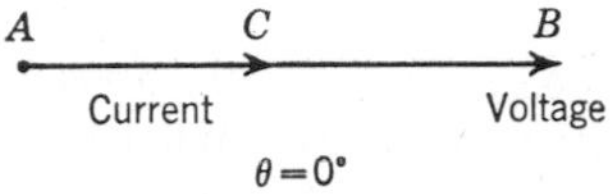

Let us assume that the voltage is larger than the current. Draw a line *AB* from left to right as in Fig. 17-2 to represent the voltage vector. Place an arrowhead on the vector at *B* pointing to the right.

A   *C*   *B*

Current   Voltage

$\theta = 0°$

Fig. 17-2. The voltage and current vectors are "in phase" in a circuit containing only resistance.

Point *A* is the "tail" of the vector, and point *B* is the "head" of the vector. Since the current occurs at the *same time* as the voltage, the current vector must be drawn in the *same direction* as the voltage vector. Draw a line starting from the original point *A* to the right to *C* with an arrow pointing to the right. This current vector is drawn smaller than the voltage vector because the current is smaller than the voltage. The phase angle θ is 0°.

Example 17-1. A 22-ohm electric iron is operated from a 110-volt 60-cycle line. Draw a vector diagram, and find the current and power used by the iron.

Solution:

Given: $E = 110$ volts   Find: $I = ?$
$R = 22$ ohms $P = ?$

1. Draw the vector diagram. Since the iron may be assumed to be made of a purely resistive element, the vector diagram will be the same as that shown in Fig. 17-2.

2. In a purely resistive circuit, Ohm's law may be used.

$$E = IR \tag{2-1}$$
$$110 = I \times 22$$
$$I = \frac{110}{22} = 5 \text{ amp} \qquad Ans.$$

3. Find the power.

$$P = I \times E \tag{7-1}$$
$$P = 110 \times 5 = 550 \text{ watts} \qquad Ans.$$

Problems

1. An electric soldering iron draws 0.8 amp from a 120-volt 60-cycle line. What is its resistance? How much power will it consume?

2. What a-c voltage is required to force 0.02 amp through an 8,000-ohm radio resistor? What is the power used?

3. Find the current and power drawn from a 110-volt 60-cycle line by a tungsten lamp whose hot resistance is 275 ohms.

4. What is the current drawn by a 200-watt incandescent lamp from a 110-volt 60-cycle line? What is the hot resistance of the lamp?

5. Find the power used by a 24-ohm soldering iron which draws 5 amp.

6. Find the voltage needed to operate a 500-watt electric percolator if it draws 4.5 amp. What is its resistance?

JOB 17-2: ALTERNATING-CURRENT CIRCUITS CONTAINING ONLY INDUCTANCE

When an a-c voltage is impressed across a coil, it will produce an alternating current. The changing current will produce changing lines of force around the turns of the coil. The changing lines of force will cut across the wires forming the coil and induce an emf in the coil. This emf is a "back emf" which acts to oppose the original voltage. This opposition, called the inductive reactance, will reduce the current below that which would flow if there were no "cuttings" or back emf. This reactance does more than just reduce the current. It also prevents the current from appearing at the same time as the voltage. The current will be pushed back in *time* as well as in amount. We say that the current "lags" behind the voltage which produces it. In a perfect coil—one which has only inductance and zero resistance—the current will lag behind the voltage by an amount of time equal to the time required for $\frac{1}{4}$ cycle. It is easier to discuss this "time lag" in terms of the number of electrical degrees for $\frac{1}{4}$ cycle than in units of time. We say that the current lags the voltage by 90°, since $\frac{1}{4}$ cycle equals $\frac{1}{4} \times 360° = 90°$.

The current that flows as a result of an a-c voltage across a coil will be an alternating current with the same frequency as the a-c voltage. The difference between this and the resistive circuit is that in the inductive circuit the current does *not* rise and fall in step with the voltage. The current remains forever 90 electrical degrees *behind* the voltage as shown in Fig. 17-3. The current lags behind the voltage by 90°, or the voltage "leads" the current by 90°. In an inductive circuit, the voltage and current are "out of phase" by 90°. The phase angle θ in an inductive circuit is 90°.

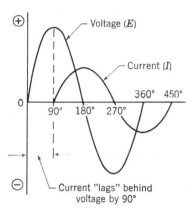

Fig. 17-3. The voltage and current are out of phase in an a-c circuit containing only inductance.

Vector Diagram. Since the voltage and current are out of phase by 90°, the vectors must be drawn in two different directions 90° apart. In addition to this, we must show which vector is the "leading" vector and which is the "lagging" vector. To show quantities occurring "before" or "after" another, we shall use the numbers on a clock. Let us consider the hour hand of a clock as a vector. A vector pointing to 3 o'clock occurs after a vector pointing to 12 o'clock, or noon. Similarly, a vector pointing to 3 o'clock occurs before a vector pointing to 6 o'clock.

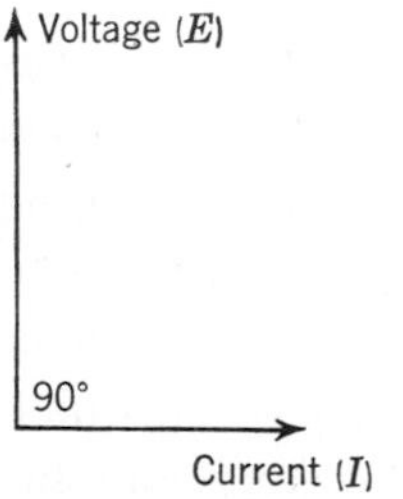

We can now proceed to draw a vector diagram for an inductive circuit. Draw a line with an arrow pointing to the right as shown in Fig. 17-4. This will represent the current I in the circuit. Since the voltage leads the current by 90°, we shall be forced to draw the voltage vector in such a way so as to be 90° before the current vector. If the current vector already points to 3 o'clock, the voltage vector must point to 12 o'clock in order to lead the current vector by 90°.

Fig. 17-4. The voltage vector leads the current vector by 90° in a purely inductive circuit.

The amount of current that will flow in a "pure" inductance is found by Ohm's law. However, since a "pure" inductance contains zero resistance, the R is replaced by X_L. Ohm's law for a pure inductance will then be

$$E_L = I_L \times X_L \qquad (15\text{-}4)$$

Power. In a purely resistive circuit, the voltage and current occur at the same time, or are in phase. The power is equal to the multiplication of the current by the voltage—just as in a d-c circuit. However, as we have just seen, the voltage and the current do not always occur at the same time. In this event, only a portion of the current will occur at the same time as the voltage. In these a-c circuits in which the voltage and current are *not* in phase, the power consumed will be equal to the voltage multiplied by only that portion of the current *in phase with it*. The amount of this *in-phase* current is equal to the current multiplied by the cosine of the phase angle.

$$\text{In-phase current} = I \times \cos \theta \qquad (17\text{-}1)$$

The general formula for power in an a-c circuit is

$$P = E \times \text{in-phase current} \qquad (17\text{-}2)$$

By substitution, we obtain

Formula

$$P = E \times I \times \cos \theta \qquad (17\text{-}3)$$

In a pure inductance, the power will be

$$P = E \times I \times \cos 90°$$
$$P = E \times I \times 0$$
$$P = 0 \text{ watts}$$

Thus, the average power used by a pure inductance is zero. Actually, the inductance uses power to build up its magnetic field during one quarter of a cycle, but it delivers an equal amount of power back to the source while the field is collapsing during the second quarter of its cycle. The net result is that zero power is used by the inductance. A perfect inductance may be considered to be just like a perfect flywheel, which accumulates power during one revolution and delivers an equal amount of power back to the engine during its second revolution.

Example 17-2. A 10-henry filter choke coil is connected across a 120-volt 60-cycle a-c line. Assuming that the coil has zero resistance, find the current and the power drawn. Draw the vector diagram.

Solution:

$$\text{Given: } L = 10 \text{ henrys} \qquad \text{Find: } I = ?$$
$$E = 120 \text{ volts} \qquad \qquad P = ?$$
$$f = 60 \text{ cps}$$

1. Find the inductive reactance.

$$X_L = 6.28 \times fL = 6.28 \times 60 \times 10 = 3,768 \text{ ohms} \qquad (15\text{-}3)$$

2. Find the current.

$$E_L = I_L \times X_L \qquad (15\text{-}4)$$
$$120 = I_L \times 3,768$$
$$I_L = \frac{120}{3,768} = 0.0318 \text{ amp} \qquad Ans.$$

3. Draw the vector diagram. See Fig. 17-4.
4. Find the power.

$$P = E \times I \times \cos \theta \qquad (17\text{-}3)$$
$$P = 120 \times 0.0318 \times \cos 90°$$
$$P = 120 \times 0.0318 \times 0 = 0 \text{ watts} \qquad Ans.$$

Problems

1. Find the current sent through a 0.03-henry coil by a voltage of 188.4 volts at a frequency of 1 kc.
2. Find the current and power drawn by a 200-mh coil which is connected to a 31.4-volt source at a frequency of 1,000 cps.
3. What voltage is needed to force 0.08 amp through an inductance of 0.5 henry at a frequency of 100 cps?
4. What voltage at 10 kc is necessary to send a current of 20 ma through an inductance of 50 mh? What is the power consumed?
5. What must be the reactance of a filter choke in order for it to pass 80 ma of current when the voltage is 240 volts? What must be the inductance of the choke if the frequency is 60 cps?

JOB 17-3: ALTERNATING-CURRENT CIRCUITS CONTAINING ONLY CAPACITANCE

When an alternating voltage is impressed across a capacitor, the capacitor will be alternately charged and discharged. While it is charging, the flow of electrons to the plate of the capacitor is largest at the instant the charge is begun. This is so because there are no electrons already on the plate to exert an opposing force. As more and more electrons accumulate on the plate of the capacitor, they exert a greater and greater force which tends to stop the flow of electrons to the plate. When the capacitor is fully charged to the voltage of the source, the flow of current falls to zero, since the back pressure is equal to the pressure of the charging source. Notice that the maximum current occurs when the voltage is zero and a zero current flows when the voltage is a maximum. If the capacitor is continually charged and discharged by a source of alternating voltage, the relation between current and voltage will be that which is shown in Fig. 17-5.

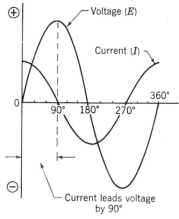

FIG. 17-5. The voltage and current are out of phase in an a-c circuit containing only capacitance.

This indicates that in a capacitive circuit the current *leads* the voltage or the voltage *lags* behind the current. This condition does not exist until the circuit is in operation for a few seconds, as it is obviously impossible for the current to start at any value other than zero. However, once the circuit is in operation, the phase relations are adjusted so that the current will *lead* the voltage by ¼ cycle or 90 electrical degrees. As with an inductance, this applies only to a "perfect" capacitor —one in which there is no resistance due to the resistance of the capacitor plates or leads.

The current that flows as a result of an a-c voltage across a capacitor will be an alternating current with the same frequency as the a-c voltage. The current remains forever 90 electrical degrees *ahead* of the voltage. The current *leads* the voltage or the voltage *lags* behind the current by 90°. The phase angle θ in a capacitive circuit is 90°.

Vector Diagram. To express this leading current by vectors, the vectors must be drawn 90° apart. Draw a line with an arrow pointing to the right as shown in Fig. 17-6. This will represent the current I in the circuit. Since the voltage *lags* the current by 90°, we shall be forced to draw the voltage vector in such a way so as to be 90° *after* the current. Since the current vector already points to 3 o'clock, the voltage vector must point to 6 o'clock in order to *lag* the current vector by 90°.

Current (I)

90°

↓ Voltage (E)

FIG. 17-6. The voltage vector lags the current vector by 90° in a purely capacitive circuit.

The amount of current in a "pure" capacitance is found by Ohm's law. However, since a "pure" capacitance contains zero resistance, R is replaced by X_c. Ohm's law for a pure capacitance will then be

$$E_c = I_c \times X_c \qquad (16\text{-}7)$$

Power. Since the voltage and current in a pure capacitive circuit are 90° out of phase, the power used is equal to zero. This fact is obtained by substituting in formula (17-3) for a-c power.

$$P = E \times I \times \cos \theta \qquad (17\text{-}3)$$
$$P = E \times I \times \cos 90°$$
$$P = E \times I \times 0$$
$$P = 0 \text{ watts}$$

Example 17-3. A 10-μf bypass capacitor in the cathode circuit of a 6V6 beam-power amplifier passes 300 ma at a frequency of 0.4 kc. Find (a) the voltage drop across the capacitor and (b) the power consumed.

Solution:

Given: $C = 10 \ \mu$f   Find: $E = $?
 $I = 300$ ma $= 0.3$ amp
 $f = 0.4$ kc $= 400$ cps

a. Find the reactance of the capacitor.

$$X_c = \frac{159,000}{f \times C} = \frac{159,000}{400 \times 10} = \frac{159}{4} = 40 \text{ ohms (approx)} \qquad (16\text{-}6)$$

Find the voltage drop.

$$E_c = I_c \times X_c \qquad (16\text{-}7)$$
$$E_c = 0.3 \times 40 = 12 \text{ volts} \qquad Ans.$$

b. Find the power.
$$P = E \times I \times \cos \theta \qquad (17\text{-}3)$$
$$P = 12 \times 0.3 \times \cos 90°$$
$$P = 12 \times 0.3 \times 0$$
$$P = 0 \text{ watts} \qquad Ans.$$

Problems

1. A voltage of 9 volts at a frequency of 10 kc is impressed across a 4-μf capacitor. Find (a) the current and (b) the power used.
2. What current will flow through a 0.000015-farad capacitor if the voltage across it is 10.6 volts at a frequency of 100 cps?
3. The cathode resistor for a 6J5 class A amplifier is bypassed with a 0.1-μf capacitor. What current will flow if the voltage across it is 45 volts at a frequency of 300 cps?
4. What is the reactance of a 0.06-μf coupling capacitor to an audio frequency of 2 kc? What current will flow if the voltage across the capacitor is 6 volts?

5. The potential difference between two wires having a distributed capacity of 20 $\mu\mu$f is 2 volts. Find the flow of current between the wires if one of them carries a 1,000-kc current.

6. Find the voltage across a 10-μf filter capacitor if it passes 1 amp at a frequency of 60 cps.

7. What must be the reactance of a capacitor in order for it to pass 1 amp of current when the voltage is 100 volts? What is the capacitance of the capacitor if the frequency is 1,000 kc?

JOB 17-4: THE PYTHAGOREAN THEOREM

In our next job we shall find the total voltage across a series a-c circuit by adding the voltages *even though the voltages do not appear at the same time!* The formulas for this total voltage and for all our work in a-c power are applications of the *Pythagorean theorem.*

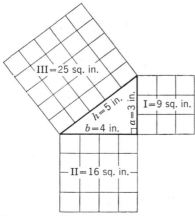

This basic mathematical law about a *right triangle* was discovered by a Greek scholar named Pythagoras about 2,500 years ago. In Fig. 17-7, squares are drawn on each of the three sides of the right triangle. The length of the sides of each square is equal to the length of the side of the triangle on which it is drawn. Pythagoras discovered that the *sum of the areas of the squares on the two legs of a right triangle is exactly equal to the area of the square erected on the hypotenuse.*

Fig. 17-7. Pictorial representation of the Pythagorean theorem: $a^2 + b^2 = h^2$.

This is true for *any right triangle.* Thus,

$$\text{Area I} + \text{area II} = \text{area III}$$
$$9 \quad + \quad 16 \quad = \quad 25$$

Since the area of a square is equal to a side times itself,

$$\text{Area I} = a \times a = a^2$$
$$\text{Area II} = b \times b = b^2$$
$$\text{Area III} = h \times h = h^2$$

The theorem may be stated as the following rule.

Rule: The sum of the squares of the legs of a right triangle is equal to the square of the hypotenuse.

Formula

$$a^2 + b^2 = h^2 \qquad (17\text{-}4)$$

where a and b = legs of a right triangle

h = hypotenuse of a right triangle

The formula may be solved for h by taking the square root of both sides.

$$\sqrt{a^2 + b^2} - \sqrt{h^2}$$
$$\sqrt{a^2 + b^2} = h \qquad (17\text{-}4a)$$

Example 17-4. Find the hypotenuse of a right triangle whose altitude is 5 in. and whose base is 12 in.

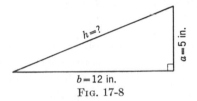

$b = 12$ in.

FIG. 17-8

Solution: The diagram is shown in Fig. 17-8.

$$h = \sqrt{a^2 + b^2} \qquad (17\text{-}4a)$$
$$h = \sqrt{5^2 + 12^2}$$
$$h = \sqrt{25 + 144}$$
$$h = \sqrt{169} = 13 \text{ in.} \qquad Ans.$$

Example 17-5. Find the altitude a in a right triangle whose hypotenuse h is 17 in. and whose base b is 15 in.

Solution:

Given: $h = 17$ in.   Find: $a = ?$

$b = 15$ in.

$$a^2 + b^2 = h^2 \qquad (17\text{-}4)$$
$$a^2 + 15^2 = 17^2$$
$$a^2 + 225 = 289$$
$$a^2 = 289 - 225$$
$$a^2 = 64$$
$$a = \sqrt{64} = 8 \text{ in.} \qquad Ans.$$

Problems

Find the unknown side in each of the following right triangles:

Problem	a	b	h
1	6	8	?
2	7	24	?
3	?	63	65
4	33	?	65
5	14	22.5	?
6	17.5	6	?
7	?	20	20.5
8	6.5	?	42.5

JOB 17-5: ALTERNATING-CURRENT CIRCUITS CONTAINING RESISTANCE AND INDUCTANCE

Figure 17-9 shows a 100-ohm resistor connected in series with an inductance whose reactance is 100 ohms at a frequency of 60 cps. A series current of 0.85 amp produces a voltage drop of 85 volts across both the resistor and the inductance. In a series circuit, the total voltage is ordinarily found by adding the voltages across all the parts of the circuit. This rule was used in d-c circuits, but can we use it for a-c circuits? Since the current in a series circuit remains unchanged throughout the circuit, we may draw the waveforms for the currents and voltages across each part of the circuit on the same drawing.

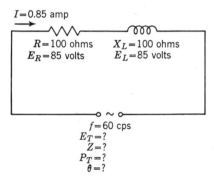

FIG. 17-9. An a-c series circuit containing resistance and inductance.

Figure 17-10 shows the relationship of each voltage to the unchanging current. The voltage across the resistor E_R is *in phase* with the current I; the voltage across the inductance E_L *leads* the current I by 90°; E_L *leads* E_R by 90°. To obtain the total voltage we must add the voltages across all parts of the circuit. But how are we going to add voltages that do not happen at the same time? The only way to do this is to add the individual *instantaneous* voltages that *do* occur at the same time. Thus, in Fig. 17-11, the instantaneous values of e_R and e_L are added for different instants of time.

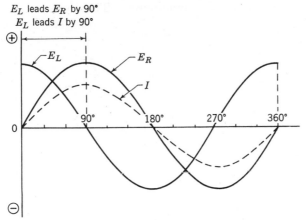

FIG. 17-10. Voltages and currents in a series a-c circuit containing resistance and inductance.

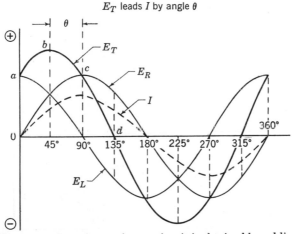

FIG. 17-11. The total voltage in a series a-c circuit is obtained by adding the instantaneous voltages instant by instant.

At 0°, $e_R = 0$ and e_L is a maximum. Therefore

$$E_T = e_R + e_L$$
$$E_T = 0 + e_L$$
$$E_T = e_L \quad \text{(point } a\text{)}$$

At 45°, $e_R = e_L$ and

$$E_T = e_R + e_L$$

or $\qquad E_T$ = twice the value of either $\qquad$ (point b)

At 90°, $e_L = 0$ and e_R is a maximum. Therefore

$$E_T = e_R + e_L$$
$$E_T = e_R + 0$$
$$E_T = e_R \quad \text{(point } c)$$

At 135°, $e_R = e_L$, but they are of opposite polarity. Therefore

$$E_T = e_R + (-e_L)$$
$$E_T = 0 \quad \text{(point } d)$$

By continuing in this manner, adding the voltages instant by instant the waveform for the total voltage is obtained as shown in Fig. 17-11. Notice that the maximum value of E_T (at 45°) is *still leading* the current maximum. In this particular problem, since R and X_L are equal, the angle of lead is equal to 45°. For other values of R and X_L, angle θ will change.

Apparently, then, although we *do* add the voltages to get the total voltage, the addition is not just a simple arithmetic addition. We can see this more clearly if we draw the voltages and currents as vectors on the same unchanging current base as shown in Fig. 17-12a. This vector diagram shows exactly the same relationships that were shown in Fig. 17-10 in waveform. The voltage across the resistor is still in phase with the current, and the voltage across the inductance still leads the current by 90°.

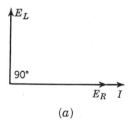 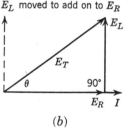

(a)   (b)

Fig. 17-12. (a) Vector diagram for a series a-c circuit containing resistance and inductance. (b) E_T represents the vector sum of E_R and E_L.

Addition of Vectors. The total voltage E_T is obtained by adding the vector E_L to the vector E_R. Place the tail of E_L on the head of E_R, and draw it in its original direction and length. The distance from the origin of the vectors to the head of the final vector is the sum of the vectors. In this instance, the vector E_T represents the sum of the vectors E_R and E_L as shown in Fig. 17-12b. The phase angle θ is the angle by which the total voltage leads the current. In this problem, the angle is 45° and is the same angle shown on the waveform diagram of Fig. 17-11. By applying the Pythagorean theorem to Fig. 17-12b, we obtain

Formula

$$E_T{}^2 = E_R{}^2 + E_L{}^2 \qquad (17\text{-}5)$$

Total Impedance. To find the impedance of the series a-c circuit, we must add R and X_L vectorially as was done with the voltages. This is shown in Fig. 17-13. The voltages in Fig. 17-13a are replaced by their Ohm's law values in Fig. 17-13b. Now, by dropping out the common factor of the current I, we obtain the *impedance triangle* of Fig. 17-13c.

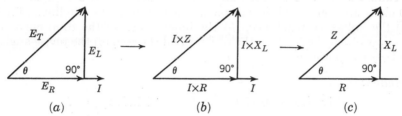

(a)   (b)   (c)

FIG. 17-13. Z represents the vector sum of R and X_L.

Applying the Pythagorean theorem to Fig. 17-13c, we obtain

Formulas

$$Z^2 = R^2 + X_L{}^2 \qquad (17\text{-}6)$$

and

$$Z = \sqrt{R^2 + X_L{}^2} \qquad (17\text{-}7)$$

And by trigonometry,

$$\cos \theta = \frac{a}{h}$$

or

$$\cos \theta = \frac{R}{Z} \qquad (17\text{-}8)$$

The power is still given by

$$P = E \times I \times \cos \theta \qquad (17\text{-}3)$$

Example 17-6. In Fig. 17-9, find (a) the total voltage, (b) the impedance, (c) the phase angle, and (d) the power.

Solution:

a.
$$E_T{}^2 = E_R{}^2 + E_L{}^2 = 85^2 + 85^2 \qquad (17\text{-}5)$$
$$= 7{,}225 + 7{,}225$$
$$= 14{,}450$$
$$E_T = \sqrt{14{,}450} = 120 \text{ volts} \qquad \textit{Ans.}$$

b. $Z = \sqrt{R^2 + X_L^2}$ (17-7)

$Z = \sqrt{100^2 + 100^2} = \sqrt{10,000 + 10,000} = \sqrt{20,000}$

$Z = 141$ ohms   *Ans.*

c. $\cos \theta = \dfrac{R}{Z} = \dfrac{100}{141} = 0.709$ (17-8)

$\theta = 45°$ *Ans.*

d. $P = E \times I \times \cos \theta$ (17-3)

$P = 120 \times 0.85 \times \cos 45° = 120 \times 0.85 \times 0.709$

$P = 72.3$ watts   *Ans.*

Example 17-7. An inductance of 0.17 henry and a resistance of 50 ohms are connected in series across a 110-volt 60-cycle line. Find (*a*) the inductive reactance, (*b*) the impedance, (*c*) the total current, (*d*) the voltage drop across the resistor and the coil, (*e*) the phase angle, and (*f*) the power used.

Solution:

Given: $L = 0.17$ henry   Find: $X_L = $?
$R = 50$ ohms $Z = $?
$E_T = 110$ volts $I_T = $?
$f = 60$ cps $E_R = $?
                              $E_L = $?
                              $\theta = $?
                              $P = $?

a. $X_L = 6.28fL = 6.28 \times 60 \times 0.17 = 64$ ohms   *Ans.*

b. $Z = \sqrt{R^2 + X_L^2} = \sqrt{50^2 + 64^2}$ (17-7)

$= \sqrt{2,500 + 4,096}$

$= \sqrt{6,596} = 81$ ohms   *Ans.*

c. Since the total opposition is the impedance Z, formula (4-7) becomes

$E_T = I_T \times Z$ (17-9)

$110 = I_T \times 81$

$I_T = \frac{110}{81} = 1.36$ amp   *Ans.*

d. Since

$I_T = I_R = I_L = 1.36$ amp   (4-1)

$E_R = I_R \times R_R$ $E_L = I_L \times X_L$

$E_R = 1.36 \times 50 = 68$ volts $E_L = 1.36 \times 64 = 87$ volts

e. $\cos \theta = \dfrac{R}{Z} = \dfrac{50}{81} = 0.6173$ (17-8)

$\theta = 52°$ *Ans.*

f.
$$P = E \times I \times \cos \theta \qquad (17\text{-}3)$$
$$P = 110 \times 1.36 \times \cos 52°$$
$$P = 110 \times 1.36 \times 0.617$$
$$P = 92.5 \text{ watts} \qquad Ans.$$

In the series circuit, the total voltage of 110 volts leads the total current of 1.36 amp by 52°.

Problems

1. A resistance of 5 ohms is in series with a coil whose inductive reactance is 12 ohms. If the total voltage is 104 volts, find (*a*) the impedance, (*b*) the total current, (*c*) the voltage drop across each part, (*d*) the phase angle, and (*e*) the power.

2. A 112-volt 60-cycle a-c voltage is applied across a series circuit of a 50-ohm resistor and a 100-ohm inductive reactance. Find (*a*) the impedance, (*b*) the total current, (*c*) the voltage drop across each part, (*d*) the phase angle, and (*e*) the power.

3. A 66-volt 220-cps a-c voltage is applied across a series circuit of a 20-ohm resistor and a 0.05-henry coil. Find the total current and the phase angle.

4. Part of the oscillator circuit for a continuous-wave transmitter is shown in Fig. 17-14. Find the current from point *A* to point *B* if the voltage drop is 70 volts.

5. A 20-ohm resistor is in series with a 0.03-henry dimmer coil. If the 230-volt 60-cycle a-c voltage is applied to the circuit, find (*a*) the current and (*b*) the power used.

6. A lightning protector circuit contains a 63.7-mh coil in series with a 7-ohm resistor. What current will flow when it is tested with a 110-volt 60-cycle a-c voltage?

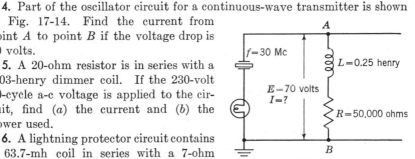

FIG. 17-14. A portion of the oscillator circuit for a continuous-wave transmitter.

7. A filter choke coil is connected in series with a 400-ohm resistor. When the voltage across the circuit is 120 volts, the current is 0.12 amp. Find the inductance of the coil if the frequency is 60 cps. *Hint:* See Job 15-4.

8. To measure the inductance of an audio choke, a 2,000-ohm resistor is connected in series with the choke. A 110-volt 60-cycle voltage is impressed across the circuit, and the current is measured at 10 ma. Find the inductance of the coil.

9. A 40-volt emf at 1,000 cycles is impressed across a loudspeaker of 5,000 ohms resistance and 1.5 henrys inductance. Find the current and power drawn.

10. Find the inductive reactance of a single-phase motor if the line voltage is 220 volts, the line current is 20 amp, and the resistance of the motor coils is 8 ohms. What is the angle of lag?

JOB 17-6: RESISTANCE AND CAPACITANCE IN SERIES

Figure 17-15 shows a 5-ohm resistor connected in series with a capacitance whose reactance is 12 ohms at a frequency of 60 cps.

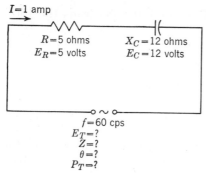

$I=1$ amp

$R=5$ ohms $X_C=12$ ohms
$E_R=5$ volts $E_C=12$ volts

$f=60$ cps
$E_T=?$
$Z=?$
$\theta=?$
$P_T=?$

FIG. 17-15. An a-c series circuit containing resistance and capacitance.

A series current of 1 amp produces a voltage drop of 5 volts across the resistor and 12 volts across the capacitor.

The total voltage across the circuit can be found by adding the voltage drops across each part. But, just as in the last job, since the voltages are *not* in phase, they must be added vectorially. The phase relations in a capacitive circuit are shown in Fig. 17-16a. The voltage across the resistor E_R is in phase with the current I; the voltage across the capacitor E_c *lags* the current I by 90°; E_c *lags* E_R by 90°.

Addition of the Vectors. In Fig. 17-16b, the total voltage E_T is obtained by adding the vector E_c to the vector E_R. Place the tail of E_c on the head of E_R, and draw it in its original direction and length.

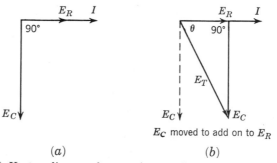

E_C moved to add on to E_R

(a)   (b)

FIG. 17-16. (a) Vector diagram for a series a-c circuit containing resistance and capacitance. (b) E_T represents the vector sum of E_R and E_c.

The distance from the origin of vectors to the head of the final vector is the sum of the vectors. In this instance, the vector E_T represents the sum of the vectors E_R and E_c. The phase angle θ is the angle by which the total voltage *lags* behind the current. By applying the Pythagorean theorem to Fig. 17-16b, we obtain

Formula

$$E_T{}^2 = E_R{}^2 + E_c{}^2 \qquad (17\text{-}10)$$

Total Impedance. To find the impedance of the series a-c circuit, we must add R and X_c vectorially as was done with the voltages. This is shown in Fig. 17-17. The voltages in Fig. 17-17a are replaced by their Ohm's law values in Fig. 17-17b. Now, by dropping out the

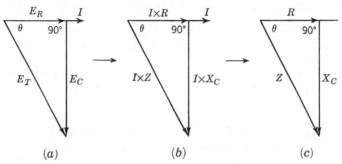

(a) (b) (c)

FIG. 17-17. Z represents the vector sum of R and X_c.

common factor of the current I, we obtain the *impedance triangle* of Fig. 17-17c.

Applying the Pythagorean theorem to Fig. 17-17c, we obtain

Formulas

$$Z^2 = R^2 + X_c^2 \qquad (17\text{-}11)$$

and
$$Z = \sqrt{R^2 + X_c^2} \qquad (17\text{-}12)$$

And by trigonometry,

$$\cos \theta = \frac{a}{h}$$

or
$$\cos \theta = \frac{R}{Z} \qquad (17\text{-}8)$$

The power is still given by

$$P = E \times I \times \cos \theta \qquad (17\text{-}3)$$

Example 17-8. In Fig. 17-15, find (a) the total voltage, (b) the impedance, (c) the phase angle, and (d) the power.

Solution:

a.
$$E_T{}^2 = E_R{}^2 + E_c{}^2 = 5^2 + 12^2 \qquad (17\text{-}10)$$
$$= 25 + 144$$
$$= 169$$
$$E_T = \sqrt{169} = 13 \text{ volts} \qquad Ans.$$

b.
$$Z = \sqrt{R^2 + X_c^2} \qquad (17\text{-}12)$$
$$= \sqrt{5^2 + 12^2}$$
$$= \sqrt{25 + 144}$$
$$Z = \sqrt{169} = 13 \text{ ohms} \qquad Ans.$$

c. $$\cos \theta = \frac{R}{Z} = \frac{5}{13} = 0.3846 \qquad (17\text{-}8)$$

$$\theta = 67° \quad \text{(approx)} \quad Ans.$$

d. $P = E \times I \times \cos \theta \qquad\qquad (17\text{-}3)$
  $P = 13 \times 1 \times \cos 67° = 13 \times 0.385 = 5$ watts $\quad Ans.$

Example 17-9. A capacitance of 4 µf and a resistance of 30 ohms are connected in series across a 100-volt 1-kc a-c source. Find (a) the capacitive reactance, (b) the impedance, (c) the total current, (d) the voltage drop across the resistor and the capacitor, (e) the phase angle, and (f) the power.

Solution:

Given: $C = 4$ µf Find: $X_c = ?$
$R = 30$ ohms $Z = ?$
$E_T = 100$ volts $I_T = ?$
$f = 1$ kc $= 1,000$ cps $E_R = ?$
$E_c = ?$
$\theta = ?$
$P = ?$

a. $X_c = \dfrac{159,000}{f \times C} = \dfrac{159,000}{1,000 \times 4} = \dfrac{159}{4} = 40$ ohms $\quad$ (approx)

b. $$Z = \sqrt{R^2 + X_c^2} \qquad (17\text{-}12)$$
$$= \sqrt{30^2 + 40^2}$$
$$= \sqrt{900 + 1,600}$$
$$Z = \sqrt{2,500} = 50 \text{ ohms} \quad Ans.$$

c. $$E_T = I_T \times Z \qquad (17\text{-}9)$$
$$100 = I_T \times 50$$
$$I_T = \tfrac{100}{50} = 2 \text{ amp} \quad Ans.$$

d. Since

$$I_T = I_R = I_c = 2 \text{ amp} \qquad (4\text{-}1)$$

$E_R = I_R \times R_R$ $\qquad\qquad$ $E_c = I_c \times X_c$
$E_R = 2 \times 30 = 60$ volts $\quad Ans.$ $\quad E_c = 2 \times 40 = 80$ volts $\quad Ans.$

e. $$\cos \theta = \frac{R}{Z} = \frac{30}{50} = 0.6000 \qquad (17\text{-}8)$$

$$\theta = 53° \quad \text{(approx)} \quad Ans.$$
f. $P = E \times I \times \cos \theta = 100 \times 2 \times 0.6 = 120$ watts $\quad Ans.$

In the series circuit, the total voltage of 100 volts lags the total current of 2 amp by 53°.

Problems

1. A 119-volt 60-cycle a-c voltage is applied across a series circuit of an 8-ohm resistor and a capacitor whose reactance is 15 ohms. Find (a) the impedance, (b) the total current, (c) the voltage drop across each part, (d) the phase angle, and (e) the power.

2. A 134-volt 60-cycle a-c voltage is applied across a series circuit of a 30-ohm resistor and a 60-ohm capacitive reactance. Find (a) the impedance, (b) the total current, (c) the voltage drop across each part, (d) the phase angle, and (e) the power.

3. A 113-volt 100-cps a-c voltage is applied across a series circuit of a 100-ohm resistor and a 15.9-μf capacitor. Find (a) the impedance, (b) the total current, (c) the voltage drop across each part, (d) the phase angle, and (e) the power.

4. Find the current and angle of lag for a series circuit of a 10-ohm resistor and an 8-μf capacitor if the applied voltage is 110 volts at 60 cps.

5. In the tone-control circuit shown in Fig. 17-18, find the impedance of the control unit to frequencies of 1,000 cps and 10 kc.

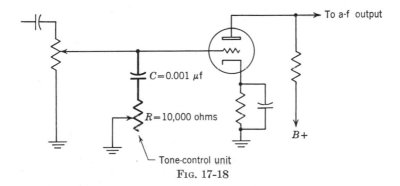

$C = 0.001 \ \mu f$

$R = 10,000$ ohms

Tone-control unit

To a-f output

$B+$

FIG. 17-18

6. In the resistance-coupled stage shown in Fig. 17-19, the voltage drop between points A and B is 1.414 volts. If the frequency of the current between these points is 10 kc, find the voltage drop across the 1,000-ohm resistor.

7. When the value of an unknown capacitor was calculated by the imped-ance method, a 300-ohm resistor was placed in series with the capacitor. A 110-volt 60-cycle a-c voltage caused a current of 0.22 amp to flow. Find (a) the impedance of the circuit, (b) the reactance of the capacitor, and (c) the capacitance of the capacitor.

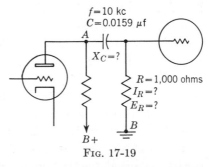

$f = 10$ kc
$C = 0.0159 \ \mu f$

A

$X_C = ?$

$R = 1,000$ ohms
$I_R = ?$
$E_R = ?$

B

$B+$

FIG. 17-19

8. A 10,000-ohm resistor and a capacitor are placed in series across a 60-cycle line. If the voltage across the resistor is 50 volts and across the capacitor 100 volts, find (a) the current in the resistor, (b) the current in the capacitor, (c) the reactance of the capacitor by Ohm's law, and (d) the capaci-tance of the capacitor.

JOB 17-7: RESISTANCE, INDUCTANCE, AND CAPACITANCE IN SERIES

Figure 17-20 shows a 16-ohm resistor, an inductive reactance of 80 ohms, and a capacitive reactance of 50 ohms connected in series across a frequency of 60 cps. A series current of 0.5 amp produces a voltage drop of 8 volts across the resistor, 40 volts across the inductance, and 25 volts across the capacitance.

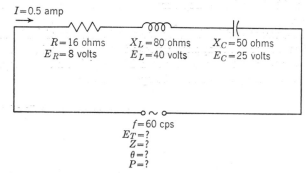

$I = 0.5$ amp

$R = 16$ ohms $X_L = 80$ ohms $X_C = 50$ ohms
$E_R = 8$ volts $E_L = 40$ volts $E_C = 25$ volts

$f = 60$ cps
$E_T = ?$
$Z = ?$
$\theta = ?$
$P = ?$

Fig. 17-20. An a-c series circuit containing resistance, inductance, and capacitance

The total voltage across the entire circuit may be found by adding the voltage drops across each part. However, since the voltages are *not* in phase, they must be added vectorially. The phase relations in the circuit are shown in Fig. 17-21a. The voltage across the resistor E_R is in phase with the current I. The voltage across the inductance E_L *leads* the current I by 90°. The voltage across the capacitance E_c *lags* the current I by 90°. Since E_L and E_c are exactly 180° out of phase and acting in exactly *opposite* directions, the voltage E_c is denoted by a minus sign.

Addition of Vectors. When there are three vectors, it is best to add only two at a time. To add the vector E_c to E_L, place the tail of E_c on the head of E_L and draw it in its original direction and length which will be straight *down* as shown in Fig. 17-21b. Since these vectors are acting in opposite directions, their *sum* is actually the *difference* between the vectors as indicated by E_d. After this addition, the vector diagram looks like Fig. 17-22a. Notice that the effect of the capacitor has disappeared. The 40 volts of coil voltage have exactly balanced the 25 volts of capacitive voltage and have left an excess of 15 volts of coil voltage. These 15 volts of coil voltage must now be added vectorially to the 8 volts of resistance voltage. In Fig. 17-22b, the total voltage E_T is obtained by adding the vector E_d to the vector E_R. Place the tail of E_d on the head of E_R, and draw it in the proper direction. If E_c is larger than E_L, the vector E_d will have a *downward* direction. The distance from the origin of the vectors to the head of the final vector is the sum of the vectors. In this instance, the vector E_T represents the sum of the vectors $E_R + E_L + E_c$. The phase angle θ is the angle by which the total voltage

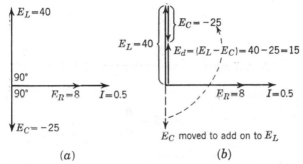

(a) (b)

FIG. 17-21. (a) Vector diagram for a series a-c circuit containing resistance, inductance, and capacitance. (b) E_d represents the vector sum of E_L and E_c.

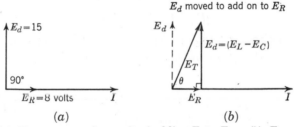

(a) (b)

FIG. 17-22. (a) E_d represents the result of adding E_c to E_L. (b) E_T represents the vector sum of $E_R + E_L + E_c$.

will lead the current. If E_c were larger than E_L, the total voltage would *lag* behind the current by this angle. By applying the Pythagorean theorem to Fig. 17-22b, we obtain

Formula

$$E_T^2 = E_R^2 + (E_L - E_c)^2 \qquad (17\text{-}13)$$

Total Impedance. To find the impedance of the series a-c circuit, we must add R, X_L, and X_c vectorially as was done with the voltages. This is shown in Fig. 17-23, resulting in the impedance triangle of Fig. 17-23c.

Applying the Pythagorean theorem to Fig. 17-23c, we obtain

Formulas

$$Z^2 = R^2 + (X_L - X_c)^2 \qquad (17\text{-}14)$$

and

$$Z = \sqrt{R^2 + (X_L - X_c)^2} \qquad (17\text{-}15)$$

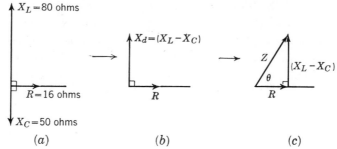

FIG. 17-23. Z represents the vector sum of $R + X_L + X_c$.

And by trigonometry,

$$\cos \theta = \frac{a}{h}$$

or

$$\cos \theta = \frac{R}{Z} \qquad (17\text{-}8)$$

The power is still given by

$$P = E \times I \times \cos \theta \qquad (17\text{-}3)$$

Example 17-10. In Fig. 17-20, find (a) the total voltage, (b) the impedance, (c) the phase angle, and (d) the power.

Solution:

a.
$$E_T{}^2 = E_R{}^2 + (E_L - E_c)^2 \qquad (17\text{-}13)$$
$$E_T{}^2 = 8^2 + (40 - 25)^2$$
$$E_T{}^2 = 8^2 + 15^2 = 64 + 225 = 289$$
$$E_T = \sqrt{289} = 17 \text{ volts} \qquad Ans.$$

b.
$$Z = \sqrt{R^2 + (X_L - X_c)^2} \qquad (17\text{-}15)$$
$$Z = \sqrt{16^2 + (80 - 50)^2}$$
$$Z = \sqrt{16^2 + 30^2} = \sqrt{256 + 900} = \sqrt{1,156}$$
$$Z = 34 \text{ ohms} \qquad Ans.$$

c.
$$\cos \theta = \frac{R}{Z} = \frac{16}{34} = 0.4706 \qquad (17\text{-}8)$$
$$\theta = 62° \qquad (\text{approx}) \qquad Ans.$$

d. $P = E \times I \times \cos \theta$ (17-3)
$$P = 17 \times 0.5 \times \cos 62° = 17 \times 0.5 \times 0.471 = 4 \text{ watts} \qquad Ans.$$

Example 17-11. An 18-ohm resistor, a 4-μf capacitor, and a 2.5-mh inductance are connected in series across a 60-volt 1-kc a-c source. Find (a) the capacitive reactance, (b) the inductive reactance, (c) the impedance, (d) the total current, (e) the voltage drop across each part, (f) the phase angle, and (g) the power.

Solution:

Given: $R = 18$ ohms   Find: $X_c = ?$
        $C = 4 \mu f$ $X_L = ?$
        $L = 2.5$ mh $= 0.0025$ henry $Z = ?$
        $E_T = 60$ volts $I_T = ?$
        $f = 1$ kc $= 1,000$ cps $E_R = ?$
                                         $E_L = ?$
                                         $E_c = ?$
                                         $\theta = ?$
                                         $P = ?$

a. $X_c = \dfrac{159,000}{f \times C} = \dfrac{159,000}{1,000 \times 4} = \dfrac{159}{4} = 40$ ohms   *Ans.*

b. $X_L = 6.28fL = 6.28 \times 1,000 \times 0.0025$ (15-3)
            $= 6.28 \times 2.5 = 16$ ohms   *Ans.*

c. $Z = \sqrt{R^2 + (X_c - X_L)^2}$ (17-15)

(Notice that X_c is written first because X_c is larger than X_L.)

$$Z = \sqrt{18^2 + (40 - 16)^2} = \sqrt{18^2 + 24^2}$$
$$= \sqrt{324 + 576}$$
$$= \sqrt{900}$$
$$Z = 30 \text{ ohms} \quad Ans.$$

d. $E_T = I_T \times Z$ (17-9)
               $60 = I_T \times 30$
               $I_T = \frac{60}{30} = 2$ amp   *Ans.*

e. Since
            $I_T = I_R = I_L = I_c = 2$ amp   (4-1)

$E_R = I_R \times R_R$ $E_c = I_c \times X_c$
$E_R = 2 \times 18 = 36$ volts   *Ans.* $E_c = 2 \times 40 = 80$ volts   *Ans.*

            $E_L = I_L \times X_L$
            $E_L = 2 \times 16 = 32$ volts   *Ans.*

f. $\cos \theta = \dfrac{R}{Z} = \dfrac{18}{30} = 0.6000$ (17-8)
              $\theta = 37°$ (approx)   *Ans.*

g. $P = E \times I \times \cos \theta = 60 \times 2 \times 0.6 = 72$ watts   *Ans.*

In the series circuit, since the capacitive reactance is larger than the inductive reactance, the total voltage of 60 volts *lags* behind the total current of 2 amp by 37°.

Example 17-12. A rectifier delivers 200 volts at 120 cps to a filter circuit consisting of a 30-henry filter choke coil and a 20-μf capacitor connected as shown in Fig. 17-24. How much 120-cps voltage appears across the capacitor which feeds into the plate supply? Has this filter succeeded in removing the a-c component from the plate supply? *Solution:* The circuit diagram is shown in Fig. 17-24.

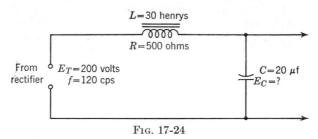

$$L = 30 \text{ henrys}$$
$$R = 500 \text{ ohms}$$

From rectifier $E_T = 200$ volts $f = 120$ cps

$$C = 20 \ \mu f$$
$$E_C = ?$$

FIG. 17-24

1. Find the reactance of the coil.

$$X_L = 6.28fL \qquad (15\text{-}3)$$
$$X_L = 6.28 \times 120 \times 30$$
$$X_L = 22{,}600 \text{ ohms} \qquad Ans.$$

2. Find the reactance of the capacitor.

$$X_c = \frac{159{,}000}{f \times C} = \frac{159{,}000}{120 \times 20} = \frac{1{,}590}{24} = 66 \text{ ohms} \qquad Ans. \qquad (16\text{-}6)$$

3. Find the impedance.

$$Z = \sqrt{R^2 + (X_L - X_c)^2} = \sqrt{500^2 + (22{,}600 - 66)^2} \quad (17\text{-}15)$$
$$= \sqrt{500^2 + 22{,}542^2}$$
$$= \sqrt{250{,}000 + 508{,}140{,}000}$$
$$= \sqrt{508{,}390{,}000}$$
$$Z = 22{,}547 \text{ ohms} \qquad Ans.$$

Notice that R was so small in comparison with $(X_L - X_c)$ that it had practically no effect on the value of $(X_L - X_c)$.

4. Find the series current.

$$E_T = I_T \times Z \qquad (17\text{-}9)$$
$$200 = I_T \times 22{,}547$$
$$I_T = \frac{200}{22{,}547} = 0.0089 \text{ amp} \qquad Ans.$$

5. Find the voltage across the capacitor.

$$E_c = I_c \times X_c \qquad (16\text{-}7)$$
$$E_c = 0.0089 \times 66 = 0.59 \text{ volt} \qquad Ans.$$

Therefore this is a satisfactory filter, since only 0.59 volt out of the total of 200 volts of 120-cps alternating current can get through to the plate supply.

Problems

1. A 16-ohm resistor, an 83-ohm inductive reactance, and a 20-ohm capacitive reactance are in series. A 130-volt 60-cycle emf is impressed on the circuit. Find (a) the impedance, (b) the series current, (c) the voltage drops across all the parts, (d) the phase angle, and (e) the power.

2. A coil of 2.07-mh inductance, a 0.3-μf capacitor, and a 36-ohm resistor are connected in series across a 127.5-volt 10-kc a-c source. Find (a) the impedance, (b) the total current, (c) the phase angle, and (d) the power.

3. A 125-volt 100-cycle power supply is connected across a 4,000-ohm resistor, a 0.5-μf capacitor, and a 10-henry coil connected in series. Find (a) the individual reactances, (b) the impedance, (c) the total current, (d) the phase angle, and (e) the power.

4. The antenna circuit of a radio receiver consists of a 0.2-mh inductance and a 0.0001-μf capacitance. If the resistance of the antenna is small enough to be considered to be zero, what is the impedance of the antenna to a 1,200-kc signal? If this frequency induces a voltage of 100 μv in the antenna, what current will flow?

5. In a circuit similar to Fig. 17-24, $E_T = 250$ volts, $f = 120$ cps, $L = 25$ henrys, $R = 400$ ohms, and $C = 25$ μf. What amount of the 120-cycle voltage will appear across the capacitor?

6. A wave trap to eliminate a 13-kc frequency is made of a 30-mh inductance of 40 ohms resistance and a 0.005-μf capacitor in series. What is the impedance of the circuit?

7. A 10.8-volt 100-kc emf is applied across a series circuit of a 6-ohm resistance, a 0.5-mh coil, and a 5,000-$\mu\mu$f capacitance. What is the total current?

8. A 300-ohm 100-μh resistor is in series with a capacitance of 2 μf. Find the impedance of the circuit at (a) 500 cps, (b) 5 kc, and (c) 500 kc.

JOB 17-8: SERIES RESONANCE

Example 17-13. A 30-henry coil, a 250-ohm resistor, and a variable capacitor are connected in series across a 110-volt 60-cycle line. When the capacitor is adjusted to 0.2344 μf, find the impedance of the circuit.

Solution:

$$\text{Given:} \begin{aligned} L &= 30 \text{ henrys} \\ R &= 250 \text{ ohms} \\ C &= 0.2344 \ \mu\text{f} \\ E &= 110 \text{ volts} \\ f &= 60 \text{ cps} \end{aligned} \qquad \text{Find:} \ Z = \ ?$$

1. Find the inductive reactance.

$$X_L = 6.28fL = 6.28 \times 60 \times 30 = 11,304 \text{ ohms} \qquad Ans. \quad (15\text{-}3)$$

2. Find the capacitive reactance.

$$X_c = \frac{159,000}{f \times C} = \frac{159,000}{60 \times 0.2344} = \frac{15,900}{1.4064} = 11,304 \text{ ohms} \quad Ans.$$

3. Find the impedance.

$$Z = \sqrt{R^2 + (X_c - X_L)^2} = \sqrt{250^2 + (11,304 - 11,304)^2}$$
$$= \sqrt{250^2 + 0^2}$$
$$= \sqrt{250^2}$$
$$Z = 250 \text{ ohms} \quad Ans.$$

Notice that for these particular values of L and C, the inductive reactance and the capacitive reactance are exactly equal. Since their actions are directly opposed to each other, the total effect of both is equal to zero and the impedance of the circuit is equal to just the resistance of the circuit. This condition is called *resonance*. Series resonance is the condition of *smallest* circuit resistance. At resonance, since the reactance effect is zero, the *largest* amount of current will flow.

Any change in the values of either L or C would give *different* values of X_L and X_c, whose sum would no longer be zero. Under these conditions, since the reactance effect is *larger* than zero, the current that flows will be *smaller* than the flow at resonance. In addition, since the values of the reactances depend on the frequency, any change in the frequency results in *different* values of reactances whose sum again would *not* be zero. Apparently, for any combination of L and C in series, there is only *one* frequency for which X_L can equal X_c. This frequency is called the *resonant frequency*.

At this frequency, a large current will flow in the series circuit, since the reactance is zero at the resonant frequency. At any other frequency, since the sum of X_L and X_c is *not* equal to zero, the impedance will be *larger* and the current will be *smaller*.

Why Is the Resonant Frequency Important? The antenna of a radio receiver is receiving signals from many stations at the same time. Each station broadcasts at a different frequency. Each different frequency induces a signal voltage in the antenna so that at any one time there may be many different signal voltages in the same antenna. How shall we separate one of these signals from all the rest?

We can separate one frequency from the rest if we can find an L and C combination which is *resonant* to that same frequency which we are trying to separate. Only this frequency will encounter a *zero impedance* and therefore will produce a *large* current. All other frequencies will encounter large impedances, and the currents at these frequencies will be practically zero. The tuner of a receiver is a series circuit of an inductance and a capacitance which can be made resonant to different frequencies by changing the values of the capacitance. Thus it will select and pass on to the amplifying system only one frequency at a time.

There are many other uses for the series-resonant circuit. In the superheterodyne receiver, the oscillator must deliver a definite frequency to the mixer tube. Values of L and C are chosen to make the combination resonant to that particular frequency. Band pass filters and acceptance circuits are other common applications of the series-resonant circuit.

Calculating the Resonant Frequency. At resonance, the inductive reactance is equal to the capacitive reactance. Write the equation.

$$X_L = X_c \qquad\qquad (17\text{-}16)$$

Substitute reactances.

$$\frac{6.28fL}{1} = \frac{159,000}{f \times C}$$

Cross-multiply.

$$f^2 \times 6.28 \times L \times C = 159,000$$

Solve for f.

$$f^2 = \frac{159,000}{6.28 \times L \times C}$$

Divide.

$$f^2 = \frac{25,318}{L \times C}$$

Take the square root of both sides.

$$f = \sqrt{\frac{25,318}{L \times C}}$$

Formula

$$f = \frac{159}{\sqrt{L \times C}} \qquad\qquad (17\text{-}17)$$

where f = frequency, cps
$\quad L$ = inductance, henrys
$\quad C$ = capacitance, μf

If we use the units of measurement commonly used in radio and television work, the formula retains the same form *but* both the frequency and the inductance are expressed in different units.

Formula

$$f = \frac{159}{\sqrt{L \times C}} \qquad (17\text{-}18)$$

where f = frequency, *kilocycles per second*

     L = inductance, *microhenrys*

     C = capacitance, *microfarads.*

Example 17-14. Calculate the resonant frequency of a tuning circuit if the inductance is 300 μh and the capacitor is set at a capacity of 0.0003 μf.

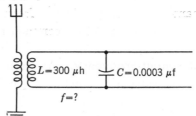

L=300 μh C=0.0003 μf

f=?

FIG. 17-25. A simple tuning circuit.

Solution: The diagram of the circuit is shown in Fig. 17-25.

$$f = \frac{159}{\sqrt{L \times C}} \qquad (17\text{-}18)$$

$$f = \frac{159}{\sqrt{300 \times 0.0003}}$$

$$f = \frac{159}{\sqrt{0.09}} = \frac{159}{0.3} = 530 \text{ kc} \qquad Ans.$$

Example 17-15. An inductance of 30 μh and a capacitor of 15 $\mu\mu$f are used in series in a Hartley-type oscillator. Find the resonant frequency.

Solution: The diagram of the circuit is shown in Fig. 17-26. If formula (17-18) is used, 15 $\mu\mu$f must be changed into microfarads.

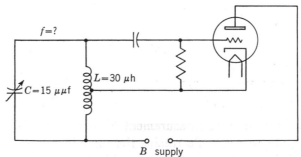

f=?

L=30 μh

C=15 $\mu\mu$f

B supply

FIG. 17-26. A series-fed Hartley-type oscillator.

$$15 \ \mu\mu f = 15 \div 10^6 = 0.000015 \ \mu f$$

$$f = \frac{159}{\sqrt{L \times C}} = \frac{159}{\sqrt{30 \times 0.000015}} \qquad (17\text{-}18)$$

$$= \frac{159}{\sqrt{0.00045}}$$

$$f = \frac{159}{0.0212} = 7,500 \ \text{kc} \qquad Ans.$$

Problems

1. Find the resonant frequency of a tuning circuit similar to Fig. 17-25 if $L = 250 \ \mu h$ and $C - 40 \ \mu\mu f$.

2. What is the resonant frequency of a series circuit if the inductance is $270 \ \mu h$ and the capacitance is $0.003 \ \mu f$?

3. What is the resonant frequency of a Hartley-type oscillator if the coil has an inductance of $40 \ \mu h$ and the capacitance is set at $160 \ \mu\mu f$?

4. Find the resonant frequency of the series-resonant section of the band-pass filter shown in Fig. 17-27.

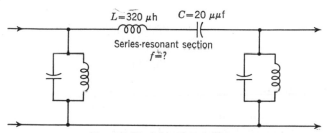

Fig. 17-27. A bandpass filter.

5. Find the resonant frequency of the series-resonant section of the wave trap or band-elimination filter shown in Fig. 17-28.

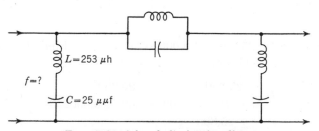

Fig. 17-28. A band-elimination filter.

6. A 3-mh coil and a 40-$\mu\mu f$ capacitor are connected as shown in Fig. 17-29 to form the secondary side of an i-f transformer. What is its resonant frequency? Explain why the secondary is a series-tuned circuit while the primary is a parallel circuit.

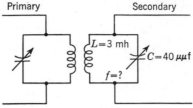

FIG. 17-29. The secondary of the i-f transformer is a series-resonant circuit.

7. Find the resonant frequency of an antenna circuit if the inductance is 50 μh and the capacitance is 0.0002 μf.

JOB 17-9: FINDING THE INDUCTANCE OR CAPACITANCE NEEDED TO MAKE A SERIES-RESONANT CIRCUIT

Formula (17-18) may be transformed to find formulas which may be used to find the inductance or capacitance needed to form a series-resonant circuit at a given frequency.

Formulas

$$L = \frac{25,300}{f^2 \times C} \tag{17-19}$$

$$C = \frac{25,300}{f^2 \times L} \tag{17-20}$$

where L = inductance, μh
 C = capacitance, μf
 f = frequency, kc per second

Example 17-16. What value of inductance must be placed in series with a 253-$\mu\mu$f tuning capacitor in order to provide resonance for a 500-kc signal?

Solution:

Given: $C = 253\ \mu\mu f = 0.000253\ \mu f$ Find: $L = ?$
 $f = 500$ kc

$$L = \frac{25,300}{f^2 \times C} = \frac{25,300}{500 \times 500 \times 0.000253} \tag{17-19}$$

$$= \frac{25,300}{25 \times 2.53}$$

$$= \frac{2,530,000}{25 \times 253}$$

$$L = \frac{10,000}{25} = 400\ \mu h \qquad Ans.$$

Example 17-17. An inductance of 40 μh is in series with a capacitor in a Hartley-type oscillator circuit. Find the value of the capacitance needed to produce resonance to a frequency of 5,000 kc.

Solution:

$$\text{Given: } L = 40 \ \mu\text{h} \qquad\qquad \text{Find: } C = ?$$
$$f = 5{,}000 \text{ kc}$$

$$C = \frac{25{,}300}{f^2 \times L} = \frac{25{,}300}{5{,}000 \times 5{,}000 \times 40} \qquad (17\text{-}20)$$

$$= \frac{25{,}300}{1{,}000{,}000{,}000}$$

$$C = 0.0000253 \ \mu\text{f} = 25.3 \ \mu\mu\text{f} \qquad Ans.$$

Problems

1. What value of inductance must be connected in series with a 0.0003-μf capacitor in order that the circuit be resonant to a frequency of 1,000 kc?

2. What value of capacitance must be connected in series with a 50-μh coil in order that the circuit be resonant to a frequency of 2,000 kc?

3. What value of inductance will produce resonance to 50 cycles if it is placed in series with a 20-μf capacitor?

4. What value of capacitance must be used in series with a 30-μh inductance in order to produce an oscillator frequency of 6,000 kc?

5. What value of capacitance must be added in series with a solenoid of 0.2-henry inductance in order to be resonant to 60 cps?

6. What capacity is necessary in series with a 100-μh coil to produce a wave trap for a 1,200-kc signal?

7. What is the inductance of the secondary winding of an r-f transformer if it is in series with a 0.00035-μf capacitor and is resonant to a frequency of 1,000 kc?

8. What is the capacity of an antenna circuit whose inductance is 50 μh if it is resonant to 1,500 kc?

9. A 0.00004-μf capacitance is in series with the secondary of an r-f transformer. What must be the inductance of the coil if the secondary is to be resonant to 500 kc?

10. What must be the minimum and maximum values of the capacitor needed to produce resonance with a 240-μh coil to frequencies between 500 and 1,500 kc?

JOB 17-10: REVIEW OF SERIES A-C CIRCUITS

The voltages and currents in a series a-c circuit are not usually in phase with each other. Alternating-current voltages may not be added arithmetically but only by means of vector addition.

A vector is a straight line drawn with a definite length and in a definite direction. In a-c electricity, the direction of the vector indicates the *time* at which the voltage or current occurs in relation to another voltage or current.

Vectors drawn in the same direction are in phase.

Vectors drawn in different directions are out of phase.

Vectors are added by placing the tail of one vector on to the head of another and drawing the vector with the original length and direction.

In a purely resistive circuit:

The voltage is in phase with the current.

$$E_T = E_1 + E_2 + E_3 \qquad (4\text{-}2)$$
$$E_T = I_T \times R_T \qquad (4\text{-}7)$$
$$R_T = R_1 + R_2 + R_3 \qquad (4\text{-}3)$$
$$P = E \times I \qquad (7\text{-}1)$$

In a purely inductive circuit:

The voltage leads the current by 90°.

$$E_T = E_1 + E_2 + E_3 \qquad (4\text{-}2)$$
$$E_L = I_L \times X_L \qquad (15\text{-}4)$$
$$X_T = X_1 + X_2 + X_3 \qquad (17\text{-}21)$$
$$P = E \times I \times \cos \theta \qquad (17\text{-}3)$$

In a purely capacitive circuit:

The voltage lags the current by 90°.

$$E_T = E_1 + E_2 + E_3 \qquad (4\text{-}2)$$
$$E_c = I_c \times X_c \qquad (16\text{-}7)$$
$$X_T = X_1 + X_2 + X_3 \qquad (17\text{-}21)$$
$$P = E \times I \times \cos \theta \qquad (17\text{-}3)$$

In an a-c series circuit of resistance and inductance:

The total voltage leads the current by some angle θ.

$$E_T{}^2 = E_R{}^2 + E_L{}^2 \qquad (17\text{-}5)$$
$$Z = \sqrt{R^2 + X_L{}^2} \qquad (17\text{-}7)$$
$$E_T = I_T \times Z \qquad (17\text{-}9)$$
$$\cos \theta = \frac{R}{Z} \qquad (17\text{-}8)$$
$$P = E \times I \times \cos \theta \qquad (17\text{-}3)$$

In an a-c series circuit of resistance and capacitance:

The total voltage lags the current by some angle θ.

$$E_T{}^2 = E_R{}^2 + E_c{}^2 \qquad (17\text{-}10)$$
$$Z = \sqrt{R^2 + X_c{}^2} \qquad (17\text{-}12)$$
$$E_T = I_T \times Z \qquad (17\text{-}9)$$
$$\cos\theta = \frac{R}{Z} \qquad (17\text{-}8)$$
$$P = E \times I \times \cos\theta \qquad (17\text{-}3)$$

In an a-c series circuit of resistance, inductance, and capacitance:

The total voltage will lead or lag the current, depending on the values of X_L and X_c. If X_L is larger than X_c, the voltage will lead the current. If X_L is smaller than X_c, the voltage will lag behind the current. The angle of lead or lag is given by the angle θ.

$$E_T{}^2 = E_R{}^2 + (E_L - E_c)^2 \qquad (17\text{-}13)$$
$$Z = \sqrt{R^2 + (X_L - X_c)^2} \qquad (17\text{-}15)$$
$$E_T = I_T \times Z \qquad (17\text{-}9)$$
$$\cos\theta = \frac{R}{Z} \qquad (17\text{-}8)$$
$$P = E \times I \times \cos\theta \qquad (17\text{-}3)$$

Series resonance is the condition at which the inductive reactance is exactly equal to the capacitive reactance. For any given combination of coil and capacitor, there is only one frequency at which this situation can occur. This frequency is called the resonant frequency.

$$f = \frac{159}{\sqrt{L \times C}} \qquad (17\text{-}18)$$

where f = frequency, kc per second
L = inductance, μh
C = capacitance, μf

The inductance or capacitance needed to make a circuit resonant to a given frequency is given by the formulas

$$L = \frac{25{,}300}{f^2 \times C} \qquad (17\text{-}19)$$

$$C = \frac{25{,}300}{f^2 \times L} \qquad (17\text{-}20)$$

where all units are measured in the units given for formula (17-18).

Problems

1. What is the voltage drop across a 3,000-ohm resistor carrying 60 ma of current at a frequency of 60 cps?

2. Find the current and power drawn by a 20-mh coil from a 125.6-volt 10-kc source?

3. A filter choke passes 60 ma of current when it is connected across a 120-volt 60-cycle line. What is its inductance?

4. Find the voltage drop across a 0.05-μf capacitor if it passes 50 ma at a frequency of 1 kc?

5. A 50-volt emf at 1-kc frequency is impressed across a 1,000-ohm resistor in series with a 1-henry coil. Find (a) the impedance, (b) the total current, (c) the voltage drop across each part, (d) the phase angle, and (e) the power drawn.

6. A 120-volt 1-kc a-c voltage is applied across a series circuit of a 200-ohm resistor and a 1.6-μf capacitor. Find (a) the impedance, (b) the total current, (c) the voltage drop across each part, (d) the phase angle, and (e) the power drawn.

7. An antenna circuit consists of a 10-ohm resistance, a 0.5-mh inductance, and a 50-$\mu\mu$f capacitance. Find its impedance to a frequency of (a) 1,000 kc and (b) 500 kc.

8. A 1,000-ohm 100-μh coil is in series with a capacitance of 5 μf. Find the impedance at (a) 500 cps, (b) 5 kc, and (c) 500 kc.

9. The secondary of a transformer is made of a 50-mh coil and a 100-$\mu\mu$f capacitor. To what frequency is it resonant?

10. What capacitance is needed in series with a 0.5-mh coil in order to produce resonance to 10 kc?

Test—Series A-C Circuits

1. A 100-volt emf at 5 kc is impressed across a 2,000-ohm resistor in series with a 0.1-henry coil. Find (a) the impedance of the circuit, (b) the total current, (c) the voltage drop across each part, (d) the phase angle, and (e) the power drawn by the circuit.

2. A 500-ohm resistor, a 0.5-mh coil, and a 0.02-μf capacitor are connected in series across a 13.8-volt 100-kc a-c source. Find (a) the impedance of the circuit, (b) the total current, and (c) the phase angle.

3. What is the resonant frequency of a series a-c circuit consisting of a 0.02-mh coil and a 0.0005-μf capacitor?

4. What inductance is needed in series with a 0.00025-μf capacitor in order to produce resonance to a 100-kc wave?

CHAPTER 18

PARALLEL A-C CIRCUITS

JOB 18-1: SIMPLE PARALLEL A-C CIRCUITS

The general rules for solving d-c parallel circuits are also applicable to the solution of a-c parallel circuits.

1. The voltages across all branches are equal to each other and to the total voltage.

$$E_T = E_1 = E_2 = E_3 \qquad (5\text{-}1)$$

2. The total current is equal to the sum of all the branch currents.

$$I_T = I_1 + I_2 + I_3 \qquad (5\text{-}2)$$

Parallel Circuits Containing Only Resistance. We can add the branch currents as indicated by formula (5-2) only if the branch currents are in phase. If they are out of phase, they may be added *only* by vector addition. Let us draw the vector diagrams for each branch of the circuit shown in Example 18-1 to discover the phase relationships in this type of circuit.

Vector Diagrams. Since the voltage in a parallel circuit is constant, the voltage is used as the reference line upon which to draw the vectors. In Fig. 18-1a, the current I_1 is drawn in the same direction as the voltage because the current in the purely resistive iron is in phase with the voltage. In Fig. 18-1b, the smaller current through the lamp I_2 is also drawn in the same direction as the voltage because the current through a purely resistive lamp is in phase with the voltage.

(a)   (b)

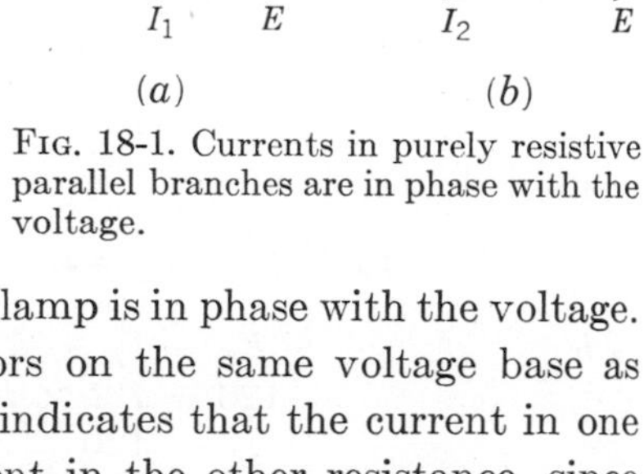

Fig. 18-1. Currents in purely resistive parallel branches are in phase with the voltage.

Now let us draw both sets of vectors on the same voltage base as shown in Fig. 18-2a. This diagram indicates that the current in one resistance is in phase with the current in the other resistance, since they are both drawn in the same direction. To find the total current, it is necessary only to add the two current vectors. This is done, as with any vector quantities, by adding the tail of vector I_2 on to the head of vector I_1 as shown in Fig. 18-2b. The total current is then the distance from the origin of the vectors to the head of the last vector. Since the two currents are in phase, the total current may be found by the direct arithmetical addition of the currents, using formula (5-2).

(*a*)   (*b*)

FIG. 18-2. (*a*) Resistive branch currents are in phase with each other.   (*b*) I_T represents the vector sum of I_1 and I_2.

Example 18-1.   A 20-ohm electric iron and a 100-ohm lamp are connected in parallel across a 120-volt 60-cycle a-c line.   Find (*a*) the total current, (*b*) the total resistance, and (*c*) the total power drawn by the circuit.

Solution: The diagram for the circuit is shown in Fig. 18-3.

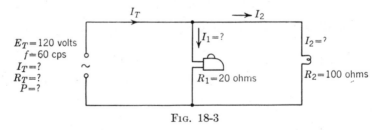

FIG. 18-3

a. Find the branch currents.   Since

$$E_T = E_1 = E_2 = E_3 = 120 \text{ volts} \qquad (5\text{-}1)$$

$$E_1 = I_1 \times R_1 \qquad\qquad E_2 = I_2 \times R_2$$
$$120 = I_1 \times 20 \qquad\qquad 120 = I_2 \times 100$$
$$I_1 = \tfrac{120}{20} = 6 \text{ amp} \qquad I_2 = \tfrac{120}{100} = 1.2 \text{ amp}$$

Find the total current.

$$I_T = I_1 + I_2 = 6 + 1.2 = 7.2 \text{ amp} \qquad Ans. \qquad (5\text{-}2)$$

b. $$E_T = I_T \times R_T \qquad\qquad\qquad (4\text{-}7)$$
$$120 = 7.2 \times R_T$$
$$R_T = \frac{120}{7.2} = 16.7 \text{ ohms} \qquad Ans.$$

c. In a purely resistive set of branch circuits, the total current is in phase with the total voltage.   The phase angle is therefore equal to 0°.

$$P = E \times I \times \cos \theta = 120 \times 7.2 \times \cos 0° \qquad (17\text{-}3)$$
$$P = 120 \times 7.2 \times 1 = 864 \text{ watts} \qquad Ans.$$

Parallel Circuits Containing Only Inductance.   This type of circuit is illustrated in Fig. 18-6 for Example 18-2 below.

Vector Diagrams.   Since the voltage in a parallel circuit is constant, the voltage is used as the reference line upon which to draw the vectors.   In Fig. 18-4a, the current I_{L_1} is drawn lagging the voltage by 90°.   In Fig. 18-4b, the current I_{L_2} is also drawn lagging the voltage by 90°, since the current in *any* inductance lags the voltage by 90°. Now let us draw both sets of vectors on the same voltage base as shown in Fig. 18-5a.   This diagram indicates that the current in one coil is in phase with the current in the second coil, since they are both drawn in the same direction.   To find the total current, it is necessary only to add the two current vectors.   This is done, as with any vector quantities, by adding the tail of vector I_{L_2} on to the head of vector I_{L_1} as shown in Fig. 18-5b.   The total current is then the

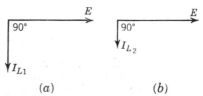

(a)   (b)

FIG. 18-4. Currents in purely inductive parallel branches lag the voltage by 90°.

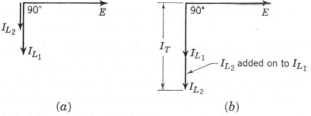

(a)   (b)

FIG. 18-5. (a) Inductive branch currents are in phase with each other.   (b) I_T represents the vector sum of I_{L_1} and I_{L_2}.

distance from the origin of the vectors to the head of the last vector. Since the two currents are in phase, the total current may be found by the direct arithmetical addition of the currents, using formula (5-2).   The difference between this circuit and the purely resistive circuit lies in the fact that the total current *lags* behind the total voltage by 90°.   The phase angle $\theta = 90°$.

Example 18-2.   Two coils of 20 and 30 ohms reactance, respectively, are connected in parallel across a 120-volt 60-cycle a-c line.   Find (a) the total current, (b) the impedance, and (c) the power drawn by the circuit.

Solution: The diagram for the circuit is shown in Fig. 18-6.

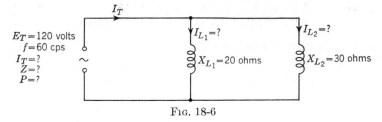

FIG. 18-6

a. Find the branch currents.   Since

$$E_T = E_1 = E_2 = 120 \text{ volts} \qquad (5\text{-}1)$$

$$
\begin{array}{ll}
E_1 = I_1 \times X_1 & E_2 = I_2 \times X_2 \\
120 = I_1 \times 20 & 120 = I_2 \times 30 \\
I_1 = \tfrac{120}{20} = 6 \text{ amp} & I_2 = \tfrac{120}{30} = 4 \text{ amp}
\end{array}
$$

Find the total current.

$$I_T = I_1 + I_2 = 6 + 4 = 10 \text{ amp} \qquad Ans. \qquad (5\text{-}2)$$

b.
$$E_T = I_T \times Z \qquad (17\text{-}9)$$
$$120 = 10 \times Z$$
$$Z = \tfrac{120}{10} = 12 \text{ ohms} \qquad Ans.$$

c. In a purely inductive set of branch circuits, the total current lags behind the voltage by 90°.   The phase angle is therefore equal to 90°.

$$P = E \times I \times \cos \theta = 120 \times 10 \times \cos 90° \qquad (17\text{-}3)$$
$$P = 120 \times 10 \times 0 = 0 \text{ watts} \qquad Ans.$$

Parallel Circuits Containing Only Capacitance.   This type of circuit is illustrated in Fig. 18-9 for Example 18-3 below.

Vector Diagrams.   Since the voltage in a parallel circuit is constant, the voltage is used as the reference line upon which to draw the vectors.   In Fig. 18-7*a*, the current I_{c_1} is drawn *leading* the voltage by 90°.   In Fig. 18-7*b*, the current I_{c_2} is also drawn *leading* the voltage by 90°, since the current in *any* capacitance leads the voltage by 90°.

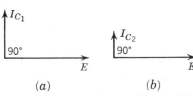

(*a*)   (*b*)

FIG. 18-7. Currents in purely capacitive parallel branches lead the voltage by 90°.

Now let us draw both sets of vectors on the same voltage base as shown in Fig. 18-8*a*.   This diagram indicates that the current in one capacitor is in phase with the current in the second capacitor, since they are both drawn in the same direction.   To find the total current, it is necessary only to add the two cur-

rent vectors.   This is done, as with any vector quantities, by adding
the tail of vector I_{c_2} on to the head of vector I_{c_1} as shown in Fig. 18-8b.
The total current is then the distance from the origin of the vectors to
the head of the last vector.   Since the two currents are in phase, the
total current may be found by the direct arithmetical addition of the

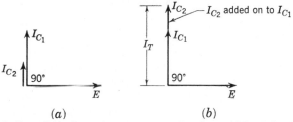

(a)   (b)

Fig. 18-8. (a) Capacitive branch currents are in phase with each other.   (b) I_T
represents the vector sum of I_{c_1} and I_{c_2}.

currents, using formula (5-2).   The difference between this and the
other two circuits lies in the fact that the total current *leads* the total
voltage by 90°.   The phase angle $\theta = 90°$.

Example 18-3.   Two capacitors of 30 and 40 ohms reactance
respectively, are connected across a 120-volt 60-cycle a-c line.   Find
(a) the total current, (b) the impedance, and (c) the power drawn by
the circuit.

Solution: The diagram for the circuit is shown in Fig. 18-9.

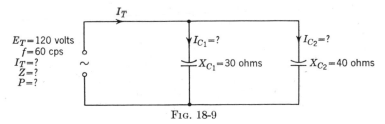

Fig. 18-9

a. Find the branch currents.   Since

$$E_T = E_1 = E_2 = 120 \text{ volts} \qquad\qquad (5\text{-}1)$$

$$E_1 = I_1 \times X_1 \qquad\qquad E_2 = I_2 \times X_2$$
$$120 = I_1 \times 30 \qquad\qquad 120 = I_2 \times 40$$
$$I_1 = \tfrac{120}{30} = 4 \text{ amp} \qquad\qquad I_2 = \tfrac{120}{40} = 3 \text{ amp}$$

Find the total current.

$$I_T = I_1 + I_2 = 4 + 3 = 7 \text{ amp} \qquad Ans. \qquad (5\text{-}2)$$

b.
$$E_T = I_T \times Z \qquad\qquad\qquad (17\text{-}9)$$
$$120 = 7 \times Z$$
$$Z = \tfrac{120}{7} = 17.1 \text{ ohms} \qquad Ans.$$

c. In a purely capacitive set of branch circuits, the total current leads the voltage by 90°. [The phase angle is therefore equal] to 90°.

$$P = E \times I \times \cos \theta = 120 \times 7 \times \cos 90° \qquad (17\text{-}3)$$
$$P = 120 \times 7 \times 0 = 0 \text{ watts} \qquad Ans.$$

Summary

In a parallel a-c circuit

1. The voltage across any branch is equal to the total voltage.

2. The current in a resistor is in phase with the voltage.

3. The current in an inductance lags the voltage by 90°.

4. The current in a capacitance leads the voltage by 90°.

5. Currents that are in phase with each other may be added arithmetically, using formula (5-2).

6. Ohm's law, $E_T = I_T \times Z$ [formula (17-9)], may be used for total values.

7. The power depends on the angle of lead or lag as shown by formula (17-3). ($P = E \times I \times \cos \theta$.)

Problems

1. A 10-ohm electric heater and a 50-ohm incandescent lamp are placed in parallel across a 120-volt 60-cycle a-c line. Find (*a*) the total current, (*b*) the total resistance, and (*c*) the power drawn.

2. Two toy-train solenoids used in semaphore signals have inductive reactances of 24 and 48 ohms, respectively. They are connected in parallel across the 12-volt winding of the power transformer. Find (*a*) the total current, (*b*) the impedance, and (*c*) the power drawn.

3. Two capacitors of 100 and 200 ohms capacitive reactance, respectively, are connected in parallel across a 100-volt 60-cycle a-c line. Find (*a*) the total current, (*b*) the impedance, and (*c*) the power drawn.

4. A 40-ohm soldering iron and a 100-ohm incandescent lamp are connected in parallel across a 110-volt 60-cycle a-c line. Find (*a*) the total current, (*b*) the total resistance, and (*c*) the power drawn.

5. Find the total current, impedance, and power used by the circuit shown in Fig. 18-10.

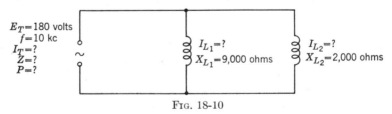

$E_T = 180$ volts
$f = 10$ kc
$I_T = ?$
$Z = ?$
$P = ?$

$I_{L_1} = ?$
$X_{L_1} = 9{,}000$ ohms

$I_{L_2} = ?$
$X_{L_2} = 2{,}000$ ohms

Fig. 18-10

6. A radio mechanic replaced a leaky coupling capacitor with a parallel combination of two capacitors as shown in Fig. 18-11. If the voltage drop across the capacitors is 0.5 volt at a frequency of 1 kc, find the current in each capacitor, the total current, and the impedance of the combination.

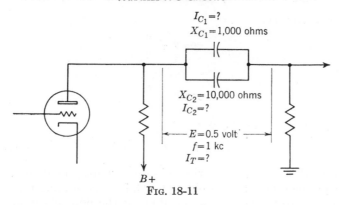

FIG. 18-11

JOB 18-2: RESISTANCE AND INDUCTANCE IN PARALLEL

Figure 18-13 shows a 24-ohm resistance and a 30-ohm inductive reactance in parallel across a 12-volt 60-cycle a-c source. The total current drawn by the circuit can be found by adding the currents in each branch. However, if they are not in phase, they must be added vectorially. The phase relations in the circuit are shown in Fig. 18-12a. The current in the resistance is in phase with the voltage, and the current in the inductance lags the voltage by 90°.

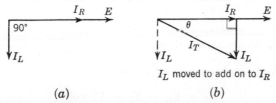

I_L moved to add on to I_R

(a)   (b)

FIG. 18-12. (a) Vector diagram for a parallel a-c circuit containing resistance and inductance. (b) I_T represents the vector sum of I_R and I_L.

Addition of the Vectors. In Fig. 18-12b, the total current I_T is obtained by adding the vector I_L to the vector I_R. Place the tail of I_L on the head of I_R, and draw it in its original direction and length. The distance from the origin of vectors to the head of the final vector is the sum of the vectors. In this instance, the vector I_T represents the sum of the vectors I_R and I_L. The phase angle θ is the angle by which the total current *lags* behind the total voltage. By applying the Pythagorean theorem to Fig. 18-12b, we obtain

Formula

$$I_T^2 = I_R^2 + I_L^2 \qquad (18\text{-}1)$$

By Ohm's law,

$$E_T = I_T \times Z \qquad (17\text{-}9)$$

By trigonometry,

$$\cos\theta = \frac{a}{h}$$

Formula

$$\cos\theta = \frac{I_R}{I_T} \tag{18-2}$$

The power is still given by

$$P = E \times I \times \cos\theta \tag{17-3}$$

Example 18-4. A toy electric-train semaphore is made of a 24-ohm lamp in parallel with a solenoid coil of 30 ohms inductive reactance. If it operates from the 12-volt winding of the 60-cycle power transformer, find (a) the total current, (b) the impedance, (c) the phase angle, and (d) the power drawn.

Solution: The diagram of [the circuit is shown in] Fig. 18-13.

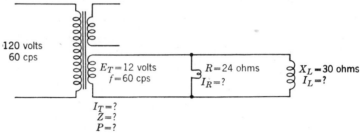

120 volts
60 cps

$E_T = 12$ volts
$f = 60$ cps

$R = 24$ ohms
$I_R = ?$

$X_L = 30$ ohms
$I_L = ?$

$I_T = ?$
$Z = ?$
$P = ?$

Fig. 18-13. An a-c parallel circuit containing resistance and inductance.

a. Find the branch currents. Since

$$E_T = E_R = E_L = 12 \text{ volts} \tag{5-1}$$

$$E_R = I_R \times R \qquad\qquad E_L = I_L \times X_L$$
$$12 = I_R \times 24 \qquad\qquad 12 = I_L \times 30$$
$$I_R = \frac{12}{24} = 0.5 \text{ amp} \qquad I_L = \frac{12}{30} = 0.4 \text{ amp}$$

Find the total current.

$$I_T{}^2 = I_R{}^2 + I_L{}^2 = 0.5^2 + 0.4^2 \tag{18-1}$$
$$= 0.25 + 0.16$$
$$I_T{}^2 = 0.41$$
$$I_T = \sqrt{0.41} = 0.64 \text{ amp} \qquad Ans.$$

b.

$$E_T = I_T \times Z \tag{17-9}$$
$$12 = 0.64 \times Z$$
$$Z = \frac{12}{0.64} = 18.75 \text{ ohms} \qquad Ans.$$

c.
$$\cos \theta = \frac{I_R}{I_T} = \frac{0.5}{0.64} = 0.7812 \qquad (18\text{-}2)$$
$$\theta = 39° \qquad Ans.$$

d.
$$P = E \times I \times \cos \theta = 12 \times 0.64 \times \cos 39° \qquad (17\text{-}3)$$
$$= 12 \times 0.64 \times 0.781$$
$$P = 6 \text{ watts} \qquad Ans.$$

In the parallel circuit, the total current of 0.64 amp lags the total voltage of 12 volts by 39°.

Example 18-5. The purpose of the "high-pass" circuit shown in Fig. 18-14 is to permit high frequencies to pass on to the load but to prevent the passage of low frequencies. Find the effectiveness of the circuit by calculating (a) the branch currents, (b) the total current, and (c) the per cent of the total current in the resistor for (1) a 1-kc audio frequency and (2) a 1,000-kc radio frequency.

Solution: The diagram for the circuit is shown in Fig. 18-14.

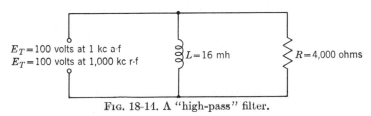

$E_T = 100$ volts at 1 kc a-f
$E_T = 100$ volts at 1,000 kc r-f
$L = 16$ mh
$R = 4,000$ ohms

FIG. 18-14. A "high-pass" filter.

1. For the 1-kc audio frequency, $f = 1,000$ cps, $L = 0.016$ henry.

a.
$$X_L = 6.28fL = 6.28 \times 1,000 \times 0.016 \qquad (15\text{-}3)$$
$$X_L = 6.28 \times 16 = 100 \text{ ohms} \qquad Ans.$$

Find the branch currents. Since

$$E_T = E_R = E_L = 100 \text{ volts} \qquad (5\text{-}1)$$

$E_R = I_R \times R$
$100 = I_R \times 4,000$

$I_R = \dfrac{100}{4,000} = 0.025$ amp

$E_L = I_L \times X_L$
$100 = I_L \times 100$

$I_L = \dfrac{100}{100} = 1$ amp

b.
$$I_T{}^2 = I_R{}^2 + I_L{}^2 = 0.025^2 + 1^2 \qquad (18\text{-}1)$$
$$= 0.000625 + 1$$
$$I_T{}^2 = 1.000625$$
$$I_T = \sqrt{1.000625} = 1 \text{ amp} \qquad Ans.$$

c. Find the per cent of the total current passing through the resistor.

$$\text{Per cent} = \frac{I_R}{I_T} \times 100 = \frac{0.025}{1} \times 100 = 2.5\% \qquad Ans.$$

That is, 2.5 per cent of the 1-kc audio frequency passes through the resistor.

2. For the 1,000-kc radio frequency: Since 1,000 kc is 1,000 times as large as the audio frequency of 1 kc, the X_L at 1,000 kc will be equal to 1,000 times the X_L at 1 kc. Therefore,

$$X_L = 1,000 \times 100 = 100,000 \text{ ohms}$$

Find the branch currents.   Since

a. $$E_T = E_R = E_L = 100 \text{ volts} \tag{5-1}$$

$$E_R = I_R \times R \qquad\qquad E_L = I_L \times X_L$$
$$100 = I_R \times 4,000 \qquad\qquad 100 = I_L \times 100,000$$

$$I_R = \frac{100}{4,000} = 0.025 \text{ amp} \qquad I_L = \frac{100}{100,000} = 0.001 \text{ amp}$$

b. $$I_T{}^2 = I_R{}^2 + I_L{}^2 = 0.025^2 + 0.001^2 \tag{18-1}$$
$$= 0.000625 + 0.000001$$
$$I_T{}^2 = 0.000626$$
$$I_T = \sqrt{0.000626} = 0.025 \text{ amp} \qquad Ans.$$

c. Find the per cent of the total current passing through the resistor.

$$\text{Per cent} = \frac{I_R}{I_T} \times 100 = \frac{0.025}{0.025} \times 100 = 100\% \qquad Ans.$$

That is, practically 100 per cent of the 1,000-kc radio frequency passes through the resistor.

The circuit is evidently a good high-pass circuit, since it passes practically 100 per cent of the high radio frequency and only 2.5 per cent of the low audio frequency.   The majority of the low audio frequency finds an easy path through the coil (I_L for the 1-kc audio frequency equals the total current of 1 amp).

Problems

1. A 24-ohm resistor and a 10-ohm inductive reactance are in parallel across a 120-volt, 60-cycle a-c line.   Find (a) the total current, (b) the impedance, (c) the phase angle, and (d) the power drawn.

2. Repeat Prob. 1 for a 1,000-ohm resistor and a 100-ohm inductive reactance.

3. A 50-ohm resistor and a 0.2-henry coil are in parallel across a 100-volt, 100-cps a-c line.   Find (a) the total current, (b) the impedance, (c) the phase angle, and (d) the power drawn.

4. In Fig. 18-15a, find the per cent of the total a-f current that passes through the resistor.   Find the per cent of the total r-f current that passes through the resistor.   On the basis of these answers, may the circuit be classified as a high-pass circuit?

5. Repeat Prob. 4 for the circuit shown in Fig. 18-15b.

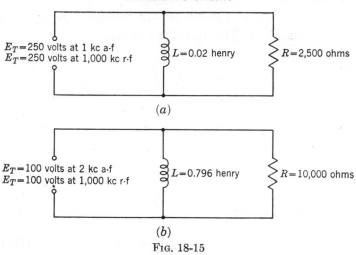

(a)

(b)

Fig. 18-15

JOB 18-3: RESISTANCE AND CAPACITANCE IN PARALLEL

Figure 18-17 shows a 20-ohm resistance and a 15-ohm capacitive reactance in parallel across a 60-volt 60-cycle a-c source. The total current drawn by the circuit can be found by adding the currents in each branch. However, if they are not in phase, they must be added vectorially. The phase relations in the circuit are shown in Fig. 18-16a. The current in the resistance I_R is in phase with the voltage, and the current in the capacitor I_c leads the voltage by 90°.

Addition of the Vectors. In Fig. 18-16b, the total current I_T is obtained by adding the vector I_c to the vector I_R. Place the tail of I_c

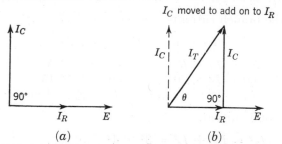

(a) (b)

Fig. 18-16. (a) Vector diagram for a parallel a-c circuit containing resistance and capacitance. (b) I_T represents the vector sum of I_R and I_c.

on the head of I_R, and draw it in its original direction and length. The distance from the origin of the vectors to the head of the final vector is the sum of the vectors. In this instance, the vector I_T represents the sum of the vectors I_R and I_c. The angle θ is the angle

by which the total current *leads* the total voltage.   By applying the
Pythagorean theorem to Fig. 18-16*b*, we obtain

Formula

$$I_T{}^2 = I_R{}^2 + I_c{}^2 \tag{18-3}$$

By Ohm's law,

$$E_T = I_T \times Z \tag{17-9}$$

By trigonometry,

$$\cos \theta = \frac{a}{h}$$

$$\cos \theta = \frac{I_R}{I_T} \tag{18-2}$$

The power is still given by

$$P = E \times I \times \cos \theta \tag{17-3}$$

Example 18-6. A 20-ohm resistor and a capacitor of 15 ohms
capacitive reactance at 60 cycles are connected in parallel across a
60-volt 60-cycle a-c source.   Find (*a*) the total current, (*b*) the impedance, (*c*) the phase angle, and (*d*) the power drawn by the circuit.
Solution: The diagram for the circuit is shown in Fig. 18-17.

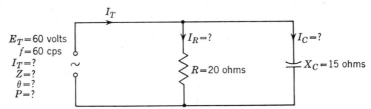

Fig. 18-17. An a-c parallel circuit containing resistance and capacitance.

a. Find the branch currents.   Since

$$E_T = E_R = E_c = 60 \text{ volts} \tag{5-1}$$

$$\begin{array}{ll} E_R = I_R \times R & E_c = I_c \times X_c \\ 60 = I_R \times 20 & 60 = I_c \times 15 \\ I_R = \tfrac{60}{20} = 3 \text{ amp} & I_c = \tfrac{60}{15} = 4 \text{ amp} \end{array}$$

Find the total current.

$$I_T{}^2 = I_R{}^2 + I_c{}^2 = 3^2 + 4^2 \tag{18-3}$$
$$= 9 + 16$$
$$I_T{}^2 = 25$$
$$I_T = \sqrt{25} = 5 \text{ amp} \qquad Ans.$$

b.
$$E_T = I_T \times Z \tag{17-9}$$
$$60 = 5 \times Z$$
$$Z = \tfrac{60}{5} = 12 \text{ ohms} \qquad Ans.$$

c.
$$\cos \theta = \frac{I_R}{I_T} = \frac{3}{5} = 0.6000 \qquad (18\text{-}2)$$
$$\theta = 53° \qquad Ans.$$

d.
$$P = E \times I \times \cos \theta = 60 \times 5 \times \cos 53° \qquad (17\text{-}3)$$
$$= 60 \times 5 \times 0.6$$
$$P = 180 \text{ watts} \qquad Ans.$$

In the parallel circuit, the total current of 5 amp leads the total voltage of 60 volts by 53°.

Example 18-7. The purpose of the "low-pass" circuit shown in Fig. 18-18 is to permit low frequencies to pass on to the load but to prevent the passage of high frequencies. Find the effectiveness of the circuit by calculating the per cent of the total current in the resistor for (*a*) a 1-kc audio-frequency and (*b*) a 1,000-kc radio frequency.
Solution: The diagram for the circuit is shown in Fig. 18-18.

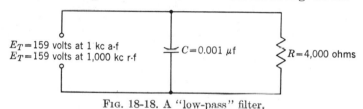

Fig. 18-18. A "low-pass" filter.

The division of the total current in a parallel a-c circuit is similar to the division of the current in a parallel d-c circuit. In Job 5-9, the formulas for the division of the total current in a parallel d-c circuit [formulas (5-6) and (5-7)] was illustrated in Example 5-25. In a-c circuits, the formula becomes

$$I_1 = \frac{Z_2}{Z_1 + Z_2} \times I_T \qquad (18\text{-}4)$$

In a resistance-capacitance circuit, we may use

Formula

$$I_R = \frac{X_c}{R + X_c} \times I_T \qquad (18\text{-}5)$$

The fraction $X_c/(R + X_c)$ represents the portion of the total current passing through the resistor. It may be changed to a per cent by multiplying by 100.

a. Find the reactance of the capacitor to the 1-kc frequency.

$$X_c = \frac{159,000}{f \times C} = \frac{159,000}{1000 \times 0.001} \qquad (16\text{-}6)$$

$$X_c = \frac{159,000}{1} = 159,000 \text{ ohms} \qquad Ans.$$

Find the per cent of the total current in the resistor.

$$\text{Per cent} = \frac{X_c}{R + X_c} \times 100$$

$$= \frac{159,000}{4,000 + 159,000} \times 100$$

$$\text{Per cent} = \frac{159,000}{163,000} \times 100 = 97.5\% \qquad Ans.$$

b. Find the reactance of the capacitor to the 1,000-kc frequency.

$$X_c = \frac{159,000}{f \times C} = \frac{159,000}{1,000,000 \times 0.001} \qquad (16\text{-}6)$$

$$X_c = \frac{159,000}{1,000} = 159 \text{ ohms} \qquad Ans.$$

Find the per cent of the total current in the resistor.

$$\text{Per cent} = \frac{X_c}{R + X_c} \times 100$$

$$= \frac{159}{159 + 159,000} \times 100$$

$$\text{Per cent} = \frac{159}{159,159} \times 100 = 0.09\% \qquad Ans.$$

That is, practically all the 1-kc current goes through the resistor and practically none of the 1,000-kc current gets through. The circuit is evidently, then, a good low-pass circuit. The majority of the 1,000-kc r-f current finds an easy path through the low reactance of the capacitor at this high frequency.

Problems

1. An 8-ohm resistor and a 15-ohm capacitive reactance are in parallel across a 120-volt 60-cycle a-c line. Find (*a*) the total current, (*b*) the impedance, (*c*) the phase angle, and (*d*) the power drawn by the circuit.

2. A 26.5-ohm resistor and a 3-μf capacitor are in parallel across a 106-volt 1-kc a-c source. Find (*a*) the total current, (*b*) the impedance, (*c*) the phase angle, and (*d*) the power drawn.

3. Repeat Prob. 1 for a 120-ohm resistor and a 60-ohm capacitive reactance.

4. An 8,000-ohm cathode resistor is bypassed with a 4-μf capacitor in a 500-cps circuit as shown in Fig. 18-19.

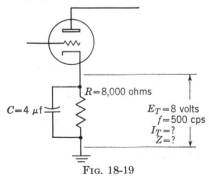

$R = 8,000$ ohms
$C = 4\ \mu f$
$E_T = 8$ volts
$f = 500$ cps
$I_T = ?$
$Z = ?$

FIG. 18-19

If the voltage drop across the combination is 8 volts, find (a) the total current and (b) the impedance of the combination.

5. In Fig. 18-20a, find the per cent of the total a-f current that passes through the resistor. Find the per cent of the total r-f current that passes through the resistor. On the basis of these answers, may the circuit be classified as a low-pass circuit?

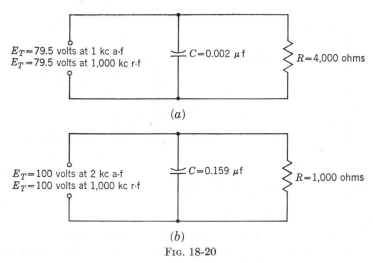

$E_T = 79.5$ volts at 1 kc a-f
$E_T = 79.5$ volts at 1,000 kc r-f $C = 0.002 \mu f$ $R = 4,000$ ohms

(a)

$E_T = 100$ volts at 2 kc a-f
$E_T = 100$ volts at 1,000 kc r-f $C = 0.159 \mu f$ $R = 1,000$ ohms

(b)

Fig. 18-20

6. Repeat Prob. 5 for the circuit shown in Fig. 18-20b.

7. In a grid-leak circuit similar to Fig. 16-5, $C = 250 \mu\mu f$ and $R = 1$ Megohm. If a 5-kc a-f signal causes a voltage drop of 0.6 volt, find (a) the total current and (b) the impedance of the combination.

JOB 18-4: RESISTANCE, INDUCTANCE, AND CAPACITANCE IN PARALLEL

Figure 18-23 shows a 30-ohm resistor, a 40-ohm inductive reactance, and a 60-ohm capacitive reactance connected in parallel across a 120-volt 60-cycle a-c line. $I_R = 4$ amp, $I_L = 3$ amp, and $I_c = 2$ amp. The total current drawn by the circuit may be found by adding the currents in each branch. However, since the currents are not in phase, they must be added vectorially. The phase relations in the circuit are shown in Fig. 18-21a. The current in the resistor I_R is in phase with the voltage. The current in the capacitor I_c *leads* the voltage by 90°. The current in the inductance I_L *lags* the voltage by 90°. Since I_L and I_c are exactly 180° out of phase and acting in exactly *opposite* directions, the current I_L is denoted by a minus sign.

Addition of Vectors. When there are three vectors, it is best to add only two at a time. To add the vector I_c to I_L, place the tail of

I_c on the head of I_L and draw it in its original length and direction, which will be straight *up* as shown in Fig. 18-21b.   Since these vectors are acting in *opposite* directions, their *sum* is actually the *difference* between the vectors as indicated by I_d.   That is, the addition of I_c to I_L is really found by $I_d = I_L - I_c$.   After this addition, the

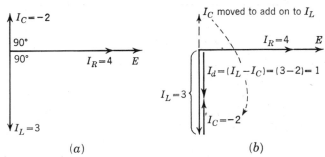

(a)   (b)

Fig. 18-21. (a) Vector diagram for a parallel a-c circuit containing resistance, inductance, and capacitance.   (b) I_d represents the vector sum of I_L and I_c.

vector diagram looks like Fig. 18-22a.   Notice that the effect of the capacitor current has disappeared.   The 3 amp of coil current has exactly balanced the 2 amp of capacitor current and has left an excess of 1 amp of coil current.   This 1 amp of coil current must now be added to the 4 amp of resistance current.   In Fig. 18-22b, the total current I_T is obtained by adding the vector I_d to the vector I_R.   Place the tail of I_d on the head of I_R, and draw it in the proper direction.

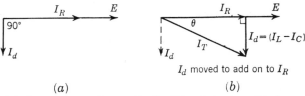

(a)   (b)

Fig. 18-22. (a) I_d represents the result of adding I_c to I_L.   (b) I_T represents the vector sum of $I_R + I_c + I_L$.

If I_c were larger than I_L, the vector I_d would have an *upward* direction. The distance from the origin of the vectors to the head of the last vector is the sum of the vectors.   In this instance, the vector I_T represents the sum of the vectors $I_R + I_L + I_c$.   The angle θ is the angle by which the total current *lags* the voltage.   If I_c were larger than I_L, the total current would *lead* the voltage by this angle.   By applying the Pythagorean theorem to Fig. 18-22b, we obtain

Formula

$$I_T{}^2 = I_R{}^2 + (I_L - I_c)^2 \qquad (18\text{-}6)$$

By Ohm's law,

$$E_T = I_T \times Z \qquad (17\text{-}9)$$

By trigonometry,

$$\cos \theta = \frac{a}{h}$$

$$\cos \theta = \frac{I_R}{I_T} \qquad (18\text{-}2)$$

The power is still given by

$$P = E \times I \times \cos \theta \qquad (17\text{-}3)$$

Example 18-8. A 30-ohm resistor, a 40-ohm inductive reactance, and a 60-ohm capacitive reactance are connected in parallel across a 120-volt 60-cycle a-c line. Find (a) the total current, (b) the impedance, (c) the phase angle, and (d) the power drawn by the circuit.

Solution: The diagram for the circuit is shown in Fig. 18-23.

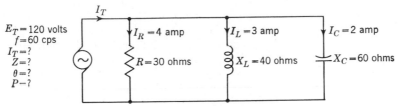

$E_T = 120$ volts
$f = 60$ cps
$I_T = ?$
$Z = ?$
$\theta = ?$
$P = ?$

$I_R = 4$ amp $R = 30$ ohms

$I_L = 3$ amp $X_L = 40$ ohms

$I_C = 2$ amp $X_C = 60$ ohms

I_T

Fig. 18-23. An a-c parallel circuit containing resistance, inductance, and capacitance.

a. Find the branch currents. Since

$$E_T = E_1 = E_2 = 120 \text{ volts} \qquad (5\text{-}1)$$

$$
\begin{array}{ll}
E_R = I_R \times R & E_L = I_L \times X_L \\
120 = I_R \times 30 & 120 = I_L \times 40 \\
I_R = \frac{120}{30} = 4 \text{ amp} & I_L = \frac{120}{40} = 3 \text{ amp}
\end{array}
$$

$$
\begin{array}{l}
E_c = I_c \times X_c \qquad (16\text{-}7)\\
120 = I_c \times 60 \\
I_c = \frac{120}{60} = 2 \text{ amp} \qquad Ans.
\end{array}
$$

Find the total current.

$$
\begin{aligned}
I_T{}^2 &= I_R{}^2 + (I_L - I_c)^2 \qquad (18\text{-}6)\\
&= 4^2 + (3 - 2)^2 = 4^2 + 1^2 \\
&= 16 + 1 \\
I_T{}^2 &= 17 \\
I_T &= \sqrt{17} = 4.12 \text{ amp} \qquad Ans.
\end{aligned}
$$

b.
$$E_T = I_T \times Z \qquad\qquad (17\text{-}9)$$
$$120 = 4.12 \times Z$$

$$Z = \frac{120}{4.12} = 29.1 \text{ ohms} \qquad Ans.$$

c.
$$\cos \theta = \frac{I_R}{I_T} = \frac{4}{4.12} = 0.9708 \qquad (18\text{-}2)$$
$$\theta = 14° \qquad Ans.$$

d.
$$P = E \times I \times \cos \theta = 120 \times 4.12 \times \cos 14° \qquad (17\text{-}3)$$
$$= 120 \times 4.12 \times 0.971$$
$$P = 480 \text{ watts} \qquad Ans.$$

Problems

1. A 24-ohm resistor, a 6-ohm inductive reactance, and a 15-ohm capacitive reactance are in parallel across a 120-volt 60-cycle line. Find (*a*) the total current, (*b*) the impedance, (*c*) the phase angle, and (*d*) the power drawn by the circuit.

2. Repeat Prob. 1 for a 30-ohm resistor, a 60-ohm inductive reactance, and a 40-ohm capacitive reactance across the same line in parallel.

3. A 50-ohm resistor, a 0.02-henry coil, and a 3-μf capacitor are connected in parallel across a 100-volt 1-kc a-c source. Find (*a*) the reactance of the coil and capacitor, (*b*) the current drawn by each branch, (*c*) the total current, (*d*) the impedance, (*e*) the phase angle, and (*f*) the power drawn by the circuit.

4. Repeat Prob. 3 for a 2,200-ohm resistor, a 20-henry coil, and a 0.8-μf capacitor in parallel across a 220-volt 60-cycle a-c line.

JOB 18-5: PARALLEL-SERIES A-C CIRCUITS

Up to this point we have been considering only circuits which contained only "pure" inductances and capacitances. Actually, such pure components do not exist. There is always some resistance in every coil or capacitor. This resistance must be taken into account whenever the resistance is an appreciable value as compared with the reactance of the component. In addition, most motor loads may be considered to be a series combination of resistance and inductance or resistance and capacitance. For example, an *induction motor* may be considered to be a series combination of resistance and inductance in which the current *lags* behind the impressed voltage. A *synchronous motor* may be considered to be a series combination of resistance and capacitance in which the current *leads* the impressed voltage. The amount of lead or lag depends on the relative amounts of resistance in series with the inductance or capacitance.

Example 18-9.   An induction motor of 5 ohms impedance draws a current lagging by 26°.   It is in parallel with a synchronous motor of 12 ohms impedance which draws a current leading by 37°.   If the applied voltage is 120 volts at 60 cps, find (*a*) the current drawn by each motor, (*b*) the total current drawn, (*c*) the impedance, (*d*) the phase angle, and (*e*) the power drawn by the circuit.

Solution: The diagram for the circuit is shown in Fig. 18-24.

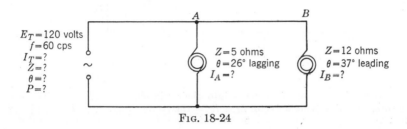

FIG. 18-24

a. Find the current in each branch.   Since

$$E_T = E_A = E_B = 120 \text{ volts} \qquad (5\text{-}1)$$

$$E_A = I_A \times Z_A \qquad E_B = I_B \times Z_B$$
$$120 = I_A \times 5 \qquad 120 = I_B \times 12$$
$$I_A = \tfrac{120}{5} = 24 \text{ amp lagging} \qquad I_B = \tfrac{120}{12} = 10 \text{ amp leading}$$

b. The total current is found by adding the currents in the two branches.   However, they are out of phase and must be added vectorially.   The phase relations are shown in Fig. 18-25.   This diagram

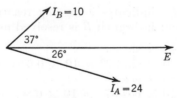

FIG. 18-25. Leading and lagging currents in a parallel circuit.

indicates that the current in branch *A* *lags* the voltage by 26° and the current in branch *B* *leads* the voltage by 37°.   To add vectors which are out of phase by angles *other* than 90°, each vector must be *resolved* into its component parts which are at right angles to each other. This is shown for each current in Fig. 18-26.   The horizontal component is called the "in-phase" component I_x.   The vertical component is called the "reactive" component I_y.   This resolution into components is merely a reversal of the process of adding vectors.   In Fig. 18-26*a*, by trigonometry, we obtain

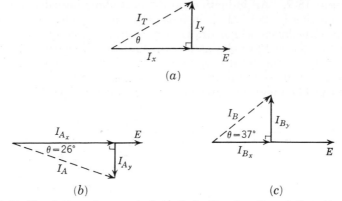

FIG. 18-26. Resolution of currents into their "in-phase" and "reactive" components. (a) Resolving a vector I_T. I_T = the vector sum of $I_x + I_y$. (b) Resolving a vector I_A. I_A = the vector sum of $I_{A_x} + I_{A_y}$. (c) Resolving a vector I_B. I_B = the vector sum of $I_{B_x} + I_{B_y}$.

Formulas

$$\sin \theta = \frac{I_y}{I_T} \qquad\qquad \cos \theta = \frac{I_x}{I_T}$$

$$I_y = I_T \times \sin \theta \qquad (18\text{-}7) \qquad I_x = I_T \times \cos \theta \qquad (18\text{-}8)$$

Resolving, in Fig. 18-26b, the current in branch A into its components,

$$\begin{aligned}
I_{A_y} &= I_A \times \sin \theta & (18\text{-}7)\\
&= 24 \times \sin 26° = 24 \times 0.44 = -10.56 \text{ amp}\\
I_{A_x} &= I_A \times \cos \theta & (18\text{-}8)\\
&= 24 \times \cos 26° = 24 \times 0.9 = 21.6 \text{ amp}
\end{aligned}$$

The minus sign in I_{A_y} indicates a lagging reactive component. In Fig. 18-26c, the current in branch B is resolved into its components.

$$\begin{aligned}
I_{B_y} &= I_B \times \sin \theta & (18\text{-}7)\\
&= 10 \times \sin 37° = 10 \times 0.6 = 6 \text{ amp}\\
I_{B_x} &= I_B \times \cos \theta & (18\text{-}8)\\
&= 10 \times \cos 37° = 10 \times 0.8 = 8 \text{ amp}
\end{aligned}$$

Addition of Vectors. Vector I_A and vector I_B may now be added by adding the components of the vectors. Since all the x components are in phase, they may be added arithmetically. Since all the y components are in phase, they also may be added arithmetically. Care must be taken to use the proper signs. x components to the right are plus (+) and to the left are minus (−). y components upward are plus (+) and downward are minus (−).

Formulas

$$I_{T_x} = I_{A_x} + I_{B_x} \qquad\qquad (18\text{-}9)$$
$$I_{T_y} = I_{A_y} + I_{B_y} \qquad\qquad (18\text{-}10)$$

Therefore,

$$I_{T_x} = I_{A_x} + I_{B_x} \tag{18-9}$$
$$= 21.6 + 8 = 29.6 \text{ amp}$$
$$I_{T_y} = I_{A_y} + I_{B_y} \tag{18-10}$$
$$= -10.56 + 6 = -4.56 \text{ amp}$$

Now, the total x component I_{T_x} and the total y component I_{T_y} may be added vectorially. Figure 18-27a shows the components for both branches drawn on the same voltage base. Figure 18-27b shows the total of the horizontal, or "in-phase," currents and the total of the vertical, or "reactive," currents. Figure 18-27c shows the vector sum

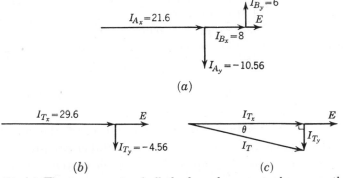

(a)

(b)   (c)

FIG. 18-27. (a) The components of all the branch currents drawn on the same voltage base. (b) $I_{T_x} = I_{A_x} + I_{B_x}$ and $I_{T_y} = I_{A_y} + I_{B_y}$. (c) I_T represents the vector sum of I_{T_x} and I_{T_y}.

of the these total components. I_T represents the total current in the circuit. The angle θ represents the angle by which the total current *lags* the voltage in this circuit. If the sum of the reactive components were positive, the current would lead the voltage by this angle θ. In Fig. 18-27c, by the Pythagorean theorem, we obtain

Formula

$$I_T{}^2 = (I_{T_x})^2 + (I_{T_y})^2 \tag{18-11}$$

By Ohm's law,

$$E_T = I_T \times Z \tag{17-9}$$

By trigonometry, we obtain

Formula

$$\cos \theta = \frac{I_{T_x}}{I_T} \tag{18-12}$$

The power is still given by

$$P = E \times I \times \cos \theta \tag{17-3}$$

We may now proceed to find the total current I_T.

$$I_T{}^2 = (I_{T_x})^2 + (I_{T_y})^2 \qquad\qquad (18\text{-}11)$$
$$= (29.6)^2 + (-4.56)^2$$
$$= 876.2 + 20.8$$
$$I_T{}^2 = 897$$
$$I_T = \sqrt{897} = 30 \text{ amp} \qquad (approx) \qquad Ans.$$

c.
$$\cos\theta = \frac{I_{T_x}}{I_T} = \frac{29.6}{30} = 0.986 \qquad\qquad (18\text{-}12)$$
$$\theta = 10° \; lagging \qquad Ans.$$

d.
$$E_T = I_T \times Z \qquad\qquad (17\text{-}9)$$
$$120 = 30 \times Z$$
$$Z = \tfrac{120}{30} = 4 \text{ ohms} \qquad Ans.$$

e. $P = E \times I \times \cos\theta = 120 \times 30 \times \cos 10° \qquad\qquad (17\text{-}3)$
$$P = 120 \times 30 \times 0.986 = 3,546 \text{ watts} \qquad Ans.$$

From this last example we can determine the procedure to follow in solving parallel-series a-c circuits:

1. Find (a) the reactance, (b) the impedance, (c) the current, and (d) the phase angle for each branch of the parallel circuit.

2. Draw the vector diagram for the branch currents on the same voltage base.

3. Resolve the current in each branch into its components.

$$I_y = I_T \times \sin\theta \qquad\qquad (18\text{-}7)$$
$$I_x = I_T \times \cos\theta \qquad\qquad (18\text{-}8)$$

Note: y components of lagging currents are negative $(-)$. y components of leading currents are positive $(+)$.

4. Find the total in-phase current I_{T_x} and the total reactive current I_{T_y}.

$$I_{T_x} = I_{A_x} + I_{B_x} \qquad\qquad (18\text{-}9)$$
$$I_{T_y} = I_{A_y} + I_{B_y} \qquad\qquad (18\text{-}10)$$

5. Find the total current.

$$I_T{}^2 = (I_{T_x})^2 + (I_{T_y})^2 \qquad\qquad (18\text{-}11)$$

6. Find the impedance.
$$E_T = I_T \times Z \qquad\qquad (17\text{-}9)$$

7. Find the phase angle.

$$\cos\theta = \frac{I_{T_x}}{I_T} \qquad\qquad (18\text{-}12)$$

8. Find the total power.

$$P = E \times I \times \cos\theta \qquad\qquad (17\text{-}3)$$

Example 18-10. An induction motor of 6 ohms resistance and 8 ohms inductive reactance is in parallel with a synchronous motor of 8 ohms resistance and 15 ohms capacitive reactance and a third parallel branch of 15 ohms resistance.   Find (*a*) the total current drawn from a 150-volt 60-cycle source, (*b*) the total impedance, (*c*) the phase angle, and (*d*) the power drawn by the circuit.

Solution: The diagram for the circuit is shown in Fig. 18-28.

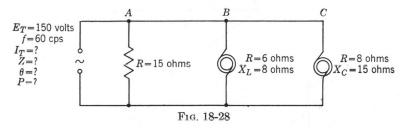

$E_T = 150$ volts
$f = 60$ cps
$I_T = ?$
$Z = ?$
$\theta = ?$
$P = ?$

$R = 15$ ohms

$R = 6$ ohms
$X_L = 8$ ohms

$R = 8$ ohms
$X_C = 15$ ohms

Fig. 18-28

a. 1. Find the series impedance, current, and phase angle for each branch.

For branch A:

$$Z = R = 15 \text{ ohms}$$

$$I_A = \frac{E}{R} = \frac{150}{15} = 10 \text{ amp} \qquad (2\text{-}1)$$

$$\cos \theta = \frac{R}{Z} = \frac{15}{15} = 1 \qquad (17\text{-}8)$$

Therefore $\theta = 0°$

The current is in phase with the voltage.

For branch B:

$$Z = \sqrt{R^2 + X_L{}^2} = \sqrt{6^2 + 8^2} = \sqrt{36 + 64} = \sqrt{100} = 10 \text{ ohms}$$

$$I_B = \frac{E}{Z} = \frac{150}{10} = 15 \text{ amp} \qquad (15\text{-}8)$$

$$\cos \theta = \frac{R}{Z} = \frac{6}{10} = 0.6000 \qquad (17\text{-}8)$$

Therefore $\theta = 53°$

The current *lags* the voltage by 53°.

For branch C:

$$Z = \sqrt{R^2 + X_C{}^2} = \sqrt{8^2 + 15^2} = \sqrt{64 + 225} = \sqrt{289} = 17 \text{ ohms}$$

$$I_C = \frac{E}{Z} = \frac{150}{17} = 8.8 \text{ amp} \qquad (16\text{-}7)$$

$$\cos \theta = \frac{R}{Z} = \frac{8}{17} = 0.4706 \qquad (17\text{-}8)$$

Therefore $\theta = 62°$

The current *leads* the voltage by 62°.

2. Draw the vector diagram for the branch currents on the same voltage base as shown in Fig. 18-29a.

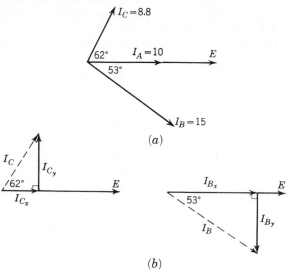

(a)

(b)

FIG. 18-29. (a) Leading and lagging currents in a parallel circuit.   (b) Resolution of each current into its "in-phase" and "reactive" components.

3. Resolve the current in each branch into its components as shown in Fig. 18-29b.   Calculate the components.

For branch A:

$$I_{A_x} = I_A \times \cos \theta \qquad\qquad (18\text{-}8)$$
$$= 10 \times \cos 0° = 10 \times 1 = 10 \text{ amp}$$
$$I_{A_y} = I_A \times \sin \theta \qquad\qquad (18\text{-}7)$$
$$= 10 \times \sin 0° = 10 \times 0 = 0 \text{ amp}$$

For branch B:

$$I_{B_x} = I_B \times \cos \theta \qquad\qquad (18\text{-}8)$$
$$= 15 \times \cos 53° = 15 \times 0.6 = 9 \text{ amp}$$
$$I_{B_y} = I_B \times \sin \theta \qquad\qquad (18\text{-}7)$$
$$= 15 \times \sin 53° = 15 \times 0.8 = -12 \text{ amp}$$

Note: The minus sign in I_{B_y} indicates a lagging reactive component.

For branch C:

$$I_{C_x} = I_C \times \cos \theta \qquad\qquad (18\text{-}8)$$
$$= 8.8 \times \cos 62° = 8.8 \times 0.470 = 4.14 \text{ amp}$$
$$I_{C_y} = I_C \times \sin \theta \qquad\qquad (18\text{-}7)$$
$$= 8.8 \times \sin 62° = 8.8 \times .88 = 7.74 \text{ amp}$$

4. Draw all the components on the same voltage base as shown in Fig. 18-30a. The total in-phase current I_{T_x} and the total reactive current I_{T_y} may now be found.

$$I_{T_x} = I_{A_x} + I_{B_x} + I_{C_x} \qquad\qquad (18\text{-}9)$$
$$= 10 + 9 + 4.14 = 23.14 \text{ amp}$$
$$I_{T_y} = I_{A_y} + I_{B_y} + I_{C_y} \qquad\qquad (18\text{-}10)$$
$$= 0 + (-12) + 7.74 = -4.26 \text{ amp}$$

Note: The minus sign in I_{T_y} indicates a lagging reactive component.

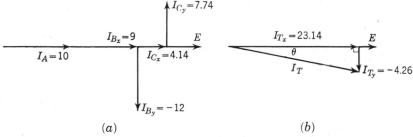

(a)   (b)

FIG. 18-30. (a) The components of all the branch currents drawn on the same voltage base. (b) I_T represents the vector sum of $I_{T_x} + I_{T_y}$.

5. Draw the vector diagram for the total current by adding I_{T_x} and I_{T_y} vectorially as shown in Fig. 18-30b. Notice that I_{T_y} is drawn downward because I_{T_y} is negative. Find I_T.

$$I_T{}^2 = (I_{T_x})^2 + (I_{T_y})^2 \qquad\qquad (18\text{-}11)$$
$$= (23.14)^2 + (-4.26)^2$$
$$= 535.5 + 18.1 = 553.6$$
$$I_T = \sqrt{553.6} = 23.5 \text{ amp lagging} \qquad Ans.$$

b. Find the impedance.

$$E_T = I_T \times Z \qquad\qquad (17\text{-}9)$$
$$150 = 23.5 \times Z$$
$$Z = \frac{150}{23.5} = 6.38 \text{ ohms} \qquad Ans.$$

c. Find the phase angle.

$$\cos \theta = \frac{I_{T_x}}{I_T} \qquad\qquad (18\text{-}12)$$
$$\cos \theta = \frac{23.14}{23.5} = 0.9847$$

Therefore $\theta = 10°$ lagging   *Ans.*

d. Find the power drawn by the circuit.

$$P = E \times I \times \cos \theta = 150 \times 23.5 \times \cos 10° \qquad (17\text{-}3)$$
$$P = 150 \times 23.5 \times 0.985 = 3{,}472 \text{ watts} \qquad Ans.$$

The total current of 23.5 amp *lags* the total voltage of 150 volts by 10°.

Example 18-11. For the circuit shown in Fig. 18-31, find (*a*) the total current, (*b*) the total impedance, (*c*) the phase angle, and (*d*) the power drawn by the circuit.

Solution: The diagram for the circuit is shown in Fig. 18-31.

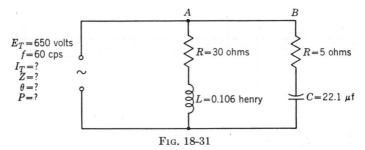

Fig. 18-31

a. 1. Find the reactance, series impedance, current, and phase angle for each branch.

For branch A:

$$X_L = 6.28fL = 6.28 \times 60 \times 0.106 = 40 \text{ ohms} \quad (15\text{-}3)$$
$$Z = \sqrt{R^2 + X_L{}^2} = \sqrt{30^2 + 40^2} \qquad (15\text{-}6)$$
$$= \sqrt{900 + 1{,}600}$$
$$Z = \sqrt{2{,}500} = 50 \text{ ohms}$$
$$I = \frac{E}{Z} = \frac{650}{50} = 13 \text{ amp} \qquad (15\text{-}8)$$
$$\cos \theta = \frac{R}{Z} = \frac{30}{50} = 0.6000 \qquad (17\text{-}8)$$

therefore
$$\theta = 53°$$

The current of 13 amp lags the total voltage by 53°.

For branch B:

$$X_c = \frac{159{,}000}{f \times C} = \frac{159{,}000}{60 \times 22.1} = 12 \text{ ohms} \qquad (16\text{-}6)$$
$$Z = \sqrt{R^2 + X_c{}^2} = \sqrt{5^2 + 12^2} \qquad (16\text{-}8)$$
$$= \sqrt{25 + 144}$$
$$Z = \sqrt{169} = 13 \text{ ohms}$$

$$I = \frac{E}{Z} = \frac{650}{13} = 50 \text{ amp} \qquad (15\text{-}8)$$

$$\cos \theta = \frac{R}{Z} = \frac{5}{13} = 0.3846 \qquad (17\text{-}8)$$

Therefore

$$\theta = 67°$$

The current of 50 amp leads the total voltage by 67°.

2. Draw the vector diagram for the branch currents on the same voltage base as shown in Fig. 18-32a.

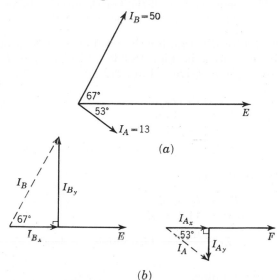

(a)

(b)

FIG. 18-32. (a) Leading and lagging currents in a parallel circuit.   (b) Resolution of each current into its "in-phase" and "reactive" components.

3. Resolve the current in each branch into its components as shown in Fig. 18-32b.   Calculate the components.

For branch A:

$I_{A_z} = I_A \times \cos \theta = 13 \times \cos 53° = 13 \times 0.6 = 7.8 \text{ amp} \quad (18\text{-}8)$
$I_{A_y} = I_A \times \sin \theta = 13 \times \sin 53° = 13 \times 0.8 = -10.4 \quad (18\text{-}7)$

For branch B:

$I_{B_z} = I_B \times \cos \theta = 50 \times \cos 67° = 50 \times 0.385 = 19.25 \quad (18\text{-}8)$
$I_{B_y} = I_B \times \sin \theta = 50 \times \sin 67° = 50 \times 0.92 = 46 \quad (18\text{-}7)$

4. Draw all the components on the same voltage base as shown in Fig. 18-33a.   The total in-phase current I_{T_z} and the total reactive current I_{T_y} may now be found.

$$I_{T_z} = I_{A_z} + I_{B_z} = 7.8 + 19.25 = 27.05 \text{ amp} \quad (18\text{-}9)$$
$$I_{T_y} = I_{A_y} + I_{B_y} = -10.4 + 46 = 35.6 \text{ amp} \quad (18\text{-}10)$$

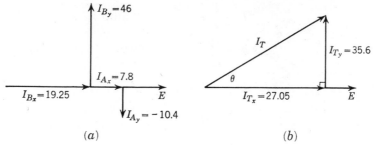

FIG. 18-33. (a) The components of all the branch currents drawn on the same voltage base. (b) I_T represents the vector sum of I_{T_x} and I_{T_y}.

5. Draw the vector diagram for the total current by adding I_{T_x} and I_{T_y} vectorially as shown in Fig. 18-33b. Notice that I_{T_y} is drawn *upward* because I_{T_y} is positive. Find I_T.

$$I_T{}^2 = (I_{T_x})^2 + (I_{T_y})^2 \qquad (18\text{-}11)$$
$$= 27.05^2 + 35.6^2$$
$$= 729 + 1{,}267 = 1{,}996$$
$$I_T = \sqrt{1{,}996} = 44.6 \text{ amp leading} \qquad Ans.$$

b. Find the impedance.

$$E_T = I_T \times Z \qquad (17\text{-}9)$$
$$650 = 44.6 \times Z$$
$$Z = \frac{650}{44.6} = 14.6 \text{ ohms} \qquad Ans.$$

c. Find the phase angle.

$$\cos \theta = \frac{I_{T_x}}{I_T} \qquad (18\text{-}12)$$
$$\cos \theta = \frac{27.05}{44.6} = 0.605$$

Therefore $\qquad\qquad \theta = 53° \text{ leading} \qquad Ans.$

d. Find the power drawn by the circuit.

$$P = E \times I \times \cos \theta = 650 \times 44.6 \times \cos 53° \qquad (17\text{-}3)$$
$$P = 650 \times 44.6 \times 0.605 = 17{,}540 \text{ watts} \qquad Ans.$$

The total current of 44.6 amp *leads* the total voltage of 650 volts by 53°.

Problems

Find (a) the total current, (b) the impedance, (c) the phase angle, and (d) the power drawn by each circuit shown in Fig. 18-34.

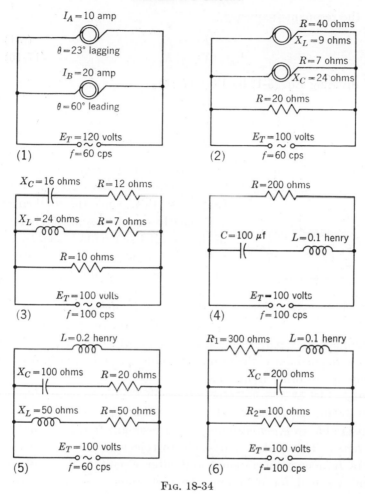

Fig. 18-34

JOB 18-6: PARALLEL RESONANCE

In a series circuit, it is possible to adjust the values of a coil and a capacitor so that their reactances will be equal for a definite frequency. The frequency at which the inductive and capacitive reactances are equal is the resonant frequency. Since the actions of the reactances are directly opposed to each other, the total reactance is zero and the impedance of the circuit becomes just the resistance of the circuit. Under these conditions, the current in the circuit will be a maximum.

Now let us arrange the coil and capacitor in *parallel* as shown in Fig. 18-35.

At the resonant frequency,

$$E_L = E_c \tag{5-1}$$
$$X_L = X_c \tag{17-16}$$

By dividing Eq. (5-1) by Eq. (17-16),

$$\frac{E_L}{X_L} = \frac{E_c}{X_c}$$

or
$$I_L = I_c \tag{18-13}$$

Since the currents are exactly opposed to each other, the total current is equal to $I_L - I_c$, or practically zero. At the resonant frequency, then, since the total current is very nearly equal to zero, the impedance of the circuit to currents at that frequency will be very large. At any other frequency, since X_L is not equal to X_c, the currents will no longer be equal. The sum of the unequal currents may be quite large, which indicates a low impedance.

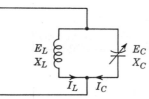

FIG. 18-35. A parallel-resonant circuit.

To summarize, a parallel-resonant circuit will offer a very large impedance to currents at the resonant frequency and a low impedance to currents at all other frequencies.

Uses.   Just as a series-resonant circuit is able to *accept* currents at the resonant frequency and reject all others, a parallel-resonant circuit is able to *reject* currents at the resonant frequency and accept all others. This makes it possible to reject or "trap" a wave of a definite frequency in antenna and filter circuits. It is also a convenient method for obtaining the high impedance required in the primary of coupling transformers.

Resonant Frequency.   The formula for the resonant frequency of a parallel circuit is the same as that for a series circuit.

$$f = \frac{159}{\sqrt{L \times C}} \tag{17-18}$$

where f = frequency, kc per second
    L = inductance, μh
    C = capacitance, μf

Example 18-12.   A 200-μh coil and a 50-$\mu\mu$f capacitor are connected in parallel to form a "wave trap" in an antenna. What is the resonant frequency that the circuit will reject?

Solution:

Given: $L = 200\ \mu h$ Find: $f = ?$
$C = 50\ \mu\mu f = 0.00005\ \mu f$

$$f = \frac{159}{\sqrt{L \times C}} \qquad\qquad (17\text{-}18)$$

$$= \frac{159}{\sqrt{200 \times 0.00005}} = \frac{159}{\sqrt{0.01}} = \frac{159}{0.1}$$

$$f = 1,590\ kc \qquad Ans.$$

Finding the Inductance or Capacitance Needed to Produce Resonance

Example 18-13. A 0.1-mh coil and a variable capacitor are connected in parallel to form the primary of an i-f transformer as shown in Fig. 18-36. If the circuit is to be resonant to 456 kc, what must be the value of the capacitor?

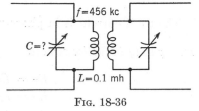

$f = 456$ kc

$C = ?$

$L = 0.1$ mh

FIG. 18-36

Solution: The diagram for the circuit is shown in Fig. 18-36.

1. Change 0.1 mh into 100 μh
2. Find the required capacitance

$$C = \frac{25,300}{f^2 \times L} \qquad\qquad (17\text{-}20)$$

$$C = \frac{25,300}{456^2 \times 100}$$

$$C = \frac{25,300}{207,900 \times 100} = 0.0012\ \mu f \qquad Ans.$$

Problems

1. Find the resonant frequency of a wave trap using a 45-$\mu\mu f$ capacitor and a 20-μh inductance.

2. Find the resonant frequency of a band-stop filter made of a 160-μh coil and a 40-$\mu\mu f$ capacitor in parallel.

3. The inductance of a parallel-resonant circuit used as a wave trap in an antenna circuit is 100 μh. What must be the value of the parallel capacitance in order to reject an 800-kc wave?

4. The capacitor of a high-impedance primary of a transformer tuned to 460 kc is 100 $\mu\mu f$. What is the value of the inductance?

5. The tank circuit of an oscillator contains a coil of 320 μh. What is the value of the capacitance at the resonant frequency of 1,000 kc?

6. The tank circuit of an impedance-coupled a-f amplifier circuit uses an inductance of 10 henrys. Find the value of the capacitance necessary to produce resonance at (*a*) 500 cps and (*b*) 1 kc.

7. What is the inductance of the coil in a 23.4-Mc trap of a video i-f amplifier which uses a capacitor of 50 $\mu\mu$f?

8. The RCA model 630TCS chassis uses an absorption-type wave trap in the second picture i-f circuit. If the trap capacitance is 56 $\mu\mu$f and it is resonant to 19.75 Mc, what is the value of the inductance?

JOB 18-7: REVIEW OF PARALLEL A-C CIRCUITS

In a purely resistive circuit:

$$E_T = E_1 = E_2 = E_3 \qquad\qquad (5\text{-}1)$$
$$E_T = I_T \times R_T \qquad\qquad (4\text{-}7)$$
$$I_T = I_1 + I_2 + I_3 \qquad\qquad (5\text{-}2)$$
$$P = E \times I \times \cos\theta \qquad\qquad (17\text{-}3)$$

The total current is in phase with the total voltage.

In a purely inductive circuit:

$$E_T = E_1 = E_2 = E_3 \qquad\qquad (5\text{-}1)$$
$$E_T = I_T \times Z \qquad\qquad (17\text{-}9)$$
$$I_T = I_1 + I_2 + I_3 \qquad\qquad (5\text{-}2)$$
$$P = E \times I \times \cos\theta \qquad\qquad (17\text{-}3)$$

The total current lags the total voltage by 90°.

In a purely capacitive circuit:

$$E_T = E_1 = E_2 = E_3 \qquad\qquad (5\text{-}1)$$
$$E_T = I_T \times Z \qquad\qquad (17\text{-}9)$$
$$I_T = I_1 + I_2 + I_3 \qquad\qquad (5\text{-}2)$$
$$P = E \times I \times \cos\theta \qquad\qquad (17\text{-}3)$$

The total current leads the total voltage by 90°.

In an a-c parallel circuit of resistance and inductance:

$$I_T{}^2 = I_R{}^2 + I_L{}^2 \qquad\qquad (18\text{-}1)$$
$$E_T = I_T \times Z \qquad\qquad (17\text{-}9)$$
$$\cos\theta = \frac{I_R}{I_T} \qquad\qquad (18\text{-}2)$$
$$P = E \times I \times \cos\theta \qquad\qquad (17\text{-}3)$$

The total current lags the total voltage by angle θ.

In an a-c parallel circuit of resistance and capacitance:

$$I_T^2 = I_R^2 + I_c^2 \qquad\qquad (18\text{-}3)$$

$$E_T = I_T \times Z \qquad\qquad (17\text{-}9)$$

$$\cos\theta = \frac{I_R}{I_T} \qquad\qquad (18\text{-}2)$$

$$P = E \times I \times \cos\theta \qquad\qquad (17\text{-}3)$$

The total current leads the total voltage by angle θ.

In an a-c parallel circuit of resistance, inductance, and capacitance:

$$I_T^2 = I_R^2 + (I_L - I_c)^2 \qquad\qquad (18\text{-}6)$$

$$E_T = I_T \times Z \qquad\qquad (17\text{-}9)$$

$$\cos\theta = \frac{I_R}{I_T} \qquad\qquad (18\text{-}2)$$

$$P = E \times I \times \cos\theta \qquad\qquad (17\text{-}3)$$

The total current will lead or lag the total voltage, depending on the values of I_L and I_c. If I_L is larger than I_c, the current will lag the voltage. If I_L is smaller than I_c, the current will lead the voltage. The angle of lead or lag is given by the angle θ.

Parallel-series A-C Circuits

1. Find the reactance, the impedance, the current, and the phase angle for each branch.

2. Resolve the current in each branch into its components.

$$I_y = I_T \times \sin\theta \qquad\qquad (18\text{-}7)$$

$$I_x = I_T \times \cos\theta \qquad\qquad (18\text{-}8)$$

(y components of lagging currents are negative.)

3. Find the total "in-phase" and total "reactive" currents.

$$I_{T_x} = I_{A_x} + I_{B_x} \qquad\qquad (18\text{-}9)$$

$$I_{T_y} = I_{A_y} + I_{B_y} \qquad\qquad (18\text{-}10)$$

4. Find the total current.

$$I_T^2 = I_{T_x}^2 + I_{T_y}^2 \qquad\qquad (18\text{-}11)$$

5. Find the impedance.

$$E_T = I_T \times Z \qquad\qquad (17\text{-}9)$$

6. Find the phase angle.

$$\cos\theta = \frac{I_{T_x}}{I_T} \qquad\qquad (18\text{-}12)$$

7. Find the total power.

$$P = E \times I \times \cos \theta \qquad (17\text{-}3)$$

Parallel Resonance. A parallel resonant circuit will offer a very large impedance to currents at the resonant frequency and a low impedance to currents at all other frequencies.

$$f = \frac{159}{\sqrt{L \times C}} \qquad (17\text{-}18)$$

where L = inductance, μh
  C = capacitance, μf
  f = frequency, kc

Finding the Inductance or Capacitance Needed to Produce a Resonant Circuit

$$L = \frac{25,300}{f^2 \times C} \qquad (17\text{-}19)$$

$$C = \frac{25,300}{f^2 \times L} \qquad (17\text{-}20)$$

where L, C, and f are measured in the same units as called for in formula (17-18).

Problems

1. Two capacitors of 500 and 750 ohms reactance, respectively, are connected in parallel across a 25-volt 25-cycle a-c source. Find (a) the total current, (b) the impedance, and (c) the power drawn by the circuit.

2. A 0.01-henry coil and a 5,000-ohm resistor are connected in parallel to form a filter circuit. Find the per cent of the total current passing through the resistor for (a) a 1-kc a-f frequency and (b) a 1,000 r-f frequency. (c) Is this filter a high-pass or a low-pass filter?

3. A 200-ohm resistor and a 0.1-henry coil are connected in parallel across a 100-volt 1-kc a-c source. Find (a) the current in each branch, (b) the total current, (c) the impedance of the circuit, (d) the phase angle, and (e) the power drawn by the circuit.

4. A 500-ohm resistor in a cathode circuit similar to Fig. 18-19 is bypassed with a 5-μf capacitor. If a 1-kc frequency causes a voltage drop of 10 volts across the resistor, find (a) the current in each branch, (b) the total current, and (c) the impedance of the combination.

5. A 3,000-ohm resistor, a 1,200-ohm inductive reactance, and an 800-ohm capacitive reactance are connected in parallel across a 240-volt line. Find (a) the total current, (b) the impedance, (c) the phase angle, and (d) the power drawn by the circuit.

6. A 0.5-μf capacitor, a 1-henry coil, and a 2,000-ohm resistor are connected in parallel across a 220-volt 60-cycle a-c line. Find (a) the total current, (b) the impedance, (c) the phase angle, and (d) the power drawn by the circuit.

7. In a circuit similar to that used for Prob. 1 in Fig. 18-34, $I_A = 8$ amp with $\theta = 30°$ lagging, $I_B = 15$ amp with $\theta = 60°$ leading, and $E_T = 120$ volts at 60 cps. Find (a) the total current, (b) the impedance, (c) the phase angle, and (d) the power drawn by the circuit.

8. In a circuit similar to that used for Prob. 6 in Fig. 18-34, $R_1 = 100$ ohms, $L = 0.2$ henry, $X_c = 500$ ohms, $R_2 = 200$ ohms, $E_T = 100$ volts, and $f = 100$ cps. Find (a) the total current, (b) the impedance, (c) the phase angle, and (d) the power drawn by the circuit.

9. A 0.001-μf capacitor and a coil are connected in parallel to form the primary of an i-f transformer similar to that shown in Fig. 18-36. What must be the inductance of the coil in order for the circuit to be resonant to a frequency of 460 kc?

10. The plate circuit of the 6J6 converter in the RCA model 648 PTK television receiver contains a 1-μh coil in parallel with a capacitance and resonant to 21.25 Mc. What is the capacitance?

Test—Parallel A-C Circuits

1. Two coils of 20 and 48 ohms reactance, respectively, are connected in parallel across a 120-volt 60-cycle a-c line. Find (a) the total current, (b) the impedance, and (c) the power drawn by the circuit.

2. A 0.1-μf capacitor, a 0.005-henry coil, and a 1,000-ohm resistor are connected in parallel across a 100-volt 10-kc a-c source. Find (a) the reactance of the coil and the capacitor, (b) the current drawn by each branch, (c) the total current, (d) the impedance, (e) the phase angle, and (f) the power drawn by the circuit.

3. In a circuit similar to that used for Prob. 1 in Fig. 18-34, $I_A = 6$ amp with $\theta = 60°$ leading, $I_B = 10$ amp with $\theta = 45°$ lagging, and $E_T = 120$ volts at 60 cps. Find (a) the total current, (b) the impedance, (c) the phase angle, and (d) the power drawn by the circuit.

4. The inductance of a high-impedance primary of a transformer is 1,000 μh. What is the value of capacitance needed to produce resonance to 460 kc?

CHAPTER 19

ALTERNATING-CURRENT POWER

JOB 19-1: POWER AND POWER FACTOR

The power in any electrical circuit is obtained by multiplying the voltage by the current flowing at that time. In a d-c circuit, the unchanging voltage E is multiplied by the unchanging current I to give the power P. The formula for this was given in Job 7-1 as $P = E \times I$. In an a-c circuit, the voltage and current are constantly changing. The power at any instant of time is obtained by multiplying the instantaneous voltage by the instantaneous current.

$$P_i = e \times i \tag{19-1}$$

Power in a Resistive Circuit. In a purely resistive circuit, each instantaneous current occurs at the same time as the instantaneous voltage which produced it. Since the worth of all the instantaneous values is the effective value, the power in a resistive circuit is found by multiplying the effective voltage by the effective current.

$$P = E \times I \tag{19-2}$$

Power in a Reactive Circuit. In an inductive circuit, the current will lag behind the voltage by some angle θ as shown in Fig. 19-1a. The power in this circuit will *not* be equal to the product of the voltage by the current, since they do not act at the same time. The actual power is equal to the voltage multiplied by *only that portion of the line current which is in phase with the voltage*. In Fig. 19-1b, OE represents the line voltage. OA represents the total line current as measured by an ammeter. This total line current may be resolved into its two component parts: OB, a component in phase with the voltage (the effective current), and BA, a component 90° out of phase with the voltage (the reactive current). By multiplying each of the current vectors of Fig. 19-1b by the line voltage, we can obtain a vector diagram for the power in an inductive circuit as shown in Fig. 19-1c. *OA* represents the *apparent power* as measured by a voltmeter and an ammeter and is equal to $P = E \times I$. This apparent power is measured in volt-amperes, *not* watts. *OB* represents the *effective power* as measured by a wattmeter *W*. *BA* represents the *reactive power* or var power.

The vector diagram of Fig. 19-1c indicates that the apparent power is made of two component parts—the effective power and the reactive

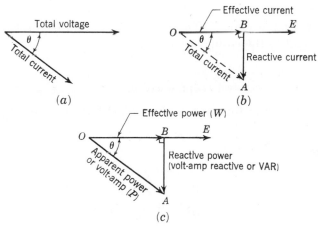

FIG. 19-1. (a) Current lags behind the voltage in an inductive circuit. (b) Resolution of the total current into its effective and reactive components. (c) Vector diagram of the power.

power. The apparent power may be likened to the power delivered to a flywheel. The *portion* of the apparent power which is delivered to the shaft to operate some device is similar to the effective power. The *portion* of the apparent power which is delivered by the flywheel *back* to the engine to keep it running is similar to the reactive power. The reactive power does no work itself. In an inductive electrical circuit it represents the power stored in the magnetic field (similar to the flywheel) and then returned to the line as the field collapses. This power merely moves back and forth between the coil and the line. In Fig. 19-1c,

$$\cos \theta = \frac{W}{P} \tag{19-3}$$

By cross multiplication,

$$W = P \times \cos \theta \tag{19-4}$$

Solving for P,

$$P = \frac{W}{\cos \theta} \tag{19-5}$$

where P = apparent power, volt-amp
  W = effective power, watts
  θ = phase angle of the circuit, degrees

Power Factor.   The ratio of the effective power as read by a watt-meter W to the apparent power P is called the *power factor* (pf).

Formula

$$\text{pf} = \frac{W}{P} \tag{19-6}$$

By comparing formulas (19-3) and (19-6), we can see that the power factor is equal to the cosine of angle θ.

Formula

$$\text{pf} = \cos\theta \tag{19-7}$$

By substituting pf for $\cos\theta$ in formulas (19-3) to (19-5), we obtain

Formulas

$$\text{pf} = \frac{W}{P} \tag{19-6}$$

$$W = P \times \text{pf} \tag{19-8}$$

$$P = \frac{W}{\text{pf}} \tag{19-9}$$

The power factor may be expressed as a decimal or as a per cent. For example, a pf of 0.8 may be written as 80 per cent.   In this sense, the pf describes the *portion* of the volt-ampere input which is actually effective in operating the device.   Thus, an 80 per cent pf means that the device uses only 80 per cent of the volt-ampere input in order to operate.

Power in a Capacitive Circuit.   An identical set of relationships exists in a capacitive circuit, except that the apparent power P will *lead* the effective power W by an angle θ.

Example 19-1.   Find the power factor of a washing-machine motor if it draws 5 amp and 440 watts from a 110-volt 60-cycle line.

Solution:

Given: I = 5 amp   Find: pf = ?
  E = 110 volts
  W = 440 watts
  f = 60 cps

$$\text{pf} = \frac{W}{P} = \frac{440}{110 \times 5} = \frac{440}{550} = 0.8 = 80\% \qquad Ans. \quad (19\text{-}6)$$

Example 19-2.   A capacitor-type motor operating at a 70 per cent pf draws 10 amp from a 110-volt a-c line. Find (a) the apparent power and (b) the effective power.

Solution:

$$\text{Given: pf} = 70\% = 0.70 \qquad \text{Find: } P = ?$$
$$I = 10 \text{ amp} \qquad\qquad\qquad W = ?$$
$$E = 110 \text{ volts}$$

a. $P = I \times E = 10 \times 110 = 1{,}100$ volt-amp   *Ans.*   (7-1)
b. $W = P \times \text{pf} = 1{,}100 \times 0.70 = 770$ watts   *Ans.*   (19-8)

Example 19-3.   A capacitor-type motor draws 750 watts at a power factor of 75 per cent.   Find the volt-ampere of apparent power drawn by the motor.

Solution:

$$\text{Given: } W = 750 \text{ watts} \qquad \text{Find: } P = ?$$
$$\text{pf} = 75\% = 0.75$$

$$P = \frac{W}{\text{pf}} = \frac{750}{0.75} = 1{,}000 \text{ volt-amp} \qquad Ans. \qquad (19\text{-}9)$$

Example 19-4.   An impedance coil of 3 ohms resistance and 4 ohms inductive reactance is connected across a 24-volt 60-cycle a-c source. Find (a) the pf, (b) the current drawn, and (c) the effective power consumed by the coil.

Solution:

$$\text{Given: } R = 3 \text{ ohms} \qquad \text{Find: pf} = ?$$
$$X_L = 4 \text{ ohms} \qquad\qquad I = ?$$
$$E = 24 \text{ volts} \qquad\qquad W = ?$$
$$f = 60 \text{ cps}$$

a. Find the impedance.

$$Z = \sqrt{R^2 + X_L^2} = \sqrt{3^2 + 4^2} = \sqrt{9 + 16} = \sqrt{25} = 5 \text{ ohms}$$

Find the pf.   Since

$$\cos \theta = \frac{R}{Z} \qquad\qquad\qquad (17\text{-}8)$$

and
$$\cos \theta = \text{pf} \qquad\qquad\qquad (19\text{-}7)$$
we obtain

Formula

$$\text{pf} = \frac{R}{Z} \qquad\qquad\qquad (19\text{-}10)$$

where pf = power factor of the circuit
      R = resistance of circuit, ohms
      Z = impedance of circuit, ohms

Therefore,

$$\text{pf} = \frac{R}{Z} = \frac{3}{5} = 0.60 = 60\% \qquad Ans.$$

b. Find the current drawn.

$$I = \frac{E}{Z} = \frac{24}{5} = 4.8 \text{ amp} \qquad Ans. \qquad (17\text{-}9)$$

c. Find the effective power.   Since

$$W = P \times \text{pf} \qquad (19\text{-}8)$$

and
$$P = E \times I \qquad (7\text{-}1)$$

By substituting $E \times I$ for P in formula (19-8), we obtain

Formula

$$W = E \times I \times \text{pf} \qquad (19\text{-}11)$$

where W = effective power, watts
E = effective voltage, volts
I = effective current, amp
pf = power factor

Therefore,

$$W = E \times I \times \text{pf} \qquad (19\text{-}11)$$
$$W = 24 \times 4.8 \times 0.6$$
$$W = 69 \text{ watts} \qquad Ans.$$

Example 19-5.   An induction motor operating at 80 per cent pf draws 1,056 watts from a 110-volt a-c line.   Find the current.

Solution:

Given: pf = 80%   Find: I = ?
W = 1,056 watts
E = 110 volts

$$W = E \times I \times \text{pf} \qquad (19\text{-}11)$$
$$1{,}056 = 110 \times I \times 0.8$$
$$1{,}056 = 88 \times I$$

$$I = \frac{1{,}056}{88} = 12 \text{ amp} \qquad Ans.$$

Problems

1. Find the power factor of a refrigerator motor if it draws 288 watts and 3 amp from a 120-volt 60-cycle line.

2. Find the effective power used by a capacitor-type jig-saw motor operating at a power factor of 75 per cent if it draws 4 amp at 120 volts.

3. The lights and motors in a shop draw 16 kw of power.   The power factor of the entire load is 80 per cent.   Find the volt-amperes of power delivered to the shop.

4. A capacitance of 5 ohms resistance and 12 ohms reactance is connected across a 117-volt 60-cycle a-c line. Find the power factor and the effective power.

5. A motor operating at 90 per cent pf draws 270 watts from a 120-volt line. Find the current drawn.

6. Find the pf of a motor in an air-conditioning unit if it draws 500 watts and 5 amp from a 120-volt line.

7. An industrial load draws 15 amp from a 230-volt line at a pf of 85 per cent. Find the volt-amperes of apparent power and the effective power taken from the line.

8. A 40-volt emf at 1 kc is impressed across a loudspeaker of 5,000 ohms resistance and 1.5 henrys inductance. Find (a) the impedance, (b) the pf, (c) the current drawn, and (d) the effective power drawn by the speaker.

9. A 10-hp motor operates at an efficiency of 80 per cent and a pf of 90 per cent. Find the volt-amperes of apparent power delivered to the motor. *Hint:* Find the watt input to the motor by the efficiency formula (9-2).

10. An inductive load operating at a phase angle of 53° draws 1,200 watts from a 120-volt line. Find the current taken.

11. Find the current drawn from a 230-volt line by a motor if it uses 6 kw of power at a pf of 0.65.

12. A 120-volt 2-hp motor operates at an efficiency of 80 per cent. Find the power input to the motor. If the current drawn by the motor is 20 amp, find the pf.

JOB 19-2: TOTAL POWER DRAWN BY COMBINATIONS OF REACTIVE LOADS

As we learned in Job 7-2, the total power in a circuit may be found by adding the power taken by the individual parts. If the power drawn by one branch is not in phase with the power drawn by another branch, however, the addition of the power must be made by *vector addition*. This will be done, as in Job 18-5, by resolving the power into its components and adding the components.

Resolving the Apparent Power into Its Components. In an inductive circuit, since the current lags behind the voltage, the apparent power will also lag behind the effective power as shown in Fig. 19-1c. By trigonometry,

1. Using the cosine function,

$$\cos \theta = \frac{W}{P} \qquad (19\text{-}3)$$

$$W = P \times \cos \theta \qquad (19\text{-}4)$$

$$P = \frac{W}{\cos \theta} \qquad (19\text{-}5)$$

2. Using the sine function, we obtain

Formulas

$$\sin \theta = \frac{\text{var power}}{P} \qquad (19\text{-}12)$$

By cross multiplication,

$$\text{var power} = P \times \sin \theta \qquad (19\text{-}13)$$

Solving for P,

$$P = \frac{\text{var power}}{\sin \theta} \qquad (19\text{-}14)$$

3. Using the tangent function, we obtain

Formula

$$\tan \theta = \frac{\text{var power}}{W} \qquad (19\text{-}15)$$

Applying the Pythagorean theorem, we obtain

Formula

$$P^2 = W^2 + (\text{var } P)^2 \qquad (19\text{-}16)$$

Combinations of Devices of Equal Power Factors

Example 19-6.   Find (a) the total apparent power, (b) the total pf, (c) the total effective power, and (d) the total current of the combination shown in Fig. 19-2.

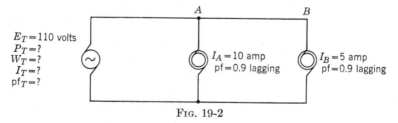

FIG. 19-2

a. Find the phase angle for each branch.   Since the pfs are equal, the phase angles will be equal.

$$\cos \theta = \text{pf} \qquad (19\text{-}7)$$
$$\cos \theta = 0.9$$
$$\theta = 26°$$

Draw the vectors for the power in each branch on the same voltage base as shown in Fig. 19-3a.   This diagram indicates that the power in one branch is in phase with the power in the second branch, since they are both drawn in the same direction.   To find the total apparent power, it is necessary only to add the two power vectors.   This is done, as with any vector quantities, by placing the tail of P_B on the head of P_A and drawing it in its original length and direction.   This is shown in Fig. 19-3b.   The total apparent power is then the distance from the origin of the vectors to the head of the final vector.   Since the two powers are in phase, the total apparent power may be found by the direct arithmetical addition of the P_A and P_B.   As seen from the vector addition, when two devices operate at the same pf, it means that the power taken by each is taken at the same time as the power

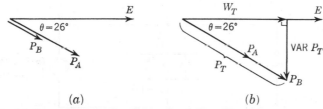

(a)   (b)

FIG. 19-3. (a) P_A and P_B are in phase, since they act at the same power factor. (b) P_T equals the vector sum of $P_A + P_B$; W_T equals the total effective power; var P_T equals the total reactive power.

taken by the other.   The total pf is the same as the pf of each device. The total current is the arithmetic sum of the currents in all the branches.

Formulas

$$P_T = P_A + P_B \qquad\qquad (19\text{-}17)$$
$$I_T = I_A + I_B \qquad\qquad (5\text{-}2)$$
$$\text{pf}_T = \text{pf}_A = \text{pf}_B \qquad\qquad (19\text{-}18)$$
$$W_T = P_T \times \text{pf}_T \qquad\qquad (19\text{-}19)$$
$$\text{var } P_T = P_T \times \sin\theta \qquad\qquad (19\text{-}20)$$

Find the apparent power for each branch.   Since

$$E_T = E_A = E_B = 110 \text{ volts} \qquad\qquad (5\text{-}1)$$
$$P_A = I_A \times E_A = 10 \times 110 = 1{,}100 \text{ volt-amp} \qquad (7\text{-}1)$$
$$P_B = I_B \times E_B = 5 \times 110 = 550 \text{ volt-amp} \qquad (7\text{-}1)$$

The total apparent power will therefore be

$$P_T = P_A + P_B \qquad\qquad (19\text{-}17)$$
$$P_T = 1{,}100 + 550$$
$$P_T = 1{,}650 \text{ volt-amp} \qquad Ans.$$

b. Find the total pf.

$$\text{pf}_T = \text{pf}_A = \text{pf}_B = 0.9 \qquad Ans. \qquad (19\text{-}18)$$

c. Find the total effective power.

$$W_T = P_T \times \text{pf}_T = 1{,}650 \times 0.9 = 1{,}485 \text{ watts} \qquad Ans. \quad (19\text{-}19)$$

d. Find the total current.

$$I_T = I_A + I_B = 10 + 5 = 15 \text{ amp} \qquad Ans. \qquad (5\text{-}2)$$

Combinations of Devices of Different Power Factors

Example 19-7. Find (*a*) the total effective power, (*b*) the total apparent power, (*c*) the total pf, and (*d*) the total current of the combination shown in Fig. 19-4.

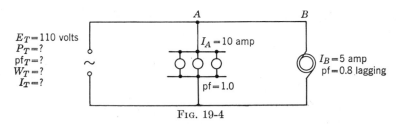

$E_T = 110$ volts
$P_T = ?$
$pf_T = ?$
$W_T = ?$
$I_T = ?$

$I_A = 10$ amp

$pf = 1.0$

$I_B = 5$ amp
$pf = 0.8$ lagging

Fig. 19-4

Solution: When the power in one branch is not in phase with the power in another branch, the apparent powers must be resolved into their components and the components added as shown below.

a. 1. Find the apparent power *P*, the effective power *W*, the phase angle θ, and the var power (var *P*) for each load.

For branch A:

$$P_A = I_A \times E_A = 110 \times 10 = 1{,}100 \text{ volt-amp} \qquad (7\text{-}1)$$
$$W_A = P_A \times pf_A = 1{,}100 \times 1 = 1{,}100 \text{ watts} \qquad (19\text{-}8)$$

Since

$$pf_A = \cos \theta = 1.0, \ \theta = 0° \qquad (19\text{-}7)$$
$$\text{var } P_A = P_A \times \sin \theta \qquad (19\text{-}13)$$
$$= 1{,}100 \times \sin 0°$$
$$= 1{,}100 \times 0$$
$$\text{var } P_A = 0 \text{ var}$$

For branch B:

$$P_B = I_B \times E_B = 5 \times 110 = 550 \text{ volt-amp} \qquad (7\text{-}1)$$
$$W_B = P_B \times pf_B = 550 \times 0.8 = 440 \text{ watts} \qquad (19\text{-}8)$$

Since

$$pf_B = \cos \theta = 0.8, \ \theta = 37° \qquad (19\text{-}7)$$
$$\text{var } P_B = P_B \times \sin \theta \qquad (19\text{-}13)$$
$$= 550 \times \sin 37°$$
$$= 550 \times 0.6$$
$$\text{var } P_B = -330 \text{ var}$$

2. Draw the vector diagram for the apparent powers on the same voltage base as shown in Fig. 19-5*a*.

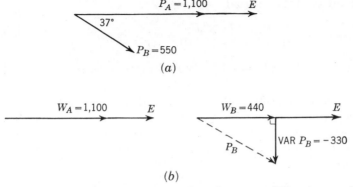

(a)

FIG. 19-5. (a) P_A and P_B are not in phase, since they act at different power factors. (b) Resolution of each power into its effective and reactive components.

3. Resolve the power in each branch into its components as shown in Fig. 19-5b.

4. Draw all the components on the same voltage base as shown in Fig. 19-6a. The total effective power W_T and the total reactive power var P_T may now be found.

$$W_T = W_A + W_B = 1{,}100 + 440 = 1{,}540 \text{ watts} \qquad Ans. \qquad (19\text{-}21)$$
$$\text{var } P_T = \text{var } P_A + \text{var } P_B = 0 + (-330) = -330 \text{ var} \qquad (19\text{-}22)$$

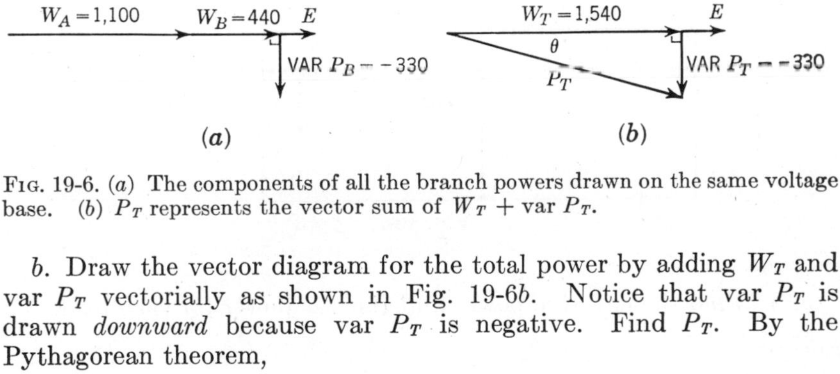

FIG. 19-6. (a) The components of all the branch powers drawn on the same voltage base. (b) P_T represents the vector sum of $W_T + \text{var } P_T$.

b. Draw the vector diagram for the total power by adding W_T and var P_T vectorially as shown in Fig. 19-6b. Notice that var P_T is drawn *downward* because var P_T is negative. Find P_T. By the Pythagorean theorem,

$$\begin{aligned}
P_T{}^2 &= W_T{}^2 + \text{var } P_T{}^2 \qquad\qquad (19\text{-}23)\\
&= 1{,}540^2 + (-330)^2\\
&= 2{,}371{,}000 + 108{,}900 = 2{,}480{,}000\\
P_T &= \sqrt{2{,}480{,}000} = 1{,}575 \text{ volt-amp} \qquad Ans.
\end{aligned}$$

c. Find the total pf.

$$\text{pf}_T = \frac{W_T}{P_T} = \frac{1{,}540}{1{,}575} = 0.977 = 97.7\% \qquad Ans. \qquad (19\text{-}24)$$

d. Find the total current.

$$P_T = I_T \times E_T \qquad (7\text{-}2)$$
$$1{,}575 = I_T \times 110$$
$$I_T = \frac{1{,}575}{110} = 14.3 \text{ amp} \qquad Ans.$$

Alternate Solution: The phase angle and the apparent power may be found by applying the tangent formula to the right triangle shown in Fig. 19-6*b*.   This solution is simpler, since it does not involve the labor of squaring numbers and finding the square root of the sum.

a. Find the phase angle in Fig. 19-6*b*.

$$\tan \theta_T = \frac{\text{var } P_T}{W_T} = \frac{330}{1{,}540} = 0.214; \text{ therefore } \theta = 12° \qquad (19\text{-}25)$$
$$\text{pf} = \cos \theta = \cos 12° = 0.978 = 97.8\% \qquad Ans. \quad (19\text{-}7)$$

b. Find the total apparent power.

$$P_T = \frac{W_T}{\text{pf}_T} = \frac{1{,}540}{\cos 12°} = \frac{1{,}540}{0.978} = 1{,}574 \text{ volt-amp} \qquad Ans. \quad (19\text{-}26)$$

Example 19-8.   Find (*a*) the total effective power, (*b*) the total power factor, and (*c*) the total apparent power for the circuit shown in Fig. 19-7.

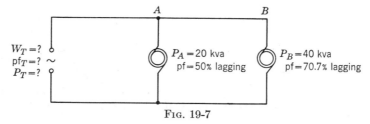

$W_T = ?$
$\text{pf}_T = ? \sim$
$P_T = ?$

$P_A = 20$ kva
pf = 50% lagging

$P_B = 40$ kva
pf = 70.7% lagging

Fɪɢ. 19-7

Solution:

a. 1. Find the effective power and the var power for each load.

For load A:

$$\text{pf} = \cos \theta = 0.500; \text{ therefore } \theta = 60° \qquad (19\text{-}7)$$
$$W_A = P_A \times \text{pf}_A = 20 \times 0.5 = 10 \text{ kw} \qquad (19\text{-}8)$$
$$\text{var } P_A = P_A \times \sin \theta = 20 \times \sin 60° = 20 \times 0.866 = -17.32 \text{ kvar}$$

For load B:

$$\text{pf} = \cos \theta = 0.707; \text{ therefore } \theta = 45° \qquad (19\text{-}7)$$
$$W_B = P_B \times \text{pf}_B = 40 \times 0.707 = 28.28 \text{ kw} \qquad (19\text{-}8)$$
$$\text{var } P_B = P_B \times \sin \theta = 40 \times \sin 45° = 40 \times 0.707 = -28.28 \text{ kvar}$$

2. Draw the vector diagram for the apparent powers on the same voltage base as shown in Fig. 19-8*a*.

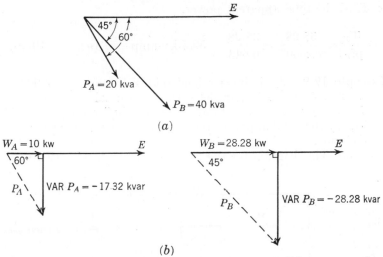

(a)

(b)

FIG. 19-8. (a) P_A and P_B are not in phase, since they act at different power factors. (b) Resolution of each power into its effective and reactive components.

3. Resolve the power in each branch into its components as shown in Fig. 19-8b.

4. Draw all the components on the same voltage base as shown in Fig. 19-9a. The total effective power W_T and the total reactive power var P_T may now be found.

$$W_T = W_A + W_B = 10 + 28.28 = 38.28 \text{ kw} \qquad Ans. \quad (19\text{-}21)$$
$$\text{var } P_T = \text{var } P_A + \text{var } P_B = (-17.32) + (-28.28) = -45.6 \text{ kvar}$$

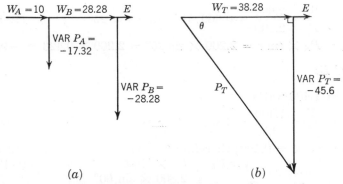

(a)   (b)

FIG. 19-9. (a) The components of all the branch powers drawn on the same voltage base. (b) P_T represents the vector sum of W_T + var P_T.

b. Find the total power factor by adding W_T and var P_T vectorially as shown in Fig. 19-9b.

$$\tan \theta_T = \frac{\text{var } P_T}{W_T} = \frac{-45.6}{38.28} = -1.191; \text{ therefore } \theta = 50° \quad (19\text{-}25)$$
$$\text{pf} = \cos \theta = \cos 50° = 0.643 = 64.3\% \qquad Ans. \qquad (19\text{-}7)$$

c. Find the total apparent power.

$$P_T = \frac{W_T}{\text{pf}_T} = \frac{38.28}{\cos 50°} = \frac{38.28}{0.643} = 59.5 \text{ kv-amp} \qquad Ans. \qquad (19\text{-}26)$$

Example 19-9. An inductive load taking 10 amp and 2,000 watts from a 220-volt line is in parallel with a motor taking 1,400 watts at a pf of 50 per cent lagging. Find (*a*) the total effective power, (*b*) the total pf, (*c*) the total apparent power, and (*d*) the total current drawn by the circuit.

Solution: The diagram for the circuit is shown in Fig. 19-10.

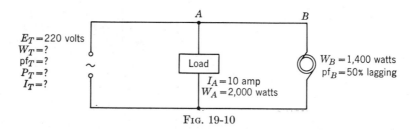

Fig. 19-10

a. 1. Find the apparent power, the effective power, the phase angle, and the var power for each load.

For load A:

$$P_A = I_A \times E_A = 10 \times 220 = 2,200 \text{ volt-amp} \qquad (7\text{-}1)$$
$$W_A = 2,000 \text{ watts}$$
$$\cos \theta = \frac{W}{P} = \frac{2,000}{2,200} = 0.909; \text{ therefore } \theta = 25° \qquad (19\text{-}3)$$
$$\text{var } P_A = P_A \times \sin \theta = 2,200 \times \sin 25° = 2,200 \times 0.423 = -931 \text{ var}$$

For load B:

$$W_B = 1,400 \text{ watts}$$
$$P_B = \frac{W}{\text{pf}} = \frac{1,400}{0.5} = 2,800 \text{ volt-amp} \qquad (19\text{-}9)$$
$$\text{pf}_B = \cos \theta = 0.500; \text{ therefore } \theta = 60° \qquad (19\text{-}7)$$
$$\text{var } P_B = P_B \times \sin \theta \qquad (19\text{-}13)$$
$$= 2,800 \times \sin 60°$$
$$= 2,800 \times 0.866$$
$$\text{var } P_B = -2,425 \text{ var}$$

2. Find the total effective and reactive power.

$$W_T = W_A + W_B = 2,000 + 1,400 = 3,400 \text{ watts} \qquad Ans.$$
$$\text{var } P_T = \text{var } P_A + \text{var } P_B = (-931) + (-2,425) = -3,356 \text{ vars}$$

b. Find the phase angle and the pf.

$$\tan \theta_T = \frac{\operatorname{var} P_T}{W_T} = -\frac{3,356}{3,400} = 0.987; \text{ therefore } \theta = 45° \quad (19\text{-}25)$$

$$\text{pf} = \cos \theta = \cos 45° = 0.707 = 70.7\% \qquad Ans. \qquad (19\text{-}7)$$

c. Find the total apparent power.

$$P_T = \frac{W_T}{\text{pf}_T} = \frac{3,400}{0.707} = 4,809 \text{ volt-amp} \qquad Ans. \quad (19\text{-}26)$$

d. Find the total current.

$$I_T = \frac{P_T}{E_T} = \frac{4,809}{220} = 21.8 \text{ amp} \qquad Ans. \qquad (7\text{-}2)$$

Summary

When the Devices Operate at the Same Power Factor

1. The total apparent power is the arithmetic sum of the apparent power taken by each load.

$$P_T = P_A + P_B \quad (19\text{-}17)$$

2. The total effective power is the arithmetic sum of the effective power taken by each load.

$$W_T = W_A + W_B \quad (19\text{-}21)$$

The total effective power is equal to the total apparent power multiplied by the total pf.

$$W_T = P_T \times \text{pf}_T \quad (19\text{-}19)$$

3. The total reactive power is the *algebraic* sum of the reactive power taken by each load.

$$\operatorname{var} P_T = \operatorname{var} P_A + \operatorname{var} P_B \quad (19\text{-}22)$$

The total reactive power is equal to the total apparent power multiplied by the sine of the phase angle.

$$\operatorname{var} P_T = P_T \times \sin \theta \quad (19\text{-}20)$$

4. The total pf is equal to the pf of each load.

$$\text{pf}_T = \text{pf}_A = \text{pf}_B \quad (19\text{-}18)$$

5. The total current is equal to the sum of the current taken by each load.

$$I_T = I_A + I_B \quad (5\text{-}2)$$

When the Devices Operate at Different Power Factors

1. Find the apparent power for each load using any of the following formulas.

$$P = E \times I \quad (7\text{-}1)$$

or

$$P = \frac{W}{\text{pf}} \quad (19\text{-}9)$$

or

$$P = \frac{W}{\cos \theta} \quad (19\text{-}5)$$

2. Find the effective and reactive power for each load.

$$W = P \times \text{pf} \quad (19\text{-}8)$$

or

$$W = P \times \cos \theta \quad (19\text{-}4)$$

$$\operatorname{var} P = P \times \sin \theta \quad (19\text{-}13)$$

Note: If the pf or the phase angle is not given, it may be found by either of the following formulas:

$$\text{pf} = \frac{W}{P} \quad (19\text{-}6)$$

$$\cos \theta = \frac{W}{P} \quad (19\text{-}3)$$

3. Find the total effective power.

$$W_T = W_A + W_B \quad (19\text{-}21)$$

4. Find the total reactive power.

$$\text{var } P_T = \text{var } P_A + \text{var } P_B$$
$$(19\text{-}22)$$

5. Find the phase angle θ.

$$\tan \theta_T = \frac{\text{var } P_T}{W_T} \quad (19\text{-}25)$$

6. Find the total pf.

$$\text{pf} = \cos \theta \quad (19\text{-}7)$$

7. Find the total apparent power.

$$P_T = \frac{W_T}{\text{pf}_T} \quad (19\text{-}26)$$

8. Find the total current drawn, using any of the following formulas.

$$P_T = E_T \times I_T \quad (7\text{-}2)$$
$$W_T = E_T \times I_T \times \cos \theta_T$$
$$(19\text{-}27)$$
$$W_T = E_T \times I_T \times \text{pf}_T$$
$$(19\text{-}28)$$

Problems

1. A refrigerator motor drawing 6 amp at 80 per cent pf leading is in parallel with a washing-machine motor drawing 8 amp at 80 per cent pf leading from a 110-volt line. Find (a) the total effective power, (b) the total pf, (c) the total apparent power, and (d) the total current drawn.

2. Motor A draws 10 amp and 800 watts from a 110-volt 60-cycle a-c line. Motor B draws 6 amp and 480 watts from the same line in parallel. Find (a) the pf of each motor, (b) the total effective power, (c) the total pf, (d) the total apparent power, and (e) the total current drawn.

3. A purely resistive lamp load (pf = 1) drawing 8 amp from a 110-volt 60-cycle line is in parallel with an induction motor taking 10 amp at 70 per cent pf. Find (a) the total effective power, (b) the total pf, (c) the total apparent power, and (d) the total current drawn.

4. A lamp bank (pf = 1) drawing 1,200 watts from a 110-volt 60-cycle line is in parallel with an induction motor taking 8 amp at a power factor of 90 per cent. Find (a) the total effective power, (b) the total pf, (c) the total apparent power, and (d) the total current.

5. Find (a) the total effective power, (b) the total pf, and (c) the total apparent power for the circuit shown in Fig. 19-11.

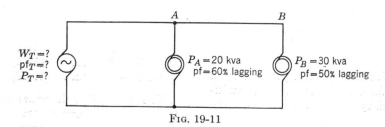

$W_T = ?$
$\text{pf}_T = ?$
$P_T = ?$

$P_A = 20$ kva
pf = 60% lagging

$P_B = 30$ kva
pf = 50% lagging

Fig. 19-11

6. A 2-kw lamp load is in parallel with a motor operating at a pf of 60 per cent lagging and drawing 3 kw from a 110-volt 60-cycle line.   Find parts (a) to (d) indicated in Prob. 4.

7. Repeat Prob. 4 for the following circuit: A motor drawing 5 kw at 80 per cent pf lagging is in parallel with a second motor drawing 8 kw at 70 per cent pf lagging from a 220-volt line.

8. Repeat Prob. 4 for the circuit shown in Fig. 19-12.

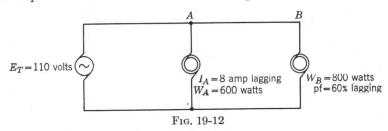

$E_T = 110$ volts

$I_A = 8$ amp lagging
$W_A = 600$ watts

$W_B = 800$ watts
pf = 60% lagging

Fig. 19-12

9. A 2-kw lamp load, a 70-kv-amp motor operating at a pf of 60 per cent lagging and a 40-kv-amp motor operating at a pf of 70 per cent lagging are connected in parallel.   Find (a) the total effective power, (b) the total pf, and (c) the total apparent power.

10. Repeat Prob. 4 for the circuit shown in Fig. 19-13.

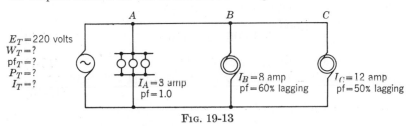

$E_T = 220$ volts
$W_T = ?$
$pf_T = ?$
$P_T = ?$
$I_T = ?$

$I_A = 3$ amp
pf = 1.0

$I_B = 8$ amp
pf = 60% lagging

$I_C = 12$ amp
pf = 50% lagging

Fig. 19-13

JOB 19-3: POWER DRAWN BY COMBINATIONS OF RESISTIVE, INDUCTIVE, AND CAPACITIVE LOADS

Power in Capacitive Loads.   When the current is out of phase with the voltage, only that portion of the current which is in phase with the voltage is useful in producing usable power.

In an inductive circuit, the current lags behind the voltage, but in a capacitive circuit, the current leads the voltage.   In such a circuit, the vector diagrams will be very similar to those of an inductive circuit, except that now the current will be a *leading* current and a *leading* power.   All the formulas developed for the inductive circuits in the last job will also apply to a capacitive circuit.   The only difference is that the reactive power will *lead* in a capacitive circuit.

Example 19-10. A lamp bank drawing 1 kw of power is in parallel with a synchronous motor drawing 2 kw at a leading pf of 80 per cent from a 220-volt 60-cycle a-c line.   Find (a) the total effective power, (b) the total pf, (c) the total apparent power, and (d) the total current drawn.

Solution: The diagram of the circuit is shown in Fig. 19-14.

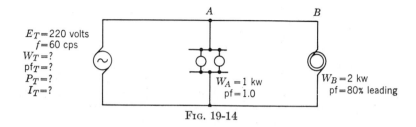

E_T=220 volts
f=60 cps
W_T=?
pf_T=?
P_T=?
I_T=?

W_A =1 kw
pf=1.0

W_B=2 kw
pf=80% leading

Fɪɢ. 19-14

a. 1. Find the apparent power, the effective power, the phase angle, and the var power for each load.

For load A:

$$W_A = 1 \text{ kw} = 1{,}000 \text{ watts} \qquad \text{(given)}$$
$$P_A = \frac{W_A}{\text{pf}} = \frac{1{,}000}{1} = 1{,}000 \text{ volt-amp} \qquad (19\text{-}9)$$
$$\text{pf} = \cos \theta = 1.0; \text{ therefore } \theta = 0° \qquad (19\text{-}7)$$
$$\text{var } P_A = P_A \times \sin \theta = 1{,}000 \times \sin 0° = 1{,}000 \times 0 = 0 \text{ var}$$
$$(19\text{-}13)$$

For load B:

$$W_B = 2 \text{ kw} = 2{,}000 \text{ watts} \qquad \text{(given)}$$
$$P_B = \frac{W_A}{\text{pf}} = \frac{2{,}000}{0.8} = 2{,}500 \text{ volt-amp} \qquad (19\text{-}9)$$
$$\text{pf} = \cos \theta = 0.8; \text{ therefore } \theta = 37° \text{ leading} \qquad (19\text{-}7)$$
$$\text{var } P_B = P_B \times \sin \theta = 2{,}500 \times \sin 37° = 2{,}500 \times 0.6 = 1{,}500 \text{ var}$$

2. Find the total effective and reactive power.

$$W_T = W_A + W_B = 1{,}000 + 2{,}000 = 3{,}000 \text{ watts} \qquad Ans.$$
$$\text{var } P_T = \text{var } P_A + \text{var } P_B = 0 + 1{,}500 = 1{,}500 \text{ var} \qquad (19\text{-}22)$$

b. Find the phase angle and the pf.

$$\tan \theta_T = \frac{\text{var } P_T}{W_T} = \frac{1{,}500}{3{,}000} = 0.5; \text{ therefore } \theta = 27° \qquad (19\text{-}25)$$
$$\text{pf}_T = \cos \theta = \cos 27° = 0.891 = 89.1\% \qquad Ans. \qquad (19\text{-}7)$$

c. Find the total apparent power.

$$P_T = \frac{W_T}{pf_T} = \frac{3,000}{0.891} = 3,367 \text{ volt-amp} \qquad Ans. \quad (19\text{-}26)$$

d. Find the total current drawn.

$$I_T = \frac{P_T}{E_T} = \frac{3,367}{220} = 15.3 \text{ amp} \qquad Ans. \qquad (7\text{-}2)$$

Example 19-11. A 10-kv-amp induction motor operating at 85 per cent lagging pf and a 5-kv-amp synchronous motor operating at 68.2 per cent leading pf are connected in parallel across a 220-volt 60-cycle a-c line. Find (a) the total effective power, (b) the total pf, (c) the total apparent power, and (d) the total current drawn.

Solution: The diagram for the circuit is shown in Fig. 19-15.

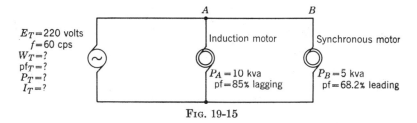

Fig. 19-15

a. 1. Find the apparent power, the effective power, the phase angle, and the var power for each load.

For the induction motor A:

$P_A = 10 \text{ kv-amp} \qquad \text{(given)}$
$W_A = P_A \times pf = 10 \times 0.85 = 8.5 \text{ kw}$ (19-8)
$pf = \cos \theta = 0.85; \text{ therefore } \theta = 32°$ (19-7)
$\text{var } P_A = P_A \times \sin \theta = 10 \times \sin 32° = 10 \times 0.53$ (19-13)
$\qquad\qquad\qquad\qquad \text{var } P_A = -5.3 \text{ kvar lagging}$

For the synchronous motor B:

$P_B = 5 \text{ kv-amp} \qquad \text{(given)}$
$W_B = P_B \times pf = 5 \times 0.682 = 3.41 \text{ kw}$ (19-8)
$pf = \cos \theta = 0.682; \text{ therefore } \theta = 47°$ (19-7)
$\text{var } P_B = P_B \times \sin \theta = 5 \times \sin 47° = 5 \times 0.73 = 3.65 \text{ kvar leading}$

2. Draw the vector diagram for the apparent powers on the same voltage base as shown in Fig. 19-16a.

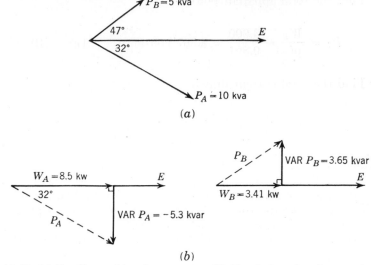

(a)

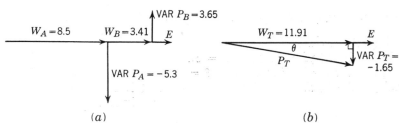

(b)

FIG. 19-16. (a) Leading and lagging powers.   (b) Resolution of each power into its effective and reactive components.

3. Resolve the power in each branch into its components as shown in Fig. 19-16b.

4. Draw all the components on the same voltage base as shown in Fig. 19-17a.   The total effective power W_T and the total reactive power var P_T may now be found.

$$W_T = W_A + W_B = 8.5 + 3.41 = 11.91 \text{ kw} \qquad Ans. \qquad (19\text{-}21)$$
$$\text{var } P_T = \text{var } P_A + \text{var } P_B = (-5.3) + 3.65 = -1.65 \text{ kvar lagging}$$

(a)   (b)

FIG. 19-17. (a) The components of all the branch powers drawn on the same voltage base.   (b) P_T represents the vector sum of $W_T + \text{var } P_T$.

b. Find the total pf by adding W_T and var P_T vectorially as shown in Fig. 19-17b.

$$\tan \theta_T = \frac{\text{var } P_T}{W_T} = \frac{-1.65}{11.91} = 0.1385; \text{ therefore } \theta = 8° \quad (19\text{-}25)$$
$$\text{pf} = \cos \theta = \cos 8° = 0.99 = 99\% \qquad (19\text{-}7)$$

c. Find the total apparent power.

$$P_T = \frac{W_T}{pf_T} = \frac{11.91}{0.99} = 12.03 \text{ kv-amp} = 12{,}030 \text{ volt-amp} \qquad Ans.$$

d. Find the total current drawn.

$$I_T = \frac{P_T}{E_T} = \frac{12{,}030}{220} = 54.7 \text{ amp lagging} \qquad Ans. \quad (7\text{-}2)$$

Example 19-12. A synchronous motor drawing 10 amp at 60 per cent leading pf from a 110-volt line is in parallel with an induction motor drawing 1 kw at 80 per cent pf lagging. Find (*a*) the total effective power, (*b*) the total pf, (*c*) the total apparent power, and (*d*) the total current drawn.

Solution: The diagram for the circuit is shown in Fig. 19-18.

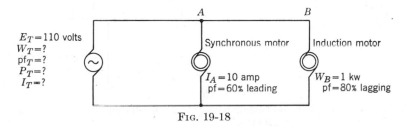

$E_T = 110$ volts
$W_T = ?$
$pf_T = ?$
$P_T = ?$
$I_T = ?$

Synchronous motor

$I_A = 10$ amp
pf = 60% leading

Induction motor

$W_B = 1$ kw
pf = 80% lagging

Fig. 19-18

a. 1. Find the apparent power, the effective power, the phase angle, and the var power for each load.

For the synchronous motor A:

$$P_A = I_A \times E_A = 10 \times 110 = 1{,}100 \text{ volt-amp} \qquad (7\text{-}1)$$
$$W_A = P_A \times PF_A = 1{,}100 \times 0.6 = 660 \text{ watts} \qquad (19\text{-}8)$$
$$pf_A = \cos\theta = 0.600; \text{ therefore } \theta = 53° \qquad (19\text{-}7)$$
$$\text{var } P_A = P_A \times \sin\theta = 1{,}100 \times \sin 53° = 1{,}100 \times 0.8 \quad (19\text{-}13)$$
$$\text{var } P_A = 880 \text{ var leading}$$

For the induction motor B:

$$W_B = 1 \text{ kw} = 1{,}000 \text{ watts} \qquad \text{(given)}$$
$$P_B = \frac{W}{pf_B} = \frac{1{,}000}{0.8} = 1{,}250 \text{ volt-amp} \qquad (19\text{-}9)$$
$$pf_B = \cos\theta = 0.800; \text{ therefore } \theta = 37° \qquad (19\text{-}7)$$
$$\text{var } P_B = P_B \times \sin\theta = 1{,}250 \times \sin 37° = 1{,}250 \times 0.6 \quad (19\text{-}13)$$
$$\text{var } P_B = -750 \text{ var lagging}$$

2. Draw the vector diagram for the apparent powers on the same voltage base as shown in Fig. 19-19*a*.

3. Resolve the power in each branch into its components as shown in Fig. 19-19b.

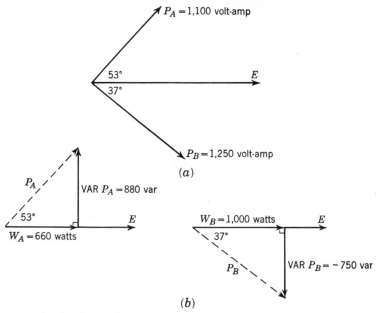

Fig. 19-19. (a) Leading and lagging powers.   (b) Resolution of each power into its effective and reactive components.

4. Draw all the components on the same voltage base as shown in Fig. 19-20a. The total effective power W_T and the total reactive power var P_T may now be found.

$$W_T = W_A + W_B = 660 + 1,000 = 1,660 \text{ watts} \quad Ans.$$
$$\text{var } P_T = \text{var } P_A + \text{var } P_B = 880 + (-750) = 130 \text{ var leading}$$

b. Find the total pf by adding W_T and var P_T vectorially as shown in Fig. 19-20b.

$$\tan \theta_T = \frac{\text{var } P_T}{W_T} = \frac{130}{1,660} = 0.078; \text{ therefore } \theta = 4° \quad (19\text{-}25)$$
$$\text{pf} = \cos \theta = \cos 4° = 0.998 = 99.8\% \quad (19\text{-}7)$$

c. Find the total apparent power.

$$P_T = \frac{W_T}{\text{pf}_T} = \frac{1,660}{0.998} = 1,663 \text{ volt-amp} \quad Ans. \quad (19\text{-}26)$$

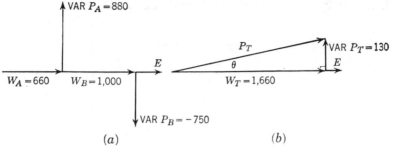

(a)   *(b)*

Fig. 19-20. (*a*) The components of all the branch powers drawn on the same voltage base. (*b*) P_T represents the vector sum of W_T and var P_T.

d. Find the total current drawn.

$$I_T = \frac{P_T}{E_T} = \frac{1{,}663}{110} = 15.1 \text{ amp leading} \qquad Ans. \qquad (7\text{-}2)$$

Problems

1. An induction motor drawing 400 volt-amp at 80 per cent lagging pf is in parallel with a synchronous motor drawing 700 volt-amp at 90 per cent leading pf. Find (*a*) the total effective power, (*b*) the total pf, and (*c*) the total apparent power.

2. Repeat Prob. 1 for a circuit containing an induction motor that draws 100 kv-amp at a pf of 85 per cent in parallel with a capacitive load that draws 80 kv-amp at a pf of 70 per cent.

3. A capacitive load drawing 20 amp at 70 per cent pf from a 120-volt 60-cycle line is in parallel with an induction motor drawing 4 kw at 70 per cent pf. Find (*a*) the total effective power, (*b*) the total pf, (*c*) the total apparent power, and (*d*) the total current drawn.

4. Repeat Prob. 3 for a circuit containing a 60 per cent pf induction motor drawing 1 kw in parallel with a synchronous motor rated at 120 volts, 15 amp, and 70 per cent pf.

5. Find the total pf of a parallel combination of a 5-kw lamp load, a 10-kw inductive load (pf = 80 per cent), and an 8-kw capacitive load (pf = 90 per cent).

6. Find (*a*) the total effective power, (*b*) the total pf, (*c*) the total apparent power, and (*d*) the total current drawn by the circuit shown in Fig. 19-21.

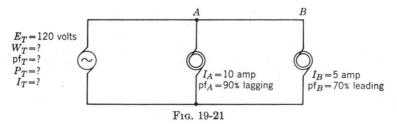

Fig. 19-21

7. Repeat Prob. 6 for the circuit shown in Fig. 19-22.

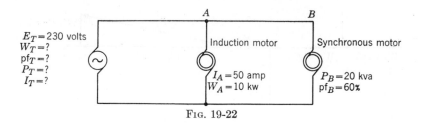

FIG. 19-22

8. An induction motor draws 20 amp at a pf of 80 per cent from a 120-volt line. What is the total pf of the circuit if (*a*) a lamp load drawing 15 amp is connected in parallel and (*b*) a capacitive load drawing 5 amp at a pf of 60 per cent leading is connected in parallel?

9. Repeat Prob. 6 for a circuit containing an induction motor taking 4 amp at 80 per cent pf lagging, a synchronous motor taking 8 amp at 50 per cent pf leading, and a lamp load taking 6 amp at 100 per cent pf, all connected in parallel across a 120-volt line.

10. Repeat Prob. 6 for a circuit containing a 100-watt inductive load at a pf of 80 per cent, a 600-watt capacitive load at a pf of 60 per cent, and an induction motor drawing 1 kw at a pf of 90 per cent, all connected in parallel across a 120-volt line.

JOB 19-4: POWER-FACTOR CORRECTION

Consider the three circuits shown in Fig. 19-23. Each circuit draws the same effective power, but at decreasing pfs.

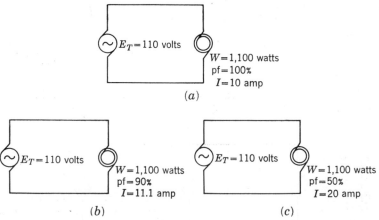

FIG. 19-23. In order to produce a constant effective power, the current must increase as the power factor decreases.

For circuit of Fig. 19-23*a*:

$$W = E \times I \times \text{pf} \qquad (19\text{-}11)$$
$$1{,}100 = 110 \times I \times 1$$
$$I = \frac{1{,}100}{110} = 10 \text{ amp}$$

For circuit of Fig. 19-23*b*:

$$W = E \times I \times \text{pf} \qquad (19\text{-}11)$$
$$1{,}100 = 110 \times I \times 0.9$$
$$1{,}100 = 99 \times I$$
$$I = \frac{1{,}100}{99} = 11.1 \text{ amp}$$

For circuit of Fig. 19-23*c*:

$$W = E \times I \times \text{pf} \qquad (19\text{-}11)$$
$$1{,}100 = 110 \times I \times 0.5$$
$$1{,}100 = 55 \times I$$
$$I = \frac{1{,}100}{55} = 20 \text{ amp}$$

By an investigation of the amount of current drawn in each of the circuits, we can see that as the pf decreases, more and more current must be supplied in order to produce the same effective power. Now, regardless of the current that is drawn to provide this 1,100 watts of effective power, the consumer pays for only 1,100 watts. Therefore, if the power company is forced to send 20 instead of 10 amp to provide 1,100 watts of power, it must provide heavier wires to carry the larger current. This is expensive. In addition, the larger the current, the greater the power lost in the transmission lines. For these reasons, the power company demands an extra premium payment if the pf falls below a certain value for a particular installation.

A low pf is generally due to the large consumption of power by underloaded induction motors which take a lagging current. In order to correct this low pf and raise it to the required value, synchronous motors, or capacitors which take a *leading* current, are placed in parallel with the inductive load. When synchronous motors are used, the required correction is accomplished by varying the pf of the synchronous motor by adjusting the excitation of its field.

Example 19-13. An induction motor takes 15-kv-amp at 220 volts and 80 per cent lagging pf. What must be the pf of a 10-kv-amp synchronous motor connected in parallel in order to raise the total pf to 100 per cent, or unity?

Solution:

Given: P = 15 kv-amp $\left.\begin{array}{l}\\ \\ \\ \end{array}\right\}$ induction motor   Find: To get a pf = 1,
        pf = 80%   pf of synchronous
        E = 220 volts   motor = ?
        P = 10 kv-amp   synchronous motor

1. Find the var P of the induction motor.
Since

$$\text{pf} = \cos \theta = 0.8, \theta = 37° \qquad (19\text{-}7)$$
$$\text{var } P = P \times \sin \theta \qquad (19\text{-}13)$$
$$\text{var } P = 15 \times \sin 37° = 15 \times 0.6 = -9 \text{ kvar lagging}$$

The vector diagram for the induction motor is shown in Fig. 19-24*a*.

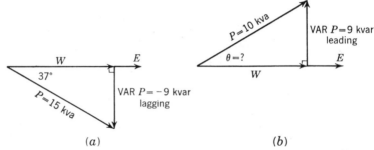

                     (*a*)   (*b*)

FIG. 19-24. (*a*) Vector diagram for the induction motor. (*b*) Vector diagram for the synchronous motor.

2. To adjust the pf to unity means that $\cos \theta = 1.0$. At unity pf, if $\cos \theta = 1.0$, θ will equal 0°. When the phase angle is 0°,

$$\text{var } P = P \times \sin \theta \qquad (19\text{-}13)$$
$$\text{var } P = P \times \sin 0°$$
$$\text{var } P = P \times 0 = 0 \text{ var}$$

Thus, to adjust a circuit to unity pf, all that is required is to make the total reactive power equal to 0 var. Since we already have 9 kvar *lagging* in the circuit, we must bring this down to zero by adding 9 kvar *leading*. This *leading* reactive power must come from the synchronous motor. The vector diagram for the synchronous motor must be as shown in Fig. 19-24*b*. We can find the phase angle for the synchronous motor from this diagram.

3. $\sin \theta = \dfrac{\text{var } P}{P} \qquad (19\text{-}12)$

$$\sin \theta = \tfrac{9}{10} = 0.9000$$
$$\theta = 64°$$

4. Find the pf of the synchronous motor.

$$\text{pf} = \cos \theta = \cos 64° \qquad (19\text{-}7)$$
$$= 0.438$$
$$\text{pf} = 43.8\% \qquad Ans.$$

Example 19-14. A 220-volt 50-amp induction motor draws 10 kw of power. An 8 kv-amp synchronous motor is placed in parallel with it in order to adjust the pf to unity. What must be the pf of the synchronous motor?

Solution:

Given: $E = 220$ volts $\Big\}$ induction motor
         $I = 50$ amp
         $W = 10$ kw
         $P = 8$ kv-amp   synchronous motor

Find: To get a pf = 1.0, pf of synchronous motor = ?

1. Find the var P of the induction motor.

$$P = I \times E = 50 \times 220 = 11,000 \text{ volt-amp} = 11 \text{ kv-amp}$$

Since

$$\cos \theta = \frac{W}{P} \qquad (19\text{-}3)$$

$$\cos \theta = \tfrac{10}{11} = 0.909$$
$$\theta = 25°$$
$$\text{var } P = P \times \sin \theta = 11 \times \sin 25° \qquad (19\text{-}13)$$
$$\text{var } P = 11 \times 0.423 = -4.65 \text{ kvar } lagging$$

2. Draw the vector diagram for the induction motor as shown in Fig. 19-25a. To adjust the pf of the circuit to unity, the vector diagram for the synchronous motor must be a *leading* power as shown in Fig. 19-25b.

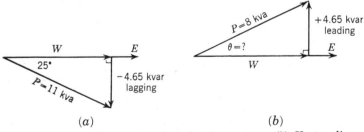

(a)   (b)

FIG. 19-25. (a) Vector diagram for the induction motor. (b) Vector diagram for the synchronous motor.

3. Find the phase angle for the synchronous motor.

$$\sin \theta = \frac{\text{var } P}{P} = \frac{4.65}{8} = 0.581 \qquad (19\text{-}12)$$
$$\theta = 36°$$

4. Find the pf of the synchronous motor.

$$\text{pf} = \cos \theta = \cos 36° = 0.809 = 80.9\% \quad Ans. \quad (19\text{-}7)$$

Note: If only the effective power W of the synchronous motor is given, find angle θ for the synchronous motor by using

$$\tan \theta = \frac{\text{lagging var } P}{W \text{ of synchronous motor}} \qquad (19\text{-}29)$$

Then
$$\text{pf} = \cos \theta \qquad (19\text{-}7)$$

Example 19-15. An induction motor takes 6.4 kw at 80 per cent pf from a 220-volt 60-cycle line. Find (*a*) the apparent power, (*b*) the lagging pf, and (*c*) the capacity of a capacitor connected across the motor terminals in order to raise the pf to unity.

Solution:

Given: W = 6.4 kw   Find: P = ?
        pf = 80%   pf = ?
        E = 220 volts C = ? to make pf$_T$ = 1.0
        f = 60 cps

a. Find the apparent power of the induction motor.

$$P = \frac{W}{\text{pf}} = \frac{6.4}{0.8} = 8 \text{ kv-amp} \qquad (19\text{-}9)$$

b.
$$\text{pf} = \cos \theta = 0.800 \qquad (19\text{-}7)$$
$$\theta = 37°$$

c. 1. Find the var P of the induction motor.

$$\text{var } P = P \times \sin \theta = 8 \times \sin 37° \qquad (19\text{-}13)$$
$$\text{var } P = 8 \times 0.6 = -4.8 \text{ kvar lagging}$$

2. In a "pure" capacitor, the current leads the voltage by 90°. Therefore, the pf = $\cos 90° = 0$. The var P will equal

$$\text{var } P = P \times \sin \theta \qquad (19\text{-}13)$$
$$\text{var } P = P \times \sin 90°$$
$$\text{var } P = P \times 1$$
or
$$\text{var } P = P$$

Thus, to balance any lagging var P such as the 4.8 kvar in this problem, it is necessary only to insert a capacitor taking 4.8 kv-amp of apparent power, since *all* the apparent power in a pure capacitor acts as a *leading* var P in direct opposition to the lagging var P already in the circuit.

3. To find the capacity of this capacitor:

Find the current drawn by the capacitor at the rated voltage. Since 4.8 kv-amp = 4,800 volt-amp,

$$P = I \times E \qquad (7\text{-}1)$$
$$4,800 = I \times 220$$
$$I = \frac{4,800}{220} = 21.8 \text{ amp}$$

Find the reactance of the capacitor.

$$E_c = I_c \times X_c \qquad (16\text{-}7)$$
$$220 = 21.8 \times X_c$$
$$X_c = \frac{220}{21.8} = 10.1 \text{ ohms}$$

Find the capacitance at 60 cycles to produce this reactance of 10.1 ohms.

$$X_c = \frac{159,000}{f \times C} \qquad (16\text{-}6)$$
$$10.1 = \frac{159,000}{60 \times C}$$
$$60 \times 10.1 \times C = 159,000$$
$$606 \times C = 159,000$$
$$C = \frac{159,000}{606} = 262 \ \mu\text{f} \qquad Ans.$$

Example 19-16. When operating at full load, an induction motor draws 800 watts and 4 amp from a 220-volt 60-cycle line. Find (*a*) the pf of the motor, (*b*) the lagging reactive power, (*c*) the apparent power drawn by a capacitor in order to raise the pf to unity, (*d*) the current drawn by this capacitor, (*e*) the reactance of the capacitor, and (*f*) the capacitance of this capacitor.

Solution:

Given: W = 800 watts   Find: pf = ?
$\quad$ I = 4 amp $\qquad\qquad$ var P = ?
$\quad$ E = 220 volts $\qquad$ P of capacitor = ?
$\quad$ f = 60 cps $\qquad\qquad$ I_c = ?
$\qquad\qquad\qquad\qquad\qquad$ X_c = ?
$\qquad\qquad\qquad\qquad\qquad$ C = ?

a. Find the pf of the motor.

1. $\qquad P = E \times I = 220 \times 4 = 880 \text{ volt-amp} \qquad (7\text{-}1)$

2. $\qquad \cos \theta = \frac{W}{P} = \frac{800}{880} = 0.909 \qquad Ans. \qquad (19\text{-}3)$
$\qquad\qquad \theta = 25°$

b. Find the lagging reactive power.

$$\text{var } P = P \times \sin \theta = 880 \times \sin 25° \qquad (19\text{-}13)$$
$$\text{var } P = 880 \times 0.423 = -372 \text{ var lagging} \qquad Ans.$$

c. In order to raise the pf to unity, the capacitor must provide 372 var of reactive power leading. Since the apparent power in a capacitor is equal to the var P, 372 volt-amp of capacitor power will exactly balance the lagging var P.

d. Find the current drawn by this capacitor.

$$P = I \times E \qquad (7\text{-}1)$$
$$372 = I \times 220$$
$$I = \frac{372}{220} = 1.69 \text{ amp} \qquad Ans.$$

e. Find the reactance of the capacitor.

$$E_c = I_c \times X_c \qquad (16\text{-}7)$$
$$220 = 1.69 \times X_c$$
$$X_c = \frac{220}{1.69} = 130 \text{ ohms} \qquad Ans.$$

f. Find the capacitance of the capacitor.

$$X_c = \frac{159,000}{f \times C} \qquad (16\text{-}6)$$
$$131.2 = \frac{159,000}{60 \times C}$$
$$131.2 \times 60 \times C = 159,000$$
$$C = \frac{159,000}{7872} = 20.2 \text{ μf} \qquad Ans.$$

Problems

1. A 440-volt line delivers 15-kv-amp to a load at 75 per cent pf lagging. To what pf should a 10-kv-amp synchronous motor be adjusted in order to raise the pf to unity when connected in parallel?

2. A 220-volt line delivers 10 kv-amp to a load at 80 per cent pf lagging. What must be the pf of an 8-kw synchronous motor in parallel in order to raise the pf to unity?

3. A 220-volt 20-amp induction motor draws 3 kw of power. A 4-kv-amp synchronous motor is placed in parallel to adjust the pf to unity. What must be the pf of the synchronous motor?

4. A bank of motors draws 20 kw at 75 per cent pf lagging from a 440-volt 60-cycle line. What must be the capacity of a static capacitor connected across the motor terminals if it is to raise the total pf to 1.0?

5. A motor draws 1,500 watts and 7.5 amp from a 220-volt 60-cycle line. What must be the capacity of a capacitor in parallel which will raise the total pf to unity?

6. A 4-hp motor operates at an efficiency of 85 per cent and a pf of 80 per cent lagging when connected across a 120-volt 60-cycle line. Find the capacity of the capacitor needed to raise the total pf to 100 per cent. *Hint:* Find the kilowatt input to the motor and proceed as before.

7. An inductive load draws 5 kw at 60 per cent pf from a 220-volt 60-cycle line. Find the kilovolt-ampere rating of the capacitor needed to raise the total pf to 100 per cent.

8. (*a*) A 30-kw motor operates at 80 per cent pf lagging. In parallel with it is a 50-kw motor which operates at 90 per cent pf lagging. Find (1) the total effective power, (2) the total pf, and (3) the total apparent power.

(*b*) Find the pf adjustment which must be made on a 20-kw synchronous motor in parallel with the motors in (*a*) in order to raise the pf of the circuit to unity.

JOB 19-5: REVIEW OF A-C POWER

The apparent power P is the product of the voltage and the current used by a circuit as measured by a-c meters.

The effective power W is the actual power used by the circuit as measured by a wattmeter.

The power factor (pf) of a circuit is the ratio of the effective power to the apparent power. It may be expressed as a decimal or as a per cent. The pf is also equal to the cosine of the phase angle of the circuit.

$$pf = \cos \theta \qquad (19\text{-}7)$$

The relations among P, W, and pf are given by

$$pf = \frac{W}{P} \quad (19\text{-}6) \qquad \text{or} \qquad \cos \theta = \frac{W}{P} \quad (19\text{-}3)$$

$$W = P \times pf \quad (19\text{-}8) \qquad \text{or} \qquad W = P \times \cos \theta \quad (19\text{-}4)$$

$$P = \frac{W}{pf} \quad (19\text{-}9) \qquad \text{or} \qquad P = \frac{W}{\cos \theta} \quad (19\text{-}5)$$

The apparent power may be resolved into its components—the effective power W and the reactive power *var*—by the following formulas:

$$W = P \times \cos \theta \qquad (19\text{-}4)$$
$$\text{var } P = P \times \sin \theta \qquad (19\text{-}13)$$

The procedure for solving problems involving resistive, inductive, and capacitive loads is as follows:

1. For each load, find

a. The apparent power, using the formula

$$P = E \times I \qquad (7\text{-}1)$$

or
$$P = \frac{W}{\text{pf}} \qquad (19\text{-}9)$$

or
$$P = \frac{W}{\cos \theta} \qquad (19\text{-}5)$$

b. The effective power, using the formula

$$W = P \times \text{pf} \qquad (19\text{-}8)$$
or
$$W = P \times \cos \theta \qquad (19\text{-}4)$$

c. The phase angle, using the formula

$$\cos \theta = \frac{W}{P} \qquad (19\text{-}3)$$

or
$$\cos \theta = \text{pf} \qquad (19\text{-}7)$$

d. The var power.

$$\text{var } P = P \times \sin \theta \qquad (19\text{-}13)$$

2. Find the total effective power.

$$W_T = W_A + W_B \qquad (19\text{-}21)$$

3. Find the total reactive power.

$$\text{var } P_T = \text{var } P_A + \text{var } P_B \qquad (19\text{-}22)$$

4. Find the phase angle for the entire circuit by adding W_T and var P_T vectorially.

$$\tan \theta_T = \frac{\text{var } P_T}{W_T} \qquad (19\text{-}25)$$

5. Find the total pf.

$$\text{pf}_T = \cos \theta_T \qquad (19\text{-}7)$$

6. Find the total apparent power.

$$P_T = \frac{W_T}{\text{pf}_T} \qquad (19\text{-}26)$$

7. Find the total current drawn, using the formula

$$P_T = I_T \times E_T \qquad (7\text{-}2)$$
or
$$W_T = E_T \times I_T \times \cos \theta_T \qquad (19\text{-}27)$$
or
$$W_T = E_T \times I_T \times \text{pf}_T \qquad (19\text{-}28)$$

Power-factor Correction

1. By synchronous motors:

a. Find the var P of the induction motor given.

b. For correction to unity pf, the leading var P of the synchronous motor must equal the lagging var P of the induction motor. Therefore, for the synchronous motor,

$$\sin \theta = \frac{\text{var } P \text{ of the induction motor}}{P \text{ of the synchronous motor}} \qquad (19\text{-}12)$$

or $$\tan \theta = \frac{\text{var } P \text{ of the induction motor}}{W \text{ of the synchronous motor}} \qquad (19\text{-}29)$$

from either of which the value of angle θ may be obtained.

c. The pf of the synchronous motor is

$$\text{pf} = \cos \theta \qquad (19\text{-}7)$$

2. By static capacitors:

a. Find the var P of the induction motor given.

b. Set this var P equal to the apparent power P drawn by the capacitor, since the apparent power of a capacitor is equal to its var P.

c. Solve for I in the formula

$$P = I \times E \qquad (7\text{-}1)$$

d. Find the reactance of the capacitor.

$$E_c = I_c \times X_c \qquad (16\text{-}7)$$

e. Find the capacitance at the given frequency.

$$X_c = \frac{159,000}{f \times C} \qquad (16\text{-}6)$$

Problems

1. A coil of 7 ohms resistance and 24 ohms reactance is connected across a 120-volt 60-cycle line. Find the pf and the current drawn.

2. A 2-hp motor operates at a pf of 80 per cent and an efficiency of 90 per cent. Find (a) the watt input to the motor and (b) the apparent power delivered to the motor.

3. A motor drawing 10 amp at 90 per cent pf lagging is in parallel with another motor drawing 8 amp at 90 per cent pf lagging from a 120-volt line. Find (a) the total effective power, (b) the total pf, (c) the total apparent power, and (d) the total current drawn.

4. A purely resistive lamp load drawing 20 amp from a 220-volt 60-cycle line is in parallel with a capacitive motor taking 8 amp at 34.2 per cent pf. Find (a) W_T, (b) pf_T, (c) P_T, and (d) I_T.

5. A 1-kw lamp load, a 20-kv-amp induction motor operating at a pf of 70 per cent, and a 15 kv-amp motor operating at a pf of 50 per cent lagging are connected in parallel. Find (a) W_T, (b) pf_T, and (c) P_T.

6. An induction motor drawing 250 volt-amp at 70 per cent pf is in parallel with a synchronous motor drawing 400 volt-amp at 60 per cent pf. Find (a) the total effective power, (b) the total pf, and (c) the total apparent power.

7. An induction motor drawing 10 amp at 80 per cent pf is in parallel with a capacitive load drawing 1 kw at 90 per cent pf from a 117-volt 60-cycle line. Find (a) the total effective power, (b) the total pf, (c) the total apparent power, and (d) the total current drawn.

8. A lamp bank drawing 10 amp, a synchronous motor drawing 8 amp at 75 per cent pf, and an induction motor drawing 5 amp at 80 per cent pf are all connected in parallel across a 230-volt 60-cycle line. Find (a) the total apparent power and (b) the total current drawn.

9. A 120-volt 20-amp induction motor draws 2 kw of power. A 1.5-kv-amp synchronous motor is placed in parallel with it to adjust the pf to unity. What is the pf of the synchronous motor?

10. An induction motor draws 1 kw from a 110-volt 60-cycle line at a pf of 70 per cent. Find (a) the apparent power, (b) the lagging var power, and (c) the capacitance needed in parallel to raise the total pf to 1.0.

Test—A-C Power

1. A purely resistive lamp load drawing 10 amp from a 230-volt 60-cycle a-c line is in parallel with a 10-kv-amp induction motor operating at a pf of 60 per cent lagging and with a synchronous motor drawing 6 kw at a pf of 77 per cent leading. Find (a) the total effective power, (b) the total pf, (c) the total apparent power, and (d) the total current drawn.

2. An induction motor draws 3 kw from a 120-volt 60-cycle a-c line at a pf of 82 per cent. Find (a) the apparent power, (b) the lagging var power, and (c) the capacitance needed in parallel to raise the total pf to unity.

BIBLIOGRAPHY

Beauchamp, William L., and John C. Mayfield: "Basic Electricity," Scott, Foresman and Company, Chicago, 1943.

Beitman, M. N.: "Most Often-needed Television Servicing Information," Supreme Publications, Highland Park, Ill., 1955.

Bishop, Calvin C.: "Alternating Currents for Technical Students," D. Van Nostrand Company, Inc., Princeton, N.J., 1942.

Cooke, Nelson M.: "Mathematics for Electricians and Radiomen," McGraw-Hill Book Company, Inc., New York, 1942.

Crawford, John Edmund: "Practical Electricity," The Bruce Publishing Company, Milwaukee, 1940.

Croft, Terrell: "Practical Electricity," 4th ed., McGraw-Hill Book Company, Inc., New York, 1940.

Dawes, Chester L.: "A Course in Electrical Engineering," Vols. I and II, 4th ed., McGraw-Hill Book Company, Inc., New York, 1952.

Dawes, Chester L.: "Industrial Electricity," Vol. I, 3d ed., 1955, and Vol. II, 2d ed., 1942, McGraw-Hill Book Company, Inc., New York.

Drew, Charles E.: "How to Pass Radio License Examinations," 2d ed., John Wiley & Sons, Inc., New York, 1947.

Fischer, Bernhard: "Radio and Television Mathematics," The Macmillan Company, New York, 1949.

Fischer, Bernhard, and Herbert Jacobs: "Elements of Mathematics for Radio, Television and Electronics," The Macmillan Company, New York, 1954.

Hellman, Charles I.: "Elements of Radio," 2d ed., D. Van Nostrand Company, Inc., Princeton, N.J., 1946.

Helt, Scott: "Practical Television Engineering," Rinehart Books, Inc., New York, 1950.

Henney, Keith: "Principles of Radio," 4th ed., John Wiley & Sons, Inc., New York, 1942.

Kuehn, Martin H.: "Mathematics for Electricians," 3d ed., McGraw-Hill Book Company, Inc., New York, 1949.

Lister, Eugene C.: "Electric Circuits and Machines," 2d ed., McGraw-Hill Book Company, Inc., New York, 1952.

Manly, Harold P., and L. O. Gorder: "Drake's Cyclopedia of Radio and Electronics," 14th ed., Frederick J. Drake & Company, Inc., Wilmette, Ill., 1951.

Marcus, Abraham: "Radio Servicing: Theory and Practice," Prentice-Hall, Inc., Englewood Cliffs, N.J., 1948.

Marcus, Abraham, and William Marcus: "Elements of Radio," 2d ed., Prentice-Hall, Inc., Englewood Cliffs, N.J., 1948.

Marshall, Samuel L., and Peter Greenleaf: "Elements of Practical Radio Mechanics," Current Books Inc., New York, 1943.

"Mathematics, Electrical Trades," Delmar Publishers, Inc., Albany, N.Y., 1948.

"MYE Technical Manual," P. R. Mallory & Company, Inc., 5th ed., Indianapolis, 1946.

Nadon, John M., and Bert J. Gelmine: "Industrial Electricity," 2d ed., D. Van Nostrand Company, Inc., Princeton, N.J., 1951.

"National Electrical Code for Electric Wiring and Apparatus," NBFU Pamphlet No. 70, National Board of Fire Underwriters, New York, 1953.

Rasch, William Edward: "Practical Electrical Mathematics," D. C. Heath and Company, Boston, 1946.

"RCA Receiving Tube Manual," Radio Corporation of America, Harrison, N.J., 1955.

Richter, H. P.: "Practical Electrical Wiring," 5th ed., McGraw-Hill Book Company, Inc., New York, 1957.

Siskind, Charles S.: "Electricity—Direct and Alternating Current," 2d ed., McGraw-Hill Book Company, Inc., New York, 1955.

Slack, Edgar P.: "Elementary Electricity," 2d ed., McGraw-Hill Book Company, Inc., New York, 1949.

Slurzberg, Morris, and William Osterheld: "Essentials of Electricity for Radio and Television," 2d ed., McGraw-Hill Book Company, Inc., New York, 1950.

Slurzberg, Morris, and William Osterheld: "Essentials of Radio," McGraw-Hill Book Company, Inc., New York, 1948.

Timbie, William H.: "Elements of Electricity," 4th ed., John Wiley & Sons, Inc., New York, 1953.

Tucker, Durwood J.: "Introduction to Practical Radio," The Macmillan Company, New York, 1945.

Wang, T. J.: "Mathematics of Radio Communication," D. Van Nostrand Company, Inc., Princeton, N.J., 1943.

VISUAL AIDS

The visual materials described below and on the following pages can be used to illustrate and complement material in this book. Both motion pictures and filmstrips are included in this visual bibliography, the character of each being identified by the abbreviations MP and FS. Immediately following such identification is the name of the producer and the year of production; if different from that of the producer, the name of the distributor is also given. Abbreviations used for these names are identified in the list of sources at the end of the bibliography. In many instances, the films can be borrowed or rented from local or state 16mm film libraries. A nationwide list of these sources is given in *A Directory of 3,300 16mm Film Libraries*, available for 70 cents from the Superintendent of Documents, U.S. Government Printing Office, Washington 25, D.C. Unless otherwise indicated, the motion pictures are 16mm sound black-and-white films and the filmstrips are 35mm black-and-white and silent. The length of motion pictures is given in minutes (min), that of filmstrips in frames (fr).

This bibliography is a selective one, and readers may also wish to consult the annual and semiannual issues of *Educational Film Guide* and *Filmstrip Guide*, standard reference catalogs available in most school, college, and public libraries.

FILMS ON MATHEMATICS

Applied Geometry (MP, Purdue, n.d., 17 min, silent). Explains nine different geometric constructions, from constructing a hexagon when the distance across corners is known to drawing an arc tangent to two circles.

Basic Algebra (FS series, SVE, 1948). Seven filmstrips with the following titles:

Addition and Subtraction of Signed Numbers (46 fr)
Equations (54 fr)
Formulas (52 fr)
Graphs (54 fr)
Introduction to Algebra (44 fr)
Introduction to Signed Numbers (43 fr)
Multiplication and Division of Signed Numbers (49 fr)

Fractions (MP series, Hunt, 1947).   Eight motion pictures, 11 min each, color or black-and-white.   Somewhat elementary but useful for review.   Titles are:

Decimal Fractions	*How to Multiply Fractions*
How to Add Fractions	*How to Subtract Fractions*
How to Change Fractions	*Introduction to Fractions*
How to Divide Fractions	*Percentage*

Introduction to Vectors: Coplanar Concurrent Forces (MP, USOE/UWF, 1945, 22 min).   Explains the meaning of scalar and vector quantities, how to add scalars and vectors, methods of vector composition and vector resolution, relationship between vector composition and vector resolution, and how vectors may be used to solve engineering problems (correlated filmstrip, same title, 36 fr).

Language of Mathematics (MP, Cor, 1950, 10 min, color or b & w).   Explains the functions and uses of the symbols used in mathematics and the need for a language of mathematics.

Mathematics (FS series, McGraw, 1952).   Ten filmstrips correlated with *Mathematics: A First Course* by Rosskopf, Aten, and Reeve.   Titles are:

Geometric Figures (29 fr)
Grouping Symbols and Order of Operations (34 fr)
Indirect Measurement (38 fr)
Mathematics in Daily Living (28 fr)
Measurement (36 fr)
Slide Rule, Part 1 (24 fr)
Slide Rule, Part 2 (27 fr)
Systems of Equations (30 fr)
Thinking in Symbols (27 fr)
Variables and Coordinates (33 fr)

Origin of Mathematics (MP, Brandon, 1941, 10 min).   Background for illustrating the history of numbers, measurement, and calculation, including methods used by cave dwellers, Egyptians, Babylonians, Greeks, Romans, and Arabs.

Periodic Functions (MP, USN/UWF, 1945, 17 min).   Defines periodic functions, illustrates the graphing of sine angles, and relates sine waves to the amount of voltage produced by a generator.

Plane Geometry (FS series, SVE, 1947–1948).   Twelve filmstrips with the following titles:

Areas (47 fr)
Basic Angles and Experimental Geometry (52 fr)
Basic Triangles (45 fr)
Common Tangents and Tangent Circles (46 fr)
Congruent and Overlapping Triangles (46 fr)
Introduction to Circles (48 fr)
Introduction to Demonstrative Geometry—Axioms, Theorems, Postulates (44 fr)
Introduction to Plane Geometry (42 fr)
Loci (47 fr)
Parallel Lines and Transversals (44 fr)
Quadrilaterals (54 fr)
Similar Polygons (44 fr)

Practical Geometry (MP series, KB, 1945–1948). Seventeen films, 10 to 12 min each, with the following titles:

Angles	*Polygons*
Angles and Arcs in Circles	*Practical Geometry*
Areas	*Properties of Triangles*
Chords and Tangents of Circles	*Pythagorean Theorem*
The Circle	*Quadrilaterals*
Congruent Figures	*Ratio and Proportion*
Indirect Measurement	*Rectilinear Coordinates*
Lines and Angles	*Similar Triangles*
Locus	

The Slide Rule: The "C" and "D" Scales (MP, USOE/UWF, 1943, 24 min), Purpose of the slide rule, parts of the rule, and how to use the "C" and "D" scales in the multiplication and division of numbers (correlated filmstrip, same title, 53 fr).

The Slide Rule: Proportion, Percentage, Squares and Square Roots (MP, USOE/UWF, 1944, 21 min). How to use the "C" and "D" scales of the slide rule to calculate proportions and percentages, how to read the "A" and "B" scales, and how to calculate squares and square roots (correlated filmstrip, same title, 44 fr).

Vectors (MP, USN/UWF, 1945, 12 min). Explains vectors, changes in angle or magnitude, how vectors are plotted, and how the resultant is found.

FILMS ON ELECTRICITY

Accent on Accuracy (MP, GE, 1952, 19 min, color). Explains the development. manufacture, and uses of General Electric's I-50 watthour meter.

Amperes, Volts, and Ohms (MP, USN/UWF, 1945, 8 min). Explains the meaning, relationship, and measurement of amperes, volts, and ohms (correlated filmstrip, same title, 23 fr).

Basic Electricity (MP, USAF/UWF, 1948, 20 min). An animated cartoon explaining the fundamentals of electricity, including voltage, current, resistance, magnetic fields, induction, primary and secondary coils, and series and parallel circuits.

Basic Electricity (FS series, Handy, n.d.). Twelve filmstrips with the following titles:

Magnetism (62 fr)	*The Generator* (77 fr)
Static Electricity (73 fr)	*Alternating Current* (90 fr)
Current Electricity (74 fr)	*Electric Motors* (66 fr)
The Electric Cell (50 fr)	*Electric Meters* (83 fr)
The Storage Battery (83 fr)	*Applications, Part* 1 (60 fr)
Electromagnetism (55 fr)	*Applications, Part* 2 (56 fr)

Basic Electronics (MP, USAF/UWF, 1948, 17 min color). An animated cartoon explaining the meaning of atoms and electrons and vacuum-tube, cathode, rectifier-tube, amplifier-tube, grid, and bridge circuits.

Basic Principles of Frequency Modulation (MP, USA/UWF, 1944, 31 min). Describes what FM is in radio communication, how it is used, and what its advantages and limitations are.

Capacitance (MP, USN/UWF, 1943, 31 min). Demonstrates electron flow through a circuit, the charging and discharging of capacitors, variations of a charge on a capacitor in relation to time, and the behavior of capacitance with alternating current (correlated filmstrip, same title, 22 fr).

The Cathode Ray Tube: How It Works (MP, USN/UWF, 1943, 15 min). Demonstrates the construction and function of various parts of the cathode-ray tube. Explains electrostatic and electromagnetic deflection and how varied currents affect the position of the spot of light on the scope.

Circuit Testing: Signal Generators (MP, USA/UWF, 1952, 26 min). Explains the theory and operation of the signal generator, including oscillating circuits, audio-oscillators, radio-frequency oscillators, and frequency meters.

Circuit Testing with Meters and Multimeters. Part 1: Theory (MP, USA/UWF, 1951, 30 min). Explains the theory and construction of meters and shows various types of meters used for circuit testing and associated external equipment.

Circuit Testing with Meters and Multimeters. Part 2: Practical Application (MP, USA/UWF, 1952, 37 min). Demonstrates how to use meters in testing transformers, capacitors, resistors, telephone loop circuits, etc.

Current and Electromotive Force (MP, USN/UWF, 1945, 11 min). Explains electron theory, the arrangement of molecules, building up of current, conductors, electromotive force, resistance, and chemical and mechanical sources of electromotive force (correlated filmstrip, same title, 38 fr).

The Diode: Principles and Applications (MP, USOE/UWF, 1945, 17 min). Principles of electron flow across a gap, basic features of the diode tube, control of electron flow in the tube, photoelectric cells, X-ray tubes, and the diode as a rectifier (correlated filmstrip, same title, 58 fr).

Electrodynamics (MP, EBF, 1936, 11 min). Explains the fundamental principles of current electricity and electromagnetism.

Electrostatics (MP, EBF, 1952, 11 min). Explains positive and negative electrification, role of insulators and conductors, movement of charges in the electroscope, the Compton electrometer, and lightning as nature's display of static electricity.

Elements of Electrical Circuits (MP, EBF, 1943, 11 min). Explains the nature of electric currents and circuits, electron motions, conductors, insulators, and factors affecting resistance. Contains animated drawings and photographic demonstrations (correlated filmstrip, same title, 89 fr).

Ohm's Law (MP, USA/UWF, 1943, 19 min). Explains the elements of electricity; electrical energy, its source, transmission, and use; composition of matter; use of force and energy; how Ohm's law functions; resistance; and the purpose and use of meters.

Principles of Electricity (MP, GE, 1945, 20 min, color). Explains the actions of electrons within an atom, the principles involved in the flow of current, magnetism and magnetic fields, and the meanings of volt, ampere, and ohm.

Radio Antennas: Creation and Behavior of Radio Waves (MP, USAF/UWF, 1942, 12 min). Explains electric and magnetic fields, generation of electromagnetic waves, behavior of radio waves in space, ground wave, reflection and refraction, the ionosphere, and causes of fading.

Radio Servicing (FS series, McGraw, 1952). Six filmstrips correlated with *Elements of Radio Servicing* by Marcus and Levy. Titles are:

Alignment. Part 1: IF Amplifier (37 fr)
Alignment. Part 2: Front End (39 fr)
Converter. Part 1: Oscillator Stage (34 fr)

Converter. Part 2: Mixer Stage (36 fr)
Converter. Part 3: Identification of Parts (39 fr)
How to Use the Signal Generator (39 fr)

RCL: Resistance, Capacitance (MP, USN/UWF, 1943, 34 min). Explains current and voltage in relation to time, voltage and current curves, the relationship of current and voltage, the measurement of voltage at source, the addition of phase components, and the effect of impedance on resonance.

Series and Parallel Circuits (MP, EBF, 1944, 11 min). Explains the relationships among resistance, current, and voltage in series circuits and in parallel circuits; the advantages of each type of circuit; and a simple series-parallel combination circuit (correlated filmstrip, same title, 86 fr).

Series and Parallel Circuits (MP, USN/UWF, 1945, 8 min). Illustrates series and parallel circuits, explaining current flow and voltage drop across each lamp (correlated filmstrip, same title, 26 fr).

Single-phase and Polyphase Circuits (MP, USOE/UWF, 1945, 17 min). Explains a single-phase synchronous generator, the use of sine curves to illustrate flow changes, a two-phase system and three-phase system, and ways to simplify wiring (correlated filmstrip, same title, 51 fr).

Split-phase Motor Principles (MP, USOE/UWF, 1945, 17 min). Construction of stator and rotor, comparison of winding in two-phase stator with split-phase stator, effects of winding resistances and inductive reactances, and use of capacitor to produce phase displacement (correlated filmstrip, same title, 48 fr).

Squirrel-cage Rotor Principles (MP, USOE/UWF, 1945, 10 min). Laws of magnetism and induced emf, electron flow in squirrel-cage rotor setting up magnetic poles which create torque, construction of squirrel-cage rotors (correlated filmstrip, same title, 28 fr).

Vacuum Tubes (MP, EBF, 1943, 11 min). Explains three functions of a vacuum tube in radio—amplifying current to operate the loudspeaker, rectifier in detection, and oscillator in the transmission station to produce the carrier wave.

Volt Ohmmeter Operation (MP, USN/UWF, 1944, 15 min). Shows how to operate a volt ohmmeter, Weston and other types, including the selection of the proper scale range, adjustment for zero on the scale, and the setup for either direct or alternating current.

Wire Sizes and Voltage Drop (MP, USOE/UWF, 1945, 13 min). Factors influencing the ability of conductors to carry electron flow, measurement of wire sizes, wire area in circular mills, voltage drop, and Ohm's law (correlated filmstrip, same title, 26 fr).

PRIMARY SOURCES OF FILMS

Brandon—Brandon Films, Inc., 200 W. 57th St., New York
Cor—Coronet Instructional Films, Coronet Bldg., Chicago 1
EBF—Encyclopaedia Britannica Films, Inc., 1150 Wilmette Ave., Wilmette, Ill.
GE—General Electric Co., 1 River Road, Schenectady 5, N. Y.
Handy—Jam Handy Organization, 2821 E. Grand Blvd., Detroit
Hunt—Johnson Hunt Productions, 6509 De Longpre Ave., Hollywood 28, Calif.
KB—Knowledge Builders, Floral Park, N. Y.
McGraw—McGraw-Hill Book Company, Inc., Text-Film Dept., 330 West 42d St., New York 36

MIT—Massachusetts Institute of Technology, Cambridge, Mass.

Purdue—Purdue University, Lafayette, Ind.

SVE—Society for Visual Education, Inc., 1345 W. Diversey Parkway, Chicago 14

USA—U.S. Dept. of the Army, Washington 25, D. C.

USAF—U.S. Dept. of the Air Force, Washington 25, D. C.

USN—U.S. Dept. of the Navy, Washington 25, D. C.

USOE—U.S. Office of Education, Washington 25, D. C. (Films distributed by United World Films)

UWF—United World Films, Inc., 1445 Park Ave., New York 29

INDEX

Power-factor Correction

1. By synchronous motors:

a. Find the var P of the induction motor given.

b. For correction to unity pf, the leading var P of the synchronous motor must equal the lagging var P of the induction motor. Therefore, for the synchronous motor,

$$\sin \theta = \frac{\text{var } P \text{ of the induction motor}}{P \text{ of the synchronous motor}} \qquad (19\text{-}12)$$

or

$$\tan \theta = \frac{\text{var } P \text{ of the induction motor}}{W \text{ of the synchronous motor}} \qquad (19\text{-}29)$$

from either of which the value of angle θ may be obtained.

c. The pf of the synchronous motor is

$$\text{pf} = \cos \theta \qquad (19\text{-}7)$$

2. By static capacitors:

a. Find the var P of the induction motor given.

b. Set this var P equal to the apparent power P drawn by the capacitor, since the apparent power of a capacitor is equal to its var P.

c. Solve for I in the formula

$$P = I \times E \qquad (7\text{-}1)$$

d. Find the reactance of the capacitor.

$$E_c = I_c \times X_c \qquad (16\text{-}7)$$

e. Find the capacitance at the given frequency.

$$X_c = \frac{159,000}{f \times C} \qquad (16\text{-}6)$$

Problems

1. A coil of 7 ohms resistance and 24 ohms reactance is connected across a 120-volt 60-cycle line. Find the pf and the current drawn.

2. A 2-hp motor operates at a pf of 80 per cent and an efficiency of 90 per cent. Find (a) the watt input to the motor and (b) the apparent power delivered to the motor.

3. A motor drawing 10 amp at 90 per cent pf lagging is in parallel with another motor drawing 8 amp at 90 per cent pf lagging from a 120-volt line. Find (a) the total effective power, (b) the total pf, (c) the total apparent power, and (d) the total current drawn.

4. A purely resistive lamp load drawing 20 amp from a 220-volt 60-cycle line is in parallel with a capacitive motor taking 8 amp at 34.2 per cent pf. Find (a) W_T, (b) pf_T, (c) P_T, and (d) I_T.

5. A 1-kw lamp load, a 20-kv-amp induction motor operating at a pf of 70 per cent, and a 15 kv-amp motor operating at a pf of 50 per cent lagging are connected in parallel. Find (a) W_T, (b) pf$_T$, and (c) P_T.

6. An induction motor drawing 250 volt-amp at 70 per cent pf is in parallel with a synchronous motor drawing 400 volt-amp at 60 per cent pf. Find (a) the total effective power, (b) the total pf, and (c) the total apparent power.

7. An induction motor drawing 10 amp at 80 per cent pf is in parallel with a capacitive load drawing 1 kw at 90 per cent pf from a 117-volt 60-cycle line. Find (a) the total effective power, (b) the total pf, (c) the total apparent power, and (d) the total current drawn.

8. A lamp bank drawing 10 amp, a synchronous motor drawing 8 amp at 75 per cent pf, and an induction motor drawing 5 amp at 80 per cent pf are all connected in parallel across a 230-volt 60-cycle line. Find (a) the total apparent power and (b) the total current drawn.

9. A 120-volt 20-amp induction motor draws 2 kw of power. A 1.5-kv-amp synchronous motor is placed in parallel with it to adjust the pf to unity. What is the pf of the synchronous motor?

10. An induction motor draws 1 kw from a 110-volt 60-cycle line at a pf of 70 per cent. Find (a) the apparent power, (b) the lagging var power, and (c) the capacitance needed in parallel to raise the total pf to 1.0.

Test—A-C Power

1. A purely resistive lamp load drawing 10 amp from a 230-volt 60-cycle a-c line is in parallel with a 10-kv-amp induction motor operating at a pf of 60 per cent lagging and with a synchronous motor drawing 6 kw at a pf of 77 per cent leading. Find (a) the total effective power, (b) the total pf, (c) the total apparent power, and (d) the total current drawn.

2. An induction motor draws 3 kw from a 120-volt 60-cycle a-c line at a pf of 82 per cent. Find (a) the apparent power, (b) the lagging var power, and (c) the capacitance needed in parallel to raise the total pf to unity.